ANALYTICAL MECHANICS
FOR ENGINEERS

By FRED B. SEELY and JAMES O. SMITH
   Advanced Mechanics of Materials, *Second Edition*

By FRED B. SEELY
   Resistance of Materials, *Third Edition*

By FRED B. SEELY and NEWTON E. ENSIGN
   Analytical Mechanics for Engineers, *Fourth Edition*

ANALYTICAL MECHANICS
FOR ENGINEERS

Fred B. Seely, M.S.

PROFESSOR OF THEORETICAL AND
APPLIED MECHANICS, EMERITUS

Newton E. Ensign, M.A. (Oxon.)

PROFESSOR OF THEORETICAL AND
APPLIED MECHANICS, EMERITUS

UNIVERSITY OF ILLINOIS

Fourth Edition

NEW YORK · JOHN WILEY & SONS, INC.
LONDON · CHAPMAN & HALL, LIMITED

Library of Congress Catalog Card Number: 52–5956

PRINTED IN THE UNITED STATES OF AMERICA

PREFACE TO FOURTH EDITION

The principal changes in the fourth edition of this book consist of the addition of many new problems and figures; the transfer of the discussion of the first moments and centroids of geometric figures (lines, areas and volumes) to the Appendix; the use of a general coplanar force system, rather than the simplest type of force system, to introduce and explain the graphical and algebraic methods of determining the resultant of a force system, after which the simpler types of coplanar force system become special cases; greater emphasis on distributed forces in determining resultants of force systems, thereby introducing the calculus method earlier in the book; the elimination in Part Four on Special Topics of the chapters on Governors and the Gyroscope, and the transfer of some of the discussion of the gyroscope to the chapter on Impulse and Momentum in Part Three, thereby reducing somewhat the size of the book; and many minor changes in the treatment of various topics throughout the book, as, for example, in the kinematics of relative motion, and in the use of the principle of conservation of energy for conservative systems.

Strong emphasis is given, as in previous editions, to the use of the general steps or procedure in analyzing problems in equilibrium and in dynamics, and new problems have been added that illustrate actual engineering conditions or applications.

The authors wish to express their appreciation of the many suggestions offered by those who have used the third edition of the book. These suggestions have been considered carefully in preparing the fourth edition.

The authors have been ably assisted by their colleague Professor Paul G. Jones who has made valuable contributions to the revision. Without his careful work it is doubtful that the revision could have been completed.

F. B. SEELY

N. E. ENSIGN

Urbana, Illinois
February 1952

PREFACE TO FIRST EDITION

This book, as its name suggests, presents those principles of mechanics that are believed to be essential for the student of engineering.

Throughout the book the aim has been to make the principles of mechanics stand out clearly; to build them up as much as possible from common experience (the student's experience); to apply the principles to concrete problems of practical value; and to emphasize the physical rather than the mathematical interpretation of the principles. Important equations are printed in bold-faced type and the statements of the more important principles are italicized.

The book is divided into three parts; namely, Statics, Kinematics, and Kinetics. Statics is presented first because of its simplicity and its direct relation to the student's experience. However, in the first two chapters are developed certain concepts and elementary principles that are fully as important in kinetics as in statics, and the authors feel that it is essential to a satisfactory grasp of mechanics, as a whole, that sufficient time and care be taken to cause these elementary concepts and principles to crystallize in the student's mind before the more general principles and problems are studied. The equilibrium of the various types of force systems are treated both by the algebraic and by the graphical method. A large number of problems involving the equilibrium of the simpler structures and machines are given, and figures illustrating the structures and machines are used freely.

Although kinematics as herein developed is mainly a preliminary to kinetics, the authors' experience indicates that the kinematic properties of motion must be isolated and developed with care if they are to be used with success in the study of the kinetics of the motion.

Both kinematics and kinetics have been developed with regard for the increasing importance of dynamics to engineers. The geometric and physical conceptions and interpretations of the quantities in kinematics have been emphasized rather than the mathematical conceptions. A treatment of acceleration is given which, it is hoped, will help to overcome some of the difficulties frequently found in the use of this quantity. The treatment of kinetics has been restricted to the more common types of motion found in engineering practice, but these motions have been treated more fully than is usual in elementary texts on mechanics. This is particularly true of plane motion. D'Alembert's principle (involving inertia forces) has been used for each type of motion as a second method of solution. The methods of procedure used in the analysis of kinetics problems are strongly emphasized both in the general discussions and in the solutions of illustrative problems.

Illustrative problems are given at the end of the more important articles and many problems are offered for solution. Great care has been exercised in selecting problems that are of practical interest and yet are easily comprehended and are free from unimportant details so that the principles used in their solution will stand out clearly. The answers to about one-half of the problems are given.

Graphical methods of representation and of solution have been used frequently in all three parts of the book. A knowledge of elementary calculus is assumed although little use is made of it in the first four chapters.

The discussion of centroids (Chapter V) is developed directly from the principle of moments—a principle given much emphasis throughout the book.

Several special topics are discussed in Section 3 of Chapter IX. They may be omitted without interfering with the continuity of the book, or any one of the topics may be studied alone without studying the whole section. Further, if it is desired to reduce the time given to kinetics, the second method of analysis of the motion of rotation or of plane motion (which employs D'Alembert's principle and inertia forces) in Section 2 of Chapter IX may be omitted. And, in general, the last part of the material in any section or chapter may be omitted without interfering with the student's progress in the first part of the next section or chapter.

The authors wish to acknowledge their indebtedness to Professor A. N. Talbot for his interest in the book during its preparation and for his helpful suggestions on the treatment of certain important topics. The authors are also indebted to Professor G. A. Goodenough for valuable material in the treatment of Governors and to Professor O. A. Leutwiler for the data and figures for a number of valuable engineering problems.

F. B. SEELY.

N. E. ENSIGN.

URBANA, ILLINOIS,
December, 1920.

CONTENTS

PART ONE. STATICS

Chapter 1. Fundamental Concepts and Definitions

1	Introduction	3
2	Rigid body	4
3	Concept of a force	4
4	External effects of a force	5
5	Characteristics of a force	5
6	Principle of transmissibility	6
7	Measure of a force. Units	6
8	Scalar and vector quantities. Vector representation of a force	7
9	Classification of forces. Definitions	8
10	Parallelogram and triangle laws	9
11	Resolution of a force	13
12	Resultant of two parallel forces	16
13	Moment of a force	17
14	Principle of moments. Varignon's theorem	19
15	Couples	23
16	Characteristics of a couple	24
17	Transformations of a couple	25
18	Vector representation of a couple. Resolution and composition of couples	27
19	Resolution of a force into a force and a couple	28
20	Methods of solution of problems	30
21	Dimensional equations	32

Chapter 2. Resultants of Force Systems

22	Introduction	36

§ 1 *Coplanar, Non-concurrent, Non-parallel Forces*

23	Graphical methods	37
24	Principle of moments	42
25	Algebraic method	44

§ 2 *Special Cases of Coplanar Force Systems*

26	Graphical methods	48
27	Algebraic method	49

§ 3 *Distributed Forces*

28	Resultant of distributed forces. Center of pressure	53

§ 4   *Non-coplanar, Concurrent Forces*

29   Graphical method   57
30   Algebraic method   57

§ 5   *Non-coplanar, Parallel Forces*

31   Algebraic method   58

§ 6   *Couples in Space*

32   Resultant of a system of couples   61
33   Composition of couples in space by means of vectors   63

§ 7   *Non-coplanar, Non-concurrent, Non-parallel Forces*

34   Algebraic method   63

CHAPTER 3.   EQUILIBRIUM OF COPLANAR FORCE SYSTEMS

§ 1   *Introduction*

35   Preliminary   66
36   Graphical conditions of equilibrium   67
37   Algebraic conditions of equilibrium   67
38   Free-body diagram   69

§ 2   *Collinear Forces*

39   Equations of equilibrium   72

§ 3   *Coplanar, Concurrent Forces*

40   Equations of equilibrium   74

§ 4   *Coplanar, Parallel Forces*

41   Equations of equilibrium   81

§ 5   *Coplanar, Non-concurrent, Non-parallel Forces*

42   Equations of equilibrium   86
43   Graphical solution of a typical problem   92
44   Procedure in the solution of problems in equilibrium   94

CHAPTER 4.   EQUILIBRIUM OF TRUSSES AND CABLES

45   Stresses in trusses   101
46   Graphical analysis of trusses   108
47   Flexible cables   111
48   The parabolic cable   112
49   The catenary   115

CHAPTER 5.   EQUILIBRIUM OF NON-COPLANAR FORCE SYSTEMS

§ 1   *Non-coplanar, Concurrent Forces*

50   Equations of equilibrium   120

§ 2 *Non-coplanar, Parallel Forces*

51 Equations of equilibrium 123

§ 3 *Non-coplanar, Non-concurrent, Non-parallel Forces*

52 Equations of equilibrium 125

CHAPTER 6. FRICTION

53 Friction defined 130
54 Coefficient of friction 131
55 Angle of friction 132
56 The laws of friction 133
57 Types of problems involving frictional forces 134
58 Pivot friction 142
59 The screw 143
60 Belt friction 146
61 Rolling resistance 150

PART TWO. KINEMATICS

CHAPTER 7. MOTION OF A PARTICLE

62 Introduction 155
63 Vector addition and subtraction 155
64 Types of motion 156
65 Linear displacement 156
66 Angular displacement 157
67 Relation between linear and angular displacements 158
68 Linear velocity and speed 158
69 Angular velocity 160
70 Relation between linear and angular velocities 163
71 Components of velocity 164
72 Linear acceleration 169
73 Acceleration in rectilinear motion 169
74 Uniformly accelerated rectilinear motion 175
75 Simple harmonic motion 178
76 Acceleration in curvilinear motion. Tangential and normal components
     of acceleration 183
77 Angular acceleration 186
78 Uniformly accelerated circular motion 187
79 Relation between linear and angular accelerations 187
80 Axial components of acceleration 190
81 Relative motion 193
82 Motion of a point relative to a rotating body. Coriolis' law 200

CHAPTER 8. MOTION OF RIGID BODIES

83 Introduction 206
84 Translation 206
85 Rotation 207

86 Plane motion 208
87 Instantaneous center 216

PART THREE. KINETICS

CHAPTER 9. FORCE, MASS, AND ACCELERATION

§ 1 *Preliminary Considerations. Kinetics of a Particle*

88 Introduction 223
89 The general kinetics problem 223
90 Characteristics of a force system 224
91 Inertia and mass 225
92 Newton's laws 226
93 Mathematical statement of Newton's second law. Units 227
94 Equations of motion for a particle 228
95 Procedure in the solution of problems in kinetics 229
96 Inertia-force method for a particle 235
97 Force proportional to displacement. Free vibration 238

§ 2 *Kinetics of Bodies*

98 Introduction. Methods of analysis 243
99 Motion of the mass center of a system of particles 245

Translation

100 Kinetics of a translating rigid body 248

Rotation

101 Kinetics of a rotating rigid body 256
102 Second method of analysis. Inertia-force method 263
103 Center of percussion 270

Plane Motion

104 Kinetics of plane motion of a rigid body 271

CHAPTER 10. WORK AND ENERGY

105 Introduction 280

§ 1 *Work and Power*

106 Work defined 281
107 Algebraic expressions for work done by a force 281
108 Work done by a couple 283
109 Work a scalar quantity. Sign and units of work 283
110 Graphical representation and calculation of work 284
111 Work done on a body by a force system 285
112 Power defined 290
113 Special equations for power 291

§ 2 *Energy*

114 Energy defined 293
115 Potential energy 294

116 Kinetic energy 296
117 Kinetic energy of a particle 296
118 Kinetic energy of a body 297
119 Non-mechanical energy 301

§ 3 *Principle of Work and Energy*

120 Preliminary 303
121 Principle of work and kinetic energy 303
122 Conservation of energy 312

§ 4 *Efficiency. Dissipation of Energy*

123 Efficiency defined 314
124 Dissipation of energy 314
125 A simple dynamometer. Prony brake 314

CHAPTER 11. IMPULSE AND MOMENTUM

126 Preliminary 318

§ 1 *Impulse*

127 Impulse and impact defined 319
128 Components of linear impulse 320
129 Moment of impulse. Angular impulse 320

§ 2 *Momentum*

130 Momentum of a particle defined 322
131 Components of momentum. Angular momentum 323
132 Linear momentum of a body 324
133 Angular momentum of a rotating rigid body 324
134 Angular momentum of a rigid body having plane motion 325

§ 3 *Principles of Impulse and Momentum*

135 Preliminary 328
136 Principle of linear impulse and linear momentum 328
137 Principle of angular impulse and angular momentum 329
138 Method of analysis of the motion of a body by means of impulse and
       momentum 330
139 Conservation of momentum 336
140 Impact 341
141 Impact of two translating bodies 342
142 The gyroscope 344

PART FOUR. SPECIAL TOPICS

CHAPTER 12. MECHANICAL VIBRATIONS

143 Introduction 353
144 Free vibrations 353
145 Simple pendulum 361

146 Compound pendulum 361
147 Free torsional vibration 362
148 Free vibration with viscous damping 368
149 Forced vibrations without damping 373
150 Vibration reduction 379

CHAPTER 13. BALANCING

151 Need for balancing 384
152 Balancing of rotating masses 385
153 Several masses in a single plane of rotation 386
154 Masses in different transverse planes 387
155 Balancing of an elongated rotor 389

APPENDIX. FIRST MOMENTS AND CENTROIDS

MOMENTS OF INERTIA

§ 1 *First Moments and Centroids*

156 First moment 394
157 Centroids 397
158 Planes and lines of symmetry 398
159 Centroids by integration 398
160 Centroids of composite figures and bodies 404
161 Theorems of Pappus and Guldinus 408
162 Graphical method of determining centroids of areas 410
163 Determination of center of gravity by experiment 411

§ 2 *Moments of Inertia of Areas*

164 Moment of inertia of an area defined 411
165 Polar moment of inertia 412
166 Radius of gyration 413
167 Parallel-axis theorem for areas 414
168 Moments of inertia by integration 415
169 Moments of inertia of composite areas 420
170 Moments of inertia of areas by graphical and approximate methods . . . 423

§ 3 *Moments of Inertia of Bodies*

171 Moment of inertia of mass defined 425
172 Radius of gyration 426
173 Parallel-axis theorem for masses 426
174 Moments of inertia with respect to two perpendicular planes 427
175 Moments of inertia of solids by integration 428
176 Moments of inertia of bodies by experimental methods 429
177 Moments of inertia of composite bodies 434

Index 439

PART ONE
Statics

Chapter 1

FUNDAMENTAL CONCEPTS
AND DEFINITIONS *

1 Introduction. The term *mechanics* is used in a broad sense to denote the science that treats of the motion of bodies, rest being considered as a special case of motion. The science of mechanics constitutes a large part of our knowledge of the laws of the universe, including the laws relating to gases and liquids as well as the laws relating to solid bodies, and it takes a prominent place in the study of astronomy and physics as well as in the study of machines and structures which are involved in engineering practice.

The purpose of analytical mechanics as developed in this book is to determine the laws by which the motions of bodies (mainly solid bodies) are governed and to apply these laws to conditions met in engineering practice.

In the development of these laws, certain concepts are assumed to be fundamental, that is, no one of them can be expressed in terms of the others or in simpler terms. Such concepts grow mainly out of our experiences, and other ideas and laws are derived from these condensed experiences.

The fundamental concepts involved in the laws of mechanics are: (1) force, which is made known to us through the tension and the compression of our muscles as a pull or a push, (2) bodies or inert material (matter) on which forces act and without which forces cannot exist, (3) space, and (4) time. A more definite understanding of force and inert bodies can be obtained only after the laws of kinetics have been developed. At present, however, it is necessary only to recognize the existence of these quantities.

In the development of the laws of mechanics, considerable use is made of mathematics. It should be kept in mind, however, that mechanics is

---

* In this introductory chapter are considered certain concepts, definitions, and principles which are used not only in the following pages but in the broad field of mechanics. The student is advised, therefore, to master the contents of this chapter in order to have a sound foundation on which to build his knowledge of the subject.

3

a physical science and that mathematics is used, mainly, to express and interpret physical laws.

For convenience, the study of mechanics is considered under three main divisions: namely, *Statics, Kinematics,* and *Kinetics.*

Statics is that branch of mechanics which treats of bodies that are acted on by balanced forces and, hence, are at rest or have uniform motion.

Kinematics is that branch of mechanics which treats of the motion of bodies without considering the manner in which the influencing factors (force and matter) affect the motion. It deals with the fundamental concepts of space and time, and the quantities, velocity and acceleration, derived therefrom. It is, therefore, sometimes called the *geometry of motion*. Kinematics forms an important part of the study of mechanics, not only because it treats of a part of the general kinetics problem in which forces are involved, but also because, in many problems which involve only motions of parts of a machine, the principles of kinematics, alone, are sufficient for the solution of the problem. Such problems are discussed in treatises on *kinematics of machinery*, in which subject the motion of such machine elements as valve gears and quick-return mechanisms, are considered.

Kinetics is that branch of mechanics which treats of bodies that are acted on by unbalanced forces and, hence, have non-uniform or accelerated motions. In particular, it treats of the change of motion of bodies and the manner in which the change is related to the factors that affect it: namely, the actions of other bodies (forces), and the properties (inertia, etc.) of the bodies themselves. Frequently the term *dynamics* is used in technical literature to denote those subdivisions of mechanics with which the idea of motion is most closely associated: namely, kinematics and kinetics.

2 Rigid body. The bodies dealt with in this book are, in general, considered to be rigid. A rigid body is defined as a body that is not deformed when acted on by external forces. In other words, the distance between any two points in a rigid body remains constant. Actual solid bodies are never rigid. The relative displacement (deformation) of their particles forms an important part of the study of *strength of materials*. But the theoretical laws that govern the motion of ideal rigid bodies may be used, usually with very small error, or with modifications, if necessary, to determine the motion of actual solid bodies.

3 Concept of a force. It was stated in Art. 1 that force is one of the fundamental concepts on which the subject of mechanics is built. A force is the action of one body on another body which changes or tends to change the state of motion of the body acted on. The idea of force, then, implies the mutual actions of two bodies, since one body cannot exert a force on another body unless the other offers a resistance to the one. A force, therefore, never exists alone. Forces always occur in pairs. Furthermore, as will be seen later when Newton's laws are discussed, the two forces are of equal magnitude and opposite direction.

Our conception of force comes mainly from our experiences in which we have been one of the bodies between which mutual actions have occurred. The resistance that is offered by one body to the action of another body arises out of the ability of a body (1) to resist a change of shape (rigidity) and (2) to resist change of motion (inertia). If a body is acted on by one force only, a change of motion of the body will always take place; but, if the body is acted on by two or more forces, it may be held at rest.

Although a single force never exists, it is convenient in the study of the motion of a body to think of a single force and to consider only the actions of other bodies on the body considered without taking into account the reactions of the body considered on the other bodies. However, the fundamental nature of force should be kept in mind.

4 External effects of a force. When a force is applied to a rigid body, the external effect on the body is either a change in the motion of the body, or resisting forces (reactions) exerted on the given body by other bodies. Both of the foregoing effects, of course, may be produced simultaneously. For example, consider a body falling freely under the action of gravity. The sole external effect of the force acting on the body (its weight *) is an acceleration g (32.2 ft per sec² approximately). If the same body is placed on the floor of an elevator which is at rest, the sole external effect of the weight is an upward reaction of the floor on the body. If now the elevator moves downward with an acceleration less than g, the effect of the weight is partly an acceleration of the body (the same as that of the elevator) and partly an upward pressure (reaction) of the floor on the body.

The internal effects of a force on a non-rigid or elastic body are stress and deformation in the body on which the force acts. The internal effects of forces are discussed in books on *strength of materials*.

5 Characteristics of a force. From experience we learn that the external effects of a force on a rigid body depend on (1) the magnitude of the force, (2) the position of the line of action of the force in the body, and (3) the sense of the force: that is, the direction along the line of action. These three properties of a force are called its *characteristics*. A change in any one of them causes a change in the external effect of the

---

* The *weight* of a body is defined as the force of attraction exerted on the body by the earth. The weight of a body varies slightly for different positions on the earth's surface.

force. In specifying the characteristics of a force, however, it is sometimes convenient to designate the action line by giving the direction * of the force and the location of any one point on the line of action. This point, as emphasized in the next article, is not necessarily the point of application of the force on the body. A discussion of the exact manner in which these characteristics influence the change of motion of a body forms an important part of the study of kinetics, and their influence on the reactions developed in holding a body at rest is considered in the study of statics.

6 Principle of transmissibility. The external effect of a force on a rigid body does not depend on the particular point on the line of action at which the force is applied. This fact is formally expressed in the principle of transmissibility. This principle states that *the external effect of a force on a rigid body is the same for all points of application along its line of action.* It will be noted that the external effect, only, remains unchanged. The internal effect of a force (stress and deformation in a solid, so-called rigid, body) may be greatly influenced by a change in the point of application along the line of action of the force.

7 Measure of a force. Units. Although we are conscious of forces of varying magnitudes, we are not able to compare the magnitudes with precision by means of our muscular sense. In order to express the magnitude of a force, some standard force must be selected as a unit in terms of which other forces may be expressed. The unit of force commonly used by the engineer is the earth pull (weight) on an arbitrarily chosen body, at a specified or standard position on the earth's surface. Examples of such units are the pound, ton, and kilogram. In this book forces will generally be expressed in pounds, a force of one pound being the earth pull on a body whose mass is one pound (for definition of mass, see Art. 91). The earth pull on any body varies slightly with its position (altitude and latitude) on the earth. For most engineering calculations, however, the variation in the weight of a body may be neglected.†

---

* To avoid confusion later, attention is called to the fact that the direction of a force will be indicated by specifying the angle θ_x that the vector representing the force (see Art. 8) makes with the positive end of the X axis, the angle being measured counterclockwise from the positive end of the axis. Thus, for a force acting upward to the right and making an angle of 30° with the X axis, $\theta_x = 30°$. For a force acting downward to the left and making an angle of 30° with the X axis, $\theta_x = 210°$, and so on. The direction of a force can also be indicated by specifying the slope of the line of action and the sense of the force (see Prob. 9).

† The earth pull on a body varies directly with g, the acceleration due to the earth pull. The extreme variation in the value of g corresponding to a change in the position of the body on the earth's surface from a high altitude at the equator to the pole is 0.6 per cent. Within the United States the maximum variation is about 0.3 per cent.

8 Scalar and vector quantities. Vector representation of a force. Quantities that possess magnitude only, as, for example, areas and volumes, are called *scalar* quantities. Many quantities involved in the study of mechanics, however, have direction as well as magnitude. Any quantity that has direction, as well as magnitude, as an inherent property is called a *vector quantity*. Thus, as stated in Art. 5, the effect of a force depends on its direction as well as its magnitude, and, hence, force is a vector quantity. Other examples of vector quantities are velocity, acceleration, and momentum.

A vector quantity may be conveniently represented wholly or in part by means of a directed straight line. Any such line is called a *vector*. Thus, the direction of a force may be represented by a straight line drawn parallel to the action line of the force, the sense being represented by an arrowhead on the line, and the magnitude by the length of the line according to some convenient scale. If the magnitude and direction only are to be represented, the vector may be laid off along any line parallel to the action line of the force. Such a vector is called a *free vector*. If, in addition, the action line of the force is to be represented, the vector must be laid off along the line of action. Such a vector is called a *localized vector*. Further, if it is desired to represent the point of application of the force, the point of application may be taken as one end of the vector.

VECTOR AND SPACE DIAGRAMS. In dealing with the forces that act on a body, it is frequently convenient to represent them by free vectors. The diagram in which are represented the free vectors is called the *vector diagram*. The diagram which represents the body and the action lines of the forces that act on the body is called the *space diagram*. Both diagrams as a rule play an important part in the complete solution of a problem and will be used frequently in the subsequent pages.

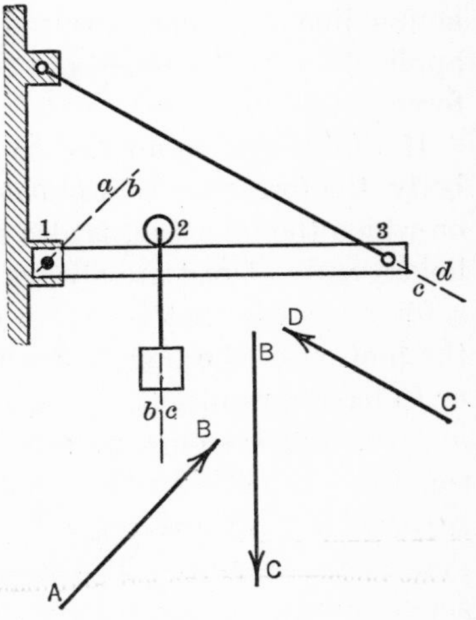

BOW'S NOTATION. In Fig. 1 is shown a wall bracket, the horizontal arm of which is acted on by three forces having points of application at 1, 2, and 3,

FIG. 1

the action lines being indicated as dashed lines and denoted by letters on the two sides of the lines as *ab*, *bc*, and *cd*, in the space diagram. The forces are represented in magnitude and direction in any convenient place by the vectors AB, BC, and CD, the lengths of the vectors representing the magnitudes of the forces according to a convenient scale. The direction of each vector is the same as that of the action line of the force which it represents, and the sense is indicated by the arrowhead.

The notation used in the foregoing illustration is known as Bow's notation and will be used frequently in the subsequent pages. According to this notation, the action line of a force is denoted by two lower-case letters, one on each side of the action line, and the vector which represents the magnitude and direction of the force is denoted by the corresponding capital letters; the sense of the force may be indicated by the order of the letters (if an arrowhead is not used); thus, the sense of the vector BA would be opposite to that of AB, etc.

9   Classification of forces.   Definitions.   Forces may be classified as surface forces and body forces, sometimes called forces of contact and forces at a distance according as the action of one body on another is exerted over a portion of the surfaces of two bodies that are in contact or is distributed throughout the bodies. The most important body force considered in mechanics is the earth pull (weight). Magnetic forces are of the same class. A surface force becomes a concentrated force when the area over which the force is distributed is so small compared to the surface of the body acted on that it may be regarded as a point. This point is called the point of application of the force. The action line of a concentrated force is a line containing the point of application of the force and having the same direction as that of the force.

If a force system applied to a body produces no external effect on the body, the forces are said to *balance* or to be in *equilibrium*, and the body on which the forces act is also said to be in equilibrium. The forces that hold a body at rest are always in equilibrium. If a body is acted on by a force system that is not in equilibrium, there always is a change in the motion of the body. Such a force system is said to be unbalanced or to have a resultant.

Two force systems are said to be *equivalent* if they will produce the same *external* effect when applied in turn to a given rigid body. The *resultant* of a force system is the simplest equivalent system to which the system will reduce. The resultant of a force system is frequently a single force. For some force systems, however, the simplest equivalent system is composed of two equal, non-collinear, parallel forces of opposite sense, called a *couple*. And still other force systems reduce to a force and a couple as the simplest equivalent system.

The process of reducing a force system to a simpler equivalent system is called *composition*. The process of expanding a force or a force system into a less simple equivalent system is called *resolution*. A *component* of a force is one of the two or more forces into which the given force may be resolved. The *anti-resultant* or *equilibrant* of a force system is the simplest force system that will balance the given system.

10 Parallelogram and triangle laws. PARALLELOGRAM LAW. The parallelogram law is the fundamental principle on which the composition and resolution of forces are based. The law may be stated as follows:

> If from a point vectors are drawn representing in direction and magnitude two concurrent forces, and if a parallelogram is constructed having these vectors as sides, the diagonal of the parallelogram drawn from the point to the opposite vertex of the parallelogram is a vector that represents in direction and magnitude the resultant of the two forces.

For example, in Fig. 2a, P and Q are two forces acting on a rigid body MN. If, from any point O in Fig. 2b, vectors OA and OB are laid off representing in magnitude and direction the forces P and Q, the vector OC represents in magnitude and direction (but not in line of action) the resultant R * of the two forces.

If the point O is taken as the intersection of the action lines of P and Q, as in Fig. 2a, then the diagonal represents the line of action of

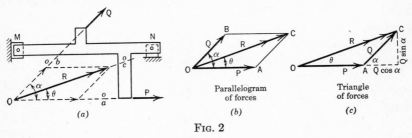

Parallelogram
of forces
(b)

Triangle
of forces
(c)

(a)

Fig. 2

the resultant as well as its magnitude and direction since the action line of the resultant of two concurrent forces must pass through the point of

---

* The fact that a force is the resultant of two or more forces is frequently indicated by two arrowheads on the vector representing the force. This fact will also be indicated sometimes by drawing the resultant force vector as a dashed line. The force R found by combining the forces P and Q by the parallelogram or triangle law, as shown in Fig. 2, is referred to as the vector (or geometric) sum of the forces. The symbol $+\!\!\!\!+$ is used to denote a vector addition. Thus, $R = P +\!\!\!\!+ Q$. The symbol $\rightarrow$ is used to denote a vector difference. Another method of indicating a vector addition or subtraction is to use the ordinary symbols $+$ and $-$, and to represent each of the vector quantities either by boldface type, or by ordinary type with a bar above the type. Thus, $\mathbf{R} = \mathbf{P} + \mathbf{Q}$ or $\bar{R} = \bar{P} + \bar{Q}$.

intersection of the action lines of the two forces. Thus, by superimposing the vector diagram (Fig. 2b) on the space diagram (Fig. 2a), all three of the characteristics (magnitude, line of action, and sense) are determined. However, in many problems, it is more convenient to use the two diagrams separately, in which procedure the vector diagram determines the magnitude and direction of the resultant, and the space diagram determines one point on the action line of the resultant; the direction of the resultant and one point on its action line determine the line of action.

TRIANGLE LAW. The triangle law is a corollary of the parallelogram law. The law may be stated as follows:

> If vectors representing in magnitude and direction two concurrent forces be drawn in order and a triangle be constructed having these vectors as sides, the third side of the triangle (the vector drawn from the beginning of the first vector to the end of the second vector) represents the resultant of the two forces in magnitude and direction.

Thus, in Fig. 2c, if OA and AC are vectors representing P and Q in magnitude and direction, the vector OC (not CO) represents the resultant R of P and Q in magnitude and direction but not in line of action. The line of action oc of the resultant passes through O (Fig. 2a), as discussed under the parallelogram law. Although the triangle law is essentially the same as the parallelogram law, its extension to more than two forces, leading to the *force polygon*, frequently makes its use more convenient than that of the parallelogram law.

ALGEBRAIC METHOD. Instead of the resultant of two concurrent forces being determined graphically, from the parallelogram or the triangle of forces, it may be found algebraically. Thus, by referring to Fig. 2c and making use of trigonometry, it may be seen that the magnitude of the resultant may be expressed by the equation

$$R = \sqrt{(P + Q \cos \alpha)^2 + (Q \sin \alpha)^2}$$

which on simplification reduces to $R = \sqrt{P^2 + Q^2 + 2PQ \cos \alpha}$. The angle θ that R makes with P is given by the expression

$$\tan \theta = \frac{Q \sin \alpha}{P + Q \cos \alpha}$$

Although it is not necessary to draw the parallelogram or triangle of forces to scale in determining the resultant by the algebraic method, the student should always make a free-hand sketch of the parallelogram or triangle when using the foregoing equations.

In a special case of considerable importance, namely, that in which the action lines of the two forces are perpendicular ($\alpha = 90°$), as in Fig. 3, $R = \sqrt{P^2 + Q^2}$, and $\tan \theta = Q/P$.

Another special case is that in which the action lines of the two concurrent forces are parallel (in this case the forces are said to be collinear). If in addition the forces have the same sense ($\alpha = 0$), $R = P + Q$. If the forces are of opposite sense ($\alpha = 180°$), $R = P - Q$.

Fig. 3

Illustrative Problem

Problem 1. Two forces, P and Q (Fig. 4a), act on a rigid body M. Find the resultant of the two forces. In other words, find the magnitude, line of action, and sense of the single force that will produce the same external effect on the

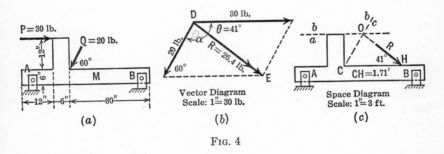

Vector Diagram
Scale: $1'' = 30$ lb.

Space Diagram
Scale: $1'' = 3$ ft.

(a)   (b)   (c)

Fig. 4

body. (In this case the external effect of the forces consists of reactions at A and B.)

GRAPHICAL SOLUTION. To find the resultant of the two forces graphically, first a vector diagram is drawn (Fig. 4b). The resultant is represented in magnitude and direction by the vector DE. The magnitude of the resultant is found, by measuring DE, to be 26.4 lb, and, by use of a protractor, the angle θ is found to be 41°, i.e., $\theta_x = 319°$. The information obtained from the vector diagram (unless superimposed on the space diagram) is not sufficient to determine the line of action of R. If, however, one point on the action line of R is found, this point and the direction already found determine the action line. For locating one point on the action line of R, the space diagram is used. Thus, in Fig. 4c the point O in which the action lines, ab and bc, of P and Q intersect is one point on the action line of R. Hence, if R is applied to the body as indicated in Fig. 4c, the external effect (reactions at A and B) would be the same as in Fig. 4a. The position of the action line can be indicated by stating the distance from C to H, which is found by measuring (to scale) to be 1.71 ft.

ALGEBRAIC SOLUTION.   Referring to Fig. 4b, we have

$$R = \sqrt{30^2 + 20^2 - 2 \times 30 \times 20 \cos 60°} = \sqrt{700} = 26.4 \text{ lb}$$

$$\frac{\sin \theta}{20} = \frac{\sin 60}{26.4}; \qquad \sin \theta = \frac{17.32}{26.4} = 0.656$$

$$\therefore \ \theta = 41° \quad \text{or} \quad \theta_x = 319°$$

$$CH = 1 \times \tan 30° + 1 \times \cot 41° = 0.577 + 1.150 = 1.73 \text{ ft}$$

Problems

NOTE. In the following problems in which the resultant of two forces is to be determined, as well as in subsequent problems in which the resultant of any system of forces is to be determined, the resultant should always be completely represented by a vector in the diagram.

2. A force P of 8 lb in the xy plane passes through the origin and makes an angle of 30° with the X axis. Another force Q of 4 lb in the same plane passes through the point 0, 2 and makes an angle of 150° with the X axis. Find the resultant of the two forces algebraically.

3. A force of magnitude 12 lb acts along the X axis to the right. Another force in the xy plane has a magnitude of 10 lb and makes an angle of 220° with the X axis, the action line passing through the origin. Find the resultant of the two forces graphically, and check the result algebraically.

4. The forces P and Q in Fig. 5 are two of the forces of an unbalanced system acting on the body M, and causing a change of motion of M along a horizontal plane indicated by the dotted line. The magnitudes of P and Q are 2 lb and $\sqrt{5}$ lb, respectively. Replace P and Q by a single force R, so that the change of motion of (external effect on) M will be the same as if P and Q were acting. (It is assumed the other forces acting on M are not changed when R replaces P and Q.)

Ans. $R = 1$ lb; $\theta_x = 270°$.

5. In Fig. 5 assume a force S of magnitude $2\sqrt{2}$ lb to act through B, the sense being downward to the left, and the line of action making an angle of 45° with the

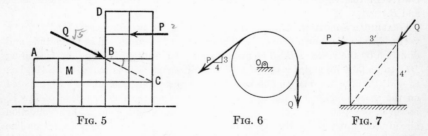

| FIG. 5 | FIG. 6 | FIG. 7 |

horizontal ($\theta_x = 225°$). If the magnitude of the force Q is $\sqrt{5}$ lb, find the resultant of S and Q.

6. The magnitudes of forces P and Q acting on the pulley as shown in Fig. 6 are 10 lb and 4 lb, respectively. Find the single force that would produce the same external effect on the pulley as the two forces, and represent this force by a vector in the diagram.   *Ans.* $R = 12.8$ lb; $\theta_x = 231° \ 20'$.

7. The magnitudes of forces P and Q acting on the body shown in Fig. 7 are 20 lb and 50 lb, respectively. Find the resultant of the two forces.

Ans. $R = 41.2$ lb; $\theta_x = 255°\ 58'$.

8. Find the force S that must be combined with the force P in the preceding problem to give as a resultant the force Q. Solve graphically and check the result algebraically.

11   Resolution of a force. Two Component Forces. The resolution of a force into two (component) forces is the reverse of the process discussed in the preceding article. For example, in Fig. 8a let W be the

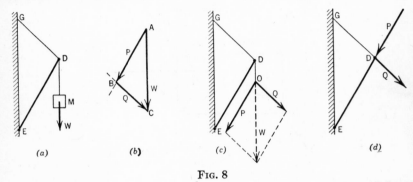

Fig. 8

weight of the body M, and let it be required to resolve W into two components, P and Q, parallel to the lines DE and DG, respectively. The forces P and Q are represented in magnitude and direction by the vectors AB and BC in the triangle of forces (Fig. 8b). This triangle was constructed by laying off (to scale) the vector AC representing the force W in magnitude and direction and constructing a triangle having AC as one side, the other two sides, AB and BC, being parallel to DE and DG, respectively. Thus, the components P and Q are represented in magnitude and direction, but not in action line, by AB and BC. The action lines of the two components must intersect at a point on the action line of W. If body M were removed (Fig. 8c) and forces P and Q were applied at any point on the action line of W such as point O (Fig. 8c) or D (Fig. 8d), the external effect (wall reactions at G and E) would be the same as that caused by the force W.

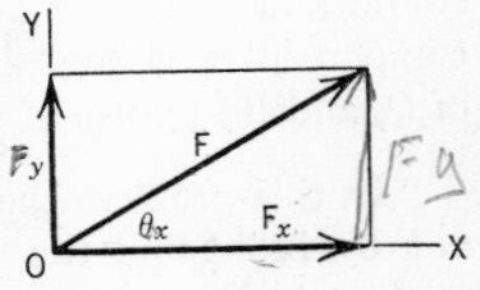

The resolution of a force into two perpendicular components is of special importance, as will be found later. In Fig. 9 is shown a force F that makes an angle θ_x with the X axis. The x and y components of the force are

Fig. 9

$$F_x = F \cos \theta_x \quad \text{and} \quad F_y = F \sin \theta_x$$

A convenient method of using rectangular components in finding the resultant of any two concurrent forces is illustrated in Prob. 9.

THREE COMPONENT FORCES. It is frequently convenient to resolve a force into three components that are mutually perpendicular. This involves only a slight extension of the parallelogram law. Thus, the force F (Fig. 10), represented by OA, may be resolved into the two

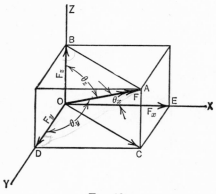

FIG. 10

rectangular components, OB and OC, and the component OC may be resolved further into two rectangular components, OD and OE. The magnitudes of the components of F in the x, y, and z directions, respectively, are

$$F_x = F \cos \theta_x \qquad F_y = F \cos \theta_y \qquad F_z = F \cos \theta_z$$

in which θ_x, θ_y, θ_z are the angles which the force makes with the x, y, and z directions, respectively.

Illustrative Problem

Problem 9. In Fig. 11a are shown two forces, P and Q,* acting on a rigid body. Determine the resultant of the two forces: (a) by resolving Q at point O into horizontal and vertical components, then finding the resultant of P and the horizontal component of Q, and finally combining this resultant with the vertical component of Q, and (b) by use of the equations of Art. 10.

* In this problem the direction of the vector representing the force Q is denoted, not by indicating the angle that the vector makes with some specified line (the angle ϕ in Fig. 11a, say), but by indicating the slope (or bevel) of the vector; the slope being denoted by the ratio of the vertical projection of any segment of the vector to the corresponding horizontal projection. This method of indicating the direction of a vector or line is frequently used in engineering problems; for one can find the function of the angle ϕ without finding the angle itself. For instance, in Fig. 11a, $\tan \phi = \frac{2}{3}$, and, hence, $\cos \phi = 3/\sqrt{13}$ and $\sin \phi = 2/\sqrt{13}$.

Solution. (a) Referring to Fig. 11b, we have

$$Q_x = Q \sin \phi = 12 \times \frac{2}{\sqrt{13}} = 6.66 \text{ lb}$$

$$Q_y = Q \cos \phi = 12 \times \frac{3}{\sqrt{13}} = 9.98 \text{ lb}$$

The resultant of P and $Q_x = 6.66 - 3 = 3.66$ lb. Referring to Fig. 11c, we have

$$R = \sqrt{(3.66)^2 + (9.98)^2} = 10.6 \text{ lb}$$

$$\theta_x = 90° + \beta = 90° + \tan^{-1} \frac{3.66}{9.98} = 90° + 20° \, 10' = 110° \, 10'$$

The action line of R must, of course, pass through the point O (Fig. 11a). This procedure of reducing the force system to two equivalent rectangular forces is of considerable importance in subsequent chapters.

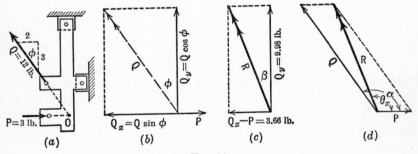

Fig. 11

(b) Referring to Fig. 11a, we see that $\phi = \tan^{-1} \frac{2}{3} = 33° \, 40'$, and, hence, $\alpha = 90° + 33° \, 40'$. Therefore, $\cos \alpha = -\sin 33° \, 40' = -0.554$, and $\sin \alpha = \cos 33° \, 40' = 0.832$. Hence, from Art. 10, we have

$$R = \sqrt{P^2 + Q^2 + 2PQ \cos \alpha} = \sqrt{12^2 + 3^2 - 2 \times 12 \times 3 \times 0.554}$$

$$= \sqrt{113.1} = 10.6 \text{ lb}$$

$$\tan \theta_x = \frac{Q \sin \alpha}{P + Q \cos \alpha} = \frac{12 \times 0.832}{3 - 12 \times 0.554} = -\frac{9.98}{3.65} = -2.73$$

$$\therefore \ \theta_x = 110° \, 10'$$

Problems

10. Resolve the force R shown in Fig. 12 into two components, P acting along BC and Q having an action line that passes through D.

Ans. $P = 200$ lb; $Q = 224$ lb.

11. If the force R shown in Fig. 12 is resolved into two components, one of which has a magnitude of 75 lb and acts downward along the line AD, what are the magnitude, line of action, and sense of the other component?

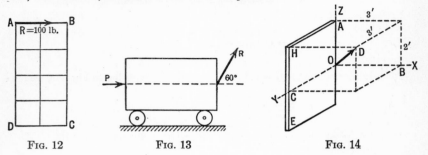

FIG. 12   FIG. 13   FIG. 14

12. A force R whose magnitude is 50 lb acts on the cart as shown in Fig. 13. If the force R is removed and a force P of 25 lb is applied as shown, what force Q in addition to P must be applied to the cart in order that the external effects (change in motion and wheel reactions) be the same as when the force R alone acts on the cart?

Ans. $Q = 43.3$ lb; $\theta_x = 90°$.

13. The vector OD in Fig. 14 represents a force of 40 lb acting on the rigid body AE. Resolve the force into components along the lines OB, OC, and OA (F_x, F_y, and F_z). If the body AE were extended to include the point D, would the external effect on the body be the same if these components were applied at D?

Ans. $F_x = 25.6$ lb; $F_y = 25.6$ lb; $F_z = 17.06$ lb.

14. A thin board in a vertical plane is 6 ft high and 4 ft wide. The board is acted on by a force of 60 lb, acting along a line joining the lower left-hand corner A to a point B 3 ft above the lower right-hand corner. The sense of the force is upward to the right. Resolve the force: (*a*) into two components, P and Q, acting along the left edge and lower edge, respectively, of the board, and (*b*) into two components, P' and Q', acting along the right-hand edge of the board and along a line connecting the upper left corner of the board to point B.

15. The action line of a force whose magnitude is 10 lb lies in the xy plane and passes through the point $(2, 0)$. The sense of the force is upward to the right, and the action line makes an angle of $45°$ with the X axis. Replace the force by an equivalent system of three forces, P, Q, and S, acting along the lines $y = 0$, $y = x$, and $x + y = 4$, respectively. *Ans.* $P = 7.07$ lb; $Q = 5$ lb; $S = 5$ lb.

16. If in Fig. 10 the magnitude of the force F is 100 lb, and the lengths of the edges OE, OD, and OB are 15 in., 12 in., and 9 in., respectively, what are the components of F along the co-ordinate axes?

12 Resultant of two parallel forces. The resultant of two parallel forces may also be found by the parallelogram law after the forces are transformed into an equivalent system of two *concurrent* forces. Let it be required to find the resultant of the parallel forces P and Q acting on the bar MN in Fig. 15. Two equal, opposite, and collinear forces F, F may be introduced as shown in Fig. 15, without causing a change in the external effect of the system since their resultant is zero. The forces P and F acting at A may be replaced by their resultant R_1, and the forces Q and F at B may be replaced by their resultant R_2. The system of two parallel forces has now been transformed into a system of two concurrent forces whose resultant may be found by use of the parallelogram law, as discussed in Art. 10. Since in Fig. 15 the vectors representing the forces are superimposed on the space diagram, the action line of the resultant is obtained in addition to its magnitude and direction.

It may be seen from Fig. 15 that $R = P + Q$ and that point C on the action line of the resultant divides the line AB into segments in-

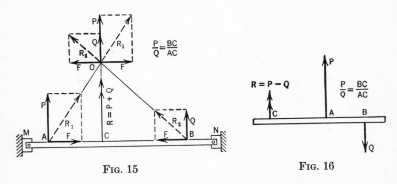

Fig. 15   Fig. 16

versely proportional to the magnitudes of the forces. (The proof is left to the student.)

If the two parallel forces are of opposite sense as shown in Fig. 16, $R = P - Q$, the action line of R is parallel to the action lines of the forces and divides the distance between them externally into segments inversely proportional to the magnitudes of the forces.

13 Moment of a force.* The moment of a force about (with respect to) a line or axis that is perpendicular to the action line of the force is defined as the product of the magnitude of the force and the perpendicular distance from the action line of the force to the axis. Thus, in Fig. 17 the moment of the force F about the axis YY is Fd. The physical significance of the moment of a force about an axis lies in the fact that it is a measure of the tendency the force would have to turn the body on which the force acts about that axis if the axis were fixed in space and in the body (or the body extended).

Since the moment Fd of the force F about YY is also the product of F and its perpendicular distance from the point O in which YY intersects the plane in which F lies, Fd may also be regarded as the moment

---

* The significance of the moment of a force appears to have first been recognized by the celebrated Italian painter, sculptor, and engineer, Leonardo da Vinci (1452–1519). However, the first definition of the moment of a force is ascribed by some writers to Father Benedetti (1530–1590).

of the force about the point O in the plane of the force. In dealing later with coplanar force systems, moments of the forces will frequently be found with respect to points in the plane of the forces. In Fig. 17 the point O is called the *moment center* and the distance d the *moment arm*.

SIGN AND UNITS. The sign of the moment of a force about a point in its plane will be regarded as positive if the sense of rotation is counter-

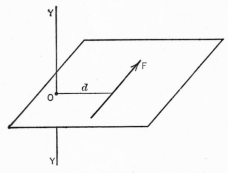

FIG. 17

clockwise. Thus, in Fig. 17 the moment of F about O is positive. Considering the moment of F about the axis YY (not the point O), the moment would be positive if viewed from the upper end of the YY axis and negative if viewed from the lower end. Later, in dealing with the moment of a force about an axis, it will be found convenient to select the axis as one of a set of co-ordinate axes and to regard the moment of

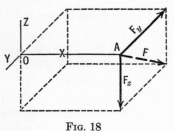

FIG. 18

a force about a co-ordinate axis as positive if the sense of rotation is counterclockwise when viewed from the positive end of the axis.

Since the moment of a force is the product of force and a length, it is expressed in pound feet, pound inches, etc.

FORCE NOT PERPENDICULAR TO MOMENT AXIS. The moment of a force about an axis that is not perpendicular to the action line of the force can be found by resolving the force into two components, one perpendicular to the moment axis and one parallel to the axis, and then finding the moment of the perpendicular component which is equal to the moment of the given force, since the moment of the parallel component about the axis is zero. Thus, in Fig. 18 the moment of F about the axis OZ is $M_z = F_y \times OA$.

Illustrative Problem

Problem 17. Find the algebraic sum of the moments about the X axis of the 30-lb and 40-lb forces shown in Fig. 19a. Assume the unit of length in the figure to be one foot.

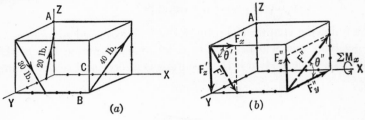

FIG. 19

SOLUTION. First the 30-lb and 40-lb forces are resolved into rectangular components as indicated in Fig. 19b. The magnitudes of the components are found to be as follows:

$$F'_x = 30 \cos \theta' = 30 \times \frac{2}{\sqrt{20}} = 13.4 \text{ lb}$$

$$F'_z = 30 \sin \theta' = 30 \times \frac{4}{\sqrt{20}} = 26.8 \text{ lb}$$

$$F''_y = 40 \cos \theta'' = 40 \times \tfrac{4}{5} = 32 \text{ lb}$$

$$F''_z = 40 \sin \theta'' = 40 \times \tfrac{3}{5} = 24 \text{ lb}$$

Hence, the moment M'_x of the 30-lb force about the X axis is $M'_x = F'_z \times 4 = 26.8 \times 4 = 107.2$ lb ft counterclockwise and hence positive, and $M''_x = -F''_z \times 4 = -24 \times 4 = -96$ lb ft clockwise and hence negative. The moments of F'_x and F''_y about the X axis are zero. Hence, $\Sigma M_x{}^* = 107.2 - 96 = 11.2$ lb ft counterclockwise as indicated.

14 Principle of moments.† Varignon's theorem. The principle of moments is of great importance in mechanics. The principle as

* The Greek letter Σ (sigma) is used to denote an algebraic summation. Thus, ΣM_x denotes the algebraic sum of the moments of the forces of a system about the X axis; ΣF_x denotes the algebraic sum of the x components of the forces of a system; etc.

† The principle of moments was first stated by Pierre Varignon (1654–1722) in his *Nouvelle Mécanique*, a work completed in 1687 but not published until 1725, three years after his death. Varignon also stated the parallelogram law in 1687, in which year the law was also stated independently by Sir Isaac Newton and Father Bernard Lami.

applied to two concurrent forces which is known as Varignon's theorem states that

> The moment of the resultant of two concurrent forces about any point in their plane is equal to the algebraic sum of the moments of the two forces about the same point.

In the following chapter the principle will be extended to more complex force systems and will be used to determine the action line of the resultant of a force system if the resultant is a force and to determine the

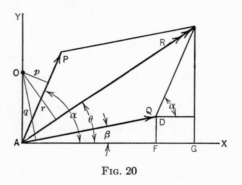

Fig. 20

moment (magnitude) and sense of the resultant if the resultant is a couple.

The fact that the principle of moments for two concurrent forces is in agreement with the parallelogram law may be shown by deducing the principle from the parallelogram law as follows: In Fig. 20 let P and Q represent two forces concurrent at A, the resultant according to the parallelogram law being R. Let O be any moment center in the plane of the forces. It is required to prove that

$$Rr = Pp + Qq$$

where p, q, and r are the moment arms of P, Q, and R, respectively. Let a set of rectangular co-ordinate axes, AX and AY, be chosen as shown in the figure, AY passing through the moment center O. Let α, β, and θ denote the angles which the action lines of P, Q, and R, respectively, make with the axis AX. From the figure it is seen that

$$AG = FG + AF$$

that is,

$$R \cos \theta = P \cos \alpha + Q \cos \beta$$

By multiplying both sides of this equation by AO, the following equation is obtained:

$$R \cdot AO \cos \theta = P \cdot AO \cos \alpha + Q \cdot AO \cos \beta$$

Hence,

$$Rr = Pp + Qq$$

It is often convenient to obtain the moment of a force about a point in its plane (or about an axis through the point perpendicular to the plane) by resolving the force, at any point on its action line, into two rectangular components and finding the algebraic sum of the moments of the two components.

In finding the moment of a force about any axis that is not perpendicular to the action line of the force, it is convenient to select the moment axis as one of a system of co-ordinate axes, and then to resolve the force into three rectangular components parallel to the co-ordinate axes and find the algebraic sum of the moments of the three components about the given axis.

Illustrative Problem

Problem 18. The magnitudes of the forces P and Q acting on the body shown in Fig. 21a are 30 lb and 40 lb, respectively. Find the algebraic sum of the moments of the two forces about the point O.

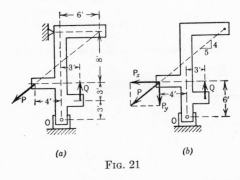

FIG. 21

SOLUTION. The force P is resolved into rectangular components as indicated in Fig. 21b. The slope of the action line of P is $\frac{4}{5}$, and the magnitudes of the components of P are found as follows:

$$P_x = 30 \times \frac{5}{\sqrt{41}} = 23.4 \text{ lb}, \qquad P_y = 30 \times \frac{4}{\sqrt{41}} = 18.75 \text{ lb}$$

Hence, by Varignon's theorem, the moment M'_0 of P about O is $M'_0 = 6P_x + 4P_y = 6 \times 23.4 + 4 \times 18.75 = 215$ lb ft, and the moment M''_0 of Q about O is $M''_0 = 3 \times 40 = 120$ lb ft. The algebraic sum of the moments of P and Q about O is then

$$\Sigma M_o = 215 + 120 = 335 \text{ lb ft}$$

Problems

19. In Fig. 12 assume a force P to act along the line AD. If the moment about C of the resultant of P and the force R shown is -200 lb ft, find the magnitude and direction of the resultant R' of P and R. Each space in the figure represents one foot.

20. In Fig. 19a a force P is applied at point B, the action line of the force lying in a plane parallel to the xz plane. The moments of P about the Y axis and Z axis are -15 lb ft and -16 lb ft, respectively. Find the force P, and represent it by a vector in the diagram. Find also the moment of the force about the X axis. Each space in the diagram represents one foot.

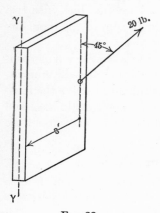

21. A force of 20 lb is exerted on the knob of a door as shown in Fig. 22. If the action line of the force lies in a plane perpendicular to the door, what is the moment of the force about the axis YY?

Ans. $M_y = 42.4$ lb ft.

22. The moment about A of the resultant of the forces P and Q in Fig. 23 is zero. If the magnitude of Q is 5 lb, find the magnitude of P.

23. In Fig. 23 a force F (not shown) is applied at point A, the action line of the force lying in the plane of the figure. The moment of F about B is -120 lb ft, and the moment about C is $+120$ lb ft. Find the magnitude and direction of F. Each space represents one foot.

Ans. $F = 50$ lb; $\theta_x = 36° 52'$.

Fig. 22

24. In Fig. 23 a force S (not shown) is applied at point B, the action line of the force lying in the plane of the figure. Determine the magnitude and direction of the force S if its horizontal component is 20 lb to the left and its moment about A is $+40$ lb ft.

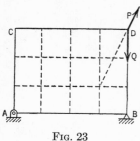

Fig. 23

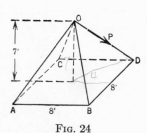

Fig. 24

25. A force P whose magnitude is 10 lb acts along the edge of the right pyramid shown in Fig. 24. Find the moment of P about the edge AB.

26. If the moment about AC of the force P shown in Fig. 24 is 112 lb ft, find the magnitude of P. *Ans.* $P = 18$ lb.

27. Find the algebraic sum of the moments about the Z axis of the 30-lb and 40-lb forces shown in Fig. 19a.

28. If the moment about CD of the force F shown in Fig. 10 is 32 lb in. and the lengths of the edges OE, OD, and OB are 7 in., 4 in., and 4 in., respectively, find the magnitude of F. *Ans.* $F = 18$ lb.

15 Couples. Two equal parallel forces that are opposite in sense and are not collinear are called a *couple*.* A couple cannot be reduced to any simpler force system. The fact that the only external effect of a couple is to produce or to prevent turning is obtained intuitively. The moment of a couple about any point in the plane of the couple (or any axis perpendicular to the plane of the couple) is defined as the algebraic sum of the moments of the forces of the couple about the point (or axis). From this definition it follows that the moment of a couple about any point in the plane of the couple (or axis perpendicular to its plane)

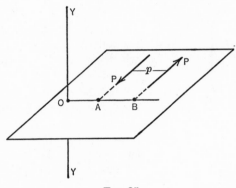

FIG. 25

is the product of the magnitude of either force of the couple and the perpendicular distance (moment arm) between the action lines of the two forces. This statement may be proved as follows: In Fig. 25, let P, P be the two forces of a couple, and let O be any point in their plane and YY any axis perpendicular to their plane. The algebraic sum of the moments of the two forces about O (or YY) is

$$P \cdot OB - P \cdot OA$$

which may be written

$$P(OB - OA) = P \cdot AB = Pp$$

Thus, if C denotes the moment (magnitude) of the couple, we may write $C = Pp$, and the moment of a couple has the same value about all points in the plane of the couple.

* The name couple was first used by Louis Poinsot (1777–1859), and his theory of couples was presented in *Éléments de Statique* (1806). Poinsot was Engineer of Roads and Bridges and in 1804 was made professor of mathematics at the Lyceum Bonaparte.

The moment of a couple will be regarded as positive if the sense of rotation is counterclockwise. The units for the moment of a couple are the same as for the moment of a force (pound foot, pound inch, etc.).

Since the moment of a couple depends only on the product of either force of the couple and the arm of the couple, it follows that the turning effect of a couple on a rigid body about an axis in the body is the same for different magnitudes and lines of

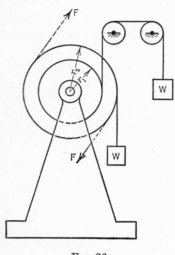

FIG. 26

action of the forces, provided that the moment and sense of the couple remains constant, and the direction of the plane of the couple does not change. For example, in Fig. 26, if cords are wrapped around two pulleys, of radii r_1 and r_2, which are keyed together, and if equal weights are attached to the ends of the cords, the pulleys will rotate exactly the same as they would if forces F, F were applied as shown by the dotted lines, provided that the moments of the two couples are the same, that is, if $W(r_2 - r_1)$ is equal to $F \cdot 2r_2$. On the other hand, if motion is to be prevented, a couple having a moment of $-(F \cdot 2r_2)$ would be required.

16   Characteristics of a couple. The external effect of a couple when applied to a rigid body is either a change in the rotational motion of the body or a resisting couple due to the actions of other bodies on the body in question. Both of the foregoing effects may, of course, be produced simultaneously. From experience we learn that the external effect of a couple depends on (1) the magnitude of the moment of the couple, (2) the sense or direction of rotation of the couple, and (3) the aspect of the plane of the couple: that is, the direction or slope of the plane (not its location). These three properties of a couple are called its *characteristics*. Since parallel planes have the same aspect, it follows from the foregoing statement that two couples that have the same moment and sense are equivalent if they lie in the same plane or in parallel planes. The fact that the external effect of a couple is independent of the position of the plane of the couple and depends only on the direction of the plane is amply verified by experience. Thus, in screwing a pipe into a joint by means of two pipe wrenches, the forces applied at the end of the wrenches constitute a couple, and it is a matter of experience that the effort required is the same, regardless of the position along the pipe at which the wrenches are applied.

17 Transformations of a couple. The foregoing comments indicate that several modifications in a couple can be made without changing any of the characteristics of the couple; namely: (a) a couple may be translated to a parallel position in its plane or to any parallel plane; (b) it may be rotated in its plane; and (c) the magnitude of the two forces of the couple and the distance between them may be changed, provided that the product of either force and the distance between the two forces remains constant. Although our acceptance of the truth of these statements is a direct outgrowth of experience, it is of value to

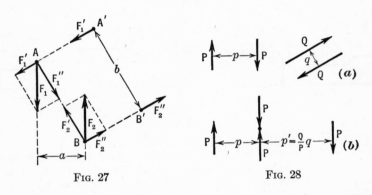

FIG. 27　　　　　　FIG. 28

show that the transformations of a couple are in accordance with the parallelogram law and the principle of transmissibility.

For example, in Fig. 27 let a couple consist of the two equal forces, F_1 and F_2, having a moment arm a. The forces may be resolved at A and B, respectively, into components so that one component, F''_1, of F_1 is equal and opposite to, and collinear with, one component, F'_2, of F_2. These two components will therefore cancel, and, hence, the couple consisting of the forces F'_1 and F''_2 ($= F'_1$) having the moment arm b is equivalent to the original couple. Further, the forces F'_1 and F''_2 may be applied at any points along their action lines, as at A' and B'.

It follows from the transformations of a couple that the resultant of any two couples in a plane (or in parallel planes) is a couple whose moment is the algebraic sum of the moments of the two couples. Consider for example the two couples, Pp and Qq, in Fig. 28a. By means of transformation c, the couple Qq may be replaced by an equivalent couple whose forces are each equal to P if the moment arm is changed from q to p', where $p' = Qq/P$ since $Pp' = Qq$. If now this transformed couple is rotated and translated, it can be placed in the position shown in Fig. 28b so that the two collinear forces P, P will cancel, leaving as a resultant of the two couples a couple whose moment is $P(p + Qq/P) = Pp + Qq$, the sense of the resultant couple in this case being negative.

By the same procedure, this resultant couple could be combined with a third couple, and so on. Hence, it follows that the resultant of any number of couples in a plane is a couple whose moment is equal to the algebraic sum of the moments of the couples.

Illustrative Problem

Problem 29. By use of the transformations of a couple, replace the couple shown in Fig. 29a by an equivalent couple whose forces are vertical and act through the points C and D.

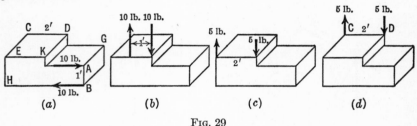

(a)   (b)   (c)   (d)

Fig. 29

SOLUTION. The couple shown in Fig. 29a may be rotated through 90° in its plane and then translated (in its plane) into the position shown in Fig. 29b by use of transformations b and a of Art. 17. By use of transformation c, the forces may be reduced from 10 lb to 5 lb, and the arm increased from 1 ft to 2 ft as shown in Fig. 29c. Finally, by use of transformation a, the couple in Fig. 29c may be translated into a parallel plane as shown in Fig. 29d. The couple in Fig. 29d has the same moment, aspect, and sense as the couple in Fig. 29a and, hence, if applied to the body, would produce the same external effect on the body as would the original couple.

Problems

30. Show by use of the transformations of a couple (applied in any order) that the couple consisting of two 20-lb forces acting on the body at A and B in Fig. 30 may be replaced by the two 10-lb forces at C and D without changing the external effect on the body.

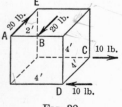

Fig. 30

31. In Fig. 30 let a couple having a clockwise moment of 60 lb-ft be applied to the body in the vertical face AD, the forces being vertical and having points of application at A and B. By use of the transformations of a couple, find an equivalent couple consisting of horizontal forces applied at E and C.

32. In Fig. 30 replace, by use of the transformations of a couple, the two couples shown by any equivalent couple, and show this couple acting on the body.

33. A couple consisting of two 8-lb forces acts on the body shown in Fig. 29a in addition to the two 10-lb forces. The forces act along the lines CE and DK, and the sense of the couple as viewed from above the body is clockwise. Transform the

couple consisting of the 8-lb forces into an equivalent couple consisting of forces parallel to HB and acting at points A and G. The length of AG is 3 ft.

③④. A couple having a clockwise moment of 30 lb ft consists of two forces acting along the lines EK and HB in Fig. 29a. The length of EH is 1.5 ft. Transform the couple into an equivalent couple whose forces are vertical and act as points C and D.

18   Vector representation of a couple.   Resolution and composition of couples.

In order to represent a couple completely by a vector, all the characteristics of the couple must be indicated. The moment of the couple may be represented to scale by the length of the vector. The aspect of the couple may be shown by drawing the vector perpendicular to the plane of the couple. The sense of the couple may be represented by an arrowhead on the vector, the usual convention being to direct the arrowhead away from the plane of the couple in the direction from which the rotation appears counterclockwise. This method of indicating the sense of a couple involves the so-called convention of the right-handed screw, since a right-handed screw having an axis perpendicular to the plane of the couple would move in the direction of the arrow if given a rotation that agrees in sense with that of the couple. Thus, in

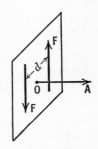

Fig. 31

Fig. 31 the vector OA completely represents the couple Fd, provided that the length of OA represents to scale the product Fd.

The fact that a couple can be completely represented by a vector is of considerable importance in problems involving the composition and resolution of couples by use of the parallelogram law. For example, if two couples in non-parallel planes be represented by vectors and the resultant of these vectors be found by the parallelogram law, the resultant vector completely represents a couple that is the resultant of the two couples. A couple may also be resolved into two couples by representing the couple by a vector and then resolving the vector, by use of the parallelogram law, into two components. The components of the vector will represent two couples whose resultant is the original couple. The two couples will have the same external effect on a body as the original couple.

Problems

35. In Fig. 19a let a 30-lb force be applied to the point C and act from C toward A. Represent by a vector the couple composed of this force and the 30-lb force shown in the figure.

36. In Fig. 30 represent by a vector the couple consisting of the two 20-lb forces.

37. A couple having a moment of 60 lb in. is required to open the blow-off valve shown in Fig. 32. Represent the couple completely by a vector, using a scale of 1 in. = 24 lb in. The valve has a right-hand screw.

38. Assume that the stem and hand wheel of the valve in Fig. 32 is replaced by the stem and two hand wheels, *A* and *B*, as shown in Fig. 33. If the wheel *A* is

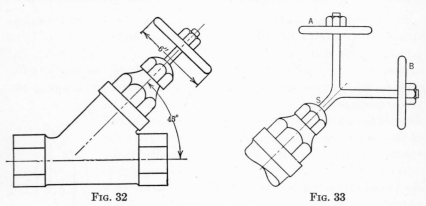

FIG. 32   FIG. 33

acted on by a couple in a horizontal plane and the wheel *B* is acted on by a couple in a vertical plane, what are the moment and sense of each of these two couples if the stem *S* is subjected to the same moment as in Prob. 37?

Ans. $C_1 = C_2 = 42.4$ lb in.

39. In Fig. 24 let a 10-lb force be applied at point *A* and act toward *C*, and let another 10-lb force be applied at point *D* and act toward *B*. Resolve the couple composed of these 10-lb forces into component couples which lie in the planes *OAC* and *OBD*.

19   Resolution of a force into a force and a couple.

In many problems in mechanics it is convenient to resolve a force into a force

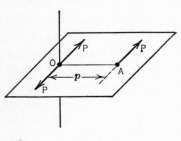

FIG. 34

parallel to the given force, and a couple in a plane containing the force. Thus, in Fig. 34 let *P* represent a force acting on a body at *A*. Let two equal, opposite, and collinear forces *P*, *P* be introduced at any point *O*, each of the forces being parallel to the original force and of the same magnitude. The three forces are equivalent to the original one, since the two equal, opposite, and collinear forces have no external effect on the body. The force system may now be considered to be a force *P* acting at *O* (parallel to the given force and of the same magnitude and sense), and a couple, the moment of which is the same as the moment of the original force about *O*. The magnitudes and action lines of the forces of this couple, however, may be changed in accordance with the transformations of a couple discussed in Art. 17.

Since a force may be resolved into a force and a couple lying in the same plane, it follows conversely that a force and a couple lying in the same plane may be combined into a resultant force in the plane, having the same magnitude, direction, and sense as the given force. For, if a force P and a couple lie in the same plane, the couple may be transformed into an equivalent couple consisting of two forces each equal to P, one of which is collinear with, and opposite in sense to, the given force. These last two forces cancel, leaving as a resultant of the system the remaining force P of the couple.

The sole effect, then, of combining a couple with a force in the plane of the couple is to move the action line of the force into a parallel position, leaving its magnitude and sense unchanged.

Illustrative Problem

Problem 40. In Fig. 35a is shown a body mounted on an axle O and acted on by a force P of 20 lb at C. Resolve the force P into a force acting through O and a couple consisting of two horizontal forces acting at A and B.

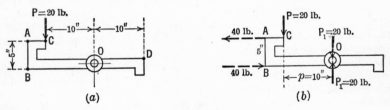

Fig. 35

SOLUTION. By introducing two equal and opposite forces P_1, P_1, acting at O and having the same magnitude as P, the external effect of P will not be changed. But the force system may now be considered to be a downward force P_1 (indicated by the dashed line) at O and a counterclockwise couple having a moment $Pp = P_1p = 20 \times 10 = 200$ lb in., the forces of which are represented by the full-lined vectors. This couple may be transformed, by rotating and translating the couple and by changing the magnitude of the forces and the moment arm (without changing the moment of the couple), to the couple represented by the 40-lb horizontal forces at A and B (Fig. 35b). Thus, the three forces represented by dashed lines (the downward 20-lb force at O and the couple consisting of the two 40-lb forces acting at A and B) are equivalent to the original force P acting at C.

Problems

41. If the force P in Fig. 5 has a magnitude of 30 lb, find the force acting at C and the couple having vertical forces acting through A and D that will replace P

without changing the external effect on the body. The squares in the figure have sides one foot long.

42. A gusset plate B (Fig. 36) is attached to another plate A by means of four rivets as shown. A force of 10,000 lb at the point O (1.5 in. below the horizontal dotted line) is transmitted to the member A. Resolve this force into a force acting along the horizontal dotted line and a couple consisting of two horizontal forces whose action lines pass through the upper and lower rivets.

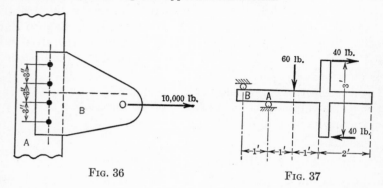

FIG. 36   FIG. 37

43. Replace the force and couple shown acting on the body in Fig. 37 by a force that will produce the same external effect (reactions at A and B). Show on the body the vector representing this force.

Ans. $R = 60$ lb downward and 3 ft to right of A.

44. Find the resultant of the 20-lb force acting at B in Fig. 30 and the couple consisting of the two 10-lb forces.

45. What single force acting on the body in Fig. 30 would produce the same external effect on the body as would be produced by the 10-lb force at D and the couple consisting of the two 20-lb forces?

46. Resolve the 60-lb force acting on the body shown in Fig. 37 into a force acting at A and a couple whose forces have action lines collinear with the action lines of the two 40-lb forces.

20   Methods of solution of problems. ALGEBRAIC AND GRAPHICAL

METHODS. In the analysis and solution of problems in mechanics, two general methods may be used: namely, algebraic and graphical methods. In the algebraic method of solution, results are calculated, whereas, in the graphical method, results are obtained by measuring distances and angles in geometric constructions. Simple graphical methods have already been used in the preceding articles in connection with forces and couples. In general, either of the two methods may be used in the solution of a problem. Some problems, however, may be solved more easily by the algebraic method, whereas other problems yield more readily to the graphical method. The operations involved in the solution of a problem by the two methods are so different that one method of solution serves as an excellent check on the other method.

METHOD OF TRIAL AND ERROR. In many engineering problems an exact answer to a problem cannot be obtained by mathematical methods of solution, and it is necessary to resort to approximate methods. A common engineering method used for computing the approximate value of an unknown quantity in an algebraic equation is called the method of trial and error, or the method of successive approximations. This method is used in the illustrative problem following this article.

DEGREE OF ACCURACY. In making computations, it is important to keep in mind the degree of accuracy that should be obtained. The degree of accuracy desired will depend, in general, on two factors, namely:

1. The degree of accuracy of the original data or quantities on which the computation is based.
2. The use that is to be made of the computed results.

The data on which many engineering computations are based are determined from experiments and, hence, are approximate values, the degree of approximation depending on the instruments and methods used, and on the care and skill of the observer. The computed results which are based on these values cannot have a greater degree of accuracy than that of the original data. In general, a sum, difference, product, or quotient of two approximate values will not have a greater degree of accuracy than that of the less accurate of the two numbers. For example, if one numerical quantity is accurate to two significant figures and another quantity to three significant figures, the product of the two numbers will not be accurate to more than two significant figures, and hence, more than two significant figures should not be retained in the result.

The degree of accuracy of results obtained by graphical methods depends on the care with which the graphical diagrams are constructed and on the scale (or scales) used in the construction. The scale should be sufficiently large to make it possible to obtain results whose accuracy is comparable to the accuracy of the original data.

Illustrative Problem

Problem 47. The equation $Q = 0.622\sqrt{2g}(b - 0.2h)h^{3/2}$ is used to determine the quantity of water flowing per unit of time over a rectangular weir of width b when the height of water above the weir is h, g being the acceleration due to gravity (32.2 ft/sec^2).

If Q equals 24.4 cu ft/sec and b equals 3 ft, compute, by the method of trial and error, the value of h to three significant figures. NOTE. This formula is valid only when $0.2h$ is small compared with b.

SOLUTION. The equation becomes $24.4 = 4.99(3 - 0.2h)h^{3/2}$, and, since $0.2h$ is small compared with 3, it may be neglected in determining the first trial value of h.

Hence,

$$24.4 = 4.99 \times 3 \times h^{3/2} \quad \text{and} \quad h = 1.38 \text{ ft}$$

The use of this value of h gives

$$24.4 = 4.99(3 - 0.2 \times 1.38)h^{3/2}; \quad \text{hence,} \quad h = 1.47 \text{ ft}$$

The equation now becomes

$$24.4 = 4.99(3 - 0.2 \times 1.47)h^{3/2} \quad \text{and} \quad h = 1.48 \text{ ft}$$

Further approximations will not change the value of the third significant figure, and, hence, $h = 1.48$ ft.

Problems

48. Find to three significant figures, by the method of trial and error, the value of x that will satisfy the equation $3x^3 + 2x = 30$.

49. In finding the diameter d of a pipe required to discharge a given quantity of water, the formula $d^5 = Ad + B$ is used. If $A = 15.5$ and $B = 400$, compute, by the method of trial and error, the value of d to three significant figures.

Ans. d = 3.40.

50. A point moves along the X axis according to the law $x = 2t^3 + 3t + 1$, where x is expressed in feet and t in seconds. Find to three significant figures the value of t when $x = 40$ ft. *Ans. t = 2.51 sec.*

51. The area of a segment of a circle is given by the equation $A = \frac{1}{2}r^2(\theta - \sin\theta)$, where r is the radius of the circle and θ is the central angle in radians. If the area of a segment of a circle whose radius is 2 in. is 1 sq in, find to four significant figures the value of θ.

21 Dimensional equations. In an algebraic equation in which the variables represent physical quantities, all the terms of the equation must be of the same dimensions, or, to express the same idea in mathematical language, an algebraic equation that expresses a relation between physical quantities must be homogeneous. The use of this principle is of assistance in checking any equation for correctness, and in determining the specific units in which a result is expressed when computed from a given correct equation. For each of these purposes the given algebraic equation is replaced by a dimensional equation.

The dimensional equation corresponding to any algebraic equation is formed by replacing each term of the given equation by a term which indicates the kinds of fundamental quantities in which the term is expressed and which also indicates the degree of the corresponding quantities in each term.

The fundamental quantities used in engineering are force, mass, length, and time (F, M, L, and T). Hence, in an equation, a term that represents an area is replaced by L^2 in the dimensional equation since an area is the square of a length. A velocity is a length divided by time and hence is represented in the dimensional equation by LT^{-1}, and similarly for other quantities. It should be noted that, in the dimensional equation, only the kinds of fundamental quantities are indicated and not the specific units used in measuring these quantities, and also that the number of such units is not indicated. Hence, numerical constants in the algebraic equation do not appear in the dimensional equation.

For example, consider the equation $ad^2 + d^3 = v$, in which a represents an area, d a length, and v a volume. Since an area is the square of a length L^2, and a volume is the cube of a length L^3, the dimensional equation is $L^4 + L^3 = L^3$, and, hence, the given equation is incorrect.

Consider also the equation $P + kv = as$, in which P represents a force, k a weight (force) per unit volume, v a volume, a an area, and s a force per unit area. The dimensional equation then may be written:

$$F + \frac{F}{L^3} \cdot L^3 = L^2 \cdot \frac{F}{L^2}$$

That is:

$$F + F = F$$

and, hence, the equation is dimensionally correct.

Furthermore, consider the equation $E = Pl/ae$, in which P represents a force in pounds, l a length in inches, a an area in square inches, and e a length in inches. Let it be required to determine the units in which E is expressed. The dimensional equation is

$$E = \frac{F \times L}{L^2 \times L} = \frac{F}{L^2}$$

Hence, in accordance with the units stated (pound and inch), E is expressed in pounds per square inch (lb/sq in. or lb/in.^{2}).

Further use is made of dimensional equations in applying the results obtained in experimental investigations on models to their full-scale counterparts. Space in this book, however, does not permit of the discussion of this subject, commonly referred to as dimensional analysis.

Problems

52. In the equation $d^4 = Ad^2 + Bd$, if d is a length, what are the dimensions of A and B?

53. Is the equation $x^3 + ax^2 + bx + ab/x = 0$ dimensionally correct if x, a, and b represent physical quantities? *Ans.* No.

54. In the equation $\omega^2 = \omega_0^2 + 2\alpha\theta$, ω and ω_0 are angular velocities expressed in radians per second, and θ is an angle in radians. If the equation is dimensionally correct, what are the dimensions of α?

55. In the Euler column formula $P = \dfrac{\pi^2 EI}{l^2}$, P is a force, l is a length, and E is a force per unit of area. What are the dimensions of I?

56. The equation $\Delta = \dfrac{1}{8}\dfrac{wl^4}{EI}$ is used to find the deflection of a cantilever beam. If l be expressed in inches, E in pounds per square inch, and I in inches to the fourth power, in what units must w be expressed in order that Δ be expressed in inches?

57. In the equation $E_k = \dfrac{1}{2}\dfrac{W}{g}v^2$, W is a force expressed in pounds, v is a velocity expressed in feet per second, and g the acceleration of gravity in feet per second per second. In what units is E_k expressed?

Review Questions

NOTE. The following review questions, as well as similar ones at the close of subsequent chapters, are meant to set before the student a definite review assignment of the essential parts of the theory covered in the chapter, by the use of which the student may test for his own satisfaction his mastery of the subject.

1. Correct the following false statement: The resultant of two concurrent forces that act on a rigid body is a single force that will replace the two forces and produce the same internal effect on the body.

2. What properties of a force are represented in a vector diagram? What properties of a force are represented in a space diagram?

3. Is the following statement correct? In finding the resultant of two concurrent forces graphically, by use of a vector diagram and a space diagram (not superimposed), only one point on the action line of the resultant is located in the space diagram, this point being the intersection of the action lines of the two given forces.

4. Is it true that the action lines of any two components of a force must intersect on the action line of the force?

5. Is the following statement correct? If a force whose action line lies in the xy plane and passes through the origin is resolved into two components, one of which lies along the X axis, the other component must lie along the Y axis.

6. Correct the following statement. The moment of a couple about a point midway between the two forces of the couple is one half as large as the moment of the same couple about a point on the action line of one of the forces.

7. Can a force be resolved into two components, one of which is perpendicular to the force?

8. How can one find the moment of the resultant of two concurrent forces without first finding the resultant?

9. If the two legs of a right triangle are vectors that completely represent two concurrent forces, why can we not regard the hypotenuse of the triangle as a vector that completely represents the resultant of the two forces?

10. One part of the following statement is untrue; indicate the part that should be omitted. If the algebraic sum of the moments of two concurrent forces about a point O in their plane is zero, it follows from the principle of moments that: (a) the resultant of the two forces is equal to zero, and (b) the action line of the resultant passes through the point O.

11. Three of the five parts of the following statement are incorrect. Correct the errors. If a force P acting on a rigid body is resolved into a force Q and a couple C, then Q must: (1) have the same magnitude as P, (2) be perpendicular to P, (3) be opposite to P; and C must: (4) have a moment equal to the product of P and the distance between P and Q, (5) have a sense the same as the sense of rotation of Q about a point on P.

12. If a force is resolved into two components, one of which is perpendicular to an axis that does not intersect the action line of the force, can the moment of the force about the axis always be found by multiplying the magnitude of the perpendicular component by the perpendicular distance of this component from the axis?

13. Indicate which one of the following choices is incorrect: A single force can always be replaced by an equivalent force system consisting of: (a) two concurrent forces, (b) two parallel forces of the same sense, (c) two parallel forces of opposite sense, (d) a force and a couple, (e) two couples.

Chapter 2

RESULTANTS OF FORCE SYSTEMS

(22) Introduction. In the preceding chapter it was shown that the resultant of any two concurrent forces or of any two parallel forces (unless the forces constitute a couple) is a single force which can be determined by use of the parallelogram law. In this chapter we shall consider force systems in which there are more than two forces, and methods of determining the resultant of each of the force systems will be discussed. Furthermore, two methods will be considered, namely, algebraic and graphical methods, for the reason that either method contributes to a better understanding of the other method. Also in the solution of a numerical problem either method can be used to check the results obtained by the other method.

The determination of the resultants of various forces systems as discussed in this chapter is of importance, mainly: (1) in the study of the conditions that the forces of a system must satisfy when they hold a body in equilibrium (Statics, Chapter 3), and (2) in the study of the laws by which the motions of bodies are governed (Part Three, Kinetics). The relations of resultants to these two purposes are discussed briefly as follows:

1. The equations of equilibrium for a given type of force system express the conditions that the forces must satisfy in order that the resultant of the system shall be zero. Therefore the resultant to which a given type of force system reduces must be known before the conditions that are required to make the resultant equal to zero can be established. Furthermore, in dealing with a force system that is in equilibrium it is frequently convenient to replace several of the forces of the balanced system by the resultant of the several forces and to deal with the resulting force system instead of the original system.

2. The motion of a body is determined by the resultant of the forces that act on the body. In the study of the motions of physical bodies, therefore, a knowledge of the resultants of the various force systems and of methods of expressing the characteristics of resultants in terms of the forces of the system must be understood.

36

The force systems to be considered in the following pages may be classified as follows:

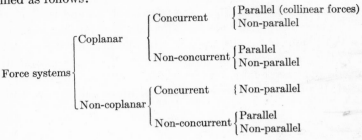

It should be observed that, in the subsequent discussion of methods of determining the resultants of force systems, extensive use is made of the following four principles and facts, namely: (1) the principle of transmissibility, (2) the parallelogram (or triangle) law, (3) the principle of moments, and (4) the action line of the resultant of two concurrent forces must pass through the point of concurrence of the action lines of the two forces.

In treating coplanar force systems, the most general coplanar system will be discussed first, that is, a system of coplanar, non-concurrent, non-parallel forces. The determination of the resultant of such a force system should present little difficulty to the student, for the reason that no principle is used that has not been discussed in the preceding chapter. After the general coplanar system is discussed, the simpler coplanar systems will be treated as special cases.

§ 1   Coplanar, Non-concurrent, Non-parallel Forces

23   Graphical methods. FIRST METHOD. The resultant of a system of non-concurrent, non-parallel forces in a plane is either a force or a couple. If the resultant is a force, it may be determined by use of the parallelogram law. In Fig. 38a are shown three non-concurrent, non-parallel forces, F_1, F_2, and F_3, acting on a body. The forces F_1 and F_2 may be combined into a resultant force R_1. R_1 and F_3 may be combined into a force R which is the resultant of the given system of forces.

If the resultant obtained by combining all except one of the forces of such a system is equal in magnitude to that one and is parallel to it and of opposite sense, the two forces constitute a couple. Furthermore, if the action lines of these two forces are collinear, the forces cancel, and the resultant of the system is equal to zero.

If the resultant of a coplanar force system is a force, and it is required to determine the magnitude and direction only of the resultant force, these two characteristics may be found by use of the triangle law. Thus, in Fig. 38b the forces F_1 and F_2 are represented in magnitude and direction by the sides AB and BC of the triangle ABC, and their resultant R_1 is represented in magnitude and direction (but not in line of action) by the third side AC of the triangle. In like manner the resultant R of R_1 and F_3, and, hence, of the three given forces, is represented in magnitude and direction by the vector AD. The following rule may then be stated: If a force polygon be constructed whose sides are vectors that

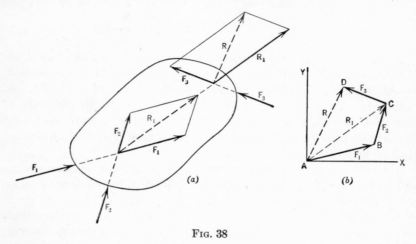

Fɪɢ. 38

represent in magnitude and direction the forces of any coplanar force system, the resultant of the system is represented in magnitude and direction by the closing side of the polygon: that is, the vector drawn from the beginning of the first vector to the end of the last vector.

A more convenient method for determining the resultant, including the action line of the resultant force, is given in the next paragraph.

SECOND METHOD. A graphical method which is especially convenient to use when the number of forces is relatively large requires the construction of two polygons: a force polygon and a string (or funicular) polygon. If the resultant is a force, the magnitude and direction of the resultant force are found from the force polygon, and one point on the action line of the resultant is found from the string polygon. Since the direction of the resultant is known from the force polygon, the location of one point on the action line will be sufficient to locate the action line.

Let the bar MN shown in Fig. 39a be acted on by three forces, F_1, F_2, and F_3, whose resultant is to be determined. The lines of action of the forces in the space diagram are denoted, in accordance with Bow's notation, by ab, bc, and cd. In Fig. 39b is constructed a force polygon whose sides AB, BC, and CD are vectors that represent the forces F_1, F_2, and F_3, respectively, in magnitude and direction. As shown earlier

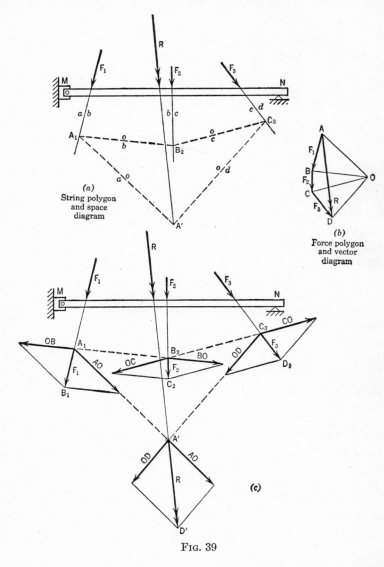

(a)
String polygon
and space
diagram

(b)
Force polygon
and vector
diagram

(c)

FIG. 39

in this article, the vector AD represents in magnitude and direction the resultant R of the three forces, and it is necessary only to determine the position of the line of action of R in order that the resultant be compeltely determined. One point on the line of action of the resultant is found in the space diagram by constructing in the space diagram a string (or funicular) polygon by the following procedure.

The forces shown in the force polygon in Fig. 39b are resolved into components as follows: From any arbitrarily chosen point O, lines are drawn to the points A, B, C, and D of the force polygon. These lines are called *rays*, and the point O is called the *pole*. The rays are vectors that represent the magnitudes and directions of the components into which the forces of the system may be resolved. Thus, in accordance with the triangle law, the force F_1, represented by the vector AB, may be resolved into components represented in magnitude and direction (but not in line of action) by the rays AO and OB. Similarly F_2, represented by the vector BC may be resolved into components BO and OC, and F_3 into components CO and OD. Thus, the original system of three forces is replaced by a system of six forces represented in magnitude and direction by the vectors AO, OB, BO, OC, CO, and OD. The action lines of the components represented by the rays are called *strings*, and, of course, the strings are drawn in the space diagram. The polygon whose sides are strings is called the string (or funicular) polygon.

The string polygon is drawn as follows: From any point A_1 on ab in the space diagram in Fig. 39a strings oa and ob are drawn parallel to the rays AO and OB. From B_2, the point of intersection of ob and bc, the string oc is drawn parallel to the ray OC, and, from C_3, the point of intersection of oc and cd, the string od is drawn parallel to OD. The point of intersection A' of the first and last strings oa and od is a point on the line of action of the resultant R of the system. Since the direction of the resultant is known from the force polygon, the location of one point on the line of action will be sufficient to locate the line of action of the resultant.

A better understanding of the significance of the string polygon may be obtained from a consideration of the construction in Fig. 39c. Here the force F_1, as well as its components AO and OB, is represented in line of action as well as in magnitude and sense. Likewise, the forces F_2 and F_3 and the components of the two forces are completely represented. The two equal and opposite forces, OB and BO, being collinear, cancel. Likewise, OC and CO cancel. There are left then only the two forces, AO and OD, and the resultant of these two forces is the resultant of the system.

Although the resultant could have been found by constructing the parallelograms of forces, as shown in Fig. 39c, the amount of geometrical construction is greater than is necessary, and the construction is shown only to give a better understanding of the string polygon. It should be noted that the string polygon $A_1B_2C_3A'$ in Fig. 39a and the polygon

$A_1B_2C_3A'$ in Fig. 39c are congruent. In constructing the string polygon it will be helpful to observe two simple rules as follows:

1. The string connecting the action lines of any two forces is denoted (in addition to the letter o) by the letter common to the notation of the two forces. Thus, the string connecting ab and bc is ob; the string connecting bc and cd is oc, etc.

2. The two strings that intersect on the action line of any force are denoted (in addition to the letter o) by the letters that denote the action line of that force. Thus, the two strings that intersect on ab are oa and ob; the strings intersecting on bc are ob and oc; etc.

If the force polygon closes, the resultant of the system will, in general, be a couple. For instance, if in Fig. 39b the end D of the vector CD that represents the last force should coincide with A, the system would be reduced to two equal parallel forces of opposite sense, represented in magnitude and direction by the two coincident vectors, AO and OD. The moment arm of the couple would be determined by measuring to scale the distance between the strings oa and od, which are parallel.

If not only the force polygon closes but the string polygon also closes, that is, if the first and last strings coincide, the resultant of the system is zero.

Illustrative Problems

Problem 58. A bar or beam 9 ft long is acted on by four forces as shown in Fig. 40. Determine the resultant of the forces by use of the force and string polygons.

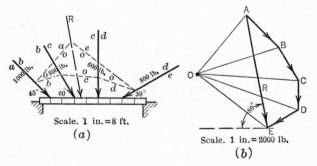

Scale. 1 in.=8 ft.

(*a*)

Scale. 1 in.= 2000 lb.

(*b*)

Fig. 40

SOLUTION. The force polygon as shown in Fig. 40b is constructed by laying off the vectors AB, BC, CD, and DE, which represent the magnitudes and the directions of the given forces. The closing side AE of the polygon represents the resultant force in magnitude and in direction. By measuring AE to scale, the magnitude of the resultant force is found to be 2450 lb, and the line AE is found to make an angle of 80° with the horizontal, as indicated in Fig. 40b.

In the space diagram (Fig. 40a) is shown the string polygon corresponding to the rays in Fig. 40b. The string polygon determines one point on the action line of the resultant, namely: the intersection of *oa* and *oe*. Therefore, the action line of the resultant passes through this point and is parallel to *AE*. By measurement the action line is found to intersect the beam at a point 3.6 ft from the left end of the beam. Hence, if the four forces were replaced by a single force *R* of 2450 lb as shown in Fig. 40a, the reactions at the ends of the beam (external effects) would be unchanged.

Problem 59. Find by the graphical method the resultant of the three forces acting on the compound pulley shown in Fig. 41a.

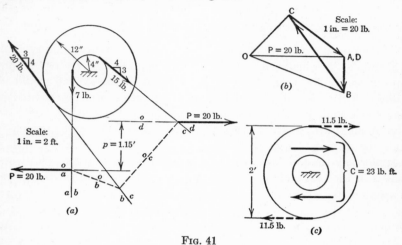

Fig. 41

SOLUTION. The force polygon shown in Fig. 41b is constructed by laying off to scale the vectors *AB*, *BC*, and *CD*, which represent the given forces in magnitude and direction. Since the force polygon closes, the resultant is not a force, and, hence, if the system has a resultant, it is a couple. For convenience, the pole *O* in Fig. 41b is selected so that the force represented by the ray *OA* has an integral value, namely: 20 lb. The string polygon is constructed in Fig. 41a. Since the string polygon does not close, the resultant is a couple consisting of two 20-lb forces acting along the strings *oa* and *od*. The moment arm of the couple, as found by measuring to scale the distance between *oa* and *od*, is 1.15 ft. Hence, the resultant of the three forces is a couple whose moment is $C = -20 \times 1.15 = -23$ lb ft, the minus sign indicating a clockwise sense. If the pole *O* had been selected at a different location, the value of each of the forces *P*, *P*, and the moment arm *p* would have differed from those shown in Fig. 41a, but the moment and sense of the couple would have been unchanged. Thus, any couple in the plane of the three forces whose moment is 23 lb ft and whose sense is clockwise, as is shown by the solid line vectors in Fig. 41c, would produce the same external effect (change in motion) on the pulley as the three given forces. One such couple is represented by broken line vectors in Fig. 41c.

㉔ **Principle of moments.** The principle of moments, as discussed in Art. 14 for the special case of two concurrent forces, may be extended to all force systems. Briefly, the principle states that the moment of the resultant of a force system is equal to the algebraic sum of the moments of the forces of the system. The principle is of great importance in the determination, by the algebraic method, of (a) the action line of the resultant of a system of forces when the resultant is a force, and (b) the moment and sense of the resultant of the force system when the resultant is a couple. A formal statement and proof of the principle of moments will not be given for each of the force systems considered since the method of proof is substantially the same for all the force systems. As applying to any system of forces in a plane the principle may be stated as follows:

> The moment of the resultant of any system of coplanar, non-concurrent, non-parallel forces about any point in the plane of the forces is equal to the algebraic sum of the moments of the forces about the same point.

In demonstrating the truth of this statement, use will be made of Fig. 39c, and of the methods of the preceding article. The given system of three forces was replaced by another system of six forces as shown in the figure. Four of these forces occur in pairs, the two forces of each pair being collinear, equal in magnitude, and opposite in sense. Obviously, the sum of the moments of the two forces of each pair with respect to any point in their plane is equal to zero. For any moment center in the plane, by use of Varignon's theorem (Art. 14), the following relations may be written:

$$\text{Moment of } F_1 = \text{moment of } AO + \text{moment of } OB$$

$$\text{Moment of } F_2 = \text{moment of } BO + \text{moment of } OC$$

$$\text{Moment of } F_3 = \text{moment of } CO + \text{moment of } OD$$

If the two sides of the foregoing equations are added, the result obtained may be stated as follows:

The sum of the moments of the forces of the system

$$= \text{moment of } AO + \text{moment of } OD$$

since the remaining terms on the right side of the equations cancel in pairs. But AO and OD are the components of the resultant force of the system, and, hence, by Varignon's theorem, the sum of the moments of AO and OD is equal to the moment of the resultant R of the system. Hence, the proposition is proved for a coplanar force system in which the resultant is a force.

If the resultant of the force system is a couple, that is, if the forces AO and OD are parallel, equal, and opposite as in Fig. 41, the proposition also holds, since the sum of the moments of AO and OD is equal to the moment of the resultant couple.

25 Algebraic method. It was shown in Art. 23 that the closing side AD of the force polygon in Fig. 38b is a vector that represents in magnitude and direction the resultant R of the three forces, F_1, F_2, and F_3. It is seen that the x component of R (R_x) is equal to the algebraic sum of the x components of the three forces ΣF_x. Thus, $R_x = \Sigma F_x$, and, similarly, $R_y = \Sigma F_y$. The resultant then is a force having com-

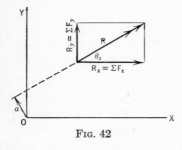

ponents parallel to the X and Y axes whose magnitudes are ΣF_x and ΣF_y as shown in Fig. 42. Since the two components of the resultant are known, the magnitude and direction of the resultant can be determined. The position of the line of action of the resultant will be determined if the distance from the origin O is found. Hence, if a denotes the perpendicular distance of the line of action

Fig. 42

from O, it follows from the principle of moments that $Ra = \Sigma M_o$, where ΣM_o denotes the algebraic sum of the moments of the forces about O. Hence, if the resultant is a force, the resultant force is completely determined by the following equations:

$$R = \sqrt{(\Sigma F_x)^2 + (\Sigma F_y)^2}$$

$$\tan \theta_x = \frac{\Sigma F_y}{\Sigma F_x} \tag{1}$$

$$Ra = \Sigma M_o$$

The sense of the moment of R (sign of Ra) must, of course, agree with that of ΣM_o. If, for instance, the sign of ΣM_o is negative, and R has the direction and sense as indicated in Fig. 42, the position of the action line of R is indicated in Fig. 42.

If both ΣF_x and ΣF_y are equal to zero, the resultant is not a force and, hence, is a couple, the moment C of which, according to the principle of moments, is the algebraic sum of the moments of the forces of the system; that is:

$$C = \Sigma M \tag{2}$$

The center about which the moments of the forces are taken may be any point in the plane of the forces, since the moment of a couple is the same about all points in the plane. The sense of rotation of the resultant couple is indicated by the sign of the algebraic summation, and the aspect of the couple, of course, is the same as that of the plane of the forces.

If ΣF_x and ΣF_y are equal to zero and ΣM is also equal to zero, the resultant is equal to zero.

Illustrative Problems

NOTE. In the solution of any of the subsequent problems, the student should present the analysis in a form as clear and concise as possible. In the solutions of the following two problems, two satisfactory forms of analysis are illustrated, an equational form in Prob. 60 and a tabular form in Prob. 61. The student is advised to note carefully the form of analysis used in each of the two problems and to use one of the two forms in the analysis of subsequent problems.

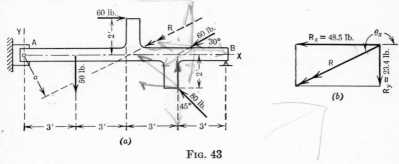

(a)

(b)

Fig. 43

Problem 60. Replace the four forces acting on the bar AB shown in Fig. 43a by a single force that will produce the same reactions at A and B as are produced by the four forces.

SOLUTION.

$$\Sigma F_x = 60 - 60 \cos 30° - 80 \cos 45°$$

$$= 60 - 51.96 - 56.56 = -48.52 \text{ lb}$$

$$\Sigma F_y = -50 - 60 \sin 30° + 80 \cos 45°$$

$$= -50 - 30 + 56.56 = -23.44 \text{ lb}$$

$$\Sigma M_A = -3 \times 50 - 2 \times 60 - 9 \times 60 \sin 30° + 9 \times 80 \sin 45° - 2 \times 80 \cos 45°$$

$$= -150 - 120 - 270 + 509 - 113 = -144 \text{ lb ft}$$

$$R = \sqrt{(48.52)^2 + (23.44)^2} = 53.8 \text{ lb}$$

$$\theta_x = 180° + \tan^{-1}\frac{23.44}{48.52} = 205° \, 47'$$

$$a = \frac{144}{53.8} = 2.67 \text{ ft}$$

Since ΣM_A is negative, the sense of the moment of R with respect to A is clockwise. In order to satisfy this requirement and also be directed downward to the left in accordance with the value for θ_x, the resultant R must have an action line as indicated in Fig. 43a.

Problem 61. Find the resultant of the system of four forces which act on the body represented in Fig. 44a. Each space represents one foot.

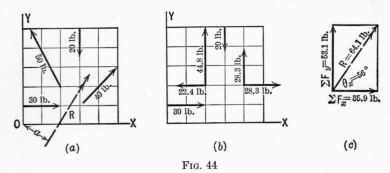

FIG. 44

SOLUTION. In finding the moments of the 40-lb and 50-lb forces about O, it will be convenient to resolve the forces at any point on their action lines into horizontal and vertical components, as shown in Fig. 44b, and find the algebraic sum of the moments of the two components of each force about O. The solution may be put in tabular form as follows:

F	$\cos \theta_x$	$\sin \theta_x$	$F_x = F \cos \theta_x$	$F_y = F \sin \theta_x$	M_o
50	$-\dfrac{1}{\sqrt{5}}$	$\dfrac{2}{\sqrt{5}}$	-22.4	44.8	134.4
20	0	-1	0.0	-20.0	-60.0
30	1	0	30.0	0.0	-30.0
40	$\dfrac{1}{\sqrt{2}}$	$\dfrac{1}{\sqrt{2}}$	28.3	28.3	56.6
			$\Sigma F_x = 35.9$	$\Sigma F_y = 53.1$	$\Sigma M_o = 101.0$

Therefore,

$$R = \sqrt{(35.9)^2 + (53.1)^2} = 64.1 \text{ lb}$$

$$\theta_x = \tan^{-1} \frac{53.1}{35.9} = 56°, \qquad a = \frac{101}{64.1} = 1.57 \text{ ft}$$

Alternative Method. Since the given system may be replaced by two parallel force systems, as shown in Fig. 44b, the problem could have been solved by finding the magnitude, line of action, and sense of the resultant of each of the parallel systems. The resultant of the given system then is the resultant of these two resultants.

Problems

NOTE. The student is expected to solve the subsequent problems algebraically unless a graphical solution is required.

62. Replace the four forces acting on the bell crank in Fig. 45 by the simplest force system that will produce the same external effect as is produced by the four forces.

63. Forces act along the sides of a hexagonal plate, as shown in Fig. 46. The length of each side of the hexagon is $\sqrt{3}$ ft. Find the resultant of the forces.

Ans. $R = 20$ lb; $\theta_x = 0$; $a = 3$ ft.

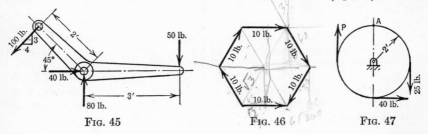

FIG. 45   FIG. 46   FIG. 47

64. In the preceding problem, assume each of the forces that act along the two right-hand sides of the hexagon to be reversed in sense, the other four forces acting as shown. Find the resultant of the six forces graphically by use of a force polygon and a string polygon.

65. The resultant of the three forces acting on the body shown in Fig. 47 is a force whose line of action passes through the point A. Find the magnitude of the force P, and then determine completely the resultant of the three forces.

66–68. In each of the three following problems the forces specified lie in the xy plane. F denotes the magnitude of a force in pounds, x and y are the co-ordinates (in feet) of a point on the action line of a force, and θ_x denotes the angle the force makes with the X axis. It is required to determine completely the resultant of each of the force systems.

66.

F	15	10	15	20
x, y	0, 1	2, 2	3, 0	3, 1
θ_x	90°	120°	0°	315°

Ans. $R = 25.9$ lb; $\theta_x = 21° 33'$; $a = 1.13$ ft.

67.

F	200	100	200	300
x, y	0, 0	0, 2	3, 2	6, 1
θ_x	60°	0°	300°	180°

Ans. $C = -620$ lb ft.

68.

F	15	12	20	18
x, y	1, 2	2, 2	1, 1	3, 0
θ_x	45°	0°	135°	270°

69. Find the resultant of the four forces acting on the body as shown in Fig. 48.

Ans. $R = 23.1$ lb; $\theta_x = 223° 57'$; $a = 1.88$ ft.

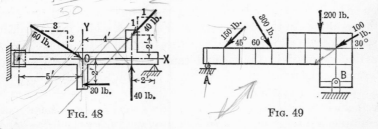

FIG. 48   FIG. 49

70. Replace the four forces acting on the body shown in Fig. 49 by the simplest system that will produce the same external effects (reactions at A and B). Each space in the diagram represents one foot.

71. Assume that the body shown in Fig. 49 is acted on by a vertically upward force P applied at point A, in addition to the four forces shown. If the resultant of the five forces is a force whose line of action passes through B, find the magnitude of P. Find also the magnitude and direction of the resultant of the five forces.

72. Three forces act along the sides of a triangular body as shown in Fig. 50. Find the resultant of the forces graphically by use of a force polygon and a string polygon. *Ans.* $C = +17.3$ lb ft.

73. In Fig. 50 assume the force that acts along the base of the triangular body to be reversed in sense and the other two forces to act as shown. Find the resultant of the three forces.

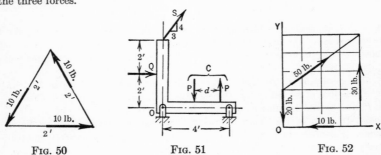

FIG. 50   FIG. 51   FIG. 52

74. The resultant of the three forces shown in Fig. 50 and a force P (not shown) is a force whose magnitude is 10 lb. The action line of the resultant is horizontal and passes through the upper vertex of the triangle. The sense of the resultant is to the right. Determine completely the force P.

75. The body shown in Fig. 51 is acted on by the forces Q and S and the couple C. The magnitudes of Q and S are 7 lb and 15 lb, respectively, and the moment of the couple is 100 lb ft. Find the resultant of the force system.

Ans. $R = 20$ lb; $\theta_x = 36°\ 52'$; $a = 2.5$ ft.

76. Find the resultant of the four forces shown in Fig. 52. Each space in the diagram represents one foot. *Ans.* $R = 50$ lb; $\theta_x = 53°\ 8'$; $a = 0.8$ ft.

§ 2 Special Cases of Coplanar Force Systems

26 Graphical methods. In Art. 23 graphical methods of determining the resultant of the most general coplanar force system were discussed. These methods are, of course, adequate for the determination of the resultants of the simpler coplanar systems, which may be regarded as special cases. However, in some cases not all of the geometrical construction required in the general case is necessary. For instance, in determining the resultant of a system of collinear forces, the construction of a string polygon is not necessary, as the line of action of the resultant force coincides with the action lines of the forces of the system, and the magnitude and sense of the resultant are found from the force polygon, which in this case is a straight line.

Likewise, in the case of a concurrent, non-parallel system of forces in a plane, the construction of a string polygon is not necessary, since the action line of the resultant force passes through the point of concurrence of the forces, and the magnitude and direction of the resultant are found from the force polygon.

In determining the resultant of a system of parallel, non-concurrent forces in a plane by the second method discussed in Art. 23, both a string polygon and a force polygon must be constructed. The force polygon for the coplanar, parallel force system will, of course, be a straight line, but the two polygons are constructed in exactly the same manner as for a coplanar, non-parallel force system.

27 Algebraic method. COLLINEAR FORCES. The equations in Art. 25 which were sufficient to determine the resultant of the most general coplanar force system obviously apply to any of the simpler coplanar systems. However, if the resultant of any of the force systems considered in this article is a force, all of the characteristics of the resultant force may be expressed by fewer equations than the three equations in Art. 25. For instance, if the forces of a coplanar system are collinear, Eqs. 1 of Art. 25 reduce to $R = \Sigma F$, and the sense of R is determined by the algebraic sign of ΣF. Therefore, the resultant of a collinear force system is a force whose magnitude and sense are determined by the equation

$$R = \Sigma F$$

and whose action line coincides with the action line of the forces.

CONCURRENT, NON-PARALLEL FORCES. The resultant of a system of concurrent, non-parallel forces in a plane is a force whose line of action passes through the point of concurrence of the forces. The magnitude and direction of the resultant are determined from Eqs. 1 of Art. 25, which reduce to

$$R = \sqrt{(\Sigma F_x)^2 + (\Sigma F_y)^2}$$

$$\theta_x = \tan^{-1} \frac{\Sigma F_y}{\Sigma F_x}$$

PARALLEL, NON-CONCURRENT FORCES. The resultant of a system of parallel, non-concurrent forces in a plane is either a force or a couple. The system will be assumed for convenience to be parallel to the Y axis. If the resultant is a force, the resultant force is parallel to the Y axis, and the magnitude R of the resultant and the distance $\bar{x}$ of the line of action of the resultant from the origin are determined from Eqs. 1 of Art. 25, which reduce to

$$R = \Sigma F$$

$$\bar{x} = \frac{\Sigma M_o}{R}$$

The sense of the resultant force is determined by the algebraic sign of ΣF.

If the resultant of the system is a couple, the moment C of the resultant couple is determined by the equation

$$C = \Sigma M$$

and the sense of the couple is indicated by the sign of the algebraic
summation.

Illustrative Problems

Problem 77. In Fig. 53a are shown four parallel forces acting on a body. Find
by the graphical method the resultant of the four forces.

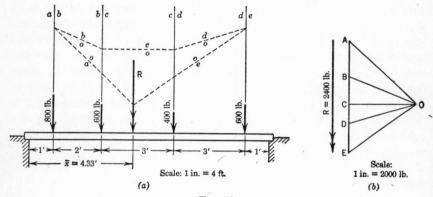

Fig. 53

SOLUTION. The force polygon $ABCDE$ is drawn to scale, as shown in Fig. 53b.
The vector AE represents the resultant force in magnitude and direction. By
measuring AE to scale, the magnitude of the resultant force is found to be 2400 lb.

The string polygon is drawn in Fig. 53a, and from this polygon one point on the
action line of the resultant is found: namely, the point of intersection of the strings
oa and oe. The action line of the resultant passes through this point and is parallel
to AE. By measuring to scale, the distance $\bar{x}$ of the action line from the left end
of the beam is found to be 4.33 ft. Hence, if the four forces were replaced by a single
force R whose magnitude is 2400 lb as shown in Fig. 53a, the reactions at the ends
of the beam (external effects) would be unchanged.

Problem 78. Find the resultant of the system of concurrent forces shown in
Fig. 54a.

ALGEBRAIC SOLUTION.

$$\Sigma F_x = 20 \cos 30° - 30 \cos 60° - 10 \cos 45° + 25 \cos 45°$$

$$= 17.32 - 15 - 7.07 + 17.67 = 12.92 \text{ lb}$$

$$\Sigma F_y = 20 \cos 60° + 30 \cos 30° - 10 \cos 45° - 25 \cos 45°$$

$$= 10 + 26.0 - 7.07 - 17.67 = 11.24 \text{ lb}$$

$$R = \sqrt{(12.92)^2 + (11.24)^2} = 17.1 \text{ lb} \qquad (\text{Fig. } 54b)$$

and

$$\theta_x = \tan^{-1}\frac{11.24}{12.92} = 41°$$

The action line of R, of course, passes through the origin.

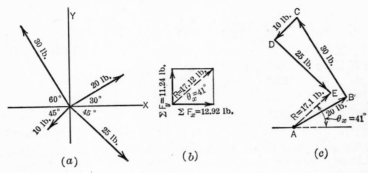

Fig. 54

GRAPHICAL SOLUTION. To determine the resultant of the system graphically, a force polygon $ABCDE$ is constructed, as shown in Fig. 54c, using a scale of 1 in. = 30 lb. The resultant is represented by the vector AE. The magnitude of the resultant R is found by measuring the length of AE to be **17.1** lb, and the angle which the resultant makes with the X axis is found by use of a protractor to be 41°.

Problems

79. Three springs lie in a vertical plane and are attached to the upper end A of a vertical post AB as shown in Fig. 55 and to a vertical wall at points C, D, and E. The tensions T_1, T_2, and T_3 in the springs are 50 lb, 140 lb, and $100\sqrt{2}$ lb, respectively. If a single spring attached at A and at a point F (not shown) on the wall would produce the same external effect on the post as the three springs, find the tension in this spring and the position of F.   *Ans.* 288 lb; $DF = 2$ ft.

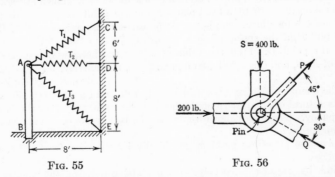

Fig. 55   Fig. 56

80. Four members of a machine are connected by means of a smooth pin as shown in Fig. 56. If the resultant of the forces P, Q, and S is equal and opposite to and collinear with the 200-lb force, find the magnitudes of the forces P and Q by the graphical method and check the results by the algebraic method.

81–83. In each of the three following problems, the forces specified lie in the xy plane and are concurrent at the origin. F denotes the magnitude of a force in pounds and θ_x the angle the force makes with the X axis. Find the resultant of each of the force systems.

81. F	80	60	50	40
θ_x	90°	150°	225°	330°

Ans. $R = 76.0$ lb; $\theta_x = 133° 57'$.

82. F	10	20	5	20
θ_x	45°	120°	180°	240°

83. F	5	4	10	8
θ_x	0°	45°	90°	315°

Ans. $R = 15.30$ lb; $\theta_x = 28° 0'$.

84. The resultant of the five forces acting on the body shown in Fig. 57 is a force equal in magnitude to the force Q and is collinear with, but opposite in sense to, the force P. Find the magnitudes of the forces P and Q.

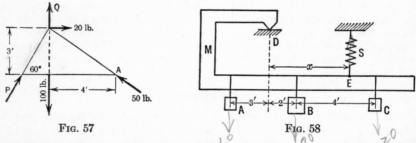

FIG. 57   FIG. 58

85. Assume that the force P in Fig. 57 is removed and that the moment about the point A of the remaining four forces is 140 lb ft counterclockwise. Determine the magnitude of the force Q and the resultant of the four forces.

86. Three bodies, A, B, and C, are hung on a frame M as shown in Fig. 58. The frame is supported at D by a fixed plane and at the point E by the spring S. The resultant of the four forces consisting of the earth pulls (weights) of A, B, and C, and the pull P of the spring on M is a force of 70 lb acting vertically downward through the point D. Find the value of P and the horizontal distance x. The weights of A, B, and C are 20 lb, 80 lb, and 20 lb, respectively.

Ans. $P = 50$ lb; $x = 4.4$ ft.

87. The compound pulley shown in Fig. 59 rotates in a clockwise direction and transmits a turning moment from the belt on the larger pulley to the belt on the smaller pulley. The forces shown represent the belt tensions. Find the resultant of the four forces.

88. Solve the preceding problem graphically by use of a force polygon and a string polygon.

89. Find, by use of a force polygon and a string polygon, the resultant of the three vertical loads acting on the truss shown in Fig. 60.

Ans. $R = -5200$ lb; $\bar{x} = 12.31$ ft to left of A.

90. Assume the 1200-lb force shown acting on the truss in Fig. 60 to be reversed in sense, and find the resultant of this force and the two forces acting at A and D as shown in the figure.

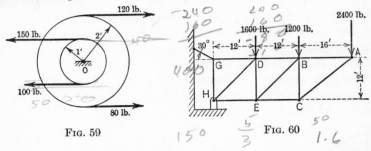

FIG. 59   FIG. 60

91–93. In each of the three following problems, the forces specified lie in the xy plane and are parallel to the Y axis. F denotes the magnitude of a force in pounds, and x denotes the distance of the force from the Y axis in feet. Find the resultant of each of the force systems.

91.

F	-40	-15	$+20$	-30	$+35$
x	-2	0	$+2$	$+4$	$+6$

Ans. $R = -30$ lb; $\bar{x} = -7$ ft.

92.

F	-10	-10	$+40$	-20
x	-1	$+1$	$+2$	$+5$

Ans. $C = -20$ lb ft.

93.

F	-80	$+50$	-20	-60	$+20$
x	0	$+1$	$+2$	$+3$	$+4$

94. A two-unit Diesel locomotive is shown in Fig. 61. The wheel loads trans-

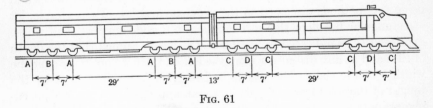

FIG. 61

mitted to each rail by wheels A, B, C, and D are 25,500 lb, 25,000 lb, 27,000 lb, and 25,500 lb, respectively. Find the resultant force on each rail.

§3   Distributed Forces

28   Resultant of distributed forces.   Center of pressure. In the force systems previously considered, the forces were assumed to be concentrated forces. The force that one body exerts on another body, however, may be distributed over a considerable area as, for example, the pressure of the water on the side of a reservoir; or over a volume as, for example, the gravitational attraction of the earth on a body. Such forces are called distributed forces. When forces are distributed over a surface, the force per unit area is called pressure. The resultant of forces distributed over a plane surface will be referred to as total pressure in the subsequent paragraphs. If forces are distributed over a plane surface and at all points are perpendicular to the surface, the distributed forces may be replaced (without changing the external effect) by an equivalent concentrated force which passes through a point on the surface called the *center of pressure*.

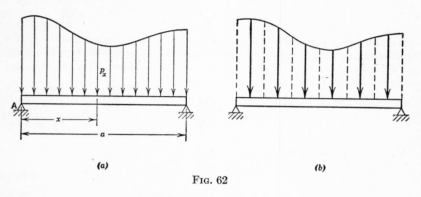

(a)   *(b)*

Fig. 62

An approximate solution for the magnitude and action line of the resultant of distributed forces can be found by replacing the distributed forces by an approximately equivalent series of concentrated forces and using the methods discussed in the previous articles. For example, let a rectangular flat floor slab a ft long and b ft wide support sand whose depth varies as indicated in Fig. 62a. Let it be assumed that the depth of the sand at any distance x from the left end A does not vary over the width b of the slab. The distributed force on the slab caused by the weight of the sand may be replaced by an approximately equivalent coplanar, parallel force system as indicated in Fig. 62b. The length of the slab may be divided into segments of equal length, and the total pressure on each segment may be considered to be a force applied at the mid-point of the segment, the magnitude of the force being equal to the product of the length of the segment and the force per unit length at the mid-point of the segment. The value of the resultant force, as determined by this procedure, will in most cases be only an approximate result, since, in general, the total pressure on any segment is not applied at the mid-point of the segment, nor is the pressure at the mid-point equal to the average pressure on the segment.

If a distributed force on an area, or on a line, or volume, varies according to a known mathematical law, the magnitude and action line of the resultant force may be found by use of the calculus, as illustrated in the following problem. The method of calculus used in this problem is widely used in the analysis and solution of engineering problems. The student should take special note of the method of dealing with a small element in setting up the problem for solution by the method of calculus.

Illustrative Problem

Problem 95. Gravel is piled on a floor (Fig. 63a) so that the beams that support the floor are subjected to a distributed force. The force per unit length on a beam varies from zero at the left end of the beam to a maximum of $p_m = 800$ lb per linear foot at the right end. Find the magnitude of the resultant of the distributed force. Also find the position of the center of pressure.

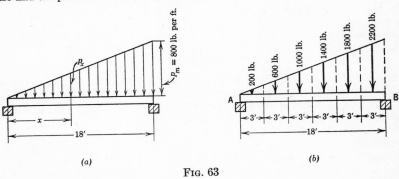

(a)   (b)

FIG. 63

EXACT SOLUTION. Let the force per unit length at any distance x from the left end of the beam be p_x lb/ft. The pressure may be assumed to be constant over an element whose length is dx, and, hence, the total pressure on this element is $dP = p_x\, dx$. But $p_x = \dfrac{x}{l} \cdot p_m$, where l is the length of the beam. Therefore, the total pressure on the beam is

$$P = \int p_x\, dx = \int_0^l \frac{x}{l}\, p_m\, dx = \frac{p_m}{2} \cdot l = 7200 \text{ lb}$$

Hence, the total pressure of the gravel (its weight) is the same in magnitude as it would be if the gravel were spread uniformly to a depth equal to one-half that of the maximum depth. The total pressure, however, would then act at the center of the beam, whereas, according to the actual distribution, the center of pressure is at a distance $\bar{x}$ from the left end of the beam such that $P\bar{x} = \int x\, dP$. Therefore,

$$\left(\frac{p_m}{2} \times l \right) \bar{x} = \int_0^l x\, \frac{x}{l}\, p_m\, dx = \frac{p_m l^2}{3}$$

Hence,

$$\bar{x} = \tfrac{2}{3}l = 12 \text{ ft}$$

APPROXIMATE SOLUTION. Let the beam be divided into six (as a convenient number) segments of equal length, as shown in Fig. 63b. The total pressures (forces) on the segments may be calculated by the method explained in the preceding article. The forces are shown in Fig. 63b, the force on each segment being assumed to act at the mid-point of the segment. The resultant of the six forces is determined as follows:

$$P = \Sigma F = 200 + 600 + 1000 + 1400 + 1800 + 2200 = 7200 \text{ lb}$$

$$P\bar{x} = \Sigma M_A = 200 \times 1.5 + 600 \times 4.5 + 1000 \times 7.5 + 1400 \times 10.5 + 1800 \times 13.5$$

$$+ \; 2200 \times 16.5 = 85,800 \text{ lb ft}$$

$$\bar{x} = \frac{85,800}{7200} = 11.92 \text{ ft}$$

It is seen that the magnitude of the resultant force obtained by the second method agrees exactly with that obtained by the first method, as might be expected since the pressure at the mid-point of each segment is equal to the average pressure on the segment. Also the value of $\bar{x}$ agrees closely with the value obtained by the first method. The agreement would be even closer if the number of segments were increased.

Problems

96. The depth of water in a rectangular tank is 6 ft. Find completely the resultant force of the water against a vertical side of the tank if the length of the side is 10 ft. The pressure at any point in the water is proportional to the distance of the point below the water surface, and the weight of water is 62.4 lb/ft³.

97. A beam 15 ft long and 1 ft wide is subjected to a pressure that varies as the ordinate to the circle $x^2 + y^2 = 225$, as indicated in Fig. 64, where y is the pressure in pounds per square foot and x is the distance in feet from the left end of the beam. Find the resultant force on the beam and the center of pressure.

Ans. $P = 176.6$ lb; $\bar{x} = 6.37$ ft.

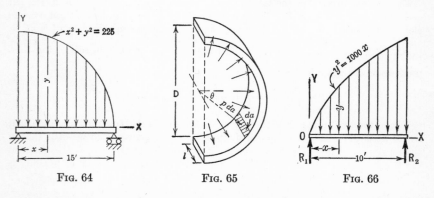

FIG. 64   FIG. 65   FIG. 66

98. In Fig. 65 is represented one half of a cylindrical vessel that is subjected to an internal fluid pressure p (force per unit area). Find an expression for the resultant of the distributed force on the half cylinder in terms of p, D, and l.

Ans. $P = pDl$.

99. A beam 10 ft long is subjected to a pressure that varies as the ordinate to the parabola $y^2 = 1000x$, as indicated in Fig. 66, where y is force per unit length of the beam in pounds per linear foot, and x is the distance in feet from the left end of the beam. Find the resultant of the distributed force and the center of pressure.

100. A rectangular grain bin is 6 ft wide and 12 ft long. The depth of grain across one 6-ft end is 4 ft, and the depth increases uniformly to 6 ft at the opposite end. Find the resultant force on the bottom of the bin and also find the center of pressure, assuming the weight of the grain to be 50 lb per cu ft.

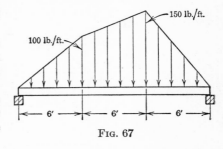

Fig. 67

Ans. $P = 18,000$ lb; $\bar{x} = 6.4$ ft.

101. The beam shown in Fig. 67 carries a distributed load which produces a pressure on the beam that varies as indicated in the diagram. Find the resultant force on the beam and the center of pressure.

§ 4 Non-coplanar, Concurrent Forces

29 Graphical method. The resultant of a system of non-coplanar, concurrent forces is a force (acting through the point of concurrence of the forces) that may be found by constructing a force polygon, as was done in finding the resultant of a system of coplanar, concurrent forces. The line drawn from the beginning of the first vector to the end of the last vector of the polygon is a vector that represents the resultant of the system in magnitude and direction. The force polygon is not a plane polygon, and, hence, this graphical method of determining the resultant of a non-coplanar, concurrent force system is not convenient. However, if the forces of any non-coplanar force system are projected on three co-ordinate planes, the resultant may then be conveniently found by the graphical method discussed in Art. 23, which makes use of a force and a string polygon.

30 Algebraic method. In finding the resultant of any number of non-coplanar, concurrent forces by the algebraic method, it will be convenient to take the point of concurrence of the forces as the origin of a set of rectangular axes. Each force of the system may be resolved into components along the co-ordinate axes (Art. 11). The system is thus replaced by three collinear systems, each of which may be replaced by a single force (Art. 27). Thus, the resultant of the components along the X axis is a single force along the X axis, the magnitude of which is expressed by ΣF_x. Similarly, the y components may be replaced by a single force of magnitude ΣF_y along the Y axis, etc. (Fig. 68). These three forces may be combined into a single force which is the resultant

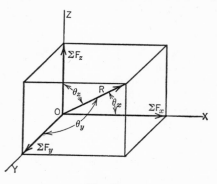

FIG. 68

of the given system and which is completely defined by the following equations:

$$R = \sqrt{(\Sigma F_x)^2 + (\Sigma F_y)^2 + (\Sigma F_z)^2}$$

$$\cos \theta_x = \frac{\Sigma F_x}{R} \qquad \cos \theta_y = \frac{\Sigma F_y}{R} \qquad \cos \theta_z = \frac{\Sigma F_z}{R}$$

where θ_x, θ_y, and θ_z are the angles that the action line of the resultant makes with the co-ordinate axes, as shown in Fig. 68.

Problems

102–104. In the following problems the forces are concurrent at the origin. F denotes the magnitude of a force, and x, y, z are the co-ordinates of a point on the action line of a force. It is required to find the resultants of the systems.

102.	F	30 lb	70 lb	45 lb	
	x, y, z	1, 2, 2	2, 3, 6	4, 4, 7	

103.	F	110 lb	120 lb	50 lb	210 lb
	x, y, z	6, 6, 7	1, 2, −2	−2, −2, −3	3, 2, 6

Ans. $R = 276$ lb; $\theta_x = 53.0°$; $\theta_y = 50.5°$; $\theta_z = 61.0°$.

104.	F	20 lb	10 lb	20 lb	
	x, y, z	1, 1, 2	2, 3, 1	3, 2, 3	

§ 5   Non-coplanar, Parallel Forces

31   Algebraic method. The resultant of a system of non-coplanar, parallel forces is, in general, a force parallel to the system whose magnitude and sense are found from the algebraic sum of the forces ($R =$

ΣF). In determining the resultant of such a system by the algebraic method, it is convenient to select co-ordinate axes so that one axis is parallel to the forces. In Fig. 69 is shown a system of parallel forces referred to such a set of axes. The line of action of the resultant force is found by applying the principle of moments. Thus, if the algebraic sum of the moments of the forces with respect to the X axis be denoted by ΣM_x and the distance of the resultant from the X axis be denoted by $\bar{y}$, then the principle of moments is expressed by the equation $R\bar{y}$

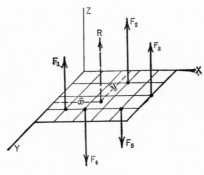

Fig. 69

$= \Sigma M_x$. In a similar manner, $R\bar{x} = \Sigma M_y$. The resultant, if a force, will then be completely defined by the following equations:

$$R = \Sigma F \qquad \bar{x} = \frac{\Sigma M_y}{R} \qquad \bar{y} = \frac{\Sigma M_x}{R}$$

If the resultant R_1 of all except one (P, say) of the forces of a non-coplanar, parallel system is equal to P, of opposite sense, and not collinear with P, then R_1 and P form a couple which is the resultant of the system. (For these conditions, $\Sigma F = 0$.) The resultant couple will, of course, lie in a plane parallel to the forces of the system (parallel to the Z axis in Fig. 69). According to the principle of moments, the moment C_x of the resultant couple with respect to the X axis is equal to the algebraic sum of the moment of the forces of the system with respect to the X axis; that is, $C_x = \Sigma M_x$. Similarly, $C_y = \Sigma M_y$. Thus, C_x and C_y are couples (components of the resultant couple) which lie in (or parallel to) the yz and xz planes, respectively. The moment of the resultant couple is given by the expression $C = \sqrt{C_x^2 + C_y^2}$ which follows from the vector representation of couples (Art. 18) and the use of the parallelogram law. Hence, the moment of the resultant couple is

$$C = \sqrt{(\Sigma M_x)^2 + (\Sigma M_y)^2}$$

Illustrative Problem

Problem 105. Find the resultant of the system of parallel forces shown in Fig. 70. Each space in the figure represents one foot.

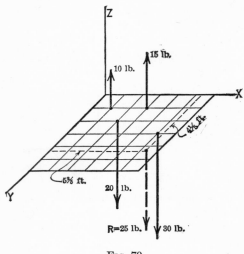

Fig. 70

SOLUTION.

$$R = \Sigma F = 10 + 15 - 20 - 30 = -25 \text{ lb}$$

$$R\bar{y} = \Sigma M_x = 20 \times 2 + 30 \times 3 - 10 \times 1 - 15 \times 1 = 105 \text{ lb ft}$$

$$R\bar{x} = \Sigma M_y = 10 \times 1 + 15 \times 3 - 20 \times 2 - 30 \times 5 = -135 \text{ lb ft}$$

$$\therefore \ \bar{x} = \tfrac{135}{25} = 5.4 \text{ ft} \quad \text{and} \quad \bar{y} = \tfrac{105}{25} = 4.2 \text{ ft}$$

Hence, the resultant is a downward force of 25 lb, as shown in Fig. 70.

Caution: Care must be taken in finding $\bar{x}$ and $\bar{y}$. For instance, in the preceding example if the value of ΣM_x (+105 lb ft) be divided by R (−25 lb), the quotient is −4.2 ft, which is *not* the value of $\bar{y}$, since a downward force of 25 lb in this position would have a moment of −105 lb ft with respect to the X axis. The signs of $\bar{x}$ and $\bar{y}$ should be determined by inspection, it being observed that the moment of the resultant ($R\bar{x}$ or $R\bar{y}$) must have the same sense of rotation as that indicated by the sign of ΣM_y or ΣM_x.

Problems

106. The force R shown in Fig 71 is the resultant of the three forces, P, Q, and S. Find the magnitudes of the three forces.   *Ans.* $P = 60$ lb; $Q = 10$ lb; $S = 30$ lb.

107. If the magnitudes of the forces P, Q, and S in Fig. 71 are 20 lb, 30 lb, and 10 lb, respectively, find the resultant of the three forces. Disregard the force R shown in the figure.

108. The resultant of the forces P, Q, and S in Fig. 71 and a fourth force T (not shown) is the force R shown in the figure. If the magnitudes of P, Q, and S are 40 lb, 20 lb, and 60 lb, respectively, find the magnitude and line of action of the force T.

109. A semi-circular plate of radius r is supported around its semi-circumferential boundary and is subjected to a vertical load (not shown) that produces a uniform

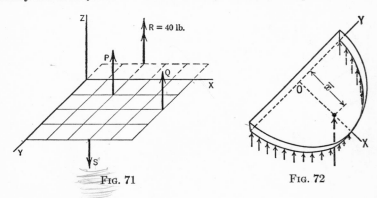

FIG. 71   FIG. 72

pressure along the support, as shown in Fig. 72. Find in terms of r the distance $\bar{x}$ of the center of the distributed upward pressure from the straight edge of the plate.

Ans. $\bar{x} = 2r/\pi$.

110–111. Find the resultant of each of the following systems of forces which are parallel to the Z axis. The values of x and y, expressed in feet, are the co-ordinates of the points where the action lines of the forces intersect the xy plane.

110. F	-150 lb	-100 lb	$+250$ lb	$+100$ lb	-200 lb
x, y	0, 4	3, 3	3, 5	4, 1	4, 0

Ans. $R = -100$ lb; $\bar{x} = -0.5$ ft; $\bar{y} = -4.5$ ft.

111. F	$+30$ lb	-40 lb	-20 lb	-20 lb	$+50$ lb
x, y	0, 2	2, 0	2, 4	4, 0	4, 2

§ 6   Couples in Space

32   Resultant of a system of couples. PROPOSITION. *The resultant of any number of couples is a couple.*

Proof. It is sufficient to prove this proposition for two couples only, since, if two couples can be combined into a single resultant couple, this couple can be combined with a third couple in exactly the same way, and so on. Thus, consider the two couples, Pp and Qq, in planes making an angle α with each other as shown in Fig. 73a. The forces Q, Q of the couple Qq can be made equal to P, P if the arm be changed to Qq/P (Art. 17) as shown in Fig. 73b. Each couple can then be rotated in its plane until the forces of the couples are parallel to the line of intersection of the two planes (Art. 17) as shown in Fig. 73c. Now let the two couples be translated until one force of each couple lies in the line of intersection of the two planes. This translation can always be made so that the two forces in this line are opposite in sense and hence will cancel, thereby

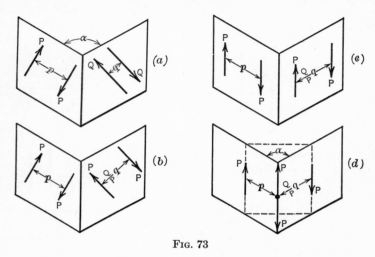

Fɪɢ. 73

leaving a couple the forces of which are P, P (Fig. 73d). The arm of this couple (as found by use of trigonometry) is

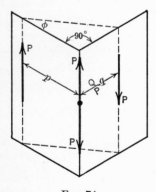

Fɪɢ. 74

$$\sqrt{p^2 + \frac{Q^2 q^2}{P^2} - 2\frac{Qqp}{P}\cos\alpha}$$

Special Case. If the angle α equals 90°, that is, if the planes of the couples are perpendicular (Fig. 74), the moment C of the resultant couple is

$$C = \sqrt{(Pp)^2 + (Qq)^2}$$

That is, the moment of the resultant couple is the square root of the sum of the squares of the moments of the two couples. The plane of the resultant couple makes an angle ϕ (Fig. 74) with the plane of the couple Pp such that

$$\tan\phi = \frac{Qq}{Pp}$$

and the sense of rotation of the resultant couple is indicated in Fig. 74.

33 Composition of couples in space by means of vectors. In order to combine a system of couples in space into a single resultant couple, each couple can first be resolved into three component couples by representing the couple by a vector C, drawn for convenience from the origin of a set of rectangular axes, as shown in Fig. 75. The vector can then be resolved into components C_x, C_y, and C_z along the co-ordinate axes. These vector components represent couples lying in the yz, zx, and xy planes, respectively. In this way, each of the couples of the system may be resolved into three component couples lying in the three co-ordinate planes and represented completely by vectors along the co-ordinate axes. The couples lying in the yz plane may now be combined into a single couple lying in the yz plane and represented by a vector along the X axis. This vector is, of course, the resultant of the x components of the vectors that represent the couples of the original system and may be designated by ΣC_x. In a similar manner, the systems of couples lying in the zx and xy planes may be replaced by equivalent couples lying in the respective planes and represented by vectors ΣC_y

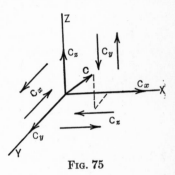

FIG. 75

and ΣC_z along the Y and Z axes. The original system of couples is thus reduced to three couples lying in the co-ordinate planes, and the resultant of the system is the resultant of these three couples and is represented by a vector which is the resultant of the three vectors, ΣC_x, ΣC_y, and ΣC_z. This resultant is $\sqrt{(\Sigma C_x)^2 + (\Sigma C_y)^2 + (\Sigma C_z)^2}$. But, since $\Sigma C_x = \Sigma M_x$, $\Sigma C_y = \Sigma M_y$, and $\Sigma C_z = \Sigma M_z$, the moment of the resultant couple may be expressed by the equation

$$C = \sqrt{(\Sigma M_x)^2 + (\Sigma M_y)^2 + (\Sigma M_z)^2}$$

The aspect of the resultant couple may be defined by the angles ϕ_x, ϕ_y, and ϕ_z which the vector representing the couple makes with the co-ordinate axes. Thus,

$$\cos \phi_x = \frac{\Sigma M_x}{C}, \qquad \cos \phi_y = \frac{\Sigma M_y}{C}, \qquad \cos \phi_z = \frac{\Sigma M_z}{C}$$

§ 7 Non-coplanar, Non-concurrent, Non-parallel Forces

34 Algebraic method. The resultant of a system of non-coplanar, non-concurrent, non-parallel forces is a force (whose action line may be made to pass through any arbitrary point) and a couple. In order to find the resultant force and couple, each force of the system may be resolved into a parallel force of equal magnitude through any point (taken for convenience as the origin of a system of co-ordinate axes) and a couple (Art. 19). Thus, the given system may be replaced by two systems: (1) a system of non-coplanar, concurrent forces acting through the origin and having the same magnitudes and directions as the forces of the original system; and (2) a system of non-coplanar couples. The resultant of the concurrent force system is a force acting through the origin and may be completely defined by the equations of Art. 30. The resultant of the system of couples is a couple which may be completely defined by the equations of Art. 33. The resultant force and resultant couple together constitute the resultant of the system which is defined by the following equations:

$$R = \sqrt{(\Sigma F_x)^2 + (\Sigma F_y)^2 + (\Sigma F_z)^2}, \qquad C = \sqrt{(\Sigma M_x)^2 + (\Sigma M_y)^2 + (\Sigma M_z)^2}$$

$$\theta_x = \cos^{-1} \frac{\Sigma F_x}{R}, \qquad\qquad \phi_x = \cos^{-1} \frac{\Sigma M_x}{C}$$

$$\theta_y = \cos^{-1} \frac{\Sigma F_y}{R}, \qquad\qquad \phi_y = \cos^{-1} \frac{\Sigma M_y}{C}$$

$$\theta_z = \cos^{-1} \frac{\Sigma F_z}{R}, \qquad\qquad \phi_z = \cos^{-1} \frac{\Sigma M_z}{C}$$

In special cases the resultant couple may vanish, leaving the force as a resultant of the system. Again in special cases the resultant force may vanish, leaving the couple as the resultant of the system. If the resultant force and the resultant couple both vanish, the resultant of the system is zero.

Review Questions

1. Correct the error in each of the following statements: (a) A ray is a line in the vector diagram that represents the magnitude and action line of a component of one of the forces in the given force system. (b) A string (or funicular) polygon is drawn in the space diagram in order to obtain the direction of the resultant force of a coplanar force system.

2. If the resultant of a coplanar force system is a couple, how is the magnitude of each of the forces of the couple determined graphically by use of a force polygon and a string polygon? How is the moment arm determined?

3. The force polygon for a given coplanar, non-concurrent, parallel force system closes. Which of the following conclusions can be drawn? (a) There is no resultant. (b) The resultant is a couple. (c) Either there is no resultant or the resultant is a couple.

4. In finding, by the algebraic method, the resultant of a coplanar, non-concurrent force system, what information about the resultant is found by applying the principle of moments: (*a*) when the resultant is a force, and (*b*) when the resultant is a couple?

5. If it is known that the resultant of a coplanar force system is a force and that the algebraic sum of the moments of the forces about a point in the plane of the forces is zero, what can be said about the resultant force?

6. A force system consisting of two couples acts on a body. (*a*) If the force system has a resultant, must it be a couple? (*b*) If the system has no resultant, must the two couples lie in the same plane?

7. Given two systems of forces that lie in the same plane, one of the systems being concurrent and the other non-concurrent. For each force in the concurrent system there is a corresponding force in the non-concurrent system having the same magnitude, direction, and sense. Which two of the following statements concerning the resultants of the two systems are correct? (*a*) If the resultant of the concurrent system is a force, the resultant of the non-concurrent system is a parallel force of equal magnitude. (*b*) If the resultant of the concurrent system is zero, the resultant of the non-concurrent system is also zero. (*c*) If the resultant of the concurrent system is zero, the resultant of the non-concurrent system is a couple. (*d*) If the resultant of the concurrent system is zero, the resultant of the non-concurrent system is either zero or a couple.

8. If the resultant of a coplanar, parallel force system is a couple and the resultant is determined graphically by use of a force polygon and a string polygon, what would be the effect of a change in the position of the pole in the force diagram?

9. If the resultant of a system of coplanar, concurrent forces is a force and the algebraic sum of the moments of the forces about a point A in the plane of the forces is zero, what restriction must be put on the location of a point B in the plane in order that the algebraic sum of the moments of the forces about B also shall be zero?

10. A system of coplanar, non-concurrent, non-parallel forces contains five forces. If the resultant of four of the forces is a couple, what conclusion can be drawn concerning the resultant of the five forces?

11. The resultant of a given coplanar, non-concurrent, non-parallel force system is a force. If $\Sigma M_A = -\Sigma M_B$, where A and B are points in the plane of the forces, what is known concerning the line of action of the resultant of the forces?

12. The forces of a non-coplanar force system are parallel to the Z axis. If $\Sigma F = 0$ and $\Sigma M_x = 0$, what conclusions can be drawn concerning the resultant of the forces?

Chapter 3

EQUILIBRIUM OF
COPLANAR FORCE SYSTEMS

§ 1   Introduction

35   Preliminary. In the preceding chapter, equations and graphical
constructions were developed for determining the resultants of various
force systems. In the present chapter are determined the algebraic and
graphical conditions of equilibrium for the various force systems: that
is, the conditions which the forces of the various systems must satisfy
in order that the force systems shall have no resultant. These conditions
may be expressed by means of algebraic equations which the forces
must satisfy, called the *equations of equilibrium*, or by stating the conditions which graphical diagrams involving the forces, such as force
and string polygons, must satisfy. Diagrams that satisfy these conditions are sometimes called *equilibrium diagrams* or *equilibrium polygons*.

Many problems in engineering practice involve bodies that are in
equilibrium under the action of a system of forces as, for example, a
bridge, roof truss, or crane. In such problems certain characteristics
of the forces acting on the body may be unknown, as, for example, the
magnitude or the direction of one or more of the forces. If the number
of unknown characteristics in a force system that is in equilibrium is not
greater than the number of equations of equilibrium for that system, the
system is said to be *statically determinate*, and all the unknown characteristics may be found from the equations of equilibrium for the system.

If the number of unknown characteristics in a force system is greater
than the number of equations of equilibrium for that particular force
system, the force system is said to be *statically indeterminate*, as, for
example, the forces that act on a horizontal beam which rests on three
or more supports and carries known vertical loads. The beam is in
equilibrium under the action of a system of coplanar, parallel forces, all
of which are known except the three upward reactions of the supports.
As is shown in Art. 41, there are only *two* independent equations of
equilibrium for such a force system, and, hence, the three reactions can-

not be found from the equations of equilibrium alone. The force system is therefore statically indeterminate.

36 Graphical conditions of equilibrium. In Chapter 2, it was shown that the resultant of an unbalanced force system in a plane is either a force or a couple. Furthermore, it was shown that, if the resultant is a force, it is represented in magnitude and in direction by the closing side of the force polygon, and that, if the resultant is a couple, the two forces of the couple act along the first and last strings of the string polygon. Hence, if the force polygon closes, the resultant cannot be a force but may be a couple. If, however, the string polygon also closes, that is, if the first and last strings along which the two forces of the couple act are collinear, the two forces cancel, and, hence, the resultant couple vanishes. There are, then, two conditions which the forces of a coplanar force system must satisfy if they have no resultant, that is, if the forces are in equilibrium.

1. The force polygon must close. If this condition is satisfied the resultant cannot be a force.
2. The string or funicular polygon must close. If this condition is satisfied the resultant cannot be a couple.

37 Algebraic conditions of equilibrium. The two conditions which the graphical diagrams for a balanced force system must satisfy,

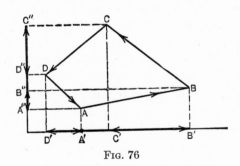

FIG. 76

as stated in the preceding article, may also be expressed algebraically. Thus, if the force polygon closes, the projections (components) of the forces on any line also form a closed polygon, as shown in Fig. 76, and, since these components are collinear, their vector sum is the same as their algebraic sum. Hence, the fact that the force polygon for the components closes may be expressed by stating that the algebraic sum of the components of the forces in any direction is equal to zero.

If the string or funicular polygon closes, the resultant cannot be a couple, since the first and last strings of the funicular polygon are collinear, and, hence, the algebraic sum of the moments, about any point, of the two equal and opposite forces which act along these strings is equal to zero. But the algebraic sum of the moments of these two forces is equal to the algebraic sum of the moments of the forces of the system. Therefore, the statement that the funicular polygon must close is equivalent to the statement that the algebraic sum of the moments of the forces of the system must equal zero. Hence, the algebraic conditions of equilibrium for a coplanar force system are:

1. The algebraic sum of the components of the forces in any direction in the plane must equal zero.
2. The algebraic sum of the moments of the forces about any point in the plane must equal zero.

An infinite number of equations could be written in accordance with these conditions by taking different directions of resolution and different moment centers, but not all of the equations would be independent. The number of independent equations is different for the various force systems, as will be discussed in the succeeding articles, but for any force system the independent equations of equilibrium are the equations which are necessary and sufficient to ensure that the resultant of that particular force system shall be equal to zero.

If a given body is in equilibrium under the influence of a statically determinate system of forces, some of which are unknown, wholly or in part, these unknowns may be found by applying the equations of equilibrium which apply to that particular system of forces.

If the number of unknowns in a system of forces which is in equilibrium is equal to the number of independent equations of equilibrium for that particular system, the determination of all the unknowns involves the use of all the equations of equilibrium. Frequently, however, it is not required to determine all the unknowns in such a system, for a single unknown only may be required, as, for example, the magnitude of a certain force, the line of action and sense of which are known. A single unknown may frequently be found by using only one of the equations of equilibrium. In applying the equilibrium equations, the work may be materially simplified by properly selecting the directions of resolution and the moment axes or moment centers.

Before applying the equations of equilibrium to any system of forces that holds a body in equilibrium, it is important to have a clear idea of the forces that act on the body. For this purpose it is highly desirable to construct a free-body diagram, which will be explained in the following article.

38 Free-body diagram. *A free-body diagram is a diagram in which are shown an isolated (free) body and all the forces exerted by other bodies on the free or isolated body considered.* It does not show the forces exerted by the considered body on other bodies. It is important to note that *all* the forces acting on the body considered must be shown; the student is likely to overlook a force and omit it from the free-body diagram. On the other hand, it must be remembered that a force cannot exist unless there is a body to exert the force; the student frequently shows a force in the free-body diagram when there is no body present to exert the force shown. The most satisfactory method of determining the forces that should be shown in the free-body diagram is to note the number of bodies that exert forces on the given body; these forces may be either forces of contact or body forces, the most important body force being the earth pull on (or weight of) a body. A body force is sometimes called a force at a distance in contrast to forces of contact.

The word *free* in the expression "free-body diagram" emphasizes the idea that all the bodies exerting forces on the considered body are removed or withdrawn and are replaced by the forces they exert; it is considered undesirable to show both the bodies *and* the forces exerted by them. However, it is sometimes convenient to indicate, by light-weight dotted lines, the faint outlines of the bodies removed, in order to make more evident the geometry and dimensions involved in the problem. For example, Fig. 77b shows the free-body diagram of the cylinder in Fig. 77a.

TYPES OF REACTION INVOLVED. In drawing a free-body diagram of a given or considered body, certain assumptions are frequently made concerning the nature of the forces (reactions) exerted by other bodies on the given body. The more common assumptions are the following: (a) If a surface of contact at which a force is applied by one body to another body has only a small degree of roughness, it may be assumed to be smooth (frictionless), and, hence, the action (or reaction) of either body on the other is directed normal to the surface of contact. (One convention for indicating a smooth surface is shown at point K in Fig. 78.) (b) A body that possesses only a small degree of bending stiffness, such as a cord, rope, or chain, may be considered to be perfectly flexible, and, hence, the pull of such a body on any other body is directed along the axis of the flexible body.

Further, in drawing the free-body diagram of a body, if one of the forces acting on the body is unknown in direction, as well as in magnitude (such as a pin reaction in a pin-connected structure), it is frequently convenient to show two rectangular components of the force instead of the single force, and thus deal with two forces, each being known in direction but unknown in magnitude. After solving for the magnitudes of the two rectangular components, their resultant, which is the desired force, may be found both in magnitude and in direction.

METHOD OF SHOWING AN INTERNAL FORCE IN THE FREE-BODY DIAGRAM. The expression "body considered" used in the definition of a free-body diagram may mean any definite portion of material and frequently is taken as a portion, only, of a physical object; such a portion may be an eye bar in a bridge or a connecting rod in a gas engine. On the other hand, the considered or given body may be taken as a group of physical bodies joined together (considered as one body), such as the whole bridge or the whole engine.

The forces in a free-body diagram, however, are always forces external to the body considered: that is, forces exerted by other (outside) bodies on the considered body. Some of the forces acting on a portion of a single body would be internal forces with respect to that (whole) body. The question then arises: How can a portion of a physical body be considered as the body in a free-body diagram if such a diagram involves only external forces? The method is as follows: Let a plane be assumed to pass through the body, severing from the body that portion of it which is to be considered in the free-body diagram. This severed portion is now considered as the "free" body, and the force (or forces) that was exerted on it at the severed (or cut) section by the other part of the body (before the severed portion was removed) is now external with respect to the severed portion and will be shown in the free-body diagram of the severed portion together with all the original external forces that act on this severed portion.

The ideas discussed in this article are illustrated in the following problem.

Illustrative Problem

Problem 112. A homogeneous cylinder weighing 100 lb and having a radius of 1 ft rests between two smooth planes, OA and OB, as shown in Fig. 77a. Member OB is attached to the vertical wall at O by a smooth pin. Similarly, the horizontal cable is attached at A and B by smooth pins. The weights of OB and AB may be assumed to be negligible. Draw a free-body diagram of: (a) the cylinder, and (b) the bar OB with one half of the cable AB attached (considered as one body).

SOLUTION. (a) The cylinder is acted on by three (and only three) bodies: namely, the earth, the vertical plane, and the bar OB. There will be, therefore, three (and only three) forces in the free-body diagram. Further, since all the surfaces of contact are assumed to be smooth, the force P exerted by the vertical wall on the cylinder will be normal to the wall and hence horizontal as shown in Fig. 77b; for the same reason Q, the force exerted by the bar OB on the cylinder, is normal to OB. Figure 77b is then the free-body diagram of the cylinder since it shows the cylinder alone or free from the other bodies (even though the bodies of contact are shown faintly as dotted lines) with all the forces acting on it. It will be observed that the forces whose magnitudes are unknown are represented by dashed-line vectors, and the forces whose magnitudes are known by solid-line vectors; this method or some other convenient method (such as representing the unknown forces by colored lines) for distinguishing between known and unknown forces is very desirable.

(b) The body for which a free-body diagram is required is shown as OBC in Fig. 77c. A plane is assumed to have been passed through the cable at its mid-point C, and the force exerted at the severed section by the left half (which has been removed) on the body OBC is shown as T; this force acts along the cable since the cable is assumed to be flexible. There are, then, three bodies acting on OBC: namely, the left half of the cable, the cylinder, and the pin at O. Hence there are three (and only three) forces acting on the body OBC: namely, the force T, the force Q per-

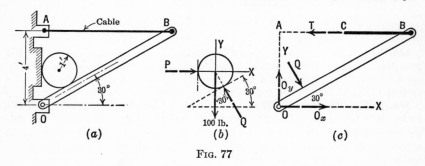

(a)   (b)   (c)

FIG. 77

pendicular to OB (equal and opposite to Q in Fig. 77b), and the pressure of the pin at O; this pin pressure is unknown in direction as well as in magnitude, for, although it is directed normal to the surfaces of contact since the pin is smooth, the point (or line) of contact on the two surfaces is unknown. It will be convenient to replace the pin pressure by its two rectangular components, O_x and O_y, as shown in Fig. 77c. It should be noted that the force at O is denoted by the same letter as the point and that the components of the force are denoted by subscripts on the letter. This has the disadvantage of using a letter for two purposes but is otherwise convenient. Another convenient notation is to denote the horizontal component of a force (or component parallel to the X axis) at a point (O, say) as H_o and the vertical component (or component parallel to the Y axis) as V_o. Another convention is to designate the reaction at a point (O, say) by R_o. This latter method has the disadvantage of requiring two subscripts to denote a component of a force. For example, the x component of a force at O would be designated by $(R_o)_x$ or R_{ox}. Some consistent and convenient notation is highly desirable in designating forces in free-body diagrams, especially for problems involving many forces.

Problems

113. In Fig. 78, two bars, HD and EB, are connected by a smooth pin at C. At H and E are smooth rollers, and the surface at K is smooth. A body M weighing 100 lb is attached to the bar EB by a flexible cable. Draw a free-body diagram of: (a) the two bars, the roller at E, and the pin at C, considered as one body, (b) the body M, (c) the bar EB, the cable, and the attached body M, considered as one body, and (d) the bar HD. Neglect the weights of the bars.

114. In the crane shown in Fig. 79 assume the weights of the members to be negligible and the pin at C to be smooth. Draw a free-body diagram of: (*a*) the entire crane, considered as one body, (*b*) the post AD, and (*c*) the member CH.

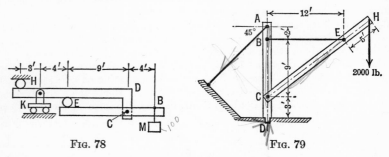

FIG. 78   FIG. 79

115. In Fig. 127 the bars AB and CD are pin-connected at A, B, and C, and the pulley D is pin-connected to CD. Draw free-body diagrams of: (*a*) the bar CD, (*b*) the bars CD and AB and the pin at B considered as one body, and (*c*) the entire system. Neglect friction and neglect weights of members.

116. In Fig. 136 the bars AD and BE are pin-connected at A, B, and C, and the pulley D is pin-connected to AD. Draw free-body diagrams of: (*a*) the bar BE, (*b*) the bar AD, the pulley D, the pin at D, the cable, and the 1000-lb body, all considered as one body, and (*c*) the entire system. Assume pins to be smooth and weights of members to be negligible.

NOTE. In the following discussion of equilibrium some readers may wish to consider the general coplanar force system as discussed in Art. 42 first and then consider the force systems discussed in Arts. 39, 40, and 41 as special cases. This method of study has the advantage of dealing with fewer equations, but it is felt that the reasoning which leads to the independent equations of equilibrium for each force system constitutes an important part of the student's development and gives an opportunity to emphasize the general method of obtaining the necessary and sufficient conditions of equilibrium for each force system. It will be observed that the method of proof in each case is to assume that the force system has a resultant and then to establish the necessary and sufficient conditions that the forces must satisfy to cause the resultant to vanish.

§ 2   Collinear Forces

39   Equations of equilibrium. A system of collinear forces is in equilibrium if the forces of the system satisfy either of the following equations:

$$\Sigma F = 0 \qquad\qquad (A)$$

or

$$\Sigma M_A = 0 \qquad\qquad (B)$$

where A is any point not on the action line of the forces.

Proof. As shown in Art. 27, if a collinear force system is not in equilibrium, the resultant of the force system is a force having the same action line as the forces and having a magnitude R which is given by the equation $R = \Sigma F$. If the forces of the system satisfy the equation $\Sigma F = 0$, the resultant is not a force, and therefore the system is in equilibrium. The equation $\Sigma M_A = 0$ is also sufficient to ensure equilibrium, for, if the forces of the system satisfy this equation, the resultant force must, in accordance with the principle of moments, pass through the point A. But this is impossible since the resultant force, if there be one, has the same line of action as the forces and hence cannot pass through A.

Therefore, if either one of the equations A and B is satisfied, the resultant is equal to zero, and hence there is but one independent equation of equilibrium for a collinear force system.

Illustrative Problem

Problem 117. Two men pull on the ends of a rope with forces of 100 lb each (Fig. 80a). What is the internal tensile force S in the rope?

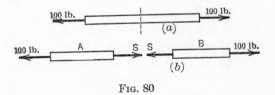

FIG. 80

SOLUTION. Suppose the rope to be divided into two parts, A and B, as shown in Fig. 80b. Consider as a free body the part A. The forces acting on A are two in number: namely, the 100-lb force and the force exerted by B on A at the cut section. The latter is the internal force S required; it is an external force with respect to part of the rope but an internal force with respect to the whole rope. This force is sometimes called total stress or merely stress in the rope. The equation of equilibrium then becomes

$$\Sigma F = S - 100 = 0$$

Therefore,

$$S = 100 \text{ lb}$$

Obviously, B could have been taken as the free body, and the same result would have been obtained. It should be noted that, although a 100-lb force is applied to each end of the rope, the stress (force) in the rope is 100 lb and not 200 lb.

TWO-FORCE MEMBER. If a body or a member of a structure is held in equilibrium by *two* forces only, the two forces must be equal, opposite, and collinear. If the body or member on which the two forces act is of prismatic form such as a straight bar or a cable and the forces are applied along the axis and at the ends of the member, the internal force (total stress) in the member is numerically equal to each of the applied forces and is collinear with them as was found in Prob. 117. Such a member is called a *two-force member*.

Examples of two-force members will be encountered in many subsequent problems, especially in determining stresses in pin-connected, pin-loaded trusses. Stresses in members that are acted on by more than two forces are considered in the subject of Strength of Materials.

§ 3 Coplanar, Concurrent Forces

40 Equations of equilibrium. A system of coplanar, concurrent forces is in equilibrium if the forces of the system satisfy the following equations:

$$\Sigma F_x = 0$$

$$\Sigma F_y = 0 \tag{A}$$

where x and y denote any two non-parallel lines in the plane. It is convenient, however, to take as the two lines a set of rectangular axes with the point of concurrence of the forces as origin.

Proof. In Art. 27 it was shown that, if a concurrent system of forces in a plane is not in equilibrium, the resultant is a force whose components are equal to ΣF_x and ΣF_y. If, then, the forces of the system satisfy the equation $\Sigma F_x = 0$, the resultant cannot have a component along the X axis, and, if the equation $\Sigma F_y = 0$ is satisfied, the resultant cannot have a component along the Y axis. Therefore, if both these equations are satisfied, the resultant cannot be a force, and hence the system must be in equilibrium. There are, then, only two independent equations of equilibrium for a coplanar, concurrent system of forces.

Another set of independent equations which are necessary and sufficient for equilibrium of the forces of a coplanar, concurrent force system may be expressed as follows:

$$\Sigma F_x = 0$$

$$\Sigma M_A = 0 \tag{B}$$

where x denotes any line in the plane (taken for convenience as one of two rectangular axes through the point of concurrence of the forces) and A is any point in the plane not on the Y axis.

Proof. If the forces of the system satisfy the equation $\Sigma F_x = 0$, the resultant cannot have a component along the X axis; that is, the resultant, if there be one, must lie along the Y axis. If the equation $\Sigma M_A = 0$ is satisfied, the resultant, if there be one, must pass through the point A in accordance with the principle of moments. It is impossible for a force to satisfy these two conditions simultaneously and hence, if both the equations are satisfied by the forces of the system, the system is in equilibrium.

A third set of equations of equilibrium for a coplanar, concurrent force system is as follows:

$$\Sigma M_A = 0$$

$$\tag{C}$$

$$\Sigma M_B = 0$$

where A and B are any two points in the plane of the forces, provided that the line joining A and B does not pass through the point at which the forces are concurrent. The proof that these equations are sufficient to ensure equilibrium will be left to the student.

THREE FORCES IN EQUILIBRIUM. If three coplanar, non-parallel forces are in equilibrium, the forces must be concurrent. In order that the three forces shall be in equilibrium, the resultant of any two of the forces must be a force that is collinear with the third force, of equal magnitude, and of opposite sense. But the resultant of the two forces will have the same line of action as the third force only if the two intersect on the action line of the third force in which case the three forces

are concurrent. This principle is of considerable importance, as it simplifies the solution of many problems. Consider, for example, the crane shown in Fig. 81a. The forces acting on the crane are the reaction R_1 at the upper end (assumed to be horizontal), the load W, the weight of the crane (not shown), and the reaction R_2 at the lower end, the direction of the latter force being unknown. The load W and the weight of the crane may be replaced by a single resultant force R, and the system will then consist of three forces:

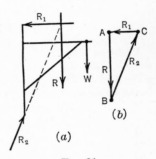

(a)

(b)

Fig. 81

R_1, R_2, and R. Since the three forces must be concurrent, R_2 must pass through the point of intersection of R_1 and R, and hence its action line is determined as indicated by the dotted line. The magnitudes of the reactions R_1 and R_2 may now be determined by drawing the force polygon (Fig. 81b). The force polygon is constructed by drawing AB to represent the known force R and by drawing from A and B lines parallel to R_1 and R_2, respectively, which intersect at C. The reaction R_1 is represented by CA, and R_2 is represented by BC.

CONVENTION CONCERNING DIRECTION AND SENSE OF AN UNKNOWN FORCE. In many problems that involve the equilibrium of force systems, the action line of one (or more) of the forces may be known, but the magnitude and sense may be unknown. If the sense of such a force is evident by inspection, the force may be shown in the free-body diagram with the proper sense. If, however, the sense of the force is not obvious by inspection, it may be assumed, and, if on solving for the unknown force the sign of the force is found to be positive, the assumed sense is correct; if the sign is negative, the sense is opposite to that assumed.

Again, in some problems in equilibrium only a point on the line of action of a force is known, the direction, sense, and magnitude of the force being unknown. In this case it will generally be convenient to represent the force in the free-body diagram by means of its two components parallel to the co-ordinate axes; the direction of each component is then known, but the sense and magnitude are unknown. If the sense of either or both of the components is evident by inspection, the component (or components) should be shown in the free-body diagram with the proper sense. If, however, the sense of a component is not evident, it may be shown as having a positive sense, and if on solving for the component the sign is found to be positive, the sense is positive as assumed; if the sign is negative, the sense is opposite to that assumed.

Illustrative Problems

Problem 118. In Fig. 82a a body A weighing 100 lb is held in equilibrium on a smooth, horizontal surface by a spring S and a cord C which passes over a frictionless pulley and carries a suspended body B whose weight is 80 lb. Determine the tension in the spring and the reaction of the horizontal surface on body A.

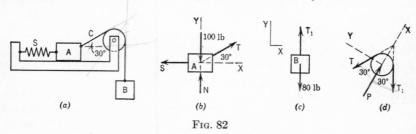

(a)   (b)   (c)   (d)

FIG. 82

SOLUTION. A free-body diagram of body A is shown in Fig. 82b. This body is acted on by a coplanar, concurrent force system consisting of the force S exerted by the spring, the force T exerted by the cord, the reaction N of the horizontal surface, and the earth pull of 100 lb. Applying the equations of equilibrium to the forces acting on body A, we have

$$\Sigma F_x = T \cos 30° - S = 0 \tag{1}$$

$$\Sigma F_y = T \sin 30° + N - 100 = 0 \tag{2}$$

Since there are three unknown quantities (S, N, and T) and only two independent equations of equilibrium for a coplanar, concurrent force system, all three of the unknown quantities cannot be found, that is, the force system is statically indeterminate. The force T will be found by considering the free-body diagrams of the body B and of the pulley. A free-body diagram of B is shown in Fig. 82c. Applying the equation of equilibrium $\Sigma F_y = 0$, we have,

$$\Sigma F_y = T_1 - 80 = 0 \quad \text{or} \quad T_1 = 80 \text{ lb}$$

This operation may perhaps be considered as evident from inspection, but it is desirable to call attention to the fact that the truth of the statement that $T_1 = 80$ lb comes only from the conditions of equilibrium.

The force T may now be found by considering the free-body diagram of the pulley and the part of the cord that passes over the pulley (Fig. 82d). The pulley is acted on by the tensions T and T_1 and the reaction of the pin at its center. Three forces in equilibrium must be either concurrent or parallel (Art. 40) and, since the forces acting on the pulley are not parallel, they must be concurrent. By selecting the axes shown in Fig. 82d, we may find the force T from the equation of equilibrium,

$$\Sigma F_y = T \cos 30° - T_1 \cos 30° = 0 \quad \text{or} \quad T = T_1 = 80 \text{ lb}$$

Substituting the value of T in Eqs. 1 and 2, we find

$$N = 60 \text{ lb} \quad \text{and} \quad S = 69.3 \text{ lb}$$

In the solution of this problem, free-body diagrams of the pulley and body B were used in the proof that the tension in the part of the cord attached to body A is equal to the weight of body B. When the tension in a cord may be determined by inspection in subsequent problems in equilibrium, the student need not show the details of the solution as was done in the solution of this problem.

Problem 119. Figure 83a represents a lower panel point of a pin-connected

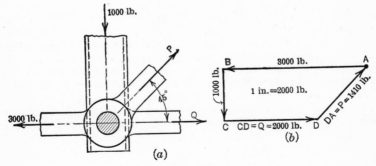

(a)

(b)

Fig. 83

Pratt truss. The stresses in two of the members are 1000 lb and 3000 lb as shown. Find the stresses P and Q in the other members.

ALGEBRAIC SOLUTION.

$$\Sigma F_x = Q + P \cos 45° - 3000 = 0 \qquad (1)$$

$$\Sigma F_y = P \sin 45° - 1000 = 0 \qquad (2)$$

From Eq. 2,

$$P = \frac{1000}{\sin 45°} = 1414 \text{ lb}$$

Substitution in Eq. 1 gives

$$Q = 3000 - 1414 \cos 45°$$

$$= 3000 - 1000 = 2000 \text{ lb}$$

GRAPHICAL SOLUTION. The problem may be solved graphically by constructing a closed force polygon as shown in Fig. 83b. The polygon is constructed as follows: Vectors AB and BC are drawn to represent the 3000-lb and 1000-lb forces, respectively. A line is then drawn from C parallel to the direction of the force Q, and a line is drawn from A parallel to the direction of the force P. These lines intersect at D. Q is then represented by CD and P by DA. The magnitudes of Q and P are found by measuring, according to the scale indicated, to be 2000 lb and 1410 lb, respectively.

Problem 120. Two bodies, A and B (Fig. 84), weighing 200 lb and 50 lb, respectively, are held in equilibrium on smooth rods by a connecting flexible cable that makes an angle θ with the horizontal. Find the reactions of the rods on the bodies, the tensile force in the cable, and the angle θ.

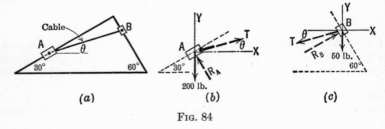

(a)   (b)   (c)

FIG. 84

SOLUTION. A free-body diagram of body A and a small part of the attached cable, considered as one body, is shown in Fig. 84b. This body is acted on by a coplanar, concurrent force system consisting of the force T exerted by the part of the cable removed (and hence is the tensile stress in the cable), the reaction R_A of the rod, and the earth pull of 200 lb. There are three unknown quantities in the diagram: namely, the magnitude and direction of T and the magnitude of R_A (T, θ, and R_A), and since there are only two equations of equilibrium for a coplanar concurrent force system, all three of the unknown quantities cannot be found; that is, the force system is statically indeterminate. Therefore a free-body diagram of the body B is drawn (Fig. 84c), to see if the force system acting on B is statically determinate. If this system is found to be statically determinate, the value of T could be found, and this value used for the force T in the force system acting on body A, thus making the force system acting on body A statically determinate.

The force system acting on B, however, is also found to be statically indeterminate since three unknown quantities (T, θ, and R_B) are involved. However, since the forces T in Fig. 84b and T in Fig. 84c are identical (except in sense), it is seen that in the two force systems there are only four unknown quantities (T, θ, R_A, R_B), and these may be found from the four equations of equilibrium (two for each of the force systems) that can be written. Applying the equations of equilibrium we have

For A

$$\Sigma F_x = T \cos \theta - R_A \sin 30° = 0 \tag{1}$$

$$\Sigma F_y = T \sin \theta + R_A \cos 30° - 200 = 0 \tag{2}$$

For B

$$\Sigma F_x = -T \cos \theta + R_B \cos 30° = 0 \tag{3}$$

$$\Sigma F_y = -T \sin \theta + R_B \sin 30° - 50 = 0 \tag{4}$$

Eliminating R_A from Eqs. 1 and 2, we find

$$T \cos (30° - \theta) = 100 \tag{5}$$

Eliminating R_B from Eqs. 3 and 4, we find

$$T \sin (30° - \theta) = 43.3 \tag{6}$$

Dividing Eq. 6 by Eq. 5, we have

$$\tan (30° - \theta) = 0.433$$

Hence,

$$30° - \theta = \tan^{-1} 0.433 = 23° \, 25', \qquad \therefore \ \theta = 6° \, 35'$$

Substituting the value of θ in Eq. 5, we find

$$T = 109 \text{ lb}$$

Substituting the values of T and θ in Eqs. 1 and 3, we find

$$R_A = 216 \text{ lb} \quad \text{and} \quad R_B = 125 \text{ lb}$$

Problems

121. In Fig. 85 is shown a bell crank mounted on a smooth pin at O and subjected to a force of 80 lb at A as shown, causing the bell crank to press against a smooth stop at B. Find the pin pressure at O and the reaction at B. Solve graphically, observing that three non-parallel forces in equilibrium must be concurrent.

$Ans.\ R_o = 115 \text{ lb};\ \theta_x = 52° \, 50';\ R_B = 51.5 \text{ lb}.$

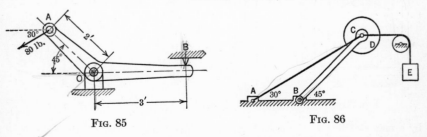

FIG. 85   FIG. 86

122. In Fig. 86, D is a cylinder whose weight is 100 lb, and E is a body whose weight is 60 lb. Find the stresses in the cable AC and the bar BC. Neglect friction at the pins.

123. A sphere weighing 100 lb rests against two smooth planes that form a V-shaped trough. The right-hand plane makes an angle of 30° with the horizontal, and the angle between the two planes is 90°. Find the reactions of the planes on the sphere. *Ans. $R_1 = 50$ lb; $R_2 = 86.6$ lb.*

124. In Fig. 87 is represented a lawn roller whose weight is 300 lb. What is the least force P that must be applied in the direction shown to cause the roller to move over a block whose height is 4 in.?

125. If the force P in the preceding problem is applied horizontally, determine the magnitude of P. *Ans. $P = 335$ lb.*

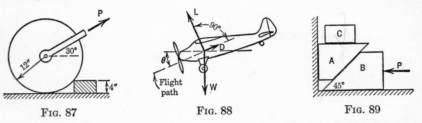

FIG. 87   FIG. 88   FIG. 89

126. In Fig. 88 an airplane is in steady flight and is acted on by the drag force D, the lift force L, and its weight W. If $D = 800$ lb and $W = 6000$ lb, determine the lift L and the angle θ that the flight path makes with the horizontal.

127. In Fig. 89 are shown two wedges, A and B, that are used to lift a body C. If body C weighs 2000 lb, find the least value of the force P that will lift the body. Assume the weights of the wedges to be negligible and all surfaces of contact to be smooth. *Ans. $P = 2000$ lb*

128. If the wedge angle in the preceding problem be changed to 60°, find the force P required to lift the 2000-lb body C.

129. A body A rests on a platform (Fig. 90). The platform is suspended from the top cross bar of a frame by two ropes B, B. The mid-points of the ropes are connected by another rope C. At the center of the rope C a vertical pull P is exerted

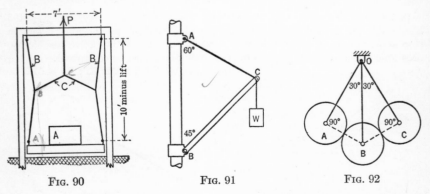

FIG. 90   FIG. 91   FIG. 92

by a man standing on the cross bar. Before the pull P is applied, the ropes B, B are vertical and 10 ft long and the rope C is horizontal and 7 ft long. The body A is placed at the center of the platform. The weight of A and the platform is 2000 lb. What force P must the man exert to support the platform: (a) 1 in. above its original position, (b) 5 in. above its original position? Solve graphically using scales 1 in. = 2 ft and 1 in. = 200 lb. *Ans. (a) $P = 335$ lb; (b) $P = 1155$ lb.*

130. The derrick shown in Fig. 91 carries a load W of 1000 lb. Determine the stresses in the cable AC and the boom BC. Assume that the weights of the cable and boom are negligible.

131. Three smooth spheres, A, B, and C (Fig. 92), having equal diameters are suspended by cords from a point O, the centers of the spheres being in a vertical plane. Each sphere weighs 100 lb. Find the tension in the cord connecting B to O.

Ans. T = 150 lb.

132. In Fig. 93 are shown two bodies, D and E, whose weights are W_D and W_E, respectively. The weights of D and E are such as to cause the angle of inclination with the horizontal of the cords A and C to be as shown in the figure. Find in terms of W_D and W_E the angle α that the cord B makes with the horizontal.

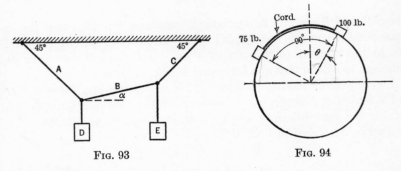

FIG. 93   FIG. 94

133. In Fig. 93 assume the weight of body D to be 300 lb and $\alpha = \tan^{-1} \frac{1}{2}$. Find the weight of body E and the tensions in the cords A, B, and C.

134. Two bodies weighing 75 lb and 100 lb rest on a smooth cylinder and are connected by a cord as shown in Fig. 94. Find the reactions of the cylinder on the bodies, the tension in the cord, and the value of θ.

Ans. R₁ $R_1 = 45$ lb; $R_2 = 80$ lb; $T = 60$ lb; $\theta = 36° 52'$.

§ 4 Coplanar, Parallel Forces

41 Equations of equilibrium. A coplanar, parallel force system is in equilibrium if the forces of the system satisfy the equations

$$\Sigma F = 0$$

$$(A)$$

$$\Sigma M_A = 0$$

where A is any point in the plane of the forces.

Proof. According to Art. 27, the resultant of a coplanar, parallel force system which is not in equilibrium is either a force or a couple. If the resultant is a force, its magnitude R is expressed by the equation $R = \Sigma F$, and, if the resultant is a couple, the magnitude of the moment C is expressed by the equation $C = \Sigma M$. Thus, if the forces of the system satisfy the equation $\Sigma F = 0$, the resultant is not a force, and, if the equation $\Sigma M_A = 0$ is satisfied, the resultant is not a couple. Hence, if both equations are satisfied, the resultant of the force system can be neither a force nor a couple, and therefore the system is in equilibrium. Two equations, then, are necessary and sufficient to ensure that the forces are in equilibrium. In other words, there are only two independent equations of equilibrium for a system of parallel forces in a plane.

Another set of equations of equilibrium for a system of coplanar, parallel forces may be written as follows:

$$\Sigma M_A = 0$$

$$(B)$$

$$\Sigma M_B = 0$$

where A and B are any two points in the plane, provided that the line connecting A and B is not parallel to the forces of the system. It will be left to the student to prove that these equations are necessary and sufficient to ensure that the forces are in equilibrium.

A graphical method of solution which makes use of a force polygon and a funicular polygon may also be used when solving a problem involving the equilibrium of a system of coplanar, parallel forces. This method is illustrated in Prob. 136.

Illustrative Problems

Problem 135. A load of 1200 lb is applied to a beam AB as shown in Fig. 95a. The left end of the beam is carried by a smooth roller resting on a second beam CD. Find the reactions on the second beam at C and D.

SOLUTION. The free-body diagram for each of the beams is shown in Figs. 95b and 95c. Considering the beam AB as a free body and using the equation $\Sigma M_A = 0$, we have

$$\Sigma M_A = 1200 \times 9 - R_B \times 12 = 0, \qquad \therefore \ R_B = 900 \text{ lb}$$

There is, then, a load of 900 lb acting on the beam CD at B. Next, considering the beam CD as a free body, we may find the two reactions R_C and R_D by applying either set of equilibrium equations of Art. 41. Thus, by using the equations $\Sigma M_C = 0$ and $\Sigma M_D = 0$, the two reactions may be found as follows:

$$\Sigma M_C = R_D \times 10 - 900 \times 6 = 0, \qquad \therefore \ R_D = 540 \text{ lb}$$

$$\Sigma M_D = -R_C \times 10 + 900 \times 4 = 0, \qquad \therefore \ R_C = 360 \text{ lb}$$

Problem 136. A beam 12 ft long carries three loads as shown in Fig. 96. Find the reactions at the ends of the beam. Solve algebraically and graphically.

ALGEBRAIC SOLUTION

$$\Sigma M_B = -12R_1 + 1000 \times 10 + 2000 \times 7 + 2000 \times 4 = 0$$

$$12R_1 = 32{,}000, \qquad \therefore \ R_1 = 2667 \text{ lb}$$

$$\Sigma M_A = 12R_2 - 1000 \times 2 - 2000 \times 5 - 2000 \times 8 = 0$$

$$12R_2 = 28{,}000, \qquad \therefore \ R_2 = 2333 \text{ lb}$$

In order to check the results, the equation $\Sigma F = 0$ may be applied. Thus,

$$2667 + 2333 - 1000 - 2000 - 2000 = 0$$

GRAPHICAL SOLUTION. In order to determine the reactions by the graphical method, a force and a funicular polygon are constructed as shown in Fig. 97. Since

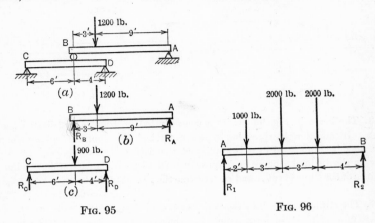

FIG. 95

FIG. 96

the forces are in equilibrium, the two polygons must close. The three known forces are represented by AB, BC, and CD. The right reaction will be represented by DE, the position of the point E being as yet unknown. Obviously the left reaction will be represented by EA since the force polygon must close. The strings oa, ob,

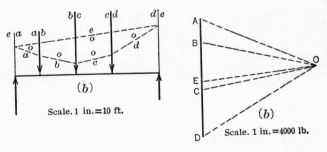

FIG. 97

oc, and od of the funicular polygon are drawn parallel to the corresponding rays. Since the string oe must intersect the string oa on ea and since oe must also intersect the string od on de, the position of the string oe is determined. The direction of the ray OE is now determined also, since it must be parallel to the string oe. Hence, E is the point where a line drawn through O parallel to oe intersects the line AD. The magnitudes of DE and EA are found, from the diagram, to be 2330 lb and 2670 lb, which agree closely with the values found by the algebraic method of solution.

Problems

137. The beam AB shown in Fig. 98 weighs 25 lb per linear foot and carries a distributed load as shown. Find the reactions of the supports at A and B.

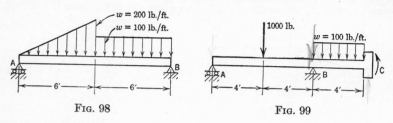

FIG. 98   FIG. 99

138. The beam in Fig. 99 carries a concentrated load and a distributed load as shown. In addition to these loads, a counterclockwise couple C whose moment has a magnitude of 2000 lb ft is applied at the right end of the beam. (A curved arrow as shown in the figure is frequently used to represent a couple.) Find the reactions of the supports at A and B. Assume the weight of the beam to be negligible.

Ans. $R_A = 650$ lb; $R_B = 750$ lb.

139. The stiffness of each of the springs shown in Fig. 100 is 10 lb per in. (The stiffness of a spring is the force required to elongate or compress the spring one unit of length.) The springs C and D are each compressed 3 in., and the springs E, F, and G are each compressed 2 in. If the total force of the block A on the yoke B is 10 lb, determine the magnitude of the force P.

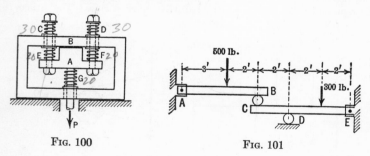

FIG. 100   FIG. 101

140. In Fig. 101 the beam CE is supported by a smooth pin at E and a smooth roller at D. The beam AB is supported by a smooth pin at A and a smooth roller between the two beams. Find the reaction of the pin at E on the beam CE. Neglect the weights of the beams.

Ans. $R_E = 0$.

141. In the preceding problem assume that the 500-lb load is changed to 1000 lb, the other data remaining as given. Find the pin reaction at E and the reaction of the roller at D on CE.

142. A block and tackle which is attached to a stake driven in the ground is used in moving a car by the method shown in Fig. 102. If the holding power of the stake is limited, which of the two arrangements shown is preferable, that shown in a or b? If the force that must be applied to the car to cause it to move is 800 lb, find the value of the force P required to move the car in each of the two arrangements. Find also the tension T in the cable connected to the stake in each case.

(a)   (b)

Fig. 102

143. In Fig. 103 is represented a differential chain hoist. Two sheaves of radii, r_1 and r_2, are fastened together, and a continuous chain passes around the small sheave, then around a movable pulley of diameter $r_1 + r_2$, and then around the larger sheave. Neglecting the resistance due to friction, find the relation between the applied force F and the load W which it will hold in equilibrium.

$$Ans. \quad F = \frac{W(r_1 - r_2)}{2r_1}.$$

$R_1 = 6 \quad W = 2000$
$R_2 = ? \quad F = 225$

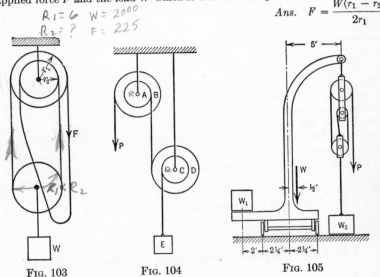

Fig. 103   Fig. 104   Fig. 105

144. In Fig. 104 the pulleys A and B are keyed together as are also the pulleys C and D. If the radius of each of the pulleys A and C is r and the radius of each of the pulleys B and D is R, find the force P required to lift a body E that weighs W lb.

$$Ans. \quad P = W \frac{r^2}{R^2}.$$

145. If the radii of the pulleys A, B, C, and D in the preceding problem are 3 in., 12 in., 4 in., and 15 in., respectively, and the weight W of the body E is 3000 lb, find the force P required to lift the body E.

146. In Fig. 105 is shown a portable crane whose weight without the counter-weight W_1 is $W = 800$ lb. What is the maximum value of W_1 that may be used in the position shown without causing the crane to overturn when carrying no load? When this value of W_1 is used, what is the maximum weight W_2 of a body that can be lifted by means of the block and tackle without causing the crane to overturn?

$$Ans. \quad W_1 = 1100 \text{ lb}; \quad W_2 = 2330 \text{ lb}.$$

147. A weightless rigid bar AB in Fig. 106 is connected to a support by a smooth pin at B and is suspended by four springs as shown. The modulus of each spring is 100 lb/in. (The modulus of a spring, or spring constant, is the force required to elongate or compress the spring one unit of length.) If there is no stress in the springs when the bar is in a horizontal position, what is the weight of the suspended body C that will cause the end A to be displaced 0.1 in.?   *Ans.* $W = 18.75$ lb.

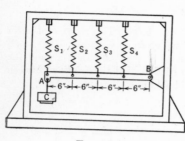

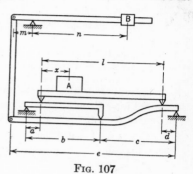

FIG. 106   FIG. 107

148. Assume in Fig. 106 that the weight of the suspended body C is 45 lb and that, after the body is attached, the upper end of the spring S_1 slips 0.3 in. in its grips. If the modulus of each spring is 100 lb/in., what will be the final tension in S_1?

149. In Fig. 107 is represented a platform scale. The weight W of a body A resting on the platform is determined by the weight w of the poise B and its position on the scale beam. Find the relation among the dimensions a, b, c, and d in order that the reading obtained be independent of the position of the body A on the platform.   *Ans.* $a/b = d/c$.

150. If in the preceding problem $W = 200$ lb, $w = 2$ lb, $a = d = 1$ in., $b = c = 8$ in., $e = 16$ in., and $m = 2$ in., what must be the value of n in order that the beam be balanced?

§ 5   Coplanar, Non-concurrent, Non-parallel Forces

42 Equations of equilibrium. A system of coplanar, non-concurrent, non-parallel forces is in equilibrium if the forces of the system satisfy the equations,

$$\Sigma F_x = 0 \qquad \Sigma F_y = 0 \qquad \Sigma M_A = 0 \qquad (A)$$

where x and y denote the co-ordinate axes and A is any point in the plane of the forces.

Proof. If a system of coplanar, non-concurrent, non-parallel forces is not in equilibrium, the resultant of the system is either a force having components equal to ΣF_x and ΣF_y or a couple having a moment equal to ΣM_A (Art. 25). If the forces of the system satisfy the equation $\Sigma F_x = 0$, the resultant, if a force, must be parallel to the Y axis since $R_x = \Sigma F_x$. If the equation $\Sigma F_y = 0$ is satisfied, the resultant, if a force, must be parallel to the X axis since $R_y = \Sigma F_y$. A force cannot be parallel to both the X and Y axes and hence, if the first two equations are satisfied, the resultant of the system cannot be a force. If the equation $\Sigma M_A = 0$ is satisfied, the resultant cannot be a couple. Therefore, if the forces of the system satisfy the three equations, the force system is in equilibrium.

Another set of independent equations of equilibrium for a non-concurrent, non-parallel system of forces in a plane may be written as follows:

$$\Sigma F_x = 0 \qquad \Sigma M_A = 0 \qquad \Sigma M_B = 0 \qquad \textbf{(B)}$$

where x denotes any line or axis in the plane of the forces and A and B are any two points in the plane, provided that the line AB is not perpendicular to the X axis.

A third set of equilibrium equations for the force system here considered may be written as follows:

$$\Sigma M_A = 0 \qquad \Sigma M_B = 0 \qquad \Sigma M_C = 0 \qquad \textbf{(C)}$$

where A, B, and C are any three non-collinear points in the plane of the forces.

It will be left to the student to prove that either set of equations **B** or **C** is necessary and sufficient to ensure the equilibrium of a coplanar, non-concurrent, non-parallel system of forces.

Any one of the above sets of equations, therefore, may be used to determine all the unknown quantities in a coplanar, non-concurrent, non-parallel force system which is in equilibrium, provided there are not more than three such unknowns.

CHOICE OF MOMENT CENTERS AND OF DIRECTIONS OF RESOLUTION. In applying the equations of equilibrium to a system of coplanar, non-concurrent, non-parallel forces in which the magnitudes (and senses) of three forces are unknown, the solution may frequently be simplified by selecting the moment centers and the directions of resolution in a particular way. For example, in Fig. 108 is represented a portion of a roof truss which is held in equilibrium by the five forces shown, of which P and R are known completely and F_1, F_2, and F_3 are unknown in magnitude. By selecting C, the intersection of the two unknown forces, F_2 and F_3, as a moment center and applying the equilibrium equation $\Sigma M_C = 0$, the force F_1 may be found from the one equation. Likewise, by choosing D as a moment center and applying a second equation of equilibrium, $\Sigma M_D = 0$, the force F_3 may be found directly. Similarly, F_2 may be found by selecting A as the moment center and applying the third equilibrium equation, $\Sigma M_A = 0$. Thus, by the proper selection of moment centers, each of the three equations involves one unknown quantity only.

As another example, consider a body which is held in equilibrium by the six forces shown in Fig. 109, all of which are completely known except F_1, F_2, and F_3, which are unknown in magnitude. The forces F_1 and F_3

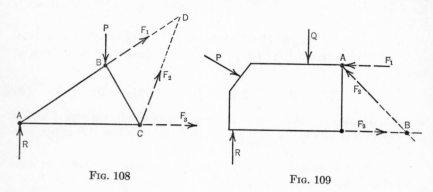

FIG. 108   FIG. 109

are parallel. By selecting B as the moment center, the force F_1 may be found from one equation: namely, $\Sigma M_B = 0$. Likewise, F_3 may be found from the single equation $\Sigma M_A = 0$, where A is the intersection of the two forces, F_1 and F_2. Further, F_2 may be found from the single equation $\Sigma F_y = 0$ provided that the y direction is chosen perpendicular to the forces F_1 and F_3.

As stated in Art. 36, the graphical conditions for equilibrium of a coplanar force system are that the force polygon must close and the string polygon must close. A graphical method which makes use of a force polygon and a string polygon is discussed in Art. 43.

Illustrative Problems

Problem 151. The wall bracket shown in Fig. 110a consists of a horizontal member AB, which is attached to the wall at A by means of a smooth pin, and a rod CB, which is attached to the member AB at B and to the wall at C by means of smooth pins. Find the tension T in the rod and the pin reaction R at A if the weights of the members are neglected.

SOLUTION. A free-body diagram of the horizontal member is shown in Fig. 110b. There are three unknown quantities in the force system: namely, T, R, and θ. Applying the three equations of equilibrium, we have

$$\Sigma M_A = T \times 12 \sin 30° - 1000 \times 10 - 400 \times 4 = 0 \tag{1}$$

$$\therefore \ T = 1930 \text{ lb}$$

$$\Sigma F_x = R \cos \theta - T \cos 30° = 0$$

$$\therefore \ R \cos \theta = 1930 \cos 30° = 1670 \text{ lb} \tag{2}$$

$$\Sigma F_y = R \sin \theta + T \sin 30° - 400 - 1000 = 0$$

$$\therefore \ R \sin \theta = 1400 - 1930 \sin 30° = 435 \text{ lb} \tag{3}$$

By solving Eqs. 2 and 3, the following results are obtained:

$$R = 1730 \text{ lb}; \qquad \theta = 14° 35'$$

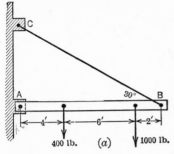
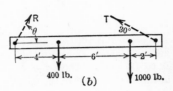

Fig. 110

Problem 152. A uniform bar AB shown in Fig. 111a is 5 ft long and weighs 100 lb. The upper end rests against a smooth vertical wall and the lower end on a smooth horizontal floor. The bar is held in equilibrium in the position shown by a cord attached at O and to a point C on the bar 1 ft from B. Find the tension in the cord.

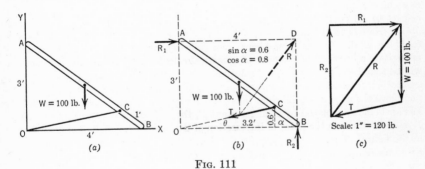

Fig. 111

ALGEBRAIC SOLUTION. The bar is held in equilibrium by the four forces, W, T, R_1, and R_2, shown in the free-body diagram in Fig. 111b. Using the equations of equilibrium, we have

$$\Sigma F_x = R_1 - T \cos \theta = 0 \tag{1}$$

$$\Sigma F_y = R_2 - T \sin \theta - 100 = 0 \tag{2}$$

$$\Sigma M_o = 4R_2 - 3R_1 - 200 = 0 \tag{3}$$

Eliminating R_1 from Eqs. 1 and 3, we find

$$R_2 = \frac{3T \cos \theta + 200}{4} \tag{4}$$

Substituting R_2 in Eq. 2, we obtain

$$T = \frac{200}{3 \cos \theta - 4 \sin \theta} \tag{5}$$

From Fig. 111*b*,

$$OC = \sqrt{(3.2)^2 + (0.6)^2} = \sqrt{10.6} \text{ ft}$$

Hence,

$$\sin \theta = \frac{0.6}{\sqrt{10.6}} \quad \text{and} \quad \cos \theta = \frac{3.2}{\sqrt{10.6}}$$

Therefore,

$$T = \frac{200\sqrt{10.6}}{9.6 - 2.4} = 90.5 \text{ lb}$$

The value of T could be found from a single equation, namely, $\Sigma M_D = 0$, if the moment of T about D were found by determining the moment arm of T (with respect to D) algebraically; the numerical calculation involved would be greater than in the method used in the foregoing solution. If the moment of T were formed by resolving T at point O into horizontal and vertical components and then using the principle of moments, it would be found that in using the equation $\Sigma M_D = 0$ the expression found for T would be the same as that given in Eq. 5.

GRAPHICAL SOLUTION. A general graphical method making use of a force polygon and a string polygon is applicable to this as well as to all other problems in equilibrium of coplanar forces. However, two special graphical methods are of interest and are discussed as follows.

A semi-graphical method could be used which would obviate the necessity of most of the numerical calculations. By this method the moment arm of T (with respect to D) could be found graphically by measuring to scale the perpendicular drawn from D to the action line of T, and then the algebraic equation $\Sigma M_D = 0$ could be used. In many problems, especially when the geometry is such as to necessitate a considerable amount of numerical calculation, a semi-graphical method will be found to give the simplest solution.

Another method which is entirely graphical makes use of the fact that three non-parallel forces in equilibrium must be concurrent. If the reactions R_1 and R_2 in Fig. 111*b* are replaced by their resultant R, the action line of R will pass through D and also through the point of intersection of the action lines of W and T as shown in the figure. The force polygon for the forces W, T, and R is shown in Fig. 111*c*. By measurement to scale it is found that $T = 90.5$ lb, $R_1 = 90$ lb, and $R_2 = 116$ lb.

Problems

153. In Fig. 49 find the magnitude of the reaction of the roller at A and the magnitude and direction of the pin reaction at B.

Ans. $A = 258$ lb; $B = 360$ lb; $\theta_x = 83°\ 12'$.

154. A uniform bar AB having a length of 4 ft and a weight of 20 lb is suspended from a fixed point O by a cord attached to the upper end A of the bar. When a couple lying in a vertical plane and having a moment of 10 lb ft is applied to the bar, the bar makes an angle θ with the vertical. Find θ.

155. A bar (Fig. 112) leans against a smooth vertical post and rests with its lower end on a smooth horizontal plane, slipping of the lower end being prevented by the cord as shown. If the weight of the bar is neglected, find the reaction of the plane at A and of the post at B, and also find the tension in the cord.

Ans. $R_A = 10.9$ lb; $R_B = 51.1$ lb; $T = 32.8$ lb.

156. Assume in Fig. 112 the point of attachment of the left end of the cord to be changed to the point midway between A and B. Find the reactions at A and B and the tension in the cord.

157. The cross section of a dam is shown in Fig. 113. The water pressure (force per unit area) on the vertical face of the dam varies as shown. The action line of

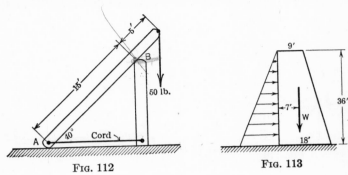

FIG. 112   FIG. 113

the weight W of the dam is **7** ft from the vertical face. If the weight per unit volume of the dam is such that the total water pressure (force) P on the vertical face is equal to $\frac{1}{2}W$, find the point on the base of the dam through which the reaction of the ground on the dam passes.

158. The upper end of a uniform ladder having a length of 20 ft and a weight of 50 lb rests against a smooth vertical wall and the lower end on a rough horizontal floor so that the ladder does not slip on the floor. A man weighing 150 lb stands on a rung of the ladder 15 ft from the lower end. If the ladder makes an angle of 60° with the floor, find the magnitude of the reaction of the wall and the magnitude and direction of the reaction of the floor on the ladder.

Ans. $R_B = 79.5$ lb; $R_A = 215$ lb; $\theta_x = 68° \; 19'$.

159. The tractor shown in Fig. 114 is used to remove a stump. The weight W of the tractor and driver is 2600 lb and the draw-bar pull P is 1000 lb. Find the total vertical reaction on the front tires and the magnitude and direction of the total reaction on the rear tires. What maximum value may the draw-bar pull P have if the front wheels do not leave the ground?

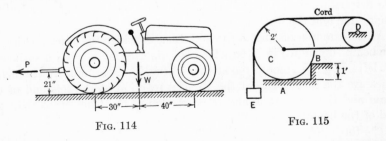

FIG. 114   FIG. 115

160. In Fig. 115, C is a smooth cylinder which weighs 60 lb, and D is a frictionless pulley. If the weight of the suspended body E is 20 lb, find the reactions at A and B on the cylinder.

161. In the preceding problem what would be the weight of the body E that would cause the reaction at A to become zero?   *Ans.* $W = 388$ lb.

162. In Fig. 116 is shown a jet-propelled airplane in steady flight (moving with constant velocity). The aerodynamic forces which act on the airplane may be considered to consist of the lift L, the tail load Q, the drag D, and a couple whose moment is C. Other forces that act on the airplane are the weight W and the thrust T from the jet. If $W = 8000$ lb, $D = 1000$ lb, and $C = 30,000$ lb in., determine the magnitudes of L, Q, and T.

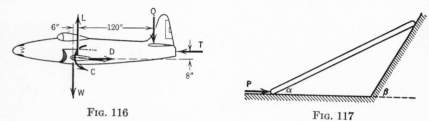

FIG. 116   FIG. 117

163. In Fig. 117 the lower end of a uniform bar that weighs W lb rests on a smooth horizontal plane and the upper end on a smooth inclined plane. Find the horizontal force P that must be applied to the lower end of the bar to hold it in equilibrium in the position shown.

$$Ans. \quad P = \frac{1}{2}\frac{W}{\tan \alpha + \cot \beta}.$$

43   Graphical solution of a typical problem.

Any problem which involves a coplanar, non-concurrent, non-parallel force system in equilibrium, in which not more than three characteristics of the forces are unknown, may be solved graphically as well as algebraically. A graphical method of solution making use of a force polygon and a string polygon for one typical problem will here be discussed. In the force system considered, all of the forces will be assumed to be known completely except two, the action line of one of these two being known and also one point on the action line of the other. The three unknown characteristics, then, are the magnitude of one of the two forces and the magnitude and the direction of the other.

As an example of such a force system, consider the forces acting on the beam shown in Fig. 118a which is supported by a smooth surface at the left end and a smooth pin at the right end. The unknown characteristics are the magnitude of the vertical reaction at the left end of the beam and the magnitude and the direction of the reaction at the right end of the beam.

The force polygon and string polygon are shown in Fig. 118. In constructing the force polygon (Fig. 118b), the lines AB, BC, and CD are first drawn to represent the magnitude and direction of the three known forces. As the magnitude of force DE is unknown, the location of E is not known, but it must lie in a vertical line through D. The rays OA, OB, OC, and OD are then drawn from O, after which the string polygon is constructed (Fig. 118a). Since the point N is the only known point on the action line of the force EA, the string polygon must be

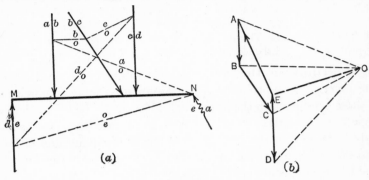

Fig. 118

started at this point. The strings oa, ob, oc, and od are drawn as shown. Since the string oe must intersect od on de and must also intersect oa on ea, its position is determined. The ray OE must be parallel to the string oe. Hence, E is the point of intersection of a vertical line through D and a line through O parallel to oe. DE then represents the left reaction, and the right reaction is represented in magnitude and in direction by EA.

Problems

164. The Fink truss shown in Fig. 119 is subjected to a wind load which is assumed to be equivalent to the three forces acting at pins A, B, and D as indicated, the forces being perpendicular to the upper chord AD. The truss rests on a smooth

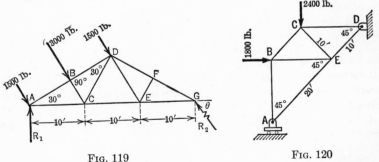

Fig. 119   Fig. 120

plate at the left end, and hence the reaction at that end is vertical. Determine completely, by use of a force polygon and a string polygon, the reactions R_1 and R_2.

Ans. $R_1 = 3460$ lb; $R_2 = 3460$ lb; $\theta = 30°$.

165. Find by use of a force polygon and a string polygon the magnitude of the reaction of the pin at A (Fig. 120) and the magnitude and direction of the reaction of the pin at D.

166. Solve Prob. 151 by use of a force polygon and a string polygon.

167. The truss shown in Fig. 60 is supported by a cable attached at G and the pin at H. Find graphically the tension in the cable and the magnitude and direction of the pin reaction at H.   *Ans.* $T = 13,900$ lb; $H = 12,100$ lb; $\theta_x = 351° 48'$.

168. The body shown in Fig. 43 is in equilibrium. Find graphically the magnitude of the reaction at B and the magnitude and direction of the pin reaction at A.

44 Procedure in the solution of problems in equilibrium.

Before proceeding to problems that are somewhat more comprehensive than those considered in the foregoing articles, it will be highly desirable to review and to outline in a logical and formal way the steps that have already been used in the solution of problems of equilibrium of forces, and to extend or generalize the procedure so that the reader may have available a concise statement of the general algebraic method of attack for use in the solution of all problems in the equilibrium of forces. The main steps in the procedure may be stated as follows:

1. Determine carefully: (*a*) what is given in the problem, and (*b*) what is required in the problem. Many of the student's difficulties arise from failure to observe this preliminary step. To make the given and the required quantities definite, they should be listed or in some other way isolated.

2. Draw a complete free-body diagram of the body, or of part of the body, or of a group of the bodies, on which are acting the forces required to be found. It will be found helpful to show all unknown forces in color or as dashed lines and known forces in black or as solid lines, thereby further emphasizing what is known and what is unknown. Further, it is desirable to show co-ordinate axes in each free-body diagram, particularly if the directions of these axes are not the same in the several diagrams.

3. Observe the type of force system shown in the free-body diagram, and write the equations of equilibrium for this type of force system.

4. Then observe whether or not there are a sufficient number of equations of equilibrium to solve for all the unknown forces. If so (that is, if the force system is statically determinate), apply the equations, and solve for *all* the unknown forces. If the force system is statically indeterminate, one or more (but not all) of the unknown forces may sometimes be found; but, in order to reduce the number of unknown forces so that the force system becomes statically determinate, the following step is necessary.

5. Draw a complete free-body diagram of one of the other bodies, or of part of a body, or of a group of the bodies, on which are acting one (or more) of the unknown forces that acts on the first free body, and apply the equations of equilibrium to the forces in this second free-body diagram. This force system does not necessarily have to be statically determinate since a solution giving *all* the unknown forces in it is *not* required; only those particular forces that will make the force system in the first free-body diagram statically determinate are required. In some problems more than one additional free-body diagram must be used in order to determine a sufficient number of forces to make the forces in the first free-body diagram statically determinate.

6. Return now to the first free-body diagram and its equations of equilibrium and complete the solution, making use, of course, of any additional equations other than equations of equilibrium that apply to the problem such as the defining equation for coefficient of friction ($F' = \mu N$).

The procedure is illustrated in the solution of the following problems.

Illustrative Problems

Problem 169. Find the force in the member AB and the x and y components of the pin pressure of D on the member EH of the frame shown in Fig. 121a. The cylinder C has a radius of 1 ft and weighs 100 lb. Assume that there is no friction at surfaces of contact of the various members. Neglect the weight of all members of the frame, and also neglect the width of members EH and FG in calculating distances. Assume that the X and Y axes are horizontal and vertical, respectively.

SOLUTION. The forces required are acting on EH, and therefore a free-body diagram of EH is drawn as shown in Fig. 121b. All five forces are unknown, and there are three equations of equilibrium for the type of force system involved. Therefore, the forces P and H must be found by considering the equilibrium of one or more

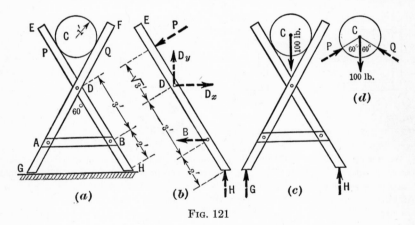

FIG. 121

of the other bodies or group of bodies before the three required forces can be found. H may be found by considering the equilibrium of all the bodies, treated as one body, as shown in Fig. 121c. The three forces constitute a parallel system for which there are two equations of equilibrium. Without formally applying these equations, it is obvious by inspection of Fig. 121c that

$$G = H = \tfrac{100}{2} = 50 \text{ lb}$$

Furthermore, P (reversed in sense) is a force acting on the cylinder C. Therefore, by drawing a free-body diagram of C as shown in Fig. 121d and applying the two equations of equilibrium for the concurrent force system, we have:

$$\Sigma F_x = P \cos 30° - Q \cos 30° = 0, \qquad \therefore P = Q$$

$$\Sigma F_y = P \sin 30° + Q \sin 30° - 100 = 0$$

$$2P \sin 30° - 100 = 0, \qquad \therefore P = 100 \text{ lb}$$

Now returning to Fig. 121b, P and H may be shown as known forces; then, by writing the three equations of equilibrium, we may find B, D_x, and D_y as follows:

$$\Sigma M_D = -B \times 3 \cos 30° + 50 \times 5 \sin 30° + 100 \times \sqrt{3} = 0, \qquad \therefore B = 115 \text{ lb}$$

$$\Sigma F_y = D_y - 100 \sin 30° + 50 = 0, \qquad \therefore D_y = 0$$

$$\Sigma F_x = D_x - B - 100 \cos 30° = 0, \qquad \therefore D_x = 201 \text{ lb}$$

Problem 170.   A smooth cylinder weighing 120 lb is supported as shown in Fig. 122a. The pin at A connecting the frame M to the vertical wall is smooth, and the weight of M may be neglected. Find the reaction of the pin at A on M, and the pressures on the cylinder at B, C, and D.

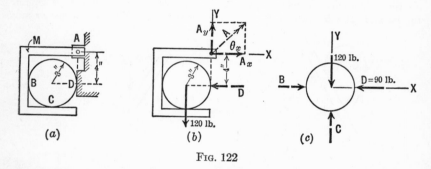

Fig. 122

SOLUTION.   The frame M and the cylinder, treated as one body, will first be taken as a free body. The free-body diagram for this body is shown in Fig. 122b, in which the components of the pin reaction A are used instead of A itself; there are three unknown forces (indicated by heavy dashed-line vectors). Since the force system involved is coplanar, non-concurrent, and non-parallel, there are three equations of equilibrium, and hence all three unknown forces can be found. Thus, applying one set of equilibrium equations to the force system in Fig. 122b, we have

$$\Sigma M_A = 120 \times 3 - 4D = 0, \qquad \therefore D = 90 \text{ lb}$$

$$\Sigma F_y = A_y - 120 = 0, \qquad \therefore A_y = 120 \text{ lb}$$

$$\Sigma F_x = A_x - D = 0, \qquad \therefore A_x = 90 \text{ lb}$$

Hence, $A = \sqrt{120^2 + 90^2} = 150$ lb, $\theta_x = \tan^{-1} \frac{120}{90} = 53° 8'$

In order to find the pressures on the cylinder at B and C, a free-body diagram of the cylinder is drawn; this is shown in Fig. 122c in which the force D is now known. There are two unknown forces, B and C, and, since the force system is coplanar and concurrent, there are two equations of equilibrium, and, hence, the two unknowns can be found. Thus,

$$\Sigma F_x = B - 90 = 0, \qquad \therefore \ B = 90 \text{ lb}$$

$$\Sigma F_y = C - 120 = 0, \qquad \therefore \ C = 120 \text{ lb}$$

Problems

171. In Prob. 169, instead of drawing a free-body diagram of EH alone, draw a free-body diagram of EH and C considered as one body, and then from Figs. 121c and d find H and Q, respectively. Now return to the free-body diagram of EH and C, and find D_x, D_y, and B.

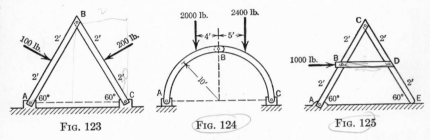

FIG. 123   FIG. 124   FIG. 125

172. Solve Prob. 170 by considering first the frame alone as a free body and next the cylinder alone as a free body.

173. Find the stress in the member BE of the crane shown in Fig. 79. Find also the magnitude and direction of the reaction of the pin at C on the member CH. Assume the weights of members to be negligible.

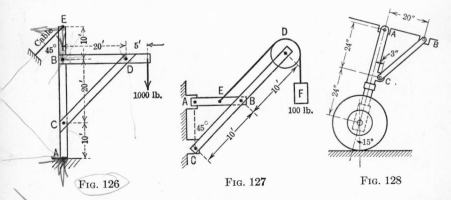

FIG. 126   FIG. 127   FIG. 128

174. The weightless bars AB and BC in Fig. 123 are connected by smooth pins at points A, B, and C. Find the horizontal and vertical components of the pin reactions at A and C.   *Ans.* $A_x = 0$; $A_y = 100$ lb; $C_x = 86.6$ lb; $C_y = 50$ lb.

175. The three-hinged arch shown in Fig. 124 is composed of two members, AB and BC, that are connected by smooth pins at points A, B, and C. Find the horizontal and vertical components of the reaction of the pins at A and B on AB.

176. The A frame shown in Fig. 125 is connected at points A, B, C, and D by smooth pins. The surface at E is also smooth. Find the stress in BD and the magnitude and direction of the reaction of the pin at C on CE.

177. In Fig. 126 find the magnitude and direction of the reaction of the pin at B on the member BD of the crane.   *Ans.* $B = 1275$ lb; $\theta_x = 191°\ 20'$.

178. Find the x and y components of the reaction of the pin at B on the member AB in Fig. 127. The drum D is frictionless and has a radius of 2 ft. Neglect the weights of the members.   *Ans.* $B_x = 157.3$ lb; $B_y = 42.4$ lb.

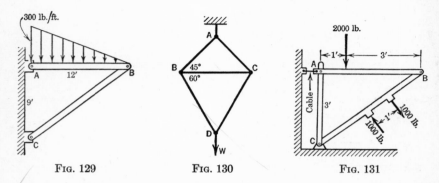

FIG. 129   FIG. 130   FIG. 131

179. In Fig. 128 is shown the landing gear of an airplane. If a vertical force of 6000 lb is transmitted from the ground to the wheel, determine the pin reactions at A and B. Assume the members of the landing gear to lie in a vertical plane.

180. The pin-connected frame shown in Fig. 129 carries a distributed load as shown. The members AB and BC each weigh 20 lb per foot of length. Find the horizontal and vertical components of the reactions of the pins at A and B on AB.

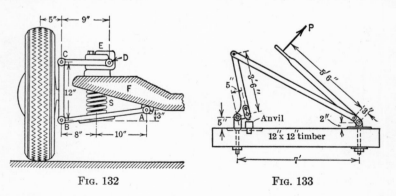

FIG. 132   FIG. 133

181. Five weightless bars are connected by smooth pins as shown in Fig. 130. Find the stress in the bar BC when a vertical load W is applied at D.

Ans. $BC = 0.788W$.

182. The pin-connected frame shown in Fig. 131 is supported by a horizontal cable at A and a smooth pin at C. Determine the tension in the cable, the reaction of the support on the pin C, and the reaction of the pin B on AB.

183. One type of front wheel suspension for an automobile is shown in Fig. 132. If the pavement exerts a force of 800 lb vertically upward through the center of the tire when the car is at rest, determine the compressive force in the vertical spring *S*. The members *CD* and *BC* are horizontal and vertical, respectively. Assume the frame *F* to be fixed, and neglect all frictional forces and the weights of the members. The pin *D* is connected to the shock absorber *E* which is rigidly attached to the frame *F*.

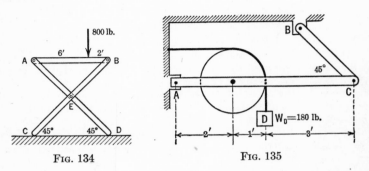

FIG. 134   FIG. 135

184. In Fig. 133 is shown a shear for cutting steel bars in a repair yard. What force *P* perpendicular to the handle is required to give a pressure of 7000 lb on the anvil when the 3-ft 6-in. arm is vertical, assuming the length of the bar connecting the arm to the handle is such as to make the handle also vertical. *Hint:* Draw a free-body diagram of the arm and also of the handle, and, in applying the equation $\Sigma M = 0$ to the forces in each diagram, use the fixed point on each body as the moment center.   *Ans. P = 34 lb.*

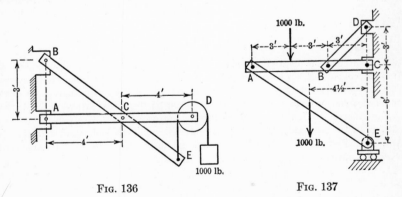

FIG. 136   FIG. 137

185. The three bars of the frame shown in Fig. 134 are connected by smooth pins at *A*, *B*, and *E*. The bars *AD* and *BC* are of equal length, and *E* is the mid-point of each of the bars. Find the magnitudes of the reactions of the pins at *A* and *B* on *AB* and the reaction of the pin at *E* on *BC*.

186. Find the reactions of the smooth pins at *A* and *C* on the bar *AC* of the pin-connected frame shown in Fig. 135. Neglect the weights of the members.
                    Ans. A = 269 lb; $\theta_x = 26° 35'$; C = 84.8 lb.

187. Find the x and y components of the reaction of the pin C on member BE in Fig. 136. The pulley at D is frictionless and has a diameter of 2 ft. Neglect the weights of the members.   *Ans.* $C_x = 3000$ lb; $C_y = -4000$ lb.

188. Find the magnitudes of the reactions of the pins at A, B, and C on the member AC of the frame shown in Fig. 137.

Ans. $A = 500$ lb; $B = 4950$ lb; $C = 4030$ lb.

Review Questions

1. Is the following statement correct? A force system is in equilibrium when the forces of the system have no resultant.

2. If a coplanar, non-concurrent force system is in equilibrium, what two graphical conditions must the forces satisfy? Explain.

3. Prove that, if the forces of a coplanar, parallel system satisfy the equations $\Sigma M_A = 0$ and $\Sigma M_B = 0$, the forces must be in equilibrium; make clear the restriction on the choice of the points A and B.

4. What is meant by a statically indeterminate force system?

5. What is wrong with the following statement? A free-body diagram is a diagram showing the body and some (but not all) of the forces that the body exerts on other bodies. *all the forces that act on it.*

6. A force system consisting of three forces is in equilibrium. If the force system is non-concurrent, what must be its classification? (See Art. 22.)

7. What is the classification of the force system that acts on member BC of the pin-connected frame shown in Fig. 135? What special name is used for this type of member?

8. Explain how the internal forces at a cross section of a body can be included in a free-body diagram.

9. Given the following equations of equilibrium for a coplanar, non-concurrent, non-parallel force system:

$$\Sigma F_x = 0, \qquad \Sigma M_A = 0, \qquad \Sigma M_B = 0$$

(*a*) What are the restrictions placed on the selection of the points A and B? (*b*) What conclusion can be drawn regarding the resultant of the given force system if the forces of the system satisfy only the first one of these equations? (*c*) What conclusions can be drawn regarding the resultant if the forces satisfy only the first two equations? (*d*) If they satisfy all three equations?

10. If in the free-body diagram of a body the point of application of a force is known, but its magnitude and direction are unknown, state two ways in which this force can be represented in the free-body diagram.

11. A system of coplanar, non-concurrent, non-parallel forces is in equilibrium, and all of the forces are known completely except two, the action line of one of these two being known and also one point A on the action line of the other. If the unknown forces are determined by use of a force polygon and a string polygon, why must the string polygon be started at the point A?

Chapter 4

EQUILIBRIUM OF
TRUSSES AND CABLES

45 Stresses in trusses. Important examples of coplanar force systems in equilibrium are met in the analysis of the internal forces in the members of trusses. The internal force in a member will be called the total stress in the member or simply the stress in the member even though the term stress in general means the intensity of the internal force or the force per unit area. In determining the stresses in trusses, only those trusses will here be considered for which the following assumptions may reasonably be made:

1. The members of the truss lie in one plane, and the external forces acting on the truss lie in the same plane, and hence the forces involved in the determination of the stresses in members of the truss form coplanar systems.

2. The members of the truss are rigid and are connected at their ends by means of smooth pins that fit perfectly to the members. This means that the deformations of the members are negligible in comparison with the dimensions of the members, and hence the geometry of the truss is not changed by deformation.

3. The applied loads and reactions on the truss act only on the pins: that is, at the ends of the members.

4. The weights of the members are negligible in comparison with the other external forces acting on the truss at the pins.

It follows from assumptions 3 and 4 that each member is a two-force member (see Art. 39), which means that the stress in each member is directed along the member and is equal to the pin pressure at either end (see Fig. 80 and Prob. 117). The stress in the member is a tensile stress if the pin pressures at the ends act outward or away from the member, or tend to pull the member apart, and a compressive stress if the pin pressures act toward the member. The usual methods of indicating the kind of stress (tension or compression) in a member is to indicate a tensile stress by a plus sign or by the letter T, and a compressive stress by a negative sign or by the letter C.

In determining the stresses in a pin-connected, pin-loaded structure algebraically, by use of the equations of equilibrium, two methods may be used: namely, the *method of joints* and the *method of sections*. In both methods a section is passed through the structure to obtain the part of the structure that is to be taken as the free body, but the difference in the methods lies chiefly in the type of force system acting on the portion of the structure that is considered as the free body. In the first method a *concurrent* force system is involved, and in the second method a *non-concurrent*, non-parallel system is dealt with.

METHOD OF JOINTS. In determining the stresses in the members of a pin-connected, pin-loaded truss by the method of joints, a section is passed through the truss, cutting members that are attached to a common pin; one such section is indicated as *aa* in Fig. 138*a*. The portion thus severed from the truss by this section (consisting of the pin and attached parts of the members) is then treated as a free body in equilibrium under the action of any known external forces that act on this body (such as the reaction at *A*) in Fig. 138*a* and the forces (stresses) exerted at the cut sections by the other portions of the members. A free-body diagram for the joint *A* in Fig. 138*a* is shown in Fig. 138*b*.

It will be noted that the method of joints involves the equilibrium of a *concurrent* force system, and, since there are two equations of equilibrium for such a force system, the section passed through the truss must not cut more than two members in which the stresses are unknown. (It is assumed that all external loads and reactions are known.)

Instead of selecting the free body as shown in Fig. 138*b*, it is sometimes convenient to treat the pin alone as the free body in equilibrium under the actions of the pressures exerted by the members on the pin as shown in Fig. 138*c*. As already noted, the stress in each member is numerically equal to the pin pressure at either end of the member, so that the two free-body diagrams lead to the same solution.

In determining the stresses in all members of a truss by the method of joints, the equations of equilibrium must be applied to the joints in turn and in such an order that not more than two unknown stresses occur in each free-body diagram. Thus, if the stress in a single member near the center of the truss is required, it is usually necessary to start at the end of the truss and consider the equilibrium of the joints in order until a joint is reached that involves the particular member. By the method of sections, discussed in the next paragraph, the stress in a single member may frequently be found by use of one free-body diagram.

METHOD OF SECTIONS. In determining the stresses in the members of a pin-connected, pin-loaded truss, by the method of sections, a section is passed through the truss, cutting members that are not attached to a common pin; two such sections are indicated as bb and cc in Fig. 138a.

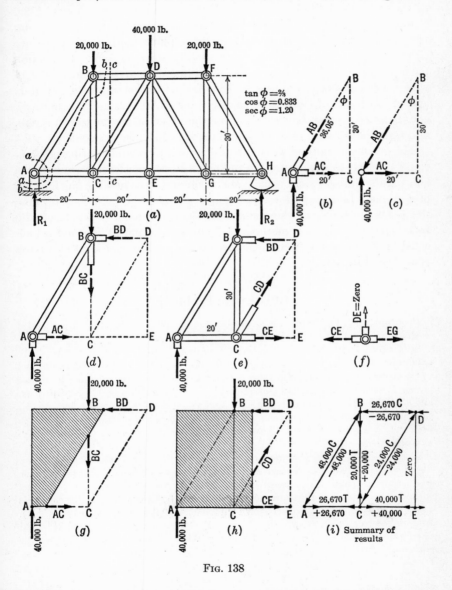

FIG. 138

The part of the truss on either side of this section is then treated as a free body in equilibrium under the action of the known external forces that act on that part and the forces (stresses) that the members of the other part exert, at the cut sections, on the part considered as the free body. Free-body diagrams are shown in Figs. 138*d* and 138*e* for the portions of the truss to the left of sections *bb* and *cc*, respectively, in Fig. 138*a*.

It will be noted that the method of sections involves the equilibrium of *non-concurrent, non-parallel* forces in a plane, and, since there are three equations of equilibrium for such a force system, the section passed through the truss must not cut more than three members in which the stresses are unknown. By a proper choice of moment centers and of directions of resolution, as discussed in Art. 42, each of the three equations may often be made to give the value of one unknown stress, and thus the solution of three simultaneous equations is avoided.

The graphical method which makes use of a force and a string polygon could be used to determine the unknown forces of the non-concurrent, non-parallel force system which acts on the free body used in the method of sections. Likewise a force polygon alone could be used to determine the unknown forces of the concurrent force system which acts on the free body used in the method of joints; a graphical method which consists of a superposition of the force polygons for each joint of a truss is discussed in Art. 46.

Illustrative Problem

Problem 189. Determine the stresses in the members of the Howe truss loaded as shown in Fig. 138*a*.

SOLUTION. By applying the equations of equilibrium to the forces in the free-body diagram of the entire truss as shown in Fig. 138*a*, the reactions R_1 and R_2 are found to be 40,000 lb each. The reactions R_1 and R_2 could be found graphically by use of the force and funicular polygons. In this problem, however, the values of R_1 and R_2 are evident from inspection. To find the stresses in members AB and AC the method of joints will be used. The free-body diagram of joint A is shown in Fig. 138*b*; it will be noted that the stress in a member is denoted by the same letters as is the member itself.

Convention Used in Designating Kind of Stress. In drawing the free-body diagram, the question arises as to whether an unknown stress should be shown as a tensile stress or as a compressive stress. One method of procedure is to show the stress with its correct sense, if the sense can be determined by inspection (or, if the sense is not evident from inspection, it is shown with a sense that seems the most plausible). If an unknown stress is shown with its correct sense, the stress will always be found to be positive whether the stress is tension or compression. This procedure has the advantage of requiring the student to visualize the forces as they act in the structure. However, it has a disadvantage in that a positive sign does not always indicate tension and a negative sign compression, as is the case in the following method. Another method of procedure is to show all unknown stresses as tension, even though it is evident from inspection that some of the stresses are compression. Then, in the solution, all stresses that are found to be positive are tension as assumed and all stresses found to be negative are compression: that is, opposite to that assumed.

In Figs. 138*b* and *c* the senses of the unknown forces AB and AC are correctly indicated and hence will be found to be positive, although one of the stresses is a compressive stress and the other a tensile stress. By applying one set of equations of equilibrium for the concurrent force system shown in Figs. 138*b* and *c*, the stresses AB and AC are found as follows:

$$\Sigma M_B = -40{,}000 \times 20 + AC \times 30 = 0, \qquad \therefore\ AC = 26{,}670 \text{ lb } T$$

$$\Sigma F_y = -AB \cos \phi + 40{,}000 = 0, \qquad \therefore\ AB = \frac{40{,}000}{0.833} = 48{,}000 \text{ lb } C$$

To find the stresses in members BC and BD let a section *bb* be passed (Fig. 138*a*) through the truss. The forces acting on the part of the truss to the left of this section form a non-concurrent force system (Fig. 138*d*), and all three stresses could be found from the three equations of equilibrium. But, since the stress in AC has already been found, only two of the three equations need be applied. Thus,

$$\Sigma M_C = -40{,}000 \times 20 + BD \times 30 = 0, \qquad \therefore\ BD = 26{,}670 \text{ lb } C$$

$$\Sigma F_y = 40{,}000 - 20{,}000 - BC = 0, \qquad \therefore\ BC = 20{,}000 \text{ lb } T$$

In a similar manner the stresses in CD and CE may be found by the method of sections. By considering the part of the truss to the left of the section *cc* (Fig. 138*e*), the stresses in these two members may be found. Thus,

$$\Sigma M_D = -40{,}000 \times 40 + 20{,}000 \times 20 + CE \times 30 = 0$$

$$\therefore\ CE = 40{,}000 \text{ lb } T$$

$$\Sigma F_y = 40{,}000 - 20{,}000 + CD \cos \phi = 0$$

$$\therefore\ CD = -20{,}000 \times \sec \phi = -20{,}000 \times 1.20 = -24{,}000 \text{ lb } C$$

It will be noted that all the stresses except CD (Fig. 138*e*) are assumed to act in the correct directions and hence are found to be positive whether they are tensile or compressive. The stress in CD is assumed to be tension, and hence the negative sign indicates that it is compression.

In considering the equilibrium of the forces which act on the pin E (Fig. 138*f*), it is evident that the stress DE is zero and that CE equals EG. Furthermore, since the truss is symmetrical with respect to the center line DE and the loads are also symmetrical with respect to this line, it is obvious that the stresses in the members of the right half of the truss are equal to the stresses in the corresponding members of the left half.

It is well to note that the stresses in the members of a truss are *internal* forces in considering the whole truss as a free body but the stresses in members that are cut by a given section passed through the truss are *external* forces with respect to the portion on either side of that section. Therefore, the portion of the truss on one side of the section may be considered to be a weightless rigid body of *any shape* provided the (external) forces acting on it have the same relative positions (and the same magnitude, of course) as in the actual body. Thus the free-body diagrams in Figs. 138*d* and *e* could be replaced by Figs. 138*g* and *h*.

Summary of Results. The results are summarized in Fig. 138*i* where the kind of stress (tension or compression) in each member is indicated by the sign + or − before the value of the stress, as well as by the letter T or C after the value of the stress. A third method of indicating the kind of stress makes use of arrows on each member which show the directions of the pressures of the member on the pins at its ends (not the pressures of the pins on the member); thus a compressive stress is represented by an arrow at each end of the member directed toward the pin at the end. Similarly a tensile stress is indicated by arrows directed toward the center of the member: that is, away from each pin.

Problems

190. In Fig. 138*a* let it be assumed that the stresses in *AB* and *BC* have been found to be 48,000 lb *C* and 20,000 lb *T*, respectively. Pass a section cutting the members *AB*, *BC*, *CD*, and *CE*, and then draw a free-body diagram of the portion of the truss to the left of this section, and solve for the two unknown stresses.

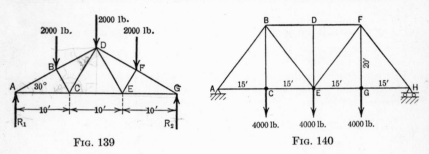

FIG. 139   FIG. 140

191. Find the stresses in the members *BD*, *DE*, and *HE* of the truss shown in Fig. 60. Note that it is not necessary to determine the reactions at *H* and *G* to solve the problem. *Ans. BD = +6800 lb; DE = +3600 lb; HE = −6800 lb.*

192. In Fig. 119 find by the method of sections the stresses in the members *BD*, *CD*, and *CE* of the Fink truss shown.

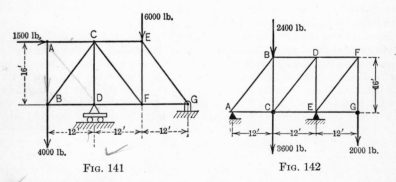

FIG. 141   FIG. 142

193. In the Fink truss shown in Fig. 139, *BC* is perpendicular to *AD* and *B* is the mid-point of *AD*. Find the stresses in the members *BC*, *BD*, *CD*, and *CE*. *Ans. BC = −1730 lb; BD = −5000 lb; CD = +1730 lb; CE = +3460 lb.*

194. Assume that the three loads are removed from the truss shown in Fig. 139 and that a vertical downward load of 3000 lb is applied at *E*. Find by use of a force and a funicular polygon the reactions R_1 and R_2. Pass a section cutting members BD, CD, and CE, and find by use of a force and a funicular polygon the stresses in these members.

195. The Pratt truss in Fig. 140 carries three loads applied at the lower panel points as shown. Find the stresses in AB, BD, BE, and CE.

Ans. $AB = -7500$ lb; $BD = -6000$ lb; $BE = +2500$ lb; $CE = +4500$ lb.

196. Assume that the three loads acting on the truss shown in Fig. 140 are replaced by a single downward vertical load of 8000 lb applied at B. Find the stresses in BD, BE, CE, and EG.

197. Find the stresses in the members AC, BC, BD, and CD of the truss shown in Fig. 141. If the diagonal BC were replaced by the diagonal AD, what would be the change in the stresses in AC and CD?

Ans. $AC = -1500$ lb; $BC = +5000$ lb; $BD = -3000$ lb; $CD = -8000$ lb.

198. Find the stresses in the members DF, DE, CE, and CD of the truss shown in Fig. 142.

199. Find, by the method of joints, the stresses in the members BC and CD of the pin-connected truss shown in Fig. 143. Find, by the method of sections, the stresses in DG, DF, and EF.

Ans. $BC = 1000$ lb; $CD = -1415$ lb; $DG = -1500$ lb; $DF = 707$ lb; $EF = 0$.

200. Find the stresses in members BD, CD, and CE of the truss shown in Fig. 144.

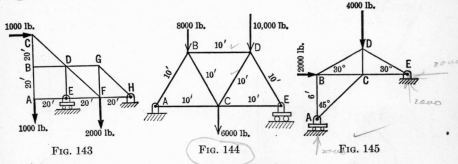

FIG. 143 FIG. 144 FIG. 145

201. Find the stresses in the members AC, BC, and BD of the truss shown in Fig. 145. *Ans.* $AC = 0$; $BC = 1465$ lb; $BD = -4000$ lb.

202. The stress in the member BD of the Warren truss shown in Fig. 146 is a compressive stress having a magnitude of 2000 lb. Determine the load P, and find the stresses in DF, DE, and CE.

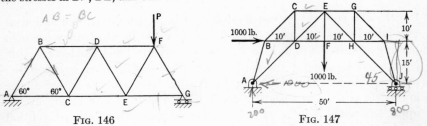

FIG. 146 FIG. 147

203. Find the stresses in the members CE, DE, DF, and AD of the truss shown in Fig. 147.

46   Graphical analysis of trusses.   A graphical method of analysis of a truss is sometimes simpler than the algebraic method. This is particularly true when the form of the truss is such that a considerable amount of calculation is necessary to determine the directions and moment arms of the forces involved. The graphical method consists essentially in constructing the force polygon for the concurrent forces at each joint and superimposing these polygons. It is evident therefore that the method of joints is used, and it is unnecessary to use the funicular polygon in addition to the force polygon as would be required if the method of sections were used. The method will be explained in detail with reference to the Howe truss shown in Fig. 148a. The truss is assumed to be subjected to known equal loads at the upper panel points, and hence the reactions at the ends of the truss are each equal to one half of the sum of the loads.

Convention Used in Designating Stresses in Members. It is convenient to use the Bow's notation (Art. 8) in which the regions on either side of the action line of a force (either external or internal) are denoted by numbers or letters as shown in Fig. 148a, and the force is denoted by the two numbers or letters adjacent to the action line of the

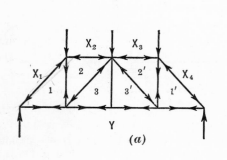
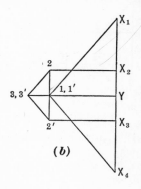

Fig. 148

force. The convention usually followed is to denote a force acting at any joint by the letters or numbers in the order in which they occur in passing around the joint in a *clockwise* direction. Thus, the left reaction is denoted by $Y-X_1$; the force exerted by the member between the regions X_1 and 1 is denoted by X_1-1 when considered as acting at the lower-left panel point and by $1-X_1$ when considered as acting at the upper-left panel point, and so on. The importance of this convention lies in the fact that the nature of the stress (whether tension or compression) in any member may be determined at once by inspection from the force polygon, as will be seen in the following discussion.

The force polygon (Fig. 148b) for the truss in Fig. 148a is constructed as follows: First consider the three concurrent forces acting on the pin at the lower-left panel point; as previously explained, these forces are equal to the stresses in the members that exert the forces on the pin. Of these three forces the left reaction $Y–X_1$ is completely known and the directions of the other two, $X_1–1$ and $1–Y$, are known. Since the three forces are in equilibrium, their force polygon must close. This polygon is constructed in Fig. 148b as follows. First a vector YX_1 representing the force $Y–X_1$ is drawn. This vector is drawn first because the force polygon must be started with a known force. The force polygon is then completed by drawing from X_1 a line $X_1 1$ parallel to $X_1–1$ in Fig. 148a and from Y a line $Y1$ parallel to $Y–1$. These two lines intersect in the point 1 in Fig. 148b, and, hence, the polygon for the lower-left panel point is $YX_1 1Y$. Since $X_1 1$ (Fig. 148b) is downward to the left, the member $X_1–1$ exerts on the lower-left pin a force downward to the left, and hence the stress in the member $X_1–1$ is a compressive stress, and similarly the stress in $1–Y$ is a tensile stress.

In like manner the force polygon for the forces exerted on the pin at the upper-left panel point is next constructed. In constructing this force polygon the vectors that represent the known forces ($1–X_1$ and $X_1–X_2$) must first be laid off because the known forces must be laid off first and in the order that the members are cut by a section in passing clockwise around the pin. But, since the vector $1X_1$ is already in the diagram, it is only necessary to lay off to the same scale the vector X_1X_2; then, from X_2 a line $X_2 2$ is drawn parallel to $X_2–2$ and from 1 a line 1 2 is drawn parallel to $1–2$. The polygon for this panel point then is $1X_1X_2 21$. From the convention already noted it is evident that the stress in $X_2–2$ is a compressive stress and that in $2–1$ is a tensile stress. In a similar manner the remaining joints are considered, and the entire polygon shown in Fig. 148b is completed; the length of any line in the polygon represents to scale the magnitude of the stress in the corresponding member.

It should be noted that the joints must be taken in an order such that at no joint are there more than two unknown forces; otherwise it would be impossible to complete the polygon for the joint.

Illustrative Problem

Problem 204. Find the stresses in the members of the truss shown in Fig. 149a. The members $X_1–1$ and $2–3$ are parallel, and the members $X_1–2$ and $Y–1$ are parallel. SOLUTION. The force polygon for the forces acting on the pins (that is, for the stresses in the members) is drawn to scale in Fig. 149b. The magnitudes of the stresses are found by measuring the lengths of the lines in the force polygon, and the kind of stress in each member is determined by the convention explained in Art. 46.

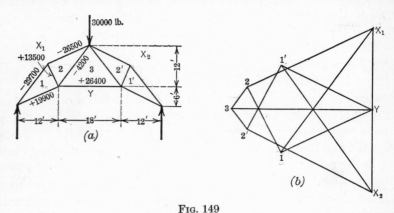

Fig. 149

The magnitudes of the stresses are shown on the members in Fig. 149a, the plus or minus sign indicating whether the stress in the member is tension or compression.

Problems

205. Find by the graphical method discussed in Art. 46 the stresses in all members of the Pratt truss shown in Fig. 140.

206. If the load P acting on the Warren truss shown in Fig. 146 is 6000 lb, find graphically the stresses in all members of the truss.

207. Find, by the graphical method, the stresses in the members of the truss shown in Fig. 150, the value of P being 10,000 lb.

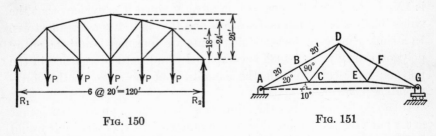

Fig. 150   Fig. 151

208. A total wind pressure of 4000 lb acts on the upper chord ABD of the truss shown in Fig. 151, the pressure being normal to the surface. Assume that this pressure is equivalent to a load of 2000 lb at B (normal to ABD) and loads of 1000 lb each at A and D, and determine the reactions at A and G by the algebraic method, and then find the stresses in the members of the truss by the graphical method.

209. Find, by the graphical method, the stresses in the members of the Fink truss shown in Fig. 119. Use values of R_1 and R_2 given in the answer to Prob. 164.

210. Determine algebraically the reactions at A and H on the truss shown in Fig. 152, and then find the stresses in all members graphically.

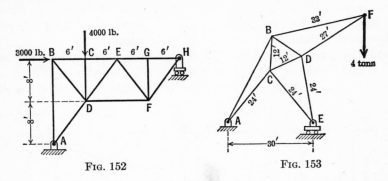

FIG. 152   FIG. 153

211. Determine the reactions at A and E on the crane shown in Fig. 153 by a semi-graphical method (see Prob. 152), and then find the stresses in all members by the graphical method. Assume that the triangle BCD is an equilateral triangle.

47 Flexible cables. In the following two articles will be discussed the equilibrium of flexible cables suspended from two points such as, for example, the cables of a suspension bridge. A cable is said to be perfectly flexible when it can offer no resistance to bending. A flexible cable, then, can transmit a force only along its axis; that is, the internal force at any cross section of a flexible cable is tangent at that section to the curve assumed by the cable. Although physical cables are not perfectly flexible, the resistance they offer to bending is generally so small that it can be neglected without serious error.

In the discussion of flexible cables it will be assumed that a cable of length l is suspended from two points, the distance between the two points being less than l, and that the cable is inextensible: that is, the length of the cable does not change when the cable is subjected to external forces or to a change in temperature. It is desired to find equations that express relations between the span a, the sag f, the length l of the cable, the internal tensile force T at any cross section of the cable, and the external forces which act on the cable (see Figs. 154 and 155). The method of obtaining the desired equations is the same as that outlined in Art. 38: namely, to pass a plane or section through the cable severing from it that portion which is to be considered in the free-body diagram. The forces that were exerted on the severed section by the other part of the cable before the severed portion was removed are now external to the severed portion, and these forces together with the original external forces that act on the severed portion constitute a coplanar force system which must satisfy the equations of equilibrium.

In the subsequent discussion, the points from which the cable is suspended will be assumed to be in the same horizontal plane. The equations relating the span, sag, etc., for a cable suspended from two points not in the same horizontal plane can be determined by the same procedure as that outlined in the preceding paragraph.

48 The parabolic cable. If a flexible cable is suspended from two points and carries a vertical load that is distributed uniformly horizontally (Fig. 154a), the curve assumed by the cable is a parabola, as will

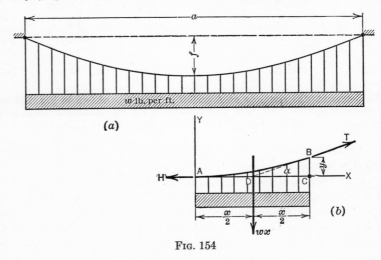

Fig. 154

presently be shown. An example of a cable carrying such a load is the cable of a suspension bridge, since the weight of the roadway is distributed uniformly horizontally, and the weights of the cables and hangers are small in comparison with the weight of the roadway and therefore may be neglected. Another example is that of a tightly stretched cable (that is, one in which the sag is small compared with the span) which carries no load except its own weight, as, for example, the cable of an electric transmission line or a telegraph wire. In this case the load carried by the cable (its weight) is distributed uniformly along the curve assumed by the cable, but, since the sag is small, the horizontal projection of an arc of the curve is approximately equal to the length of the arc, and hence the load is distributed approximately uniformly in the horizontal direction.

In order to determine the equations that express relations between the span, sag, tension, etc., a portion AB of the cable will be considered as a free body (Fig. 154b). The lowest point A of the cable will be taken as the origin of co-ordinates, and the tension at this point will be denoted by H. The tension at any point B will be denoted by T. The portion of cable AB, then, is in equilibrium under the action of the three forces, H, T, and the vertical load wx which acts through the point D midway between A and C. Since these three forces are in equilibrium, they must be concurrent, and hence the action line of T passes through D. The equations of equilibrium are:

$$\Sigma F_x = T \cos \alpha - H = 0 \tag{1}$$

$$\Sigma F_y = T \sin \alpha - wx = 0 \tag{2}$$

Eliminating T from Eqs. 1 and 2, we have

$$\tan \alpha = \frac{wx}{H}, \quad \text{but} \quad \tan \alpha = \frac{2y}{x}$$

Hence

$$\frac{2y}{x} = \frac{wx}{H}, \quad \text{or} \quad y = \frac{wx^2}{2H} \tag{3}$$

The curve, then, is a parabola with its vertex at A and its axis vertical. Eliminating α from Eqs. 1 and 2, we have

$$T = \sqrt{H^2 + w^2x^2} \tag{4}$$

In applying the foregoing equations, we are concerned with the tension at the point of support since at this point the tension is a maximum. Hence, if the span be denoted by a and the maximum value of y (that is, the sag) by f, Eqs. 3 and 4 reduce to

$$f = \frac{wa^2}{8H} \tag{5}$$

and

$$T = \frac{1}{2} wa \sqrt{1 + \frac{a^2}{16f^2}} \tag{6}$$

in which T represents the tension at the points of support.

The length of the cable will now be determined in terms of the span and sag. In any curve the length of an arc is obtained from the equation

$$s = \int \sqrt{1 + \left(\frac{dy}{dx}\right)^2}\, dx$$

From Eq. 3, $dy/dx = wx/H$. Hence, if the length of the cable be denoted by l, we have

$$l = 2 \int_0^{a/2} \sqrt{1 + \frac{w^2x^2}{H^2}}\, dx$$

Substitution of H from Eq. 5 gives

$$l = 2 \int_0^{a/2} \sqrt{1 + \frac{64f^2x^2}{a^4}}\, dx$$

The expression for l, obtained from this integral, involves a logarithmic function and is difficult to apply. An expression for l that is more convenient to use may be obtained by expanding the expression under the integral into a series and integrating the series term by term. This method leads to the following equation:

$$l = a\left[1 + \frac{8}{3}\left(\frac{f}{a}\right)^2 - \frac{32}{5}\left(\frac{f}{a}\right)^4 + \cdots\right] \qquad (7)$$

Since the sag-span ratio f/a is generally small, the series converges rapidly, and it is sufficient in most practical computations to use only the first two or three terms of the series to obtain a close approximation to the value of l.

Illustrative Problem

Problem 212. The horizontal load carried by each cable of a suspension bridge is 1000 lb per ft. The span of the bridge is 800 ft, and the sag is 50 ft. Determine the tensions at the ends and at the middle of the cable, and also find the length of the cable.

SOLUTION. From Eqs. 5 and 6,

$$H = \frac{1000 \times (800)^2}{8 \times 50} = 1{,}600{,}000 \text{ lb}$$

and

$$T = \frac{1}{2} \times 1000 \times 800 \sqrt{1 + \frac{(800)^2}{16 \times (50)^2}} = 1{,}650{,}000 \text{ lb}$$

The length of the cable may be determined by using Eq. 7. Thus,

$$l = 800\,[1 + \tfrac{8}{3}(\tfrac{50}{800})^2 - \tfrac{32}{5}(\tfrac{50}{800})^4] = 808.24 \text{ ft}$$

Problems

213. A telegraph wire weighing 0.1 lb per ft is stretched between two poles 150 ft apart. The tension in the wire at the insulators (which are in the same horizontal plane) is 500 lb. Find the sag, assuming that the weight of the wire is uniformly distributed horizontally. Find also the length of the curve assumed by the wire.

Ans. $f = 0.562$ ft; $l = 150.005$ ft.

214. Each cable of a suspension bridge carries a load of 1200 lb per ft uniformly distributed along the horizontal. The span is 1000 ft, and the sag is 50 ft. Find the maximum stress in the cable and the length of the cable.

Ans. $T = 3{,}060{,}000$ lb; $l = 1006.63$ ft.

215. A uniform cable 100 ft in length is suspended from two points in a horizontal plane which are 99 ft apart. What is the sag of the cable? *Ans. $f = 6.09$ ft.*

49 The catenary. The curve assumed by a flexible cable of uniform cross section which is suspended from two points, and which carries no load except its own weight (Fig. 155), is called a catenary. The load which causes a cable to assume the form of a catenary, then, differs from that which causes the form of a parabola in that the load is distributed uniformly along the cable in the former case, whereas in the latter case the load is distributed uniformly horizontally.

The discussion of the catenary is of practical importance only for cables in which the sag-span ratio is large, since for a small sag-span ratio

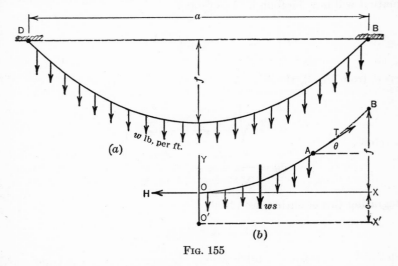

FIG. 155

the curve assumed by a cable may be regarded with small error as being a parabola, as discussed in the preceding article.

In order to determine the equations that express relations between such quantities as the sag, span, length of cable, and tension, the equilibrium of a portion OA of the cable (Fig. 155) will be considered, O being the lowest point of the cable and A any other point. The point O will be taken as the origin of co-ordinates, the weight of the cable per unit of length will be denoted by w, and the length of the arc OA will be denoted by s. The portion OA of the cable is in equilibrium under the influence of three forces: namely, the tension H at the point O, the tension T at the point A, and the weight ws. The angle that T makes with the horizontal will be denoted by θ. The equations of equilibrium for the concurrent force system are

$$\Sigma F_x = T \cos \theta - H = 0, \qquad \therefore \ T \cos \theta = H \qquad (1)$$

$$\Sigma F_y = T \sin \theta - ws = 0, \qquad \therefore \ T \sin \theta = ws \qquad (2)$$

From Eqs. 1 and 2, we obtain

$$\tan \theta = \frac{ws}{H} = \frac{s}{c} \quad \text{where} \quad \frac{H}{w} = c \text{ (a constant)}$$

Hence,

$$s = c \tan \theta \quad \text{or} \quad s = c\frac{dy}{dx} \tag{3}$$

This equation is the intrinsic equation of the catenary. The Cartesian equation will now be found. In any curve,

$$\frac{ds}{dy} = \sqrt{1 + \left(\frac{dx}{dy}\right)^2}$$

Hence, from Eq. 3, the following equation is obtained:

$$\frac{ds}{dy} = \sqrt{1 + \frac{c^2}{s^2}} = \frac{\sqrt{s^2 + c^2}}{s}$$

Therefore,

$$dy = \frac{s\,ds}{\sqrt{s^2 + c^2}}$$

Integrating this equation, we obtain

$$y + A = \sqrt{s^2 + c^2}$$

where A is a constant of integration. If now the origin is transferred to O', where $OO' = c$, then $y = c$ when $s = 0$, and hence $A = 0$. The last equation, therefore, becomes

$$y = \sqrt{s^2 + c^2} \tag{4}$$

Elimination of y from Eqs. 3 and 4 gives

$$dx = \frac{c\,ds}{\sqrt{c^2 + s^2}}$$

Integrating this equation we obtain

$$x + B = c \log_e (s + \sqrt{s^2 + c^2})$$

Since $s = 0$ when $x = 0$, $B = c \log_e c$, and hence the last equation becomes

$$x = c \log_e \frac{s + \sqrt{s^2 + c^2}}{c} = c \log_e \frac{s + y}{c} \tag{5}$$

Equation 5 can also be written in the form,

$$\sqrt{s^2 + c^2} + s = ce^{x/c} \tag{6}$$

By inverting each side of Eq. 6 and rationalizing the denominator of the left side, the following equation is obtained:

$$\sqrt{s^2 + c^2} - s = ce^{-x/c} \tag{7}$$

Adding Eqs. 6 and 7 and using Eq. 4, we have

$$y = \frac{c}{2}(e^{x/c} + e^{-x/c}) = c \cosh\frac{x}{c} \tag{8}$$

This is the Cartesian equation of the catenary. Subtracting Eq. 7 from Eq. 6, we obtain

$$s = \frac{c}{2}(e^{x/c} - e^{-x/c}) = c \sinh\frac{x}{c} \tag{9}$$

Squaring and adding Eqs. 1 and 2, we have

$$T^2 = H^2 + w^2 s^2 = w^2 c^2 + w^2 s^2 = w^2 y^2$$

Hence,

$$T = wy \tag{10}$$

In summarizing, then, the following important properties of the catenary may be stated:

1. The horizontal component of the tensile internal force T at any cross section of the cable is constant and equal to wc.

2. The vertical component of the tensile internal force T at any cross section of the cable is equal to ws.

3. The total tensile internal force T at any cross section of the cable is equal to wy.

In engineering problems that involve the catenary we are concerned particularly with the tension at the points of support, since at these points the tension is a maximum. Hence, in Eq. 10 T will be regarded as the tension at the points of support, and the values of x, y, and s will be regarded as the values of the variables at these points. Therefore, if the length of the cable be denoted by l, the span by a, and the sag by f, then the values of x, y, and s in the foregoing equations become $a/2$, $f + c$, and $l/2$, respectively.

The formulas of Art. 48 are generally used when the sag is small, since they are much easier to apply and the results obtained are sufficiently accurate for practical purposes. When the sag is large compared with the span, however, the above formulas in Art. 49 should be used.

Since the relations between the quantities as expressed by the above equations are complicated, many of the problems that involve the catenary can be solved only by trial.

Illustrative Problems

Problem 216. A cable weighing 4 lb per ft is stretched between two points in the same horizontal plane. The length of the cable is 600 ft, and the tension at the points of support is 2000 lb. Find the sag and also the distance between the points of support.

SOLUTION. From Eq. 10,

$$y = \frac{T}{w} = \frac{2000}{4} = 500 \text{ ft}$$

From Eq. 4,

$$c = \sqrt{y^2 - s^2} = \sqrt{(500)^2 - (300)^2} = 400 \text{ ft}$$

Hence,

$$f = y - c = 500 - 400 = 100 \text{ ft}$$

From Eq. 5,

$$x = c \log_e \frac{\sqrt{s^2 + c^2} + s}{c} = 400 \log_e \frac{\sqrt{(300)^2 + (400)^2} + 300}{400} = 277.2 \text{ ft}$$

Hence,

$$a = 2x = 554.4 \text{ ft}$$

Problem 217. A cable weighing 2 lb per ft of length is suspended from two points in a horizontal plane. If the maximum allowable tension in the cable is 4000 lb and the maximum permissible sag is 5 ft, what is the maximum allowable distance between the points of support?

SOLUTION. At the points of support $y = f + c$. Hence, in using Eq. 10, we have

$$4000 = 2(5 + c); \qquad \therefore c = 1995 \text{ ft} \quad \text{and} \quad y = 2000 \text{ ft}$$

Substituting the values of y and c in Eq. 8, we obtain

$$2000 = 1995 \cosh \frac{a}{3990}; \qquad \therefore \cosh \frac{a}{3990} = 1.0025$$

From a table of hyperbolic functions it is found that

$$\frac{a}{3990} = 0.07; \qquad \therefore a = 279.3 \text{ ft}$$

Since the sag-span ratio is very small, the curve assumed by the cable approximates very closely a parabola. Hence, the value of a found from Eq. 6 of Art. 48 should not differ materially from the correct value found. Thus,

$$4000 = a \sqrt{1 + \frac{a^2}{400}}$$

By rationalizing this equation and solving for a, it is found that $a = 282.4$ ft.

Problems

218. A cable 100 ft long is suspended between two points which are in the same horizontal plane and 80 ft apart. What is the sag at the mid-point of the cable?
$Ans. f = 26.54$ ft.

219. A cable weighing 2 lb per ft is stretched between two points in the same horizontal plane which are 150 ft apart. If the sag is 5 ft, what are the length of the cable and the tension at the points of support?
$Ans. l = 150.44$ ft; $T = 1130$ lb.

220. The curve assumed by the cable in Prob. 215 is actually a catenary instead of a parabola as was assumed in determining the sag. Since the sag-span ratio is small, the correct value of the sag should not differ materially from the value found. Find the correct value by use of the equations in Art. 49. $Ans. f = 6.114$ ft.

Review Questions

1. What is the essential difference between two-force members and members that are acted on by more than two forces? Which of these two classes of members occurs in a pin-connected, pin-loaded truss?

2. Correct the errors in the following statement: If the method of joints is used in determining the stresses in members of a pin-connected, pin-loaded truss, non-concurrent force systems are involved, and hence the unknown stresses in three members that meet at any joint can be found.

3. Is the graphical method used in Art. 46 for determining stresses in trusses based on the method of joints or the method of sections?

4. Is the following statement correct? In determining stresses in trusses algebraically by the method of sections, each section used may cut more than three members but cannot cut more than three members in which the stresses are unknown.

5. If the three loads on the Pratt truss shown in Fig. 140 be applied at points B, D, and F instead of at the points C, E, and G, would the stresses in any of the members be changed? If so, indicate which members.

6. If in Fig. 140 the diagonal members BE and EF be replaced by diagonal members CD and DG, respectively, what would be the change in the stresses in the diagonals? In what other members would the stresses be changed?

7. If the roller at H of the Howe truss shown in Fig. 138 be replaced by a fixed support similar to that at A, is it always possible to determine completely the external reactions? Is it possible to determine the stresses in all members? If not, indicate the members in which the stresses can be determined.

8. A cable is suspended from two points in a horizontal plane. If the total weight of the cable and the tension in the cable at its mid-point are known, explain how the slope of the cable at a point of support and the tension at this point can be determined.

9. Assume that a smooth peg is placed under the cable in Fig. 155 at O, and that the segment BO of the cable is lengthened by an amount OO' ($=c$), and that the added length of the cable hangs vertically. Show that the cable BOO' is in equilibrium.

10. A cable of indefinite length passes over two smooth pegs in the same horizontal plane. The initial sag of the portion of the cable between the pegs is large compared to the distance between the pegs. If the sag is continuously decreased by pulling the free ends of the cable over the pegs, will the tension in the cable at the pegs decrease continuously?

Chapter 5

EQUILIBRIUM OF NON-COPLANAR FORCE SYSTEMS

§ 1 Non-coplanar, Concurrent Forces

50 Equations of equilibrium. In the preceding chapters the equilibrium of coplanar force systems was considered, and in this chapter the equilibrium of non-coplanar force systems will be discussed. Consider first a system of forces that is non-coplanar and concurrent. The necessary and sufficient conditions of equilibrium for this force system are that the algebraic sums of the components of the forces along any three non-coplanar lines through the point of concurrence of the forces are equal to zero. As a matter of convenience, the three lines will be taken as a set of rectangular axes through the point of concurrence, in which case the independent equations which are necessary and sufficient to ensure equilibrium may be written:

$$\Sigma F_x = 0, \qquad \Sigma F_y = 0, \qquad \Sigma F_z = 0$$

Proof. If a concurrent system of forces in space is not in equilibrium, the resultant of the system is a force (Art. 30). If the forces of the system satisfy the equation $\Sigma F_x = 0$, the resultant, if there be one, must lie in the yz plane since $R_x = \Sigma F_x$, and, hence, $R_x = 0$. Likewise, in order to satisfy the equation $\Sigma F_y = 0$, the resultant must lie in the xz plane, and, in order to satisfy the equation $\Sigma F_z = 0$, the resultant must lie in the xy plane. It is impossible for a force to lie in the three planes simultaneously, and hence, if the forces of the system satisfy the foregoing equations, the resultant cannot be a force and, therefore, the system must be in equilibrium.

The foregoing set of equations is not the only set of equilibrium equations for the force system here considered. For example, if a non-coplanar, concurrent force system is in equilibrium it is necessary that the algebraic sum of the moments of the forces about any axis be equal to zero, and it may be shown that a set of three equations which includes one or more moment equations is sufficient to ensure equilibrium of a non-coplanar, concurrent force system. Use of such a set will be illustrated in Prob. 221.

The graphical method which makes use of a force polygon and a string polygon may be used to determine the unknown quantities in a balanced non-coplanar force system. However, if the forces are concurrent as here considered, only a force polygon is needed. In applying the graphical method, it is convenient to project the forces on three co-ordinate planes and then follow the procedure outlined in Art. 43 for coplanar forces.

Illustrative Problem

Problem 221. The wall bracket (Fig. 156) is composed of two flexible cables, AC and BC, and a stiff rod DC, which is pin-connected at D and C. The points A, B, and C lie in a horizontal plane, and A, B, and D lie in a vertical plane, D being vertically beneath E, the mid-point of AB. Find the stresses (internal forces)

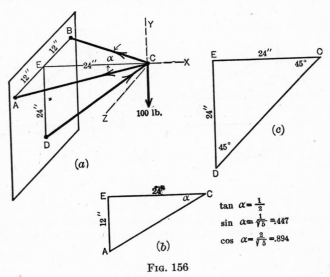

FIG. 156

in the three members when the 100-lb load acts on the bracket as shown.

SOLUTION. The pin C is in equilibrium under the action of the 100-lb load and the reactions of the three members, these reactions being equal to the stresses in the corresponding members. The forces acting on the pin at C are shown in Fig. 156a. As previously noted, the stress in a member is denoted by the same letters as is the member itself. By selecting axes as indicated and applying the equations of equilibrium, we obtain the following equations:

$\Sigma F_y = DC \cos 45° - 100 = 0,$ $\therefore DC = 141.4$ lb

$\Sigma F_z = AC \sin \alpha - BC \sin \alpha = 0,$ $\therefore AC = BC$

$\Sigma F_x = DC \cos 45° - AC \cos \alpha - BC \cos \alpha = 0,$ $\therefore DC \cos 45° = 2AC \cos \alpha$

and

$$BC = AC = \frac{DC \cos 45°}{2 \cos \alpha} = \frac{141.4 \times 0.707}{2 \times 0.894} = 55.9 \text{ lb}$$

Hence, there is a compressive stress of 141.4 lb in the rod DC and a tensile stress of 55.9 lb in each of the cables BC and AC.

The equations of equilibrium could have been selected as the last two of the foregoing set and the moment equation $\Sigma M_{AB} = 0$. Thus, the stress in the rod DC could have been obtained from the equation

$$\Sigma M_{AB} = 24 \times 0.707DC - 24 \times 100 = 0; \qquad \therefore \; DC = 141.4 \text{ lb}$$

Problems

222. A uniform plate $BCDE$ shown in Fig. 157 weighs 600 lb. The plate is held in equilibrium in a horizontal position by the three cables, AB, AC, and AF. Find the stresses in the cables.

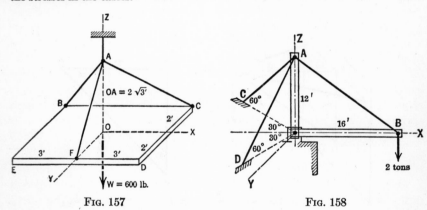

Fig. 157   Fig. 158

223. In the derrick shown in Fig. 158, find the stresses in the flexible cables AB, AC, and AD when the 2-ton load is supported at the end of the boom as shown.

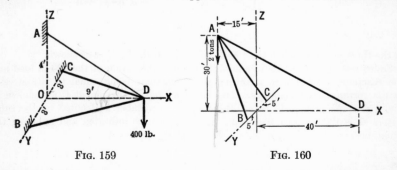

Fig. 159   Fig. 160

The supports C and D to which the cables are attached lie in the xy plane. Neglect the weights of the members.   *Ans.* $AB = 6670$ lb; $AC = AD = 6160$ lb.

224. In Fig. 159, AD is a flexible cable, and BD and CD are stiff members. The members are attached to a smooth pin at D and to the wall at A, B, and C by smooth pins. Find the stresses in AD, BD, and CD when a 400-lb load is applied as shown. Neglect the weights of the members.   *Ans.* $AD = 985$ lb; $BD = CD = 475$ lb.

225. Find the stresses in the legs AB and AC of the shear-legs derrick shown in Fig. 160 and also the tension in the cable AD. Neglect the weights of the members.

226. The upper ends A and B of two cables each 25 ft long are attached to hooks in a vertical wall. The lower ends of the cables are attached to a small ring from which a body weighing 1600 lb is suspended. The points A and B lie in a horizontal plane, and the distance between them is 30 ft. A horizontal force P, whose line of action is perpendicular to the wall, is applied to the ring so that the ring and body are moved a horizontal distance of 12 ft from the wall. What must be the value of P to hold the ring and body in equilibrium in that position?

§ 2   Non-coplanar, Parallel Forces

51   Equations of equilibrium. A system of parallel forces in space is in equilibrium if the algebraic sum of the forces is zero and the algebraic sum of the moments of the forces with respect to each of two lines is equal to zero, provided that not more than one of the lines is parallel to a plane that is parallel to the forces of the system. It will be convenient to select a set of rectangular axes so that one of the axes (the Z axis, say) is parallel to the forces. If the axes are so selected, the independent equations which are necessary and sufficient to ensure equilibrium may be written:

$$\Sigma F = 0, \qquad \Sigma M_x = 0, \qquad \Sigma M_y = 0$$

Proof. The resultant of a system of parallel forces in space which is not in equilibrium is either a force or a couple (Art. 31). If the forces of the system satisfy the equation $\Sigma F = 0$, the resultant cannot be a force since $R = \Sigma F$. If the resultant is a couple, it must lie in a plane parallel to the xz plane in order that the forces shall satisfy the equation $\Sigma M_x = 0$, and in order that the forces shall satisfy the equation $\Sigma M_y = 0$ the resultant must lie in a plane parallel to the yz plane. A plane, however, cannot be parallel to both the xz and yz planes, and hence, if the two moment equations are satisfied, the resultant cannot be a couple. Therefore, if the forces of the system satisfy the three equations, the force system is in equilibrium.

Illustrative Problem

Problem 227. In Fig. 161, ABC represents a triangular plate, the sides of which are each 2 ft in length. It is held in a horizontal position by vertical cords at the vertices. A body which weighs 200 lb is suspended from the point E which lies on the median AD, the distance DE being 6 in. Find the internal forces in the cords neglecting the weight of the plate.

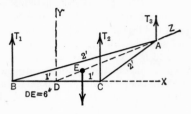

FIG. 161

SOLUTION. The forces T_1, T_2, and T_3 may be found by applying the equations of equilibrium to the forces shown in the free-body diagram of the plate. Thus,

$$\Sigma M_z = T_3 \times 2 \sin 60° - 200 \times \tfrac{1}{2} = 0, \qquad \therefore T_3 = \frac{100}{2 \sin 60°} = 57.7 \text{ lb}$$

$$\Sigma M_z = T_2 \times 1 - T_1 \times 1 = 0, \qquad \therefore T_2 = T_1$$

$$\Sigma F = T_1 + T_2 + T_3 - 200 = 0, \qquad \therefore T_1 = T_2 = 71.1 \text{ lb}$$

Problems

228. A rectangular concrete slab of uniform thickness weighs 1600 lb. The lengths of two adjacent edges, AB and AD, are 6 ft and 4 ft, respectively. The slab is held in a horizontal position by supports under the corners A, B, and D. Find the reactions of the supports when a vertical upward force of 200 lb is applied at the fourth corner C of the slab.

229. A uniform circular steel plate weighing 200 lb is supported in a horizontal position at three points, A, B, and C, on its circumference. The points are located so that the arcs AB, BC, and CA are 90°, 120°, and 150°, respectively. Find the reactions of the supports on the plate.

Ans. $R_A = 73.4$ lb; $R_B = 42.2$ lb; $R_C = 84.4$ lb.

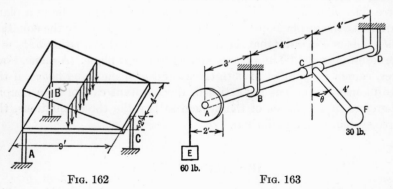

FIG. 162   FIG. 163

230. A horizontal plate shown in Fig. 162 rests on three posts, A, B, and C. Material of uniform density is piled on the plate at a depth increasing uniformly from zero at the right edge of the plate to a maximum at the left edge. If the total weight of the material is 1000 lb, find the reactions of the supports A, B, and C on the plate.

Ans. R_A = 278 lb; R_B = 389 lb; R_C = 333 lb.

231. The horizontal shaft AD shown in Fig. 163 is supported in frictionless bearings at B and D. A pulley is attached to the shaft at A, and a rigid bar CF (perpendicular to AD) is attached at C. A body weighing 60 lb is suspended from the pulley, and a sphere weighing 30 lb is attached to the bar CF, the distance from the center of the sphere to the axis of the shaft being 4 ft. Find the angle θ and the bearing reactions at B and D when the system of bodies is in equilibrium. Neglect the weights of the shaft, bar, and pulley.

232. The crank-pin pressures P_1 and P_2 on the crankshaft shown in Fig. 164 are 6000 lb and 4800 lb, respectively. Find the bearing reactions R_1 and R_2 (Fig. 164b) and the resisting moment Qq required for equilibrium of the shaft.

Ans. R_1 = 3120 lb; R_2 = 1920 lb; Qq = 64,800 lb in.

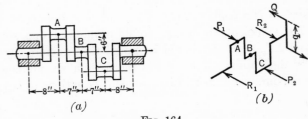

(a)   (b)

Fig. 164

233. A triangular table top is supported by legs at the three corners. The horizontal cross section of the top is a right triangle, and the length of each of the two perpendicular edges, AB and AC, is 4 ft. Find the compressive stresses in the legs of the table if the table top is subjected to a downward vertical force of 100 lb applied at a point 2 ft from AC and 1 ft from AB.

§ 3   Non-coplanar, Non-concurrent, Non-parallel Forces

52 Equations of equilibrium. A system of non-coplanar, non-concurrent, non-parallel forces is in equilibrium if the algebraic sum of the components of the forces in each of three directions is equal to zero and the algebraic sum of the moments of the forces with respect to each of three axes is equal to zero, provided that the directions of resolution are so chosen that lines drawn through any arbitrary point in these three directions are not coplanar, and that the moment axes are so chosen that lines drawn through any arbitrary point parallel to the three axes are not coplanar. It will be convenient to select the coordinate axes for the axes of resolution and for the moment axes. If the axes are so selected, the independent equations which are necessary and sufficient to ensure equilibrium may be written as follows:

$$\Sigma F_x = 0, \qquad \Sigma M_x = 0$$

$$\Sigma F_y = 0, \qquad \Sigma M_y = 0$$

$$\Sigma F_z = 0, \qquad \Sigma M_z = 0$$

Proof. The resultant of a non-concurrent, non-parallel system of forces in space, is, in general, a force and a couple (Art. 34). If the forces of the system satisfy the first three equations, the resultant force must vanish, and, if the last three equations are satisfied, the couple must vanish. If, therefore, the forces of the system satisfy the six equations, the force system is in equilibrium.

The equations of equilibrium for the force systems previously discussed can be obtained from the foregoing six equations. For example, if a force system is a coplanar, concurrent force system, two of the six equations are sufficient to ensure equilibrium, and one such set is $\Sigma F_x = 0$ and $\Sigma F_y = 0$. It should be noted that no force system can be statically determinate if there are more than six unknowns since that is the maximum number of independent equations of equilibrium.

Illustrative Problems

Problem 234. Figure 165 represents a windlass used in lifting weights. The end bearings will be regarded as smooth, and the force P applied to the crank will be assumed to be perpendicular to the axis of the cylinder and also perpendicular to the crank. Find the value of P required to hold the 450-lb weight, and also find the reactions at the bearings, assuming that the crank is inclined 30° to the vertical

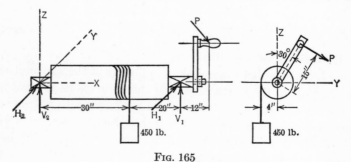

Fig. 165

SOLUTION. The co-ordinate axes will be selected as shown in the figure. There are four forces acting on the windlass: namely, the weight of 450 lb, the force P, and the reactions at the bearings. Since the bearing reactions are unknown in direction as well as in magnitude, it will be convenient to resolve them into horizontal and vertical components, H_1, V_1 and H_2, V_2, as indicated in the figure. Applying the equations of equilibrium to the system of forces acting on the windlass, we have

$$\Sigma F_y = P \cos 30° + H_1 + H_2 = 0 \tag{1}$$

$$\Sigma F_z = V_1 + V_2 - P \sin 30° - 450 = 0 \tag{2}$$

$$\Sigma M_x = 15P - 450 \times 4 = 0 \tag{3}$$

$$\Sigma M_y = P \sin 30° \times 62 + 450 \times 30 - 50V_1 = 0 \tag{4}$$

$$\Sigma M_z = 50H_1 + P \cos 30° \times 62 = 0 \tag{5}$$

The solution of these equations gives the following values:

$$P = 120 \text{ lb}, \qquad H_1 = -128.8 \text{ lb}, \qquad V_1 = 344 \text{ lb},$$

$$H_2 = 24.9 \text{ lb}, \qquad V_2 = 165.6 \text{ lb}$$

Problem 235. In Fig. 166a a bar ABC lies in a horizontal plane and is subjected to a vertical load P as shown. Determine the reaction on the bar at the fixed end A.

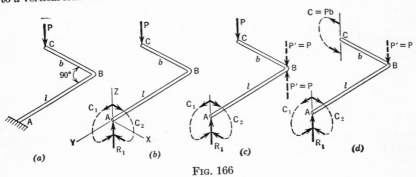

FIG. 166

SOLUTION. A free-body diagram of the bar is shown in Fig. 166b. The reaction at A may be resolved into three components: namely, an upward shearing force R_1, a bending couple C_1, and a twisting couple C_2. Since the two unknown couples can be rotated in their own plane (Art. 17), this force system is equivalent to a non-coplanar, parallel force system for which there are three independent equations of equilibrium and there are three unknowns: namely, R_1, C_1, and C_2. Applying the equations of equilibrium, we have

$$\Sigma F_z = R_1 - P = 0 \qquad \therefore\ R_1 = P$$

$$\Sigma M_x = C_1 - Pl = 0 \qquad \therefore\ C_1 = Pl$$

$$\Sigma M_y = Pb - C_2 = 0 \qquad \therefore\ C_2 = Pb$$

Another method that may be used to determine the reaction at A makes use of the resolution of the force P into a force and a couple. Let two equal and opposite forces P', P' (Fig. 166c) act at point B and have the same magnitude as P. The force system may now be considered to consist of the reaction at A (R_1, C_1, and C_2), a downward force P' at B, and a counterclockwise couple having a moment Pb. The couple may be rotated and translated to the position shown in Fig. 166d. The downward force P' (equal to P) and the counterclockwise couple C (equal to Pb) will have the same external effect on the bar as does the force P in Fig. 166a. The unknowns R_1, C_1, and C_2 now may be found by use of the equations of equilibrium, and it is evident that $R_1 = P$ and the couple formed by R_1 and P' is equal in magnitude but opposite in sense to C_1; that is, $C_1 = Pl$. Also the couple C_2 must be equal in magnitude but opposite in sense to the couple C; that is, $C_2 = Pb$.

Problems

236. In Fig. 167 is shown a vertical shaft AD that weighs 80 lb and is supported by a smooth step bearing at D and a smooth journal bearing at A. A pulley

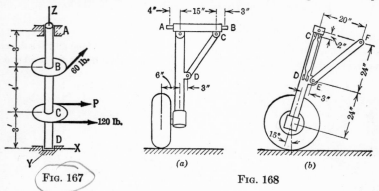

FIG. 167

(a)

FIG. 168

(b)

weighing 10 lb and having a diameter of 1 ft is keyed to the shaft at B. To this pulley a force of 60 lb is applied parallel to the Y axis. A pulley weighing 40 lb

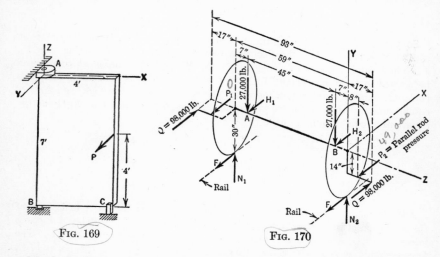

FIG. 169

FIG. 170

and having a diameter of 1 ft is keyed to the shaft at C. To this pulley two forces, P and 120 lb, are applied parallel to the X axis. If the shaft is in equilibrium, find the magnitudes P and the x, y, and z components of the bearing reactions at D and A.

237. In Fig. 168 is shown the landing gear of an airplane. A, B, and F are smooth pins that attach the landing gear to the frame of the airplane. If the reaction of the horizontal surface on the wheel is a vertical force of 8000 lb, determine the magnitudes of the reactions at the pins A and B on the landing gear. Also determine the force in the drag brace member EF.

$Ans.$ $A = 12,520$ lb; $B = 853$ lb; $EF = 6090$ lb.

238. The homogeneous door shown in Fig. 169 weighs 60 lb. The door is subjected to a force P of 100 lb acting in a direction perpendicular to the door. Determine the components of the reactions at A and B parallel to the x, y, and z axes, and determine the reaction of the stop at C on the door.

239. In Fig. 170 the forces acting on the main driving axle and wheels of a certain type of locomotive are in equilibrium. The axle is attached to the locomotive frame at A and B. Each of the vertical components of the reactions at A and B is 27,000 lb, and each of the forces Q, Q at the crank pins is equal to 98,000 lb, as shown in the figure. Let it be assumed that, when the driver is in the position shown, the frictional forces on the rails are equal, the parallel rod pressure $P_1 = 0$, and the parallel rod pressure $P_2 = 49,000$ lb. Determine the unknown forces N_1, N_2, F, H_1, and H_2.

$Ans.$ $N_1 = N_2 = 27,000$ lb; $F = 11,430$ lb; $H_1 = 102,900$ lb; $H_2 = 21,200$ lb.

Chapter 6

FRICTION

53 Friction defined. If two bodies slide or tend to slide on each other, the resisting force tangent to the surface of contact which one body offers to the other is defined as the frictional force or simply *friction*.

Friction is of great importance in engineering practice. Since it always opposes motion, it is an undesirable and expensive factor in the operation of many machines and in such cases is reduced as much as practicable by means of lubricants. In other machines it becomes a very desirable and useful element, as in various forms of brakes and friction drives. In fact, many of our normal physical activities, such as walking, would be impossible without the aid of friction.

If the frictional force at the surface of contact of two bodies prevents motion of one body relative to the other, the resistance is called *static friction*; the frictional resistance on the surface of contact of two bodies which move relative to each other is called *kinetic friction*. If the friction is static, the amount of friction developed is just sufficient to maintain equilibrium with the other forces acting on the body. That is, static friction is an adjustable force, the magnitude of which is determined from the equations of equilibrium for all the forces that act on the body. Thus, let Fig. 171 represent a body in equilibrium on a rough horizontal plane under the action of a horizontal force P, which tends to move the body, the reaction R of the plane, and the weight W of the body. Let the reaction R be resolved into two components, F and N, parallel and perpendicular, respectively, to the plane. The component F along, or tangent to, the plane is the frictional force as previously defined. The component N is called the *normal pressure*, and R is called the *total reaction*. Since the body is in equilibrium, the equation of equilibrium $\Sigma F_x = 0$ must be satisfied, and hence $F = P$; the equation $\Sigma F_y = 0$ must also be satisfied, and hence $N = W$. If the force P is gradually

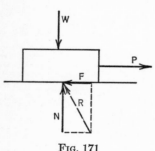

Fig. 171

130

increased, F must increase in the same ratio in order to maintain a condition of equilibrium. There is a definite limit, however, to the amount of frictional resistance that can be developed for any two surfaces of contact, and, when the value of P exceeds this limiting value, motion will ensue. The limiting or maximum value of the frictional force is called *limiting friction* and is denoted by F'. Its value depends on the normal pressure and on the roughness of the surfaces of contact.

In Fig. 171 it was seen that the frictional force F was equal to the applied force P and that the normal pressure N was equal to W, the weight of the body. However, the student should not make the mistake of assuming that, in all cases in which one body tends to slide over another, F is equal to P or to the component of P parallel to the plane, and that N is equal to W; it is important to note that in all cases both the static friction and the normal pressure are determined by the conditions of equilibrium for *all* the forces acting on the body. Consider, for example, the body shown in Fig. 172, and assume that motion of the body is impending up the plane under the influence of the applied

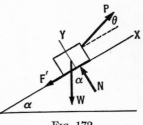

Fig. 172

force P and the other forces acting on the body. By applying the equations of equilibrium, $\Sigma F_x = 0$ and $\Sigma F_y = 0$, it is seen that

$$F' = P \cos \theta - W \sin \alpha$$
$$N = W \cos \alpha - P \sin \theta$$

54 Coefficient of friction. In order to compare the frictional properties of various pairs of materials or of the same pair of materials under varying conditions of their surfaces of contact, and in order to calculate the maximum frictional force corresponding to any normal pressure, a certain experimental constant, called the *coefficient of friction*, is used.

The *coefficient of static friction* for any two surfaces of contact is defined as the ratio of the limiting friction to the corresponding normal pressure. Thus, if the coefficient of static friction is denoted by μ, it may be expressed as follows:

$$\mu = \frac{F'}{N} \quad \text{or} \quad F' = \mu N$$

It is important to note that F' in this equation is the maximum friction the surfaces can develop: that is, the friction corresponding to impending motion. Thus, the maximum frictional force any two surfaces can develop is equal to μN. Attention should be called to the fact that the actual frictional force developed is not equal to μN but will be less than μN unless motion of one surface on the other is impending.

The value of μ must be determined experimentally, and, as previously stated, it is a constant for any two materials for a definite condition of the surfaces of contact and for moderate normal pressures. It varies considerably, however, for different conditions of the surfaces, and it varies widely for different pairs of materials, as is shown in the accompanying table, which gives the values of the coefficient of friction for dry surfaces as determined by Morin and others.

COEFFICIENT OF STATIC FRICTION

Wood on wood	0.25 to 0.50
Metal on wood	0.20 to 0.60
Metal on metal	0.15 to 0.30
Metal on leather	0.30 to 0.60
Wood on leather	0.25 to 0.50
Stone on stone	0.40 to 0.65
Metal on stone	0.30 to 0.70
Earth on earth	0.25 to 1.00
Rubber on concrete	0.75 to 0.90

If two surfaces move relative to each other, the ratio of the friction developed to the corresponding normal pressure is defined as the *coefficient of kinetic friction*. The value of the coefficient of kinetic friction for two surfaces is influenced by more factors than is the value of the coefficient of static friction. A brief discussion of the influencing factors is given in Art. 56. For values of the coefficient of kinetic friction for various conditions of rubbing surfaces the reader is referred to Goodman's *Mechanics Applied to Engineering*.

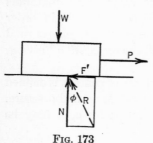

FIG. 173

55 Angle of friction. The *angle of static friction* for two surfaces of contact is defined as the angle between the directions of the total reaction and the normal pressure *when motion is impending*. Thus, in Fig. 173, if the force P is just large enough to develop the limiting friction, the angle which R, the reaction of the plane on the body, makes with the normal pressure N is the angle of static friction and is denoted by ϕ.

Since the components of R, parallel and perpendicular, respectively, to the plane, are F' and N, it is evident from the figure that $\tan \phi =$

F'/N. But, since the ratio F'/N is defined as the coefficient of static friction μ, the following important relation may be written:

$$\mu = \tan \phi$$

that is, *the coefficient of static friction is equal to the tangent of the angle of static friction.*

If the two surfaces move relative to each other, the angle between the total reaction and the normal pressure is called the *angle of kinetic friction.* Its value is somewhat less than the angle of static friction, since the frictional force after motion ensues becomes less than the limiting friction. The relation $\mu = \tan \phi$ also holds for kinetic friction, the value of μ for kinetic friction being some-what less than for static friction.

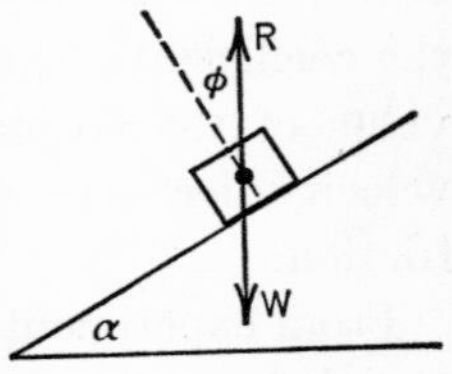

ANGLE OF REPOSE. If a body rests on an in-clined plane, as shown in Fig. 174, and is acted on by no forces except its weight W and the re-action R of the plane, and if α, the angle of in-clination of the plane to the horizontal, is such that motion of the body impends down the plane, the angle α is defined as the *angle of repose.*

FIG. 174

Since the body is in equilibrium under the action of the two forces R and W, these forces must be equal, opposite, and collinear. Hence the reaction R is vertical. Furthermore, the angle R makes with the normal to the plane is ϕ, the angle of friction. It is evident from the figure that the angles α and ϕ are equal. The angle of repose for two surfaces can be found easily by experiment, after which the coefficient of friction for the surfaces may be found from the relation $\mu = \tan \phi = \tan \alpha$.

56 The laws of friction. One of the earliest contributions to our knowledge of the laws of friction was made by Coulomb who published, in 1781, the results of experiments on the friction of plane dry surfaces. Later experiments by Morin confirmed, in the main, the results obtained by Coulomb. The results of the experiments of Morin on dry surfaces, published in 1831, may be stated as follows:

1. The frictional force on the surface of contact of two bodies when motion is impending (limiting friction) is proportional to the normal pressure; that is, the coefficient of friction is independent of the normal pressure.

2. The coefficient of static friction is independent of the area of contact.

3. The coefficient of kinetic friction is less than the coefficient of static friction and is independent of the relative velocity of the rubbing surfaces.

Although these laws are probably correct for the conditions under which the tests were made, they must be modified in order to apply to friction that is developed under conditions quite different from those found in the experiments. The pressures used in the experiments of Morin varied from ¾ lb per sq in. to 100 lb per sq in. It has been found in later experiments that for pressures less than ¾ lb per sq in. and for very great pressures the value of the coefficient of static friction increases. The highest velocity used in Morin's experiments was 10 ft per sec. For greater velocities than this it has been found in later experiments that the coefficient of kinetic friction decreases with the velocity. The experiments of Jenkin show that for extremely low velocities (the lowest velocity measured was 0.0002 ft per sec) there is an increase in the coefficient of kinetic friction. These experiments indicate that the value of the coefficient of kinetic friction gradually increases as the velocity decreases and passes without discontinuity into that of static friction.

From experiments made by Tower, Goodman, Thurston, and others, on lubricated surfaces, it has been found that the laws of friction for lubricated surfaces are almost the reverse of those stated for dry surfaces. For example, it is found that the friction of two surfaces is almost independent of the nature of the surfaces and of the normal pressure provided that there is a film of lubricant between the surfaces. Again, for lubricated surfaces, it is found that the friction is materially affected by the temperature, which is not true for moderate temperatures in the case of dry surfaces.

57 Types of problems involving frictional forces. In the following problems there are two general types:

1. In one type a body is in equilibrium under the action of a force system one (or more) of which is a frictional force, but motion of the body is impending; in other words, the frictional force developed is the limiting friction and can therefore be expressed as $F' = \mu N$. It is important to note that such a problem is a problem in equilibrium and is no different from those treated in the preceding chapter, for the equations of equilibrium apply to *all* the forces acting on the body (including friction forces and the normal pressures). But, in addition to the relationship that must exist among *all* the forces as expressed in the equations of equilibrium, there is a special relationship between two of the forces that act on the body: namely, $F' = \mu N$. This equation then is used together with the equations of equilibrium to effect a solution of some of the unknown forces. If more than one pair of rubbing surfaces

are involved there will, of course, be more than one equation of the type $F' = \mu N$.

2. In the other type of problem a body is acted on by forces one (or more) of which is a frictional force, but it is not known whether the body is in equilibrium under the action of the applied forces, because it is not known whether the frictional force (or forces) required for equilibrium can be developed on the surfaces of contact. One method of attacking such a problem is first to assume the body to be in equilibrium and then find the frictional force and corresponding normal pressure required (with the other forces) to hold the body in equilibrium by applying the equations of equilibrium. This magnitude of the frictional force is then compared to the value of the limiting friction, $F' = \mu N$, and, if it is less than F', the body will be in equilibrium, and the frictional force will have the value found from the equilibrium equations, but, if it is greater than F', the body will not be in equilibrium, and hence the problem is one of kinetics instead of statics.

Illustrative Problems

Problem 240. A lift shown in Fig. 175 slides on a vertical shaft having a square cross section 2 in. on a side. Find the greatest distance x from the edge of the shaft at which a load W can be placed and still cause the lift to slide on the shaft. Neglect the weight of the lift, and use 0.2 for the coefficient of friction.

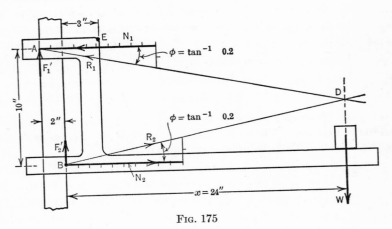

FIG. 175

GRAPHICAL SOLUTION. Since motion impends, the angle between the reaction R_1 and the normal pressure N_1 of the shaft at A is equal to the angle of friction; that is, the tangent of the angle is equal to 0.2. Hence, by laying off ten spaces along the normal and two spaces perpendicular to the normal, as shown in Fig. 175, the action line of R_1 is determined. In a similar manner the action line of R_2 is found. Now the three forces, R_1, R_2, and W, must be concurrent in order to be in equilibrium (Art. 40), and, hence, W must pass through the intersection of R_1 and R_2. The intersection of these two forces can never be nearer to the shaft than the point D, since the angle ϕ cannot be greater than $\tan^{-1} 0.2$. The distance x of D from the shaft is found by measurement to be 24 in.

ALGEBRAIC SOLUTION. The five forces, F'_1, N_1, F'_2, N_2, and W, which hold the lift in equilibrium as shown in the free-body diagram (Fig. 175), form a coplanar, non-concurrent force system, and hence there are three equations of equilibrium as follows:

$$\Sigma F_x = N_2 - N_1 = 0 \tag{1}$$

$$\Sigma F_y = -W + 0.2N_1 + 0.2N_2 = 0 \tag{2}$$

$$\Sigma M_B = -Wx + 10N_1 - 2 \times 0.2N_1 = 0 \tag{3}$$

in which

$$0.2N_1 = F'_1 \quad \text{and} \quad 0.2N_2 = F'_2$$

From Eqs. 1 and 2, we have

$$W = 0.4N_1 = 0.4N_2$$

By substituting this value of W in Eq. 3, the equation obtained is

$$-0.4N_1 \cdot x + 10N_1 - 0.4N_1 = 0$$

whence

$$x = 24 \text{ in.}$$

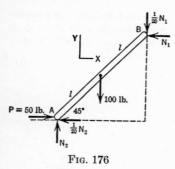

FIG. 176

Problem 241. The bar AB in Fig. 176 is a uniform bar and weighs 100 lb. If the coefficient of friction for the surfaces of contact at each end of the bar is 0.05 and a horizontal force of 50 lb is applied at the lower end A of the bar as shown: (a) will the lower end A move toward the wall, (b) will A move away from the wall, or (c) will the bar be in equilibrium?

SOLUTION. The least force P that will cause motion of A to impend toward the wall will first be found. The free-body diagram of the bar for this case is shown in Fig. 176. Applying the equations of equilibrium, we have

$$\Sigma F_x = P - \tfrac{1}{20}N_2 - N_1 = 0 \tag{1}$$

$$\Sigma F_y = N_2 - 100 - \tfrac{1}{20}N_1 = 0 \tag{2}$$

$$\Sigma M_A = N_1 \times 2l \cos 45° - \tfrac{1}{20}N_1 \times 2l \cos 45° - 100 \times l \cos 45° = 0 \tag{3}$$

From Eq. 3, we find $N_1 = 1000/19$. Substituting this value of N_1 in Eq. 2, we find $N_2 = 1950/19$. Hence, from Eq. 1,

$$P = \tfrac{1}{20} \times \tfrac{1950}{19} + \tfrac{1000}{19} = 57.8 \text{ lb}$$

A force of 50 lb therefore is not large enough to cause A to move toward the wall. The least force P that will prevent A from moving away from the wall will now be found. The free-body diagram for this case will be the same as shown in Fig. 176, except that the two frictional forces will be reversed, and the corresponding equations of equilibrium are

$$\Sigma F_x = P + \tfrac{1}{20}N_2 - N_1 = 0$$

$$\Sigma F_y = N_2 - 100 + \tfrac{1}{20}N_1 = 0$$

$$\Sigma M_A = N_1 \times 2l \cos 45° + \tfrac{1}{20}N_1 \times 2l \cos 45° - 100 \times l \cos 45° = 0$$

Eliminating N_1 and N_2 from the last three equations, we find $P = 42.7$ lb. Since the 50-lb force is greater than 42.7 lb and less than 57.8 lb, the bar will be in equilibrium.

Problem 242. Figure 177a represents a cotter joint. The angle α equals 15°, and the angle of friction for all rubbing surfaces is 12°. What is the value of the force P required to overcome the 1000-lb force applied on part A?

SOLUTION. Free-body diagrams of the block A and the cotter pin C are shown in Figs. 177b and 177c, respectively. The equations of equilibrium for the two blocks may be written as follows:

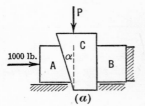

For A,

$$\Sigma F_x = 1000 + R_1 \sin 12° - R_2 \cos 27° = 0 \quad (1)$$

$$\Sigma F_y = R_1 \cos 12° - R_2 \sin 27° = 0 \quad (2)$$

For C,

$$\Sigma F_x = R_2 \cos 27° - R_3 \cos 12° = 0 \quad (3)$$

$$\Sigma F_y = R_2 \sin 27° + R_3 \sin 12° - P = 0 \quad (4)$$

By eliminating R_1 from Eqs. 1 and 2, the equation obtained is

$$R_2 = \frac{1000 \cos 12°}{\cos 39°} \quad (5)$$

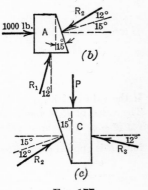

FIG. 177

By eliminating R_3 from Eqs. 3 and 4, the following equation is obtained:

$$R_2 = \frac{P \cos 12°}{\sin 39°} \quad (6)$$

By equating values of R_2 in Eqs. 5 and 6, the value of P may be found. Thus,

$$\frac{P \cos 12°}{\sin 39°} = \frac{1000 \cos 12°}{\cos 39°}$$

Therefore,

$$P = 1000 \tan 39° = 810 \text{ lb}$$

Problem 243. In Fig. 178 assume that W and α are known; assume also that the coefficient of friction μ (and hence also the angle of friction ϕ) is known. Find, in terms of θ and the known quantities, the value of P that will make motion impend up the plane. Show also that P will be a minimum when $\theta = \phi$, and find the minimum value of P.

SOLUTION. The body is in equilibrium and hence the equations of equilibrium may be applied to the system of forces acting on it. In addition to the required force P, the forces acting on the body are the weight W of the body, and the reaction of the plane. The latter force will be resolved into components N, perpendicular to the plane, and F' (equal to μN), parallel to the plane, as shown in the free-body diagram. If the X and Y axes are chosen as shown, the equations of equilibrium may be written as follows:

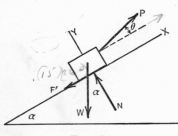

FIG. 178

$$\Sigma F_x = P \cos \theta - \mu N - W \sin \alpha = 0$$

$$\Sigma F_y = N + P \sin \theta - W \cos \alpha = 0$$

Eliminating N from the two equations we have

$$P = \frac{W (\sin \alpha + \mu \cos \alpha)}{\cos \theta + \mu \sin \theta}$$

If $\tan \phi$ be substituted for μ, this may be written

$$P = W \frac{\sin (\alpha + \phi)}{\cos (\theta - \phi)}$$

If the values of W, α, and ϕ are specified, P may be regarded as a function of θ. The value of P is a minimum when θ is equal to ϕ, since this value of θ makes $\cos (\theta - \phi)$ a maximum; the minimum value of P, then, is $W \sin (\alpha + \phi)$. If the force P is applied parallel to the plane its value becomes $W \dfrac{\sin (\alpha + \phi)}{\cos \phi}$.

Problems

244. A block weighing 60 lb rests on a plane inclined 30° to the horizontal. The coefficient of friction for the surfaces of contact is 0.2. If a horizontal force P of 50 lb is applied to the block, will the block start up the plane?

245. In Fig. 179 what must be the magnitude of the horizontal force P to cause motion to impend? The coefficient of static friction for both pairs of rubbing surfaces is 0.1. Bodies A and B weigh 50 lb and 100 lb, respectively, and the force exerted on A and B by the spring S is 100 lb. Is the action line of the force P shown correctly in the figure?

246. In Fig. 180 the coefficients of friction for the lower wedge and the horizontal surface, and for the upper wedge and the vertical surface are each 0.2. The surfaces of the wedges which are in contact are smooth. Find the least value of P that will hold the 1000-lb load. *Ans.* $P = 338$ lb.

247. In Fig. 181 the cylinder B weighs 100 lb, and the body A weighs 80 lb. If the coefficient of friction for the cylinder and the horizontal plane is 0.25 and the vertical surface is smooth, will the cylinder turn?

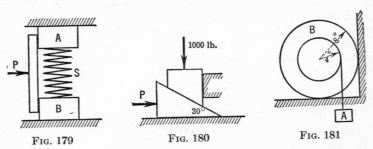

FIG. 179   FIG. 180   FIG. 181

248. A horizontal pull is exerted on one handle of a desk drawer a distance x from the center line of the drawer. The drawer has a length L parallel to the direction of pull. Show that the maximum value x can have and still allow the drawer to open is $L/2\mu$, where μ is the coefficient of friction for each side of the drawer. Assume that, when motion impends, the friction and the normal pressure on each side are concentrated at the front or back edge of the drawer and that friction on the bottom of the drawer is negligible.

249. A crown friction drive as indicated in Fig. 182 is used on screw-power presses, motor trucks, etc. The cast-iron disk B rotates at 1000 rpm and drives the crown wheel C which is faced with leather fiber. The diameter of C is 20 in. and the value of μ is 0.4. If a turning moment of 120 lb ft is transmitted to the crown-wheel shaft when slipping impends, what is the normal pressure between the disk and the crown wheel? What is the pressure on the bearings at A and D?

Ans. N = 360 lb; A = 291 lb; D = 96.9 lb.

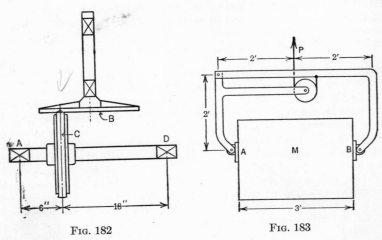

FIG. 182   FIG. 183

250. A lifting device in Fig. 183 holds a body M whose weight is 100 lb. To hold M a force P is applied to a flexible cable which passes around the lower portion of a frictionless pulley as shown. The diameter of the pulley is 6 in. What minimum coefficient of friction at A and B is necessary to hold the body M? Neglect the weights of all members of the frame.

251. If the weight W in Prob. 240 is 580 lb and x is 24 in., what vertical force P applied at E will be just sufficient to start the lift up?   *Ans.* $P = 1000$ lb.

252. A load P of 60 lb is applied to the arm shown in Fig. 184 at a distance of 2 ft from the axis of the shaft. Determine the minimum coefficient of friction required to prevent sliding of the arm on the shaft. If the coefficient of friction is equal to this minimum value, will a load P of 100 lb cause the arm to slide?

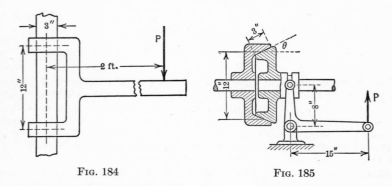

FIG. 184   FIG. 185

253. A cone clutch as shown in Fig. 185 is used to connect two shafts. If the normal pressure between the two surfaces of contact is 10 lb per sq in. and the coefficient of friction is 0.3, what is the maximum torque the clutch can transmit? Assume that the frictional force has a mean arm of 6 in. and that $\theta = 12.5°$.

Ans. 2040 lb in.

254. A ladder 10 ft long is inclined 60° to the horizontal, its upper end resting against a smooth vertical wall and its lower end on a rough horizontal plane. The center of gravity is 4.5 ft from the lower end. If the ladder is on the point of slipping, what is the coefficient of friction between the ladder and horizontal surface?

Ans. $\mu = 0.26$.

255. In Prob. 242 assume that A is fixed instead of B and that a horizontal force of 1000 lb is applied to B. Find the value of P required to make motion of B impend.

256. In Fig. 186 is shown a tandem axle unit (or assembly) used on an automobile trailer truck for carrying heavy loads. It is desirable that the front- and rear-wheel loads be equal when the brakes are applied in order that the rear tires do not tend to lift off the pavement, thus causing the unit to vibrate excessively and causing the tires to scuff against the pavement. The rocker arm BD is pinned at its center E to a bracket mounted on the truck frame. The rods FG and HI each make an angle of 30° with the horizontal when the truck is loaded and the brakes are applied. There are two rods and one rocker arm on each side of the tandem unit. The rollers at A, B, C, and D exert only vertical forces on the springs. Show that the wheel loads will be equal when the truck is loaded and moving to the left and the brakes (not shown) are applied so that the wheels slide on the pavement without turning on their axles. Assume the coefficient of friction μ to be the same for the surfaces of contact between all tires and the pavement, and neglect friction at the pins of the members. Neglect the weights of the members and assume the members to be in equilibrium. *Hint*: Consider as free bodies: (1) the front axle, wheels, and springs (as a single free body), (2) the rear axle, wheels, and springs, and (3) the rocker arm.

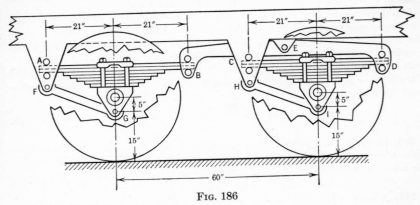

FIG. 186

257. In Prob. 256 assume the tandem unit supports a vertical load of 32,000 lb (16,000 lb on each axle). If the brakes are locked and the wheels slide on the pavement, determine the stresses in the rods FG and HI, and determine the force at pin E acting on the rocker arm BD. Assume $\mu = 0.8$ for the surfaces of contact between the tires and pavement, and neglect the weights of the members.

Ans. $FG = HI = 7380$ lb; $E = 16,280$ lb.

258. Two bodies weighing 50 lb and 100 lb rest on an inclined plane and are connected by a cord which is parallel to the plane. The body weighing 50 lb is below the one weighing 100 lb, and the coefficient of friction for the 50-lb body is $\frac{1}{5}$ and that for the 100-lb body is $\frac{1}{2}$. Find the inclination of the plane to the horizontal and the tension in the cord, when motion impends.

Ans. $\theta = 21° 48°$; $T = 9.28$ lb.

259. In Fig. 187 find the least value of P that will prevent the 800-lb body from descending and turning the wheel and axle D. Assume the axle to be smooth, and disregard the weight of the wheel and axle. Assume the coefficient of friction between AC and D to be 0.4 and the thickness of the bar AC to be negligible.

Ans. $P = 500$ lb.

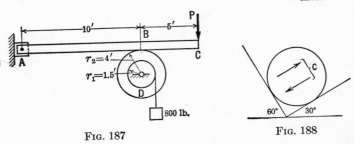

FIG. 187   FIG. 188

260. The cylinder which rests between two planes as shown in Fig. 188 weighs 3000 lb and has a diameter of 3 ft. The coefficient of friction between the cylinder and each plane is 0.25. The cylinder is acted on by a couple C whose moment is gradually increased until the cylinder starts to move. Will the cylinder move up the plane to the right or rotate about its axis? Find the minimum value of the moment of the couple that will cause the cylinder to move.

261. In the preceding problem find the least value of the coefficient of friction for the surfaces of contact between the cylinder and the 30° plane that will permit the cylinder to roll up the plane. Find the minimum value of the moment of the couple that will cause the cylinder to roll up the plane.

262. In Prob. 243 determine the force P that will just prevent motion down the plane when $\alpha > \phi$. Find also the value of θ for which P is a minimum, and determine the minimum value of P.

$$Ans. \ P = \frac{W \sin (\alpha - \phi)}{\cos (\theta + \phi)} \ ; \theta = -\phi; P = W \sin (\alpha - \phi).$$

263. In Prob. 243 determine the force P that will just start the body down the plane when $\alpha < \phi$. Find also the value of θ for which P is a minimum and determine the minimum value of P. $\quad Ans. \quad P = \dfrac{W \sin (\phi - \alpha)}{\cos (\theta + \phi)} \ ; \theta = -\phi; P = W \sin (\phi - \alpha).$

264. A body weighing W lb rests on a rough plane inclined at an angle θ to the horizontal. What horizontal force must be applied in order to start the body up the plane if the angle of friction is ϕ? Express the force in terms of W, θ, and ϕ and also in terms of W, θ, and μ. $\quad Ans. \quad P = W \tan (\theta + \phi) = W \dfrac{\sin \theta + \mu \cos \theta}{\cos \theta - \mu \sin \theta}.$

58 Pivot friction.

In Fig. 189 is shown a step bearing. Let it be required to find the expression for the frictional moment developed on the flat end of the shaft as it turns in its bearing. The assumption will be made that the coefficient of friction μ for the rubbing surfaces is constant and that the pressure on the bearing is uniformly distributed. Let the total axial load be denoted by W, the radius of the shaft by r, and the bearing area by A.

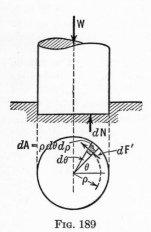

FIG. 189

Obviously the frictional moment cannot be found by obtaining the total frictional force F' from the equation $F' = \mu N$ and then multiplying this force by the moment arm, for the resultant of the frictional forces is not a force but a couple. However, the frictional force dF' on any small (differential) part dA of the area may be found from the equation $dF' = \mu \, dN$, where dN is the normal pressure on the differential area, and the moment of this frictional force may be found by multiplying the force by its moment arm ρ which of course varies with the position of dA. Hence we are here dealing with a continuously varying quantity and the total or resultant frictional moment M_F must be thought of as a summation of the products $(\rho \cdot dF')$ which involves the method of the calculus. Thus,

$$M_F = \int \rho \, dF' = \int \rho\mu \, dN$$

But

$$dN = \text{pressure per unit area times the area } dA$$

$$= \frac{W}{\pi r^2} \, dA = \frac{W}{\pi r^2} \rho \, d\rho \, d\theta$$

Therefore,

$$M_F = \frac{\mu W}{\pi r^2} \int_0^{2\pi} \int_0^r \rho^2 \, d\rho \, d\theta = \tfrac{2}{3}\mu W r$$

Problems

265. Derive the expression for the frictional moment for the hollow flat pivot (Fig. 190a) or the collar bearing (Fig. 190b).   *Ans.* $M_F = \dfrac{2}{3} \mu W \dfrac{r_2{}^3 - r_1{}^3}{r_2{}^2 - r_1{}^2}.$

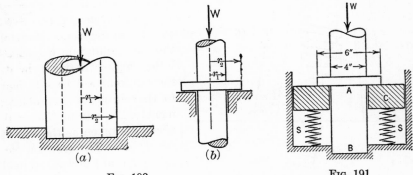

Fig. 190   Fig. 191

266. The vertical shaft in Fig. 191 carries a load $W = 400$ lb and is supported by a collar bearing at A and a step bearing at B. The hollow plate C is supported by springs S which exert a total upward force of 100 lb on the plate. The plate C is free to move vertically but is not free to rotate. If the weight of C is negligible and if $\mu_A = 0.1$ and $\mu_B = 0.05$, find the total frictional moment exerted by the two bearings on the shaft when the shaft turns.

267. Find the frictional moment on a collar bearing such as Fig. 190b when subjected to a load W of 3000 lb, if the radii of the collar are 3.5 in. and 2.5 in. and the coefficient of friction is 0.024.   *Ans.* $M_F = 218$ lb in.

59   The screw. A screw is, in effect, an inclined plane wound around a cylinder. Screws are made with square threads and with triangular threads, but square-threaded screws, only, will be considered here.

Figure 192a shows a jackscrew with square threads which is used in raising or lowering heavy loads. The radius of the base of the thread is denoted by r_1 and the outer radius by r_2; α is called the *pitch angle*, and p is called the *pitch* of the screw. Let it be required to find the force P

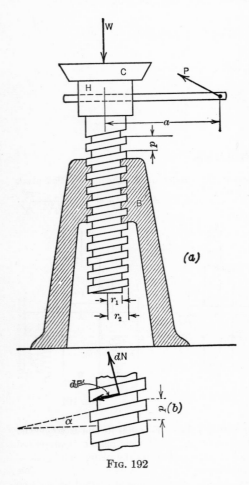

(a)

(b)

Fig. 192

which, when applied at the end of the lever of length a, is just sufficient to raise the load W. The forces that hold the screw in equilibrium are: the force P, the pressure of the cap C on the head H, and the reaction of the nut B on the screw. The last is distributed over the area of the threads in contact with the nut. If the friction between the cap and the head of the screw is neglected, the pressure of the cap on the head of the screw will be a vertical force equal to W; the problem will be solved on this assumption. Two of the six equilibrium equations which apply to this type of force system will be sufficient for the solution of the problem: namely, $\Sigma F_z = 0$ and $\Sigma M_z = 0$, where z is taken as the axis of the screw. The reaction between the nut and the thread of the screw on an element of area dA will be denoted by dR. This force may be resolved into components dN normal to the thread and dF' parallel to the thread as shown in Fig. 192b.

In taking moments about the axis of the thread it will be sufficiently accurate to consider the moment arm of dF' to be equal to the mean radius of the thread, $\frac{1}{2}(r_1 + r_2)$, which will be denoted by r. The two equilibrium equations, then, become

$$\Sigma F_z = \Sigma\, dN \cos \alpha - \Sigma\, dF' \sin \alpha - W = 0$$

$$\Sigma M_z = Pa - \Sigma r\, dN \sin \alpha - \Sigma r\, dF' \cos \alpha = 0$$

Since $dF' = \mu \, dN$, these equations may be written

$$\cos \alpha \Sigma \, dN - \mu \sin \alpha \Sigma \, dN - W = 0 \tag{1}$$

$$Pa - r \sin \alpha \Sigma \, dN - \mu r \cos \alpha \Sigma \, dN = 0 \tag{2}$$

By eliminating $\Sigma \, dN$ from Eqs. 1 and 2, the equation obtained is

$$Pa = Wr \frac{\sin \alpha + \mu \cos \alpha}{\cos \alpha - \mu \sin \alpha}$$

By substituting $\tan \phi$ for μ this equation may be written in the form

$$Pa = Wr \tan (\phi + \alpha) \tag{A}$$

If the pitch angle α is large and the angle of friction is small, the load W will cause the screw to run down unless a force is applied to prevent it. The force P required to hold the load is found by a method similar to the foregoing analysis, the only difference being that the sense of the frictional force is reversed. The least value of P required to prevent the screw from running down is given by the equation

$$Pa = Wr \tan (\alpha - \phi) \tag{B}$$

If $\alpha = \phi$ in this equation, the force P reduces to zero; that is, the load will be held by friction alone. If $\alpha < \phi$, a force is required to lower the load; the value of the force P required to lower the load is given by the equation

$$Pa = Wr \tan (\phi - \alpha) \tag{C}$$

and the sense of this force is opposite to that in the foregoing two cases.

Problems

268. The mean diameter of the screw of a square-threaded jackscrew is 2.3 in. The pitch of the thread is 0.6 in., and the coefficient of friction for the screw and nut is 0.12. What force P must be applied as in Fig. 192 at the end of a lever 18 in. long to raise a load of 5000 lb? What force is required to lower the load?

Ans. 65.5 lb; 11.8 lb.

269. The least force P applied as in Fig. 192 at the end of the lever of a jackscrew that will raise a load W is found to be 50 lb. If the coefficient of friction is $\frac{1}{8}$ and the pitch angle is $\tan^{-1} \frac{1}{10}$, find the least force that will lower the load.

270. A load W of 1000 lb is raised by the scissors jack shown in Fig. 193. The mean diameter of the screw is 1.2 in., the pitch of the thread is 0.25 in., and the coefficient of friction is 0.15. Find the moment of the couple C required to raise the load when $\theta = 30°$.   *Ans.* $C = 454$ lb in.

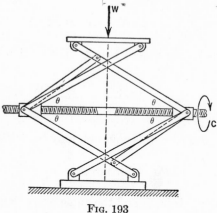

Fɪɢ. 193

271. If the coefficient of friction in Prob. 268 were zero, what force would be required to raise the load?

60   Belt friction.

Belt friction is important in the transmission of power by belt and rope drives and in resisting large loads by means of band brakes, capstans, etc. If a belt, rope, or steel band passes over a *smooth* cylinder or pulley that offers resistance to turning, no difference in the tensions in the belt, rope, or band on the two sides of the pulley can be developed since a difference in the tensions requires that there be friction on the surface of contact between the belt and pulley. The "smooth" pulley therefore could not be turned. If the cylinder or pulley is *rough*, however, the tensions will not, in general, be equal, and hence the belt would drive or turn the cylinder or pulley.

In the present article the relation between the tensions in the belt, on the two sides of a rough pulley, *when the belt is about to slip*, will be determined. It is evident that the greater tension must be just large enough to overcome the smaller tension in addition to the friction of the pulley on the belt. In Fig. 194*a* is represented a belt on a pulley, the angle of contact being α and the belt tensions being T_1 and T_2. Let T_1 be the greater tension, and let it be assumed that the belt is about to slip on the pulley. The normal pressure between the belt and the pulley per unit length of belt at any point will be denoted by p, and the tension in the belt at the same point will be denoted by T. In Fig. 194*b* is a free-body diagram of an element of belt of length Δs. The forces acting on this element are the tensions T and $T + \Delta T$ at the ends, and the reaction of the pulley. The latter force may be resolved into a component, $\Delta N = p\,\Delta s$, normal to the face of the pulley and a frictional

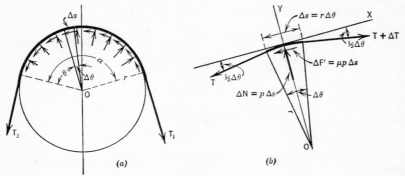

Fig. 194

component, $\Delta F' = \mu p\,\Delta s$, tangent to the face of the pulley. The equations of equilibrium may be applied as follows:

$$\Sigma F_x = (T + \Delta T)\cos\frac{\Delta\theta}{2} - T\cos\frac{\Delta\theta}{2} - \mu p\,\Delta s = 0 \tag{1}$$

$$\Sigma F_y = p\,\Delta s - (T + \Delta T)\sin\frac{\Delta\theta}{2} - T\sin\frac{\Delta\theta}{2} = 0 \tag{2}$$

Equation 1 may be written

$$\Sigma F_x = \Delta T\cos\frac{\Delta\theta}{2} - \mu pr\,\Delta\theta = 0$$

or

$$\frac{\Delta T}{\Delta\theta}\cos\frac{\Delta\theta}{2} = \mu pr$$

As $\Delta\theta$ approaches zero, $\cos\Delta\theta/2$ approaches the value unity. Hence, the limit of the left side of the equation is $dT/d\theta$, and

$$\frac{dT}{d\theta} = \mu pr \tag{3}$$

Equation 2 may be written

$$\Sigma F_y = pr\,\Delta\theta - 2T\sin\frac{\Delta\theta}{2} - \Delta T\sin\frac{\Delta\theta}{2} = 0$$

or

$$T\frac{\sin\Delta\theta/2}{\Delta\theta/2} + \frac{\Delta T}{\Delta\theta}\sin\frac{\Delta\theta}{2} = pr$$

As $\dfrac{\Delta\theta}{2}$ approaches zero, $\dfrac{\sin \Delta\theta/2}{\Delta\theta/2}$ approaches the value unity, and $\dfrac{\Delta T}{\Delta\theta}$ $\sin \dfrac{\Delta\theta}{2}$ approaches a small quantity of the second order and may be neglected. Hence the limit of the preceding equation as $\Delta\theta$ approaches zero is

$$T = pr \tag{4}$$

Eliminating pr from Eqs. 3 and 4, we find

$$\frac{dT}{T} = \mu \, d\theta \tag{5}$$

By integrating Eq. 5, the relation between T_1 and T_2 may be found as follows:

$$\int_{T_2}^{T_1} \frac{dT}{T} = \int_0^\alpha \mu \, d\theta, \quad \text{or} \quad \log_e \frac{T_1}{T_2} = \mu\alpha$$

That is,

$$\frac{T_1}{T_2} = e^{\mu\alpha}, \quad \text{or} \quad T_1 = T_2 e^{\mu\alpha} \tag{6}$$

where e is the base of natural logarithms and α is measured in radians. It should be noted that in the derivation of Eq. 6 the belt is assumed to be perfectly flexible.

Illustrative Problem

Problem 272. In the band brake shown in Fig. 195 the force P is 100 lb, the angle of contact α is 270° ($\frac{3}{2}\pi$ radians), and the coefficient of friction μ for the band and the brake wheel is 0.2. If the brake wheel rotates in a counterclockwise direction, find the tensions in the band and the frictional moment developed.

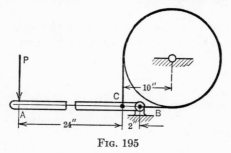

FIG. 195

SOLUTION. Since the operating lever ACB is in equilibrium, the equation $\Sigma M_B = 0$ may be applied, from which the band pull at C, that is, the tension T_2, is found. Thus,

$$\Sigma M_B = 100 \times 26 - T_2 \times 2 = 0, \qquad \therefore T_2 = 1300 \text{ lb}$$

Since T_2 is now known, the tension T_1 may be found from the belt-friction formula. Thus,

$$T_1 = T_2 \times e^{\mu\alpha} = 1300 \times (2.718)^{0.2 \times \frac{3}{2}\pi}$$

$$\log T_1 = \log 1300 + 0.3\pi \log 2.718$$

$$= 3.114 + 0.942 \times 0.434 = 3.522, \qquad \therefore T_1 = 3330 \text{ lb}$$

Frictional moment $= (T_1 - T_2) \times 10 = 2030 \times 10 = 20,300$ lb in.

Problems

273. A body weighing 1000 lb is suspended by means of a rope wound $1\frac{1}{2}$ turns around a drum. If the coefficient of friction is 0.2, what is the least force P that must be exerted at the other end of the rope to hold the body? *Ans. P = 152 lb.*

274. A rope passes around a horizontal circular beam making $1\frac{1}{2}$ turns. What is the greatest weight on one end of the rope that can be supported by a force of 1200 lb applied to the other end of the rope if the coefficient of static friction is 0.25?

275. A body weighing 400 lb is raised by means of a rope which passes over a horizontal cylinder, the angle of contact being 180°. If the coefficient of friction is 0.3, what is the least force P that will raise the body? What is the least force P that will hold the body? *Ans. P = 1026 lb; P = 156 lb.*

276. A rope is wound three times around a cylindrical post. If a pull of 60 lb at one end of the rope will just support a force of 6000 lb at the other end, what is the coefficient of friction for the surfaces of contact?

277. A boat is held at rest by means of a rope which is wound around a capstan. If a force of 3000 lb is exerted by the boat and a pull of 100 lb is exerted on the other end of the rope, find the number of turns the rope makes around the capstan, assuming the value of μ to be 0.20. *Ans. 2.71 turns.*

278. In Fig. 196 is represented a band brake, the angle of contact of the band on the brake wheel being 180°. If the coefficient of friction is 0.25, find the frictional moment developed when the brake wheel rotates clockwise. Although clockwise rotation would be desirable in order to eliminate vibration, assume the brake wheel rotates counterclockwise, and find the frictional moment developed.

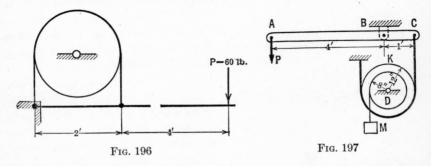

FIG. 196   FIG. 197

279. A band brake (Fig. 197) prevents the wheel K and drum D from being turned by the weight of the body M which is attached to a rope that is wound around the drum D. What is the greatest weight M can have if a force P of 20 lb applied as shown to the arm AC will just prevent the drum from turning? The friction of the drum bearing and of the pin at B may be neglected. The coefficient of friction for the band and wheel K is $2/\pi$. *Ans. W = 766 lb.*

280. In Fig. 198 what is the value of P if it just prevents downward motion of the 2000-lb weight? The rope makes one complete turn around the post. The drum turns in a frictionless bearing, and μ for the post and rope is $3/4\pi$.

281. Solve the preceding problem, assuming that the drum cannot turn and that μ for the rope and drum is $1/\pi$.

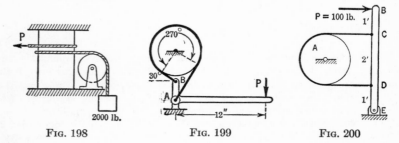

| FIG. 198 | FIG. 199 | FIG. 200 |

282. A frictional resisting moment of 1000 lb in. is exerted on the drum in Fig. 199 by the band brake when a load P of 20 lb is applied as shown. Find the value of the coefficient of friction for the band and drum. Assume the radius of the drum to be 4 in. and the drum to be rotating counterclockwise. *Ans. $\mu = 0.297$.*

283. In Fig. 200 find the moment of the couple that must be applied to the brake wheel A to cause it to rotate clockwise if the coefficient of friction is 0.2. The brake would operate more satisfactorily (with less vibration) if the bar BE were pinned at the fixed point D instead of E. What would be the moment of the couple if the bar were pinned at D?

61 Rolling resistance.

If a rigid wheel or roller which carries a vertical load rests on a *rigid* horizontal surface, a horizontal force, however small, will cause the wheel or roller to roll on the surface. If a wheel rolls over a *yielding* surface, however, a resistance to the motion is encountered, owing to the fact that the surface immediately in front of the wheel is being deformed.

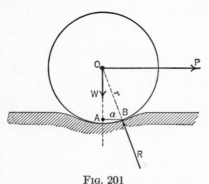

FIG. 201

In Fig. 201 is shown a wheel carrying a vertical load W. Let P be a horizontal force which causes the center of the wheel to move with a constant velocity. Since the surface on which the wheel rolls deforms under the wheel, the pressure on the surface is distributed over the area of contact. The resultant pressure or reaction of the surface on the wheel then passes through some point B in the area of contact as shown in the figure. Since the velocity of the wheel is constant, the three forces acting are in equilibrium and hence the reaction R of the surface on the wheel must pass through O, the center of the wheel. Applying the equation of equilibrium $\Sigma M_B = 0$, we have

$$\Sigma M_B = W \times AB - P \times OA = 0$$

Since the depression of the surface is usually small, OA is approximately equal to r, the radius of the wheel. By using this approximation and denoting AB by a, the value of P is found from the foregoing equation to be

$$P = \frac{Wa}{r}$$

The horizontal component of the reaction R is equal to P and is called the *rolling friction* or *rolling resistance*; the distance a is sometimes called the *coefficient of rolling resistance*. However, since a is a linear quantity and not a pure number, it is not a true coefficient. The value of a is generally expressed in inches. The laws of rolling resistance are not well established, and there is need of further investigation on the subject. It was assumed by Coulomb that the coefficient of rolling resistance is independent of the radius of the wheel. Tests by Dupuit indicate that the coefficient varies as the square root of the diameter. Whether the conclusion of the latter is correct or not, it seems reasonable to assume that the value of the coefficient depends on the diameter of the wheel. The values of the coefficient of rolling resistance given by various investigators are not in close agreement and should be used with caution.

COEFFICIENTS OF ROLLING RESISTANCE

Determined by Coulomb and Goodman

	a (inches)
Lignum vitae on oak	0.0195
Elm on oak	0.0327
Steel on steel	0.007 to 0.015
Steel on wood	0.06 to 0.10
Steel on macadam road	0.05 to 0.20
Steel on soft ground	3.0 to 5.0
Pneumatic tires on good road	0.02 to 0.022
Pneumatic tires on mud road	0.04 to 0.06
Solid rubber tire on good road	0.04
Solid rubber tire on mud road	0.09 to 0.11

Problems

284. If the rolling resistance for the wheels of a freight car is 3 lb per ton and the diameter of the car wheels is 33 in., what is the coefficient of rolling resistance?

Ans. 0.025 in.

285. What is the rolling resistance of an automobile wheel on a concrete road if the diameter of the wheel is 32 in. and if it supports a vertical load of 800 lb? Assume the coefficient of rolling resistance to be 0.02 in.

286. What is the rolling resistance of a wagon wheel on a macadam road if the diameter of the wheel is 4 ft 6 in.? Assume the coefficient of rolling resistance to be 0.2 in.   *Ans.* 14.8 lb per ton.

Review Questions

1. Show that the angle of static friction is equal to the angle of repose.

2. Show that the coefficient of static friction is equal to the tangent of the angle of friction.

3. A horizontal force P whose magnitude is known is applied to a body of known weight W that rests on a horizontal plane (see Fig. 171). If the coefficient of friction μ for the body and plane is known, how does one proceed to determine whether or not the body will move?

4. A body rests on an inclined plane. Is the friction of the plane on the body necessarily equal to the product of the normal pressure of the plane and the coefficient of friction?

5. Correct the error in the following statement: The angle between the total reaction and the normal pressure is always equal to the angle of friction.

6. If two bodies in contact are in a condition of impending motion and additional forces are applied to the bodies causing an increase in the normal pressure, does the angle of friction also increase?

7. If a body rests on a plane and motion of the body is impending, state two ways of representing the action of the plane on the body in a free-body diagram?

8. Correct the error in each of the following statements: (*a*) The coefficient of friction for two surfaces of contact is the ratio of the normal pressure to the limiting friction. (*b*) The angle of friction is the angle between the action lines of the limiting friction and the normal pressure. (*c*) The normal pressure of a plane on a body that slides or tends to slide on the plane is always equal to the component of the weight of the body in a direction normal to the plane. (*d*) The coefficient of static friction for a given pair of rubbing surfaces is not a constant for that pair of surfaces because the limiting friction developed varies with the normal pressure.

9. In obtaining the expression for the frictional moment on a flat pivot bearing, why is the moment obtained by first getting the moment of the frictional force on an elementary area dA and then finding the sum of all such moments rather than by finding the resultant of the frictional forces and then obtaining the moment of this resultant?

10. If a load is raised by a jackscrew as in Fig. 192, is the moment of the frictional force on the screw equal to the moment of the force P applied to the lever?

11. If a frictional force acts on a moving body, is the direction of the force always opposite to the direction of motion of that part of the body on which the frictional force acts?

12. A load W is being raised by a jackscrew (Fig. 192) by a force P applied at the end of the lever of the jackscrew. Under what condition will the load descend if the force P is removed?

PART TWO
Kinematics

Chapter 7

MOTION OF A PARTICLE

62 Introduction. Kinematics treats of the motion of bodies without considering the manner in which the motion is influenced, either by the forces acting on the bodies or by the character of the bodies themselves. That is, the bodies are treated as geometric solids and not as physical bodies. When the geometric solids are endowed with physical properties, we are led to a study of force, energy, momentum, etc., that is, to a study of Kinetics (Part Three).

Kinematics deals with the relations among distance, time, velocity, and acceleration. In order to establish the fundamental definitions, concepts, and relationships which are involved in the study of the motion of bodies, the kinematics of a particle will be treated first. The word *particle* is used in mechanics to denote a body whose dimensions are infinitesimally small, and hence a particle is sometimes referred to as a *material point*. In many problems a body of finite size may be treated as a particle if the dimensions of the body are small compared with the range of motion of the body.

Any body may be regarded as being made up of an infinite number of particles, and the study of the motion of a body is largely a study of the motions of the particles of which the body is composed. The study of the motion of bodies will, for the most part, be restricted to rigid bodies, and the motions considered will be limited mainly to translation, rotation, and plane motion.

63 Vector addition and subtraction. In discussing the motion of a particle in terms of the vector quantities, displacement, velocity, and acceleration, the addition and the subtraction of vectors are involved.

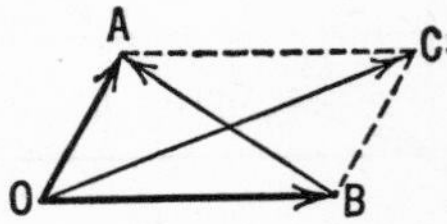

According to the parallelogram (or triangle) law, the *sum* of two vectors, such as OA and OB in Fig. 202, is the diagonal OC of the parallelogram shown in the figure. The *difference* of the two vectors, OA and OB, is the other diagonal BA of the parallelogram. This fact is also in accordance with the triangle law since the difference between two quantities is the quantity that must be added to one of the

Fig. 202

155

two quantities to make the resulting quantity equal to the other. Thus, the vector BA (not AB) must be added to the vector OB to make the resulting vector equal to OA.

The symbols $\nrightarrow$ and $\rightarrow$ will be used to denote vector addition and subtraction, respectively. (For other methods of denoting vector addition and subtraction see footnote in Art. 10.) Hence the above statements, with reference to Fig. 202, may be expressed as follows:

$$OC = OA \nrightarrow OB \quad \text{and} \quad BA = OA \rightarrow OB$$

It will be observed that the vector difference BA between OA and OB may also be obtained by reversing the sense (changing the sign) of vector OB and adding it to OA, which is analogous to the rule for algebraic subtraction. It should also be noted that the difference between OB and OA is AB (not BA). That is, $OB \rightarrow OA = AB$.

64 Types of motion. The motion of a particle or point along a straight-line path is called *rectilinear* motion. The motion of a particle along a curved path is called *curvilinear* motion. If the moving particle describes equal distances along its path in equal periods of time, however small, the motion is said to be *uniform*. If unequal distances are described by the moving particle in equal periods of time, the motion is said to be *non-uniform* or *variable*.

Thus, if the crankshaft of a steam engine revolves at a constant number of revolutions per minute, the crosshead of the engine has a non-uniform rectilinear motion, the crank pin has a uniform curvilinear motion, and any intermediate point on the connecting rod has a non-uniform, curvilinear motion.

65 Linear displacement. The linear displacement of a moving point is defined as the change of position of the point. The position of

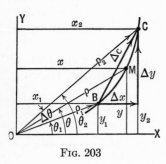

FIG. 203

a moving point, at any instant, may be specified in a number of ways, as, for example, by stating the rectangular co-ordinates or the polar co-ordinates of the point. Thus, in Fig. 203 the position, at any instant, of the point M as it travels along the curve from B to C may be specified by the rectangular co-ordinates (x, y) or by the polar co-ordinates (ρ, θ). The displacement Δc of the point as it moves from the position (x_1, y_1) or (ρ_1, θ_1) to the position (x_2, y_2) or (ρ_2, θ_2) is the straight line BC: that is, the vector drawn from B to C. This displacement may be expressed as the *vector sum* of its x and y components by the vector equation,

$$\Delta c = \Delta x \nleftrightarrow \Delta y$$

The *magnitude* and *direction* of Δc may be expressed by the two scalar equations,

$$\Delta c = \sqrt{(\Delta x)^2 + (\Delta y)^2}, \qquad \tan \phi = \frac{\Delta y}{\Delta x}$$

where ϕ is the angle between Δc and Δx.

The displacement Δc may be expressed also as the *vector difference* of the radius vectors to the two positions of the moving point. Thus,

$$\Delta c = \rho_2 \rightarrow \rho_1$$

that is, Δc is the directed distance which must be added to ρ_1 to give ρ_2. Or, in other words, ρ_2 is the vector sum of ρ_1 and Δc.

The unit of displacement is any convenient unit of length, such as the inch, foot, or mile. It will be noted, however, that displacement is a *directed* distance or length: that is, a vector quantity. Displacements, therefore, may be combined and resolved according to the parallelogram (or triangle) law like forces and other vector quantities. It is important to note that by one of the above equations the displacement Δc is expressed as the *vector sum* of two directed distances, whereas by the other equation it is expressed as the *vector difference* of two directed distances.

If the displacement of the particle is decreased indefinitely, the point C (Fig. 203) will approach the point B, and, in the limit, the chord Δc becomes coincident with the tangent to the path at B. Therefore, the direction of motion of the particle at any point on its path is tangent to the path at that point.

66 Angular displacement. The angular displacement of a line that moves in a plane is the change in the angle that the moving line makes with any fixed line or axis in the plane. The angular displacement of a moving point with respect to a given point or pole is the angular displacement of the line joining the moving point to the pole. Thus, in Fig. 203, the angular displacement $\Delta \theta$ of M relative to O, corresponding to the linear displacement Δc, is

$$\Delta \theta = \theta_2 - \theta_1$$

It is important to note that the angular displacement of a point depends upon the reference point or pole selected. If the point moves on a circular arc, the center of the circle is usually taken as the pole. The unit of angular displacement may be any convenient angular measure, such as the degree, revolution, or radian.

67   Relation between linear and angular displacements. If a point moves counterclockwise along a circular path of radius r, the linear displacement dc (Fig. 204), corresponding to an indefinitely small angular displacement $d\theta$, may be considered to be coincident with the arc ds, which is subtended by the angle $d\theta$. Since the arc of a circle is the product of the radius and the central angle, when the angle is

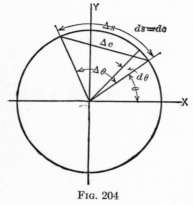

measured in radians, the relation between the linear and angular displacements may be expressed by the equation

$$ds = r\,d\theta$$

For a large angular displacement $\Delta\theta$, the corresponding linear displacement Δc is *not* equal to $r\,\Delta\theta$. The distance Δs along the arc, however, *is* expressed by $r\,\Delta\theta$.

If the moving point does not travel

Fig. 204

on a circular path, but on a path having a variable radius of curvature, the equation $ds = r\,d\theta$ may be used, provided that r is the radius of curvature of the path at the given position of the point and that $d\theta$ is measured with respect to the center of curvature as the pole.

If, however, the pole is not chosen as the center of curvature of the path (Fig. 205), the displacement may then be expressed in terms of its two components parallel and perpendicular,
respectively, to the radius vector as follows:

$$ds = \rho\,d\theta + d\rho$$

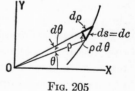

in which ρ is the radius vector to the point and *not* the radius of curvature of the path at that point. The components $\rho\,d\theta$ and $d\rho$ are called the *transverse* and *radial* components of displacement.

Fig. 205

68   Linear velocity and speed. The linear velocity of a moving particle is the time rate at which the particle is changing position, or, more briefly, the time rate of linear displacement. The direction of the velocity of the moving particle at a given point on its path is tangent to the path at that point (Art. 65). Velocity, like displacement, possesses both magnitude and direction and, therefore, is a vector quantity. The magnitude of the velocity of a point is called the *speed* of the point. Speed, therefore, is a scalar quantity. It may be defined as the time rate of describing distance (not the time rate of *displacement*).

Although the terms velocity and speed are frequently used interchangeably, it is important to associate with the word *velocity* the two properties that it possesses, for a change in the direction of a velocity is fully as important in the laws of motion of physical bodies as is a change in the speed.

If a point has a *uniform* motion along any path, the speed v of the point is the ratio of any distance Δs described by the point to the corresponding interval of time Δt. Thus, the speed is expressed as

$$v = \frac{\Delta s}{\Delta t}$$

It will be noted that, if a particle has uniform motion, whether rectilinear or curvilinear, the speed of the particle is constant. The velocity, however, is constant only in the case of uniform *rectilinear* motion, since in any curvilinear motion the velocity of the particle continually changes direction.

If the motion of the point is non-uniform, the foregoing equation does not give the speed of the point at each instant in the interval, but gives only the average speed for the time interval Δt. The instantaneous speed is the average speed over an indefinitely small period of time including the instant, or, expressed in mathematical form, the speed at any instant is

$$v = \underset{\Delta t \doteq 0}{\text{limit}} \frac{\Delta s}{\Delta t} = \frac{ds}{dt} \tag{1}$$

The direction of v, as already noted, is tangent to the path at the point on the path where the moving particle is located at the instant. In order to find the value of v by differentiation, as indicated in Eq. 1, s must be expressed in terms of t.

The unit of velocity may be any convenient unit of length per unit of time, such as foot per second (ft/sec), mile per hour (mi/hr), or centimeter per second (cm/sec).

If v is expressed as a function of t, the displacement Δs along the path in any time interval $t_2 - t_1$ may be found by integrating v with respect to t. Thus, from Eq. 1,

$$ds = v\, dt$$

Integration gives

$$\int_{s_1}^{s_2} ds = \int_{t_1}^{t_2} v\, dt$$

That is,

$$s_2 - s_1 = \Delta s = \int_{t_1}^{t_2} v\, dt \tag{2}$$

It should be noted that Δs denotes the distance the point moves along its path and not the *linear displacement* of the point unless the path of the point is a straight line.

DISTANCE-TIME AND SPEED-TIME CURVES. It is convenient to interpret Eqs. 1 and 2 graphically. Thus, let a distance-time (s–t) curve be constructed by plotting a series of points, the rectangular co-ordinates of each point being simultaneous values of s and t (Fig. 211). The slope to this curve is represented by ds/dt; but $v = ds/dt$, and hence it follows that the slope at any point of the (s–t) curve represents to some

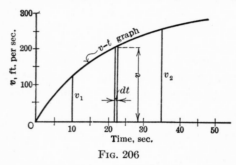

FIG. 206

scale (depending on the scales used in plotting the curve) the speed of the moving point at the corresponding instant.

Similarly, if the relation between v and t is shown graphically by plotting a speed-time (v–t) curve for the moving point as shown in Fig. 206, the area under this curve between the ordinates v_2 and v_1 represents to some scale (depending on the scales used in plotting the curve) the displacement Δs of the point along its path in the corresponding time interval $t_2 - t_1$. This is evident from a consideration of Eq. 2 and Fig. 206.

69 Angular velocity. The angular velocity of a moving line is defined as the time rate of angular displacement of the line. The angular velocity of a moving point with respect to a given point or pole is the angular velocity of the line joining the moving point to the pole. If equal angular displacements occur in equal time intervals, the motion is said to be uniform, and the angular velocity ω is expressed as the ratio of any angular displacement $\Delta\theta$ to the time interval Δt during which the displacement occurs. Thus,

$$\omega = \frac{\Delta\theta}{\Delta t}$$

If unequal angular displacements occur in equal time intervals, the motion is said to be non-uniform or variable. For such a motion the foregoing equation gives the average angular velocity during the time interval Δt. When the angular velocity varies during the interval, its value at any instant is the average velocity over an indefinitely small time interval including the instant. Or, expressed mathematically, the instantaneous angular velocity is

$$\omega = \underset{\Delta t \doteq 0}{\text{limit}} \frac{\Delta \theta}{\Delta t} = \frac{d\theta}{dt} \tag{1}$$

In order to determine the angular velocity from this equation, θ must be expressed in terms of t.

The relation between θ and t and between ω and t may be shown graphically by curves similar to those discussed in the preceding article.

The unit of angular velocity is any convenient unit of angular displacement per unit of time, such as degree per second (deg/sec), revolution per minute (rpm), or radian per second (rad/sec).

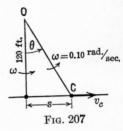

FIG. 207

Illustrative Problems

Problem 287. In Fig. 207, C is a car (considered as a point) moving on a straight road, and O is an observer in a tower directly over the road. If the car moves so that its angular velocity with respect to the observer is constant and equal to 0.10 rad/sec, find the linear velocity of the car when its position is such that θ is 0°, 30°, and 60°.

SOLUTION. From Fig. 207 it is seen that $s = 120 \tan \theta$ and, since $v = ds/dt$, we have

$$v = \frac{d(120 \tan \theta)}{dt} = 120 \sec^2 \theta \, \frac{d\theta}{dt} = 120 \sec^2 \theta \times \omega = 12 \sec^2 \theta$$

$$= 12 \times 1 = 12 \text{ ft/sec} \quad \text{when} \quad \theta = 0°$$

$$= 12 \times \tfrac{4}{3} = 16 \text{ ft/sec} \quad \text{when} \quad \theta = 30°$$

$$= 12 \times 4 = 48 \text{ ft/sec} \quad \text{when} \quad \theta = 60°$$

Problem 288. The length of the crank OA of a steam engine (Fig. 208) is denoted by r, and the length of the connecting rod BA is denoted by l. If the crank turns

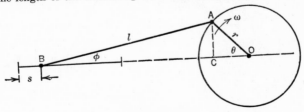

FIG. 208

with constant angular velocity ω, determine the velocity of the crosshead B in terms of r, l, ω, and the angle θ which the crank makes with the horizontal.

SOLUTION. The displacement s of the crosshead from its extreme position may be determined in terms of θ, and, since $\theta = \omega t$ in which ω is known, s may also be expressed as a function of t. Thus,

$$s = l + r - l \cos \phi - r \cos \theta$$

But

$$AC = l \sin \phi = r \sin \theta$$

and

$$l \cos \phi = \sqrt{l^2 - l^2 \sin^2 \phi} = \sqrt{l^2 - r^2 \sin^2 \theta}$$

By expanding the last expression by the binomial theorem and using only the first two terms of the expansion, we may write the preceding equation as follows with only a small error since r/l is usually small.

$$l \cos \phi = l - \frac{r^2}{2l} \sin^2 \theta$$

Therefore,

$$s = r - r \cos \theta + \frac{r^2}{2l} \sin^2 \theta$$

Hence,

$$v = \frac{ds}{dt} = r \sin \theta \frac{d\theta}{dt} + \frac{r^2}{l} \sin \theta \cos \theta \frac{d\theta}{dt}$$

$$= r\omega \left(\sin \theta + \frac{r}{l} \sin \theta \cos \theta \right) = r\omega \left(\sin \theta + \frac{r}{2l} \sin 2\theta \right)$$

Problems

289. A point moves along a straight line according to the law $s = t^3 + 8t$, where s and t are expressed in feet and seconds, respectively. Find: (a) the initial velocity of the point, (b) the displacement during the third second, and (c) the average velocity for the time interval $t = 1$ sec to $t = 3$ sec.

290. In Fig. 209 blocks A and B are pinned together. Block A slides in a horizontal slot in D, and B slides in a slot in OC as OC rotates about O with a constant angular velocity ω. When in the position shown, $\theta = 30°$, and the distance from O to the pin is 2 ft. Find, by use of Eq. 1 of Arts. 68 and 69, the linear velocity of block A in terms of ω and θ.   *Ans.* $v_A = \sqrt{3} \, \omega \sec^2 \theta$.

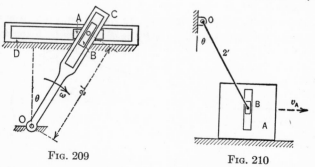

FIG. 209   FIG. 210

291. In Fig. 210 a bar OB is pin-connected to a fixed surface at O and to a block B that slides in a vertical slot in body A. If $\theta = 30°$ and body A has a velocity of

10 ft/sec to the right, find, by use of Eq. 1 of Arts. 68 and 69, the angular velocity of OB.

292. An automobile travels on a straight road with variable speed. A speed-time curve for the motion is drawn to a scale of 1 in. vertical equals 100 ft/sec, and 1 in. horizontal equals 10 sec. If the area under the curve between the ordinates corresponding to $t = 30$ sec, and $t = 90$ sec is 6 sq in., find the average speed during the 60 sec, and express it in miles per hour. *Ans.* $v = 68.2$ mi/hr.

293. A man runs 100 yd in 11 sec. If he runs x yd at a constant speed of 8 yd/sec and the remainder of the distance at a constant speed of 10 yd/sec, find the distance x.

294. A point moves along the X axis according to the law $x = (t - 1)(t - 3)$, where x and t are expressed in feet and seconds, respectively. Describe in detail the motion for the first 4 sec, indicating the direction in which the point is moving each second, and also indicating the position of the point and the magnitude and direction of the velocity at the end of each second. Draw the x–t and v–t curves for the motion.

295. In Fig. 211 is shown the $(s$–$t)$ curve for a point moving on a straight line. What is the velocity of the point when $t = 20$ sec? *Ans.* $v = 5$ ft/sec.

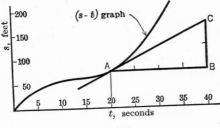

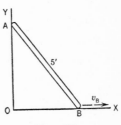

| FIG. 211 | FIG. 212 |

296. One end A of the bar AB in Fig. 212 moves downward on the Y axis according to the law $v_A = 32t$, where v_A and t are expressed in feet per second and seconds, respectively, and the other end B moves to the right on the X axis. If $OA = 4$ ft when $t = 0$, find, by use of Eq. 1 of Art. 68, the velocity of B when $OA = 3$ ft.

297. An automobile travels along a straight road a distance of 200 ft at a constant speed of 40 ft/sec and then a further distance s at a constant speed of 20 ft/sec. Find the distance s if the average speed for the entire distance is the average of the two speeds. *Ans.* $s = 100$ ft.

298. A point moves on a circle whose radius is 5 ft according to the law $s = \dfrac{t^3}{3} + \dfrac{1}{t}$, where s and t are expressed in feet and seconds, respectively. Find t when the angular velocity of the point relative to the center of the circle is zero. Find also the angular velocity when $t = \frac{1}{2}$ sec.

70 Relation between linear and angular velocities. If a point moves on a circular path, the relation between its linear and angular velocities may be found as follows: Let a point M move on a circular path of radius r (Fig. 213a), let v be the linear velocity of the point at any instant, and let ω be the angular velocity of the point, with respect to

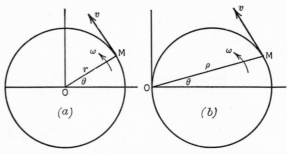

Fig. 213

the center of the circle, at the same instant. By definition,

$$v = \frac{ds}{dt} \quad \text{and} \quad \omega = \frac{d\theta}{dt}$$

But the distance ds traversed in the time dt may be expressed in terms of the corresponding angular displacement $d\theta$, by the equation $ds = r\,d\theta$ (Art. 67). Therefore,

$$v = \frac{r\,d\theta}{dt} = r\omega \tag{1}$$

Hence, at any instant, the linear velocity of a point moving on a circle is the product of its angular velocity (with respect to the center of the circle) and the radius of the circle, where the angular velocity ω is expressed in *radians* per unit of time.

If the point does not move on a circular path, the equation $v = \omega r$ is also true if r is the radius of curvature of the path at the given position of the point, and if ω is the angular velocity of the point with respect to the center of curvature as the pole.

Furthermore, if the point moves on a curve of any form and the center of curvature is not taken as the pole (Fig. 213b), then the term $\rho\omega$, where ρ denotes the radius vector to the point, gives one component only of the linear velocity, as is shown in the next article.

71 Components of velocity. It is frequently convenient to find the velocity of a moving point by determining its components, or to deal with the components of the velocity instead of the total velocity.

Two sets of components only are here determined: namely, the axial components (v_x and v_y), parallel, respectively, to the X and Y axes, and the radial and transverse components (v_R and v_T), parallel and per-pendicular, respectively, to the radius vector (Fig. 214).

Thus, since the component, in any direction, of the linear veloc-ity of a point is the time rate of the component displacement of the point in the given direction, the axial components of the velocity v of the moving point M (Fig. 214) are given by the expressions,

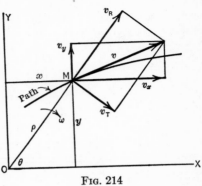

FIG. 214

$$v_x = \frac{dx}{dt} \quad \text{and} \quad v_y = \frac{dy}{dt} \quad (1)$$

or, if the co-ordinates x and y of the particle change uniformly, then,

$$v_x = \frac{\Delta x}{\Delta t} = \frac{x_2 - x_1}{t_2 - t_1} \quad \text{and} \quad v_y = \frac{\Delta y}{\Delta t} = \frac{y_2 - y_1}{t_2 - t_1}$$

Likewise, at any instant, the transverse and radial components of veloc-ity v_T and v_R are expressed as follows:

$$v_T = \frac{\rho \, d\theta}{dt} \quad \text{and} \quad v_R = \frac{d\rho}{dt} \quad (2)$$

in which $\rho \, d\theta$ and $d\rho$ are the components of displacement in the trans-verse and radial directions during the time interval dt, as shown in Art. 67 and Fig. 206, and $d\theta/dt$ is the angular velocity of the point with reference to the pole O. It will be noted that, when O is chosen as the center of curvature of the path, the transverse component of the velocity becomes the total velocity, tangent to the path, v_R then being equal to zero.

Since the pole O may be arbitrarily chosen, the components v_T and v_R are different for different positions of the pole or origin, whereas v_x and v_y are independent of the origin and depend on the directions only of the co-ordinate axes.

In obtaining the radial and transverse components of velocity, the graphical method of solution is frequently preferable to the algebraic method which makes use of Eq. 2. The graphical method is illustrated in Prob. 300.

Illustrative Problems

Problem 299. The angular velocity of the oscillating arm OM (Fig. 215) is 40 rpm when $\theta = 30°$. (a) Find by use of Eq. 2 the radial and transverse components of the velocity of the block A referred to O as the pole. (b) Show by means of a

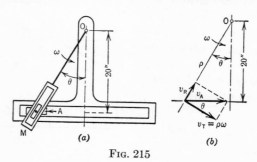

FIG. 215

diagram how the vectors v_A, v_R, and v_T are related, and then, by use of the value of v_T found from Eq. 2, find v_R and v_A.

SOLUTION. (a) From Fig. 215, we obtain

$$\rho = \frac{20}{12 \cos \theta} = \frac{5}{3} \sec \theta \text{ ft}$$

and

$$\omega = \frac{d\theta}{dt} = \frac{40 \times 2\pi}{60} = \frac{4\pi}{3} \text{ rad/sec}$$

Hence,

$$v_R = \frac{d\rho}{dt} = \frac{5}{3} \sec \theta \tan \theta \frac{d\theta}{dt} = \frac{5}{3} \sec \theta \tan \theta \times \omega$$

$$= \frac{5}{3} \times \frac{2}{\sqrt{3}} \times \frac{1}{\sqrt{3}} \times \frac{4}{3} \pi = 4.65 \text{ ft/sec} \quad \text{when} \quad \theta = 30°$$

Also

$$v_T = \rho \frac{d\theta}{dt} = \frac{5}{3} \sec \theta \times \omega$$

$$= \frac{5}{3} \times \frac{2}{\sqrt{3}} \times \frac{4\pi}{3} = 8.06 \text{ ft/sec} \quad \text{when} \quad \theta = 30°$$

(b) The total velocity of A is horizontal, and the components v_R and v_T are as shown in Fig. 215b. From the figure, it is seen that

$$v_R = v_T \tan \theta \quad \text{and} \quad v_A = v_T \sec \theta$$

Since $v_T = \rho\omega = \frac{5}{3} \sec \theta \times \omega$, we have

$$v_R = \frac{5}{3} \sec \theta \tan \theta \times \omega = \frac{5}{3} \times \frac{2}{\sqrt{3}} \times \frac{1}{\sqrt{3}} \times \frac{4\pi}{3} = 4.65 \text{ ft/sec} \quad \text{when} \quad \theta = 30°$$

and

$$v_A = \frac{5}{3} \sec^2 \theta \times \omega = \frac{5}{3} \times \frac{4}{3} \times \frac{4\pi}{3} = 9.31 \text{ ft/sec} \quad \text{when} \quad \theta = 30°$$

Problem 300. In the quick-return mechanism shown in Fig. 216, OO_1 = 18 in., and the crank OA = 8 in. If the angular veloc-ity of the crank is 40 rpm, what is the velocity of the block A? Find graphically the component of the velocity of A perpendicular to the rocker arm O_1M (the transverse component) in the po-sition shown. Find also the angular velocity of O_1M.

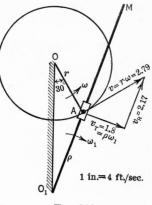

SOLUTION. The block moves on the circular path of radius r = 8 in. Let ω denote the angular velocity of A with reference to the pole O and ω_1 the angular velocity of A with reference to the pole O_1 (that is, let ω_1 denote the angular veloc-ity of O_1A, or ρ). The direction of the velocity of A is tangent to the circle, and its magnitude is

$$v = \omega r = \frac{40 \times 2\pi}{60} \times \frac{8}{12} = 2.79 \text{ ft/sec}$$

Fig. 216

By resolving v, graphically, into its transverse and radial components as shown in the figure, the following values are found:

$$v_T = 1.8 \text{ ft/sec} \quad \text{and} \quad v_R = 2.17 \text{ ft/sec}$$

But

$$v_T = \omega_1\rho = \omega_1 \times O_1A$$

By measuring, O_1A is found to be 11.7 in.
Therefore,

$$\omega_1 = \frac{1.8 \times 12}{11.7} = 1.84 \text{ rad/sec} = 17.6 \text{ rpm}$$

Problems

301. In Fig. 182 the disk B rotates at 300 rpm and turns (without slipping) the wheel C by means of the frictional force on the circumference of C. The distance from the center line of B to the point of contact between B and C is 6 in., and the diameter of C is 20 in. What is the angular velocity of C, in rpm?

302. A point moves along the parabola $y^2 = 8x$. What is the position of the point when $v_x = v_y$?

303. A disk A (Fig. 217) rotating with an angular velocity ω_1 of 50 rpm turns (without slipping) another disk B by means of friction at their surfaces of contact. A drum D is attached to the disk B and turns with it, thereby raising the body C. The radii r_1, r_2, and r_3 are 9 in., 15 in., and 6 in., respectively. Find the velocity of C in feet per second. *Ans. v_C = 1.57 ft/sec.*

304. In Fig. 218, AB is a rigid bar which oscillates, thus causing the bar OM also to oscillate. When the bars are in the position shown, the angular velocity of AB is 4 rad/sec. Find the angular velocity of OM for this position.

305. A point moves along the curve $y = \frac{1}{12}x^3$. If $v_x = 5$ ft/sec when $x = 2$ ft, find the magnitude and direction of the total velocity of the point when $x = 2$ ft. *Ans. v = 7.07 ft/sec; θ_x = 45°.*

306. In Fig. 209 the bar OC rotates with a constant angular velocity of 10 rad/sec. When it is in the position shown, $\theta = 30°$, and the distance from O to the pin is 2 ft. Find the radial and transverse components of the velocity of the block A with respect to O as a pole when OC is in the position shown.

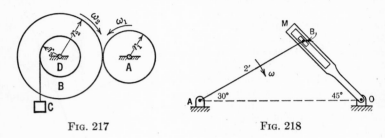

FIG. 217   FIG. 218

307. The cam shown in Fig. 219 revolves about the axis O, causing the roller A to change its x co-ordinate at the rate of 4 in. per sec when $\theta = 30°$. Find the angular velocity of the bell crank AO_1B if O_1A is 18 in.   *Ans.* $\omega = 4.24$ rpm.

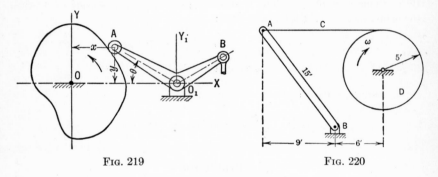

FIG. 219   FIG. 220

308. In Fig. 220 the bar AB is caused to move from a horizontal position to a vertical position by a cord C which is attached to the bar AB and wrapped around the drum D. The drum is rotating with a constant angular velocity of 3 rpm. Determine the angular velocity of AB when the cord is in the horizontal position shown.
Ans. $\omega = 0.131$ rad/sec.

309. How long will it take the bar AB in the preceding problem to move from the position shown to a vertical position?

310. A point moves in the xy plane according to the law $y = t^4 + 2t^2$, $v_x = 4t$, where x and y are expressed in feet and t in seconds. If the distance of the point from the origin is 5 ft when $t = 1$ sec, find the equation to the path in terms of x and y.   *Ans.* $4y = x^2 - 4$.

311. In Fig. 221 the vertical rod C moves downward with a velocity of 4 ft/sec, causing the bell crank AOB to rotate about O. Find the linear velocity of B when the bell crank is in the position shown.

312. In Fig. 222, A is a block that revolves about O with an angular velocity $\omega = 60$ rpm. O_1M is a rod that is pivoted at O_1 and passes through a slot in A. The lengths of OA and OO_1 are 12 in. and 6 in., respectively. Find, graphically, the radial and transverse components of the velocity of A with respect to O_1 as a pole. Find also ω_1 the angular velocity of O_1M in revolutions per minute.

Ans. $\omega_1 = 48$ rpm.

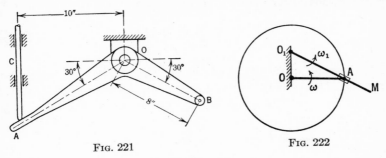

FIG. 221   FIG. 222

313. A point moves on the curve $xy = 4$ according to the law $x = 2t^2$, where x and y are expressed in feet and t in seconds. Find the magnitude and direction of the velocity of the point when $t = 1$ sec and also when $x = 1$ ft.

72 Linear acceleration. The linear acceleration of a moving point, at any instant, is defined as the time rate of change of the linear velocity of the point at the instant. If the change in the velocity in time Δt be denoted by Δv, the average acceleration for the time interval is $\Delta v/\Delta t$, and the limit of this ratio as Δt approaches zero is the instantaneous acceleration. Or, expressed mathematically,

$$a = \underset{\Delta t \doteq 0}{\text{limit}} \frac{\Delta v}{\Delta t}$$

Since velocity is a vector quantity, the change Δv in the velocity may occur as a result of a change in the magnitude, only, of the velocity as in rectilinear motion with varying speed; or a change in the direction only, as in curvilinear motion with constant speed; or a change in both magnitude and direction as in curvilinear motion with varying speed. The acceleration of a point having various types of motion will be considered in the following articles.

The unit of linear acceleration is any unit of linear velocity per unit of time, such as foot per second per second (ft/sec²) or mile per hour per second (mi/hr/sec).

73 Acceleration in rectilinear motion. In Fig. 223 let a point move so that its velocity changes in magnitude only. That is, let the point move on a straight-line path with varying speed. Let v_1 be the velocity at one instant, and let v_2 be the velocity after the time interval Δt. If the velocity changes uniformly, the magnitude of the acceleration is the ratio of any change in the velocity Δv to the time interval Δt during which the change Δv occurs. Since v_2 and v_1 have the same direction, Δv is the algebraic difference of v_2 and v_1 as well as the vector difference. Hence, the magnitude of the acceleration for uniformly accelerated, rectilinear motion is

$$a = \frac{\Delta v}{\Delta t} = \frac{v_2 - v_1}{t_2 - t_1} \tag{1}$$

If the velocity of the moving point in Fig. 223 does not change uniformly, Eq. 1 gives only the average acceleration during the period Δt. When the acceleration varies from instant to instant, its value at any

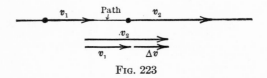

Fɪɢ. 223

instant is the average acceleration during a very small time interval including the instant. Or, expressed mathematically, the instantaneous acceleration for rectilinear motion is

$$a = \underset{\Delta t \doteq 0}{\text{limit}} \frac{\Delta v}{\Delta t} = \frac{dv}{dt} \tag{2}$$

In order to find a from this equation, v must be expressed in terms of t. Since $v = ds/dt$, the above expression may also be written

$$a = \frac{dv}{dt} = \frac{d^2s}{dt^2} \tag{3}$$

The direction of the acceleration of the point in rectilinear motion is the same as that of the change of velocity Δv, but Δv is parallel to v: that is, along the path. If v_2 is smaller than v_1, the sense of Δv is negative, that is, opposite to that of v, and hence the acceleration then is negative. A negative acceleration is sometimes called a *deceleration*.

By dividing numerator and denominator of the right side of Eq. 2 by ds, another useful form of expressing a is obtained, namely:

$$a = v \frac{dv}{ds} \tag{4}$$

In order to find a from this equation, v must be expressed in terms of s. This expression for a is especially convenient to use in problems involving the flow of fluids in which the velocity of the fluid may be measured at various points along the stream line, and from these measurements the rate of change of velocity with respect to distance may be obtained. It may be noted that the expression $v\dfrac{dv}{ds}$ may be written $\dfrac{1}{2}\dfrac{d(v^2)}{ds}$. This form of the expression is sometimes convenient to use when dealing with energy.

If a is expressed as a function of t, the change of speed in any time interval $t_2 - t_1$ may be found by integrating a with respect to t. Thus, from Eq. 2, we obtain

$$dv = a\, dt$$

Integration of this equation gives

$$\int_{v_1}^{v_2} dv = \int_{t_1}^{t_2} a\, dt$$

That is,

$$v_2 - v_1 = \Delta v = \int_{t_1}^{t_2} a\, dt \tag{5}$$

JERK. The time rate of change of acceleration in rectilinear motion is called "jerk." Thus,

$$\text{Jerk} = \frac{da}{dt} = \frac{d^3 s}{dt^3}$$

Jerk is sometimes of importance in problems involving elevators and riding vehicles since it is claimed that riding comfort is dependent on a minimum value of jerk.

SPEED-TIME AND ACCELERATION-TIME CURVES. It is convenient to interpret Eqs. 2 and 5 graphically. The relation between v and t for

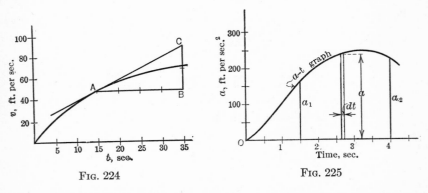

FIG. 224   FIG. 225

the rectilinear motion of a point may be shown graphically by plotting a speed-time (v–t) curve, the co-ordinates of any point on which represent simultaneous values of v and t. The slope of this curve at any point is represented by dv/dt. But $a = dv/dt$, and, hence, the slope of the $(v-t)$ curve at any point represents to some scale (depending on the scales used in plotting the curve) the acceleration of the moving point at the corresponding time. Thus, if the rectilinear motion of a point is represented by the $(v-t)$ curve in Fig. 224, the acceleration of the point when $t = 15$ sec (corresponding to point A on the $v-t$ curve) is $\dfrac{2 \times 20}{4 \times 5} = 2$ ft/sec².

Similarly, if an acceleration-time $(a-t)$ curve for the rectilinear motion of a point is plotted as indicated in Fig. 225, the area under the curve between the ordinates a_2 and a_1 represents to some scale (depending on the scales used in plotting the curve) the change in speed in the corresponding time interval $t_2 - t_1$, as is obvious from a consideration of Eq. 5 and Fig. 225.

Illustrative Problems

Problem 314. In Prob. 287 find the acceleration of the car when $\theta = 30°$.

SOLUTION. The velocity of the car corresponding to any value of θ was found to be 12 sec² θ, and, hence,

$$a = \frac{dv}{dt} = \frac{d}{dt}(12 \sec^2 \theta) = 24 \sec^2 \theta \tan \theta \, \omega$$

$$= 2.4 \sec^2 \theta \tan \theta$$

$$= 2.4 \times \frac{4}{3} \times \frac{1}{\sqrt{3}} = 1.85 \text{ ft/sec}^2 \quad \text{when} \quad \theta = 30°$$

Problem 315. Find, by use of Eq. 3 of Art. 73, the acceleration of the crosshead of a steam engine in terms of r, l, θ, and ω as defined in Prob. 288.

SOLUTION. From Prob. 288, we have

$$v = r\omega \left(\sin \theta + \frac{r}{l} \sin \theta \cos \theta \right)$$

Hence,

$$a = \frac{dv}{dt} = r\omega \left[\cos \theta + \frac{r}{l} (\cos^2 \theta - \sin^2 \theta) \right] \frac{d\theta}{dt}$$

$$= r\omega^2 \left(\cos \theta + \frac{r}{l} \cos 2\theta \right)$$

It may be noted that, when the ratio of r to l is small, the second term in the above expression becomes small, and hence the acceleration is approximately $r\omega^2 \cos \theta$, and therefore the motion of the crosshead is approximately a simple harmonic motion (Art. 75).

Problems

316. A point moves on a straight line according to the law $a = 6t^2 + 2$ where a is expressed in feet per second per second and t in seconds. If $s = 8$ ft and $v = 2$ ft/sec when $t = 0$, find the values of v and s when $t = 2$ sec.

317. Water flows in a straight pipe whose diameter is 6 in. at the rate of 1 cu ft per sec. A valve in the pipe line is operated in such a manner that the volume of water flowing is reduced at the rate of 0.1 cu ft per sec each second. Determine the acceleration of a fluid particle flowing in the pipe. *Ans.* $a = 0.509$ ft/sec^2.

318. A point starts at the origin and moves along the Y axis with constant acceleration. When $t = 3$ sec, $y = 6$ ft, and, when $t = 4$ sec, $y = 16$ ft. Find: (a) the initial velocity of the point, (b) the acceleration of the point, (c) the linear displacement during the first 2 sec, and (d) the distance traveled by the point in the first 2 sec.

319. In Fig. 209 the arm OC rotates about O with a constant angular velocity ω causing the block A to slide in the horizontal slot; blocks A and B are pinned together. When OC is in the position shown, $\theta = 30°$, and $OA = 2$ ft. Find in terms of θ and ω the linear acceleration of block A. *Ans.* $a = 2\sqrt{3}\,\omega^2 \sec^2\theta \tan\theta$.

320. Two flat circular plates 2 ft in diameter are parallel to a horizontal plane and are spaced 1 in. apart. Water is introduced through a hole in the center of the top plate and allowed to flow radially filling the space between the plates. If the water flows through the hole in the top plate at the rate of 0.5 cu ft per sec, determine the velocity and acceleration of a fluid particle at a point 6 in. from the center of the plates.

321. A car starts from rest and moves on a straight road in such a way that its acceleration at any instant is proportional to the time after starting. If the car travels a distance of 1 ft during the first second, find its speed when it has moved 8 ft from its initial position.

322. Two railway stations are connected by two straight parallel tracks. Two trains, A and B, start from rest at one station and reach the second station in 150 sec. The speed-time curve for A is shown in Fig. 226a and that for B in Fig. 226b. Train B reaches its maximum speed when $t = 80$ sec. Draw the acceleration-time curve for each train, and find the distance between the two stations. Find also the maximum speed of B. *Ans.* Distance $= 1.5$ mi; $v_{max} = 64.6$ mi/hr.

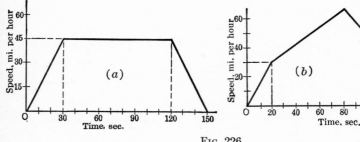

Fig. 226

323. A point starts at the origin and moves on the X axis according to the law $x = t^3 - 4t^2$. Is the speed of the point increasing or decreasing when $t = 1$? When $t = 2$? When $t = 3$?

324. An elevator is moving upward and has an upward acceleration which is increasing at the rate of 24 ft/sec^2 each second (jerk = 24 ft/sec^3). If when $t = 0$ the elevator is 2 ft above the basement floor and has an upward velocity of 4 ft/sec and an upward acceleration of 10 ft/sec^2, find its position when $t = \frac{1}{4}$ sec.

Ans. 3.38 ft above basement floor.

325. In Fig. 227 is shown the speed-displacement graph for the crosshead C of a steam engine. If the scale of abscissas is 1 in. = 1.75 ft and if BC measures 0.33 in., what is the acceleration of the crosshead when in the position shown? How may the position of C be found for which C has zero acceleration? *Ans.* $a = 443$ ft/sec^2

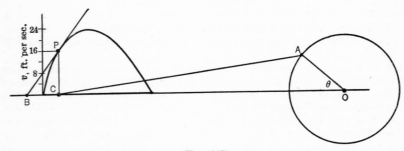

Fig. 227

326. A parachutist jumps from a balloon and falls a distance of 900 ft before his parachute starts to open. If it takes 4 sec for the parachute to open and during this time the acceleration decreases at a constant rate of 25 ft/sec^2 each second (the jerk is 25 ft/sec^3), determine the velocity of the parachutist at the instant the parachute is fully opened. (Assume the acceleration of the parachutist to be $g = 32$ ft/sec^2 before the parachute starts to open.)

327. A point starts from rest at the origin and moves along the X axis according to the law $a = 3v^{2/3}$ where a is expressed in feet per second per second and v in feet per second. Find the values of x and v when $t = 2$ sec.

Ans. $x = 4$ ft; $v = 8$ ft/sec.

328. In Fig. 228 is shown the $(v-t)$ curve for the rectilinear motion of a point. For what values of t will: (a) the acceleration of the point be zero, (b) the acceleration be a maximum, (c) the displacement be zero, and (d) the displacement be a maximum?

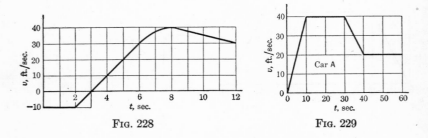

Fig. 228

Fig. 229

329. Two automobiles, A and B, start at the same time from the same place and travel in the same direction. B moves with a constant velocity of 30 ft/sec, and the velocity of A varies as shown in Fig. 229. When is car A ahead? When is B ahead? *Hint:* Draw $(s-t)$ curves for the two cars.

330. A point starts from rest and moves along the X axis for 2 sec according to the law $a = \pi \sin \frac{\pi}{2} t$ where a is expressed in feet per second per second and t in seconds. Thereafter the acceleration is constant and equal to 2 ft/sec^2 to the right. Find the velocity of the point 3 sec after starting. *Ans.* $v = 6$ ft/sec.

74 Uniformly accelerated rectilinear motion.

Many examples of rectilinear motion with constant acceleration occur in engineering practice, such as the motion of a freely falling body or of a train leaving a station under the action of a constant draw-bar pull by the locomotive. The relations among the distance, time, velocity, and acceleration, for uniformly accelerated rectilinear motion, may be deduced as follows: By definition,

$$a = \frac{\Delta v}{\Delta t} = \frac{v - u}{t}$$

or

$$v = u + at \tag{1}$$

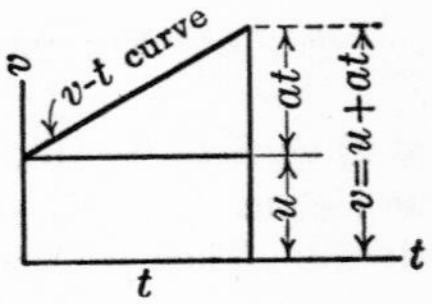

in which u and v are the initial and final velocities, respectively, corresponding to the time interval Δt or simply t. Equation 1 may also be obtained from the $(v-t)$ curve shown in Fig. 230. The slope of the curve represents the acceleration

Fig. 230

of the moving point. Hence, $a = \text{slope} = \dfrac{v - u}{t}$, or $v = u + at$.

Since the velocity increases (or decreases) uniformly, the average velocity is $\dfrac{u + v}{2}$, and the distance s traveled in time t is $\dfrac{u + v}{2} \cdot t = \dfrac{u + u + at}{2} \cdot t = (u + \frac{1}{2}at)t$. Hence,

$$s = ut + \tfrac{1}{2}at^2 \tag{2}$$

This equation also follows from the fact that s is represented by the area under the $(v-t)$ curve (Fig. 230). The rectangular part of the area is expressed by ut and the triangular part by $\frac{1}{2}at^2$. Hence, $s = ut + \frac{1}{2}at^2$. By eliminating t from Eqs. 1 and 2, the following equation is obtained:

$$v^2 = u^2 + 2as \tag{3}$$

The motion of a freely falling body is a special case of uniformly accelerated rectilinear motion, in which the acceleration is usually denoted by g and is approximately equal to 32.2 ft/sec^2.

Illustrative Problem

Problem 331. A projectile is fired from a gun with an initial velocity u making an angle θ with the horizontal (Fig. 231). Find: (a) the time of flight of the projectile to reach the level from which it started, (b) the range on a horizontal plane through the point of projection, (c) the greatest height reached, and (d) the equation to the path of the projectile. The actual motion of a projectile is influenced by a number of conditions such as rotation of the projectile due to rifling of the gun barrel, wind velocity, and air resistance. The motion of the projectile under ideal conditions (in a vacuum and without rotation) will here be considered.

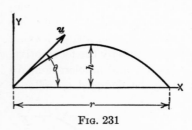

FIG. 231

SOLUTION. The motion of the projectile may be assumed to be a combination of two simultaneous motions, namely, a uniform horizontal (rectilinear) motion with a constant velocity of $u \cos \theta$ and a uniformly accelerated vertical (rectilinear) motion with a constant acceleration which is downward and equal to g ($a_y = -g = -32.2$ ft/sec^2). Let v denote the velocity after any time t. Then we may write

$$a_x = \frac{v_x - u_x}{t} = 0 \quad \text{or} \quad v_x = u_x = u \cos \theta \tag{1}$$

and

$$a_y = \frac{v_y - u_y}{t} = -g \quad \text{or} \quad v_y = u_y - gt = u \sin \theta - gt \tag{2}$$

The horizontal displacement x in any time interval t is

$$x = u \cos \theta \cdot t \tag{3}$$

and the vertical displacement y in any time interval t is the average velocity times the time interval. Hence,

$$y = u \sin \theta \cdot t - \tfrac{1}{2}gt^2 \tag{4}$$

Time of Flight. Since y equals zero when the projectile reaches the X axis, the time of flight t_r as found from Eq. 4 is

$$t_r = \frac{2u \sin \theta}{g} \tag{5}$$

Range. The range r equals the value of x in Eq. 3 when $t = t_r$. Therefore,

$$r = \frac{u^2 \sin 2\theta}{g} \tag{6}$$

Time to Reach Greatest Height. When the projectile reaches its greatest height, $v_y = 0$. Hence, the time t_h required for the projectile to reach its greatest height as found from Eq. 2 is

$$t_h = \frac{u \sin \theta}{g} \tag{7}$$

Greatest Height. The greatest height h will be given by y in Eq. 4 when t has the value t_h. Hence,

$$h = \frac{u^2 \sin^2 \theta}{2g} \tag{8}$$

The equation of the path of the projectile (called the trajectory) may be obtained by eliminating t from Eqs. 3 and 4, which gives the following equation:

$$y = x \tan \theta - \frac{gx^2}{2u^2 \cos^2 \theta} \tag{9}$$

Hence, the trajectory is a portion of a parabola with its axis vertical.

Problems

332. Deduce Eqs. 1, 2, and 3 of Art. 74 by calculus methods, starting with the equations $a = \dfrac{dv}{dt}$, $v = \dfrac{ds}{dt}$, and $a = v \dfrac{dv}{ds}$, respectively.

333. A train is moving on a straight track at a speed of 60 mi/hr toward a station at which it must stop. If the brakes can retard the train at the rate of 2 ft/sec each second, how far from the station should the brakes be applied?   *Ans.* 1936 ft.

334. A train in starting is uniformly accelerated and attains a speed of 60 mi/hr in 5 min. After it has run for a certain period of time at this speed, the brakes are applied, and it stops at a uniform rate in 4 min. If the total distance traveled is 20 mi, find the total time.   *Ans. t =* 24.5 min.

335. If the maximum allowable speed of an elevator is 800 ft/min and if it acquires this speed uniformly in a distance of 10 ft, what acceleration does it have?

336. The cam A in Fig. 232 is moving to the left, and its velocity is increasing at the rate of 20 in./sec each second. When the inclined surface of the cam comes into contact with the pin on the rod B, the velocity of the cam is 10 in./sec. What is the velocity of the rod when the cam has moved 4 in. to the left?   *Ans. v =* 8.06 in./sec.

337. A particle is dropped from rest, and in a subsequent time interval of 2 sec the particle descends 288 ft. How long had the particle been falling at the beginning of the time interval? Assume $g = 32$ ft/sec^2.

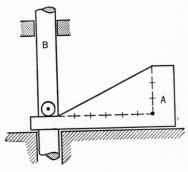

Fig. 232

338. The speed-time curve for the rectilinear motion of a point is shown in Fig. 233. Find the acceleration of the point during the period: (*a*) between 10 sec and 20 sec and (*b*) between 30 sec and 60 sec, and (*c*) the distance traveled by the point in 70 sec.   *Ans.* (*a*) $a = 0$; (*b*) $a = -0.5$ ft/sec^2; (*c*) $s = 775$ ft.

339. Boxes are carried by a conveyor belt, as shown in Fig. 234, with a constant velocity of 2 ft/sec to an inclined plane 20 ft long. The boxes slide down the plane with a constant acceleration of 0.3 ft/sec^2 until they reach a horizontal plane on which they slide with constant velocity on a smooth surface. If the spacing between the boxes is 10 ft when they are on the belt, what is the spacing when they are on the horizontal plane?

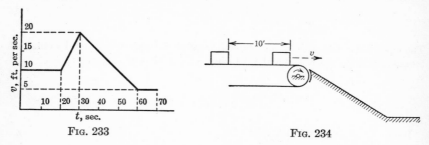

Fig. 233   Fig. 234

340. A bag of sand is dropped from a balloon that is rising with a velocity of 8 ft/sec. If the bag reaches the ground in 6 sec, how high above the ground was the balloon when the sand was dropped? Assume $g = 32$ ft/sec². *Ans.* 528 ft.

341. A stone is dropped from the ground surface into a well, and the splash is heard 3 sec later. If the velocity of sound is 1100 ft/sec, how far is the surface of the water from the ground surface? Assume $g = 32$ ft/sec². *Ans.* 132.6 ft.

342. A train starts from rest at a station A and stops at a station B which is 10 mi from A. The maximum possible acceleration of the train and the maximum possible deceleration when brakes are applied are each 12 mi/hr/min. If the maximum allowable speed is 60 mi/hr what is the least time in which the train can go from A to B? If the distance between the stations is 4 mi, what is the least time in which the train can go from A to B?

343. A stone is projected vertically upward from a point on the earth with a velocity of 96 ft/sec. Two seconds later a second stone is projected vertically upward from the same point with a velocity of 160 ft/sec. At what distance from the earth will the two stones meet? Assume $g = 32$ ft/sec².

344. A ball is thrown upward at an angle of 45° with the horizontal. It strikes a vertical wall 80 ft away at a point 20 ft above the level from which the ball was thrown. What is the initial speed of the ball? Assume $g = 32$ ft/sec².

Ans. $u = 58.4$ ft/sec.

345. A shell fired from a gun with an initial velocity of 1064 ft/sec strikes a balloon that is 1000 ft above the earth. If the angle of projection is 30°, what is the horizontal distance x of the balloon from the gun? Assume $g = 32$ ft/sec².

346. A hunter shoots at a bird which is directly overhead and is flying in a horizontal plane with a constant velocity of v ft/sec. If the bird is h ft above the hunter and the muzzle velocity of the gun is u ft/sec, show that, in order to hit the bird, the hunter should lead it: that is, aim at a point ahead of it, a distance of $\dfrac{hv}{\sqrt{u^2 - v^2}}$ ft. If $h = 100$ ft, $v = 50$ ft/sec, and $u = 800$ ft/sec, find in feet the distance the hunter should lead the bird.

347. A shell is fired from a gun on the top of a cliff 600 ft high, with a velocity of 800 ft/sec, the angle of elevation of the gun being $\sin^{-1} 0.25$. Find the range on a horizontal plane through the base of the cliff. Assume $g = 32$ ft/sec².

Ans. $R = 11,620$ ft.

75 Simple harmonic motion.

If the velocity of a point does not vary uniformly, the acceleration is not constant, and hence the equations of Art. 74 do not apply. One special case of rectilinear motion with variable acceleration is simple harmonic motion. A *simple harmonic motion* is defined as the motion of a point in a straight line such that the acceleration of the point is proportional to the distance x of the point from some fixed origin O in the line and is directed toward O. Or, expressed mathematically,

$$a = \frac{d^2x}{dt^2} = -kx \tag{1}$$

where k is a constant, and the negative sign indicates that the sense of the acceleration is opposite to that of the displacement x (Fig. 235); that is, a is negative when x is positive, and positive when x is negative.

The student should interpret physically Eq. 1 by describing in detail the motion of the point. Thus, for the motion of the point represented in Fig. 235, he should be able to show that the moving point oscillates between two fixed points (A and B, say) on the line that are equally distant from and on opposite sides of O. The motion of the point from A to B

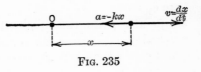

FIG. 235

and back again to A constitutes one cycle, and the time required for one cycle is called the *period*. The number of oscillations per unit time is called the *frequency*, and the maximum distance OA (or OB) of the point from O is called the *amplitude*.

The student should also be able to state the positions of the point when the velocity is zero and when a maximum, and the positions when the acceleration is zero and when a maximum.

One example of a simple harmonic motion is the motion of a body suspended from the lower end of a helical spring (Fig. 238) which is allowed to vibrate freely. The motion of the crosshead of a steam engine closely approximates a harmonic motion if the ratio of the length of the connecting rod to that of the crank is large (see Prob. 315). The motion of an oscillating pendulum also approximates closely a simple harmonic motion if the arc through which the pendulum swings is small. In fact, many of the vibrational motions so common and important in engineering problems may be assumed without serious error to be simple harmonic motions.

A convenient method of studying the features of a simple harmonic motion is to consider the motion of a point on a circular path with constant speed, and hence with constant angular velocity with respect to the center of the circle. The motion of the projection of this point on a diameter of the circle is harmonic as may be shown as follows. If the point M in Fig. 236 moves on a circle of radius r with constant speed v_M and angular velocity ω, and the time required for the point to move from A to the position shown is t, then,

$$\theta = \omega t \quad \text{and} \quad x = r \cos \theta = r \cos \omega t \tag{2}$$

Hence, the velocity of P, the projection of M on the horizontal diameter of the circle, is

$$v = \frac{dx}{dt} = -\omega r \sin \omega t = -\omega y \tag{3}$$

and

$$a = \frac{d^2 x}{dt^2} = -\omega^2 r \cos \omega t = -\omega^2 x \tag{4}$$

Therefore, the motion of P is harmonic, and the constant k in Eq. 1 is here equal to ω^2. It should be observed that the period of oscillation of the point P is the time required for the point M to make one complete revolution, and hence, if the angular velocity ω of the point M (sometimes called the *circular frequency*) is expressed in radians per second, the period T in seconds and the frequency f in cycles per second are expressed by the equations

$$T = \frac{2\pi}{\omega} \quad \text{and} \quad f = \frac{\omega}{2\pi} \tag{5}$$

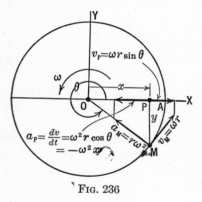

`Fig. 236

The linear velocity of M is $r\omega$ tangent to the circle, and the linear acceleration of M, as will be shown in Art. 76, is $r\omega^2$ toward the center of the circle; it should be observed that the linear displacement, velocity, and acceleration of the point P are the x components of the displacement, velocity, and acceleration, respectively, of the point M.

It is convenient to study a simple harmonic motion by means of the displacement-time, velocity-time, and acceleration-time curves. Consider for example the mechanism shown in Fig. 237a in which a crank pin C moves on a circle of radius r with constant angular velocity ω as it slides in a slot in the crosshead (this is called a Scotch crosshead).

The motion of the piston B is the same as the motion of the projection of C on the X axis and hence is harmonic. The amplitude A of the motion of the piston B (and also of the crosshead) is equal to r, the radius of the circle. The displacement-time curve for the motion of B is shown in Fig. 237b, and the velocity-time and acceleration-time curves are shown in Fig. 237c. It should be noted that at either end of the stroke

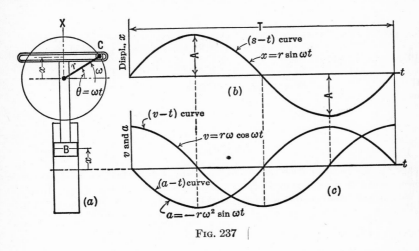

FIG. 237

v is zero and a is a maximum and that at the center of the stroke a is zero and v is a maximum. Particular attention should be called to the fact that, when v is equal to zero, a is a maximum; the student is likely to make the mistake of reasoning that $a = dv/dt$, and hence, when $v = 0$, a must also be zero. In certain types of rectilinear motion, including simple harmonic motion, the velocity may be changing rapidly through its zero value, and hence dv/dt may be large when $v = 0$. Or, to state the same idea in mathematical language, the first derivative of a function is not necessarily equal to zero when the function is equal to zero.

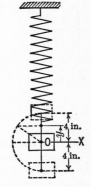

FIG. 238

Illustrative Problem

Problem 348. A body having a weight W is supported by a helical spring as shown in Fig. 238. The body is pulled down a distance of 4 in. from its equilibrium position OX and is then released and allowed to oscillate about the equilibrium position with a simple harmonic motion. The weight of the body and the stiffness of the spring are such that the acceleration of the body for any value of y is $a = d^2y/dt^2 = -60y$. Find the amplitude A and the period T of the motion. Find also the maximum velocity and maximum acceleration of the body.

SOLUTION. The amplitude is obviously $A = 4$ in. The value of ω in Eq. 4 is $\sqrt{60} = 7.75$ rad/sec, and hence the motion of the body is the same as the motion of the projection on the Y axis of a point that moves on a circle whose radius is 4 in. with a constant angular velocity of 7.75 rad/sec. Therefore, the period is

$$T = \frac{2\pi}{7.75} = 0.81 \text{ sec}$$

The maximum values of v and a occur when x and y in Eqs. 3 and 4 have their maximum values: that is, when x and y are each equal to 4 in. Hence, the maximum values of v and a are

$$v_{max} = 4\omega = 4 \times 7.75 = 31.0 \text{ in./sec} = 2.58 \text{ ft/sec}$$

$$a_{max} = 4\omega^2 = 4 \times (7.75)^2 = 240 \text{ in./sec}^2 = 20 \text{ ft/sec}^2$$

Problems

349. If the body in Prob. 348 is pulled down 3 in. instead of 4 in. and then released, what will be the period and the frequency of the motion?

350. A point moves with a simple harmonic motion the amplitude of which is ¾ in. If the period is ½ sec, determine the maximum velocity and maximum acceleration.   *Ans.* $v_{max} = 9.42$ in./sec; $a_{max} = 118.4$ in./sec^2.

351. In Fig. 239 the body C is raised by the pressure of the roller A on the cam B as the crank OA rotates with constant angular velocity ω. The length of OA is 10 in. If the linear velocity of A is 5 in./sec and the linear velocity of C is 4 in./sec when OA is in the position shown, determine the angle θ, and find the velocity of C in terms of t, assuming $t = 0$ when $\theta = 0$. Also find the magnitude and direction of the acceleration of C when OA is in the position shown.

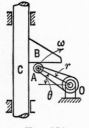

352. The maximum acceleration of a point that has a simple harmonic motion is 200 ft/sec^2, and the frequency is 4 cycles per second. Find the amplitude of the motion and the maximum velocity of the point.   *Ans.* $A = 0.317$ ft; $v = 7.96$ ft/sec.

353. If the angular velocity of C in Fig. 237a is 100 rpm and the radius r is 4 in., find the velocity and acceleration of B ½ sec after B has reached its maximum positive velocity.

Fig. 239

354. The acceleration of a point which has a simple harmonic motion is 6 in./sec^2 when the point is at one end of its path. If the velocity of the point is 2 in./sec when the point is 1 in. from one end of its path, find the length of the path.   *Ans.* 1.5 in.

355. A point moves with a simple harmonic motion such that its speed is 12 in./sec when it is 3 in. from the center of its path and 9 in./sec when it is 4 in. from the center. Determine the period and the amplitude of the motion. Determine also the maximum velocity and the maximum acceleration of the point.

    Ans. $T = 2.09$ sec; $A = 5$ in.; $v_{max} = 15$ in./sec; $a_{max} = 45$ in./sec^2.

356. The length r of the crank of the steam-engine mechanism represented in Fig. 208 is 5 in., and the length l of the connecting rod is 50 in. The engine runs at a constant speed of 300 rpm. If the motion of the crosshead B is assumed to be a simple harmonic motion, find the acceleration of the crosshead when the angle θ is 30°. Compare this value of the acceleration with the value obtained by using the expression found for the acceleration in Prob. 315.

76   Acceleration in curvilinear motion.   Tangential and normal components of acceleration. Let a point move with varying speed along the curved path shown in Fig. 240a, and let it be required to find the magnitude and direction of the linear acceleration of the moving point, at the instant it is at any point A on the path, from the defining equation

$$a = \lim_{\Delta t \doteq 0} \frac{\Delta v}{\Delta t}$$

The designation *linear* acceleration is used to distinguish it from *angular* acceleration which will be discussed in the next article.

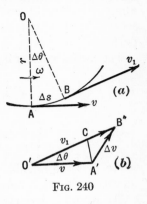

Let the time required for a small displacement AB (or Δs) be denoted by Δt, and let the velocities at A and B be denoted by v and v_1, respectively.   Also let the radius of curvature at A be denoted by r and the angular displacement with respect to the center of curvature O be denoted by $\Delta\theta$.   Now if, in Fig. 240b, $O'A'$ and $O'B'$ be laid off to represent in direction and magnitude v and v_1, respectively, the change in velocity Δv is represented by the vector $A'B'$ (Art. 63).   The

Fig. 240

average acceleration during the time interval Δt is therefore $A'B'/\Delta t$, and the instantaneous acceleration at A is the limit of this ratio as Δt (and also Δs and $\Delta\theta$) approaches zero.   If, in Fig. 240b, $O'C$ is laid off equal to $O'A'$ (or v), $A'B'$ may be expressed as the vector sum of $A'C$ and CB', and hence the acceleration may be expressed as the vector sum of two component accelerations as follows:

$$a = \lim_{\Delta t \doteq 0} \frac{A'B'}{\Delta t} = \lim_{\Delta t \doteq 0} \frac{A'C \nrightarrow CB'}{\Delta t}$$

$$= \lim_{\Delta t \doteq 0} \frac{A'C}{\Delta t} \nrightarrow \lim_{\Delta t \doteq 0} \frac{CB'}{\Delta t}$$

Since $A'C$ would represent the change in the velocity if the velocity were constant in magnitude and changed only in direction, and since the length of CB' represents the change in the magnitude, only, of the velocity, it is evident that the first of the two components is the acceleration resulting from a change in the direction, only, of the velocity, and the second component is the acceleration resulting from a change in the magnitude, only, of the velocity.

The direction and magnitude of each of these two component accelerations defined by the last two terms of the foregoing equation will now be found.

The direction of the first of the two components is the limiting direction of $A'C$ as Δt (and $\Delta\theta$) approaches zero. As $\Delta\theta$ approaches zero, the angle $O'A'C$ approaches 90°, and hence in the limit $A'C$ is perpendicular to $O'A'$ (or v), and therefore the first term represents the component of acceleration normal to the path at A. This component is directed toward the center of curvature and is denoted by a_n. Similarly, the direction of the second component is the limiting direction of CB' as $\Delta\theta$ approaches 0 and therefore is in the direction of $O'A'$ (or v). Hence, the second term represents the component of acceleration tangent to the path at A and is denoted by a_t.

The magnitudes of a_n and a_t may be found as follows:

$$a_n = \lim_{\Delta t \doteq 0} \frac{A'C}{\Delta t} = \lim_{\Delta t \doteq 0} \frac{2v \sin \frac{1}{2}\Delta\theta}{\Delta t}$$

$$= v \lim_{\Delta t \doteq 0} \frac{\Delta\theta}{\Delta t} = v \frac{d\theta}{dt} = v\omega$$

where ω is the angular velocity of the point relative to the center of curvature O. And, since $v = r\omega$, a_n may also be expressed as $r\omega^2$ or v^2/r.

The magnitude of the tangential component is

$$a_t = \lim_{\Delta t \doteq 0} \frac{CB'}{\Delta t} = \lim_{\Delta t \doteq 0} \frac{v_1 - v}{\Delta t} = \frac{dv}{dt}$$

and, since $v = ds/dt$, a_t may also be expressed as d^2s/dt^2; and as indicated in Art. 73 this may also be written $a_t = v \frac{dv}{ds} = \frac{1}{2} \frac{d(v^2)}{ds}$.

Summarizing, we may state two important theorems as follows:

I. When the velocity v of a particle or point changes in magnitude, an acceleration is produced the value of which is dv/dt; its direction at any instant is parallel to that of the velocity: that is, tangent to the path at the point at which the particle is located at the instant. This acceleration is called the tangential component of the total linear acceleration of the moving particle and may be expressed in several forms as follows:

$$a_t = \frac{dv}{dt} = \frac{d^2s}{dt^2} = v \frac{dv}{ds}$$

II. When the velocity v of a particle or point changes in direction, an acceleration is produced the value of which is $v\omega = r\omega^2 =$

v^2/r; its direction, at any instant, is perpendicular to the velocity and directed towards the center of curvature of the path, at the point where the particle is located at the instant. Thus the normal component of the linear acceleration of the moving particle may be expressed in several forms as follows:

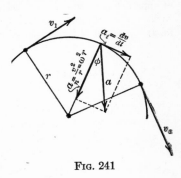

FIG. 241

$$a_n = v\omega = r\omega^2 = \frac{v^2}{r}$$

The total linear acceleration (in contrast to angular acceleration) of a point that moves on a curved path with varying speed is the resultant, or vector sum, of the normal and tangential components of acceleration as shown in Fig. 241. The magnitude and direction of the linear acceleration may be found from the following equations:

$$a = a_n \mathbin{+\!\!\!\rightarrow} a_t = \sqrt{a_n{}^2 + a_t{}^2}$$

$$\tan \phi = a_t/a_n$$

Illustrative Problems

Problem 357. A point P moves clockwise on a circular path of radius 2 ft. The angular velocity of the point with respect to the center of the circle is proportional to the square of the time after starting: that is, $\omega = kt^2$ where k is a constant and ω and t are expressed in radians per second and seconds, respectively. If the speed of the point is 64 ft/sec when $t = 2$ sec, what is the linear velocity and the linear acceleration of P when $t = \frac{1}{2}$ sec. Assume P to be at the top of the circle when $t = \frac{1}{2}$ sec as shown in Fig. 242.

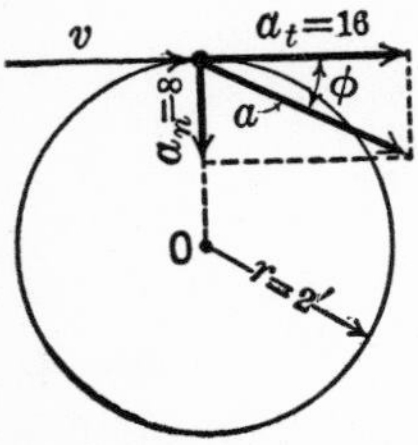

SOLUTION. The linear velocity is $v = r\omega = 2\omega = 2kt^2$, and, since $v = 64$ ft/sec when $t = 2$ sec, we have

$$64 = 2k \times 4 \quad \text{or} \quad k = 8; \qquad \therefore \ v = 16t^2$$

Hence, when $t = \frac{1}{2}$ sec;

FIG. 242

$$v_P = 16 \times (\tfrac{1}{2})^2 = 4 \text{ ft/sec}$$

and the tangential and normal components of the linear acceleration of P are

$$(a_P)_t = \frac{dv}{dt} = \frac{d}{dt}(16t^2)$$

$$= 32t = 16 \text{ ft/sec}^2 \quad \text{when} \quad t = \tfrac{1}{2} \text{ sec}$$

$$(a_P)_n = \frac{v^2}{r} = \frac{4^2}{2} = 8 \text{ ft/sec}^2 \quad \text{when} \quad t = \tfrac{1}{2} \text{ sec}$$

$$\therefore \ a_P = \sqrt{16^2 + 8^2} = 17.9 \text{ ft/sec}^2$$

Also

$$\tan \phi = \tfrac{8}{16}; \qquad \therefore \ \phi = 26° \ 34'$$

Problem 358. If a sphere as shown in Fig. 243 is held in a wind whose velocity of approach is v_0, the paths of the air particles in contact with the front part of the surface of the sphere follow the contour of the sphere, and the velocity of a particle in any position is given approximately by the equation $v = \tfrac{3}{2} \ v_0 \sin \beta$ where β

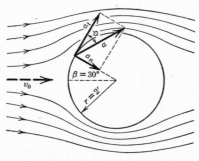

Fig. 243

is the angle between the wind direction and the radius to the particle as shown in Fig. 243. Determine the linear acceleration of a particle at a point on the sphere if $\beta = 30°$, $v_0 = 30$ mi/hr, and the radius of the sphere is 2 ft.

SOLUTION.

$$a_t = v \frac{dv}{ds} = \frac{3}{2} v_0 \sin \beta \times \frac{3}{2} v_0 \cos \beta \frac{d\beta}{ds}$$

Since $ds = r \, d\beta$, $d\beta/ds = 1/r$, and, hence,

$$a_t = \frac{9}{8} \frac{v_0^2}{r} \sin 2\beta = \frac{9}{8} \times \frac{1}{2} \times 44^2 \times 0.866 = 943 \ \text{ft/sec}^2$$

$$a_n = \frac{v^2}{r} = \frac{(\tfrac{3}{2} \times 44 \times \tfrac{1}{2})^2}{2} = \frac{33^2}{2} = 544 \ \text{ft/sec}^2$$

$$\therefore \ a = \sqrt{943^2 + 544^2} = 1090 \ \text{ft/sec}^2$$

and

$$\phi = \tan^{-1} \tfrac{544}{943} = 30°$$

77 Angular acceleration. The angular acceleration of a line is the time rate of change of the angular velocity of the line. The angular acceleration of a moving point with respect to a fixed point or pole is the angular acceleration of the line joining the moving point to the pole. If the angular velocity ω of the point changes uniformly, the angular acceleration α is expressed by the ratio of any change $\Delta\omega$ in the angular velocity to the corresponding time interval Δt. Thus,

$$\alpha = \frac{\Delta\omega}{\Delta t} = \frac{\omega_2 - \omega_1}{t_2 - t_1}$$

If the angular velocity of the point does not change uniformly, the acceleration at any instant is the average acceleration during an indefinitely small time interval including the instant. Or, expressed mathematically, the instantaneous angular acceleration is

$$\alpha = \lim_{\Delta t \doteq 0} \frac{\Delta \omega}{\Delta t} = \frac{d\omega}{dt}$$

Since $\omega = \dfrac{d\theta}{dt}$ and $\dfrac{d\omega}{dt} = \dfrac{d\omega}{d\theta}\dfrac{d\theta}{dt}$, the foregoing expression may also be written

$$\alpha = \frac{d\omega}{dt} = \frac{d^2\theta}{dt^2} = \omega \frac{d\omega}{d\theta}$$

The most convenient form for use in the solution of problems depends on the data given in the problem. The relations among θ, t, ω, and α may be shown graphically by diagrams similar to those used in Arts. 73 and 74 for s, t, v, and a.

The unit of angular acceleration is any convenient unit of angular velocity per unit of time, such as degree per second per second (deg/sec^2), revolution per minute per second (rev/min/sec), or radian per second per second (rad/sec^2).

78 Uniformly accelerated circular motion. Many problems involving the motion of a point on a circular path with constant angular acceleration occur in engineering practice. For such a motion the following relations among the angular displacement, angular velocity, angular acceleration, and time may be deduced in a manner similar to that used in Art. 74:

$$\omega = \omega_0 + \alpha t \tag{1}$$

$$\theta = \omega_0 t + \tfrac{1}{2}\alpha t^2 \tag{2}$$

$$\omega^2 = \omega_0{}^2 + 2\alpha\theta \tag{3}$$

where ω_0 and ω denote the initial and final angular velocities, respectively corresponding to any time interval t, and θ and α denote the angular displacement and angular acceleration, respectively. The derivation of the foregoing equations will be left to the student.

79 Relation between linear and angular accelerations. The relation between the linear and angular accelerations of a point that moves on a circular path may be found as follows: In Fig. 244 let a point move on the circular path shown, O being the center of the path and r the radius.   If the magnitude of the velocity of the point changes (assumed to increase), there is, at any instant during the change, a tangential acceleration given by the equation $a_t = dv/dt$.   But $v = r\omega$, and therefore $a_t = \dfrac{d}{dt}\,(r\omega) = r\dfrac{d\omega}{dt}$.   And, since $\dfrac{d\omega}{dt}$ is the angular acceleration α of the point at the instant, we have

$$a_t = r\alpha$$

Therefore, the tangential component of the linear acceleration, at any instant, of a point moving on a circular path is equal to the product of the radius of the circle and the angular acceleration of the point about the center of the circle at the same instant.

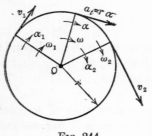

If the particle does not move on a circular path, the equation is also true provided that r is the radius of curvature of the path at the given position of the particle and that α is the angular acceleration of the particle with reference to the center of curvature.

The normal component $r\omega^2$ of the linear acceleration of the particle (not shown in Fig. 244), unlike the tangential component, is independent of the angular acceleration; it depends on the angular velocity at the instant, and not on the rate at which the angular velocity is changing at the instant.

FIG. 244

Problems for Articles 76 to 79

359. Derive the equations of Art. 78 by calculus methods, starting with the equations $\alpha = d\omega/dt$, $\omega = d\theta/dt$, and $\alpha = \omega\,d\omega/d\theta$.

360. A quarter-mile track is made up of two straight parallel sides connected at the ends by two semi-circles, each having a radius of 80 ft.   A boy runs the quarter mile in 50 sec at uniform speed.   What is the acceleration of the boy: (a) when on the straight track and (b) when on the curved portion?   *Ans.* $a = 0$; $a = 8.71$ ft/sec^2.

361. A point moves on a circle according to the law $s = t^3 + 3t$, s and t being measured in feet and seconds, respectively.   If the acceleration of the point is 13 ft/sec^2 when $t = 2$ sec, what is the radius of the circle?   *Ans.* $r = 45$ ft.

362. An airplane is flying in a straight horizontal path at an elevation h and a constant velocity v.   The airplane flies directly above a searchlight whose beam is following the airplane.   Determine the angular velocity and angular acceleration of the searchlight beam in terms of h, v, and the distance x that the airplane has flown from its position directly above the searchlight.

363. A flywheel 8 ft in diameter turns so that its angular velocity changes uniformly from 100 rpm to 10 rpm during a period of 4 sec.   Find the tangential component of the linear acceleration of a point on the rim during the 4-sec period. Find the total acceleration of a point on the rim at the end of the period.

364. Two pulleys are connected so that they turn together about the center O (Fig. 245), causing the body A to unwind and the body B to wind up. If the angular velocity of the points M and P increases uniformly from 10 rpm to 20 rpm during a period of $\frac{1}{2}$ sec, find: (a) the tangential acceleration of each of the two points at any instant during the $\frac{1}{2}$ sec, (b) the acceleration of A and of B, (c) the total acceleration of M at the beginning, and of P at the end, of the $\frac{1}{2}$-sec period. Assume that M at the beginning of the $\frac{1}{2}$-sec period and P at the end of the period are in the positions shown.

Ans. $(a_M)_t = a_A = 1.57$ ft/sec^2; $(a_P)_t = a_B = 2.09$ ft/sec^2; $a_M = 1.77$ ft/sec^2;
$a_P = 4.85$ ft/sec^2.

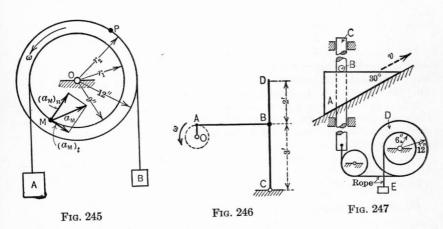

Fig. 245	Fig. 246	Fig. 247

365. The rod CD in Fig. 246 is made to oscillate by the crank OA and connecting rod AB. The angular velocity of OA is 4 rad/sec, and the angular acceleration is 8 rad/sec^2, both counterclockwise. In the position shown AB is perpendicular to OA and to CD. Thus, the velocity of A is equal to the velocity of B, and the tangential component of the acceleration of A is equal to the tangential component of the acceleration of B. The length of OA is 6 in. Find the tangential and normal components of the linear acceleration of D.

366. If at a certain instant the velocity v of A in Fig. 247 is 4 in./sec and is increasing uniformly at the rate of 10 in./sec^2, find the linear acceleration of C, the angular acceleration of the drum D, and the linear acceleration of E.

Ans. $a_C = 5$ in./sec^2; $\alpha = 0.417$ rad/sec^2; $a_E = 2.5$ in./sec^2.

367. A train, while traveling on a curve of $\frac{1}{2}$-mi radius, changes its speed uniformly from 30 mi/hr to 40 mi/hr in 20 sec. What is the total linear acceleration of the train at the beginning and at the end of the 20-sec period?

368. A point starts from rest and moves on a circle whose radius is 2 ft in such a way that the rate of change of speed at any instant is proportional to the time after starting. If the point makes one revolution in the first second, find its speed at the end of 8 revolutions.   *Ans.* $v = 150.8$ ft/sec.

369. The velocity of water flowing over a spillway (Fig. 248) is 12 ft/sec at a point A where the radius of curvature is 4 ft. If the magnitude of the velocity of the water at this point is changing at the rate of $\frac{1}{3}$ ft/sec per inch of travel, determine the acceleration of the water.

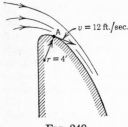

370. The pilot of a dive bomber pulls out of a dive by changing his course to a circle in a vertical plane. If the bomber travels at a constant speed of 400 mi/hr, determine the minimum radius of the circle in order that the bomber not exceed an acceleration of $5g$ (5 times the acceleration of gravity). Will the magnitude of the acceleration of the bomber when it is at the lowest point on the circle be the same as that for other positions on the circle?

Fig. 248

371. An electron is revolving in the orbit of a betatron, the diameter of the orbit being 66 in. If the velocity of the electron is 5×10^8 ft/sec and is assumed to be constant in magnitude, determine the linear acceleration of the electron.

Ans. $a = 9.09 \times 10^{16}$ ft/sec².

372. A point starts from rest and moves on a circle whose radius is 48 ft with a constant angular acceleration with respect to the center of the circle. When it has moved along the circle 32 ft from its initial position, the speed is 24 ft/sec. Find the magnitude of the linear acceleration of the point in this position.

373. A flywheel having a radius of 4 ft rotates with constant angular acceleration through 3 radians in a time interval of $\frac{1}{2}$ sec. If the angular velocity at the end of the interval is twice that at the beginning, find the total linear acceleration of a point on the rim at the beginning of the interval.   *Ans.* $a = 71.7$ ft/sec².

374. A point P moves along a certain curve according to the law $s = 6t^2 - 14t$. At the end of 2 sec, P is at a point on the curve for which the radius of curvature is 20 ft. Find the magnitude of the linear acceleration of P at that instant.

80 Axial components of acceleration. In Art. 76 the acceleration of a point was determined as the vector sum of the components of acceleration tangent and normal, respectively, to the path of the point. It is sometimes more convenient, however, to determine the acceleration of a point as the vector sum of the components of acceleration, a_x and a_y, parallel to the co-ordinate axes.

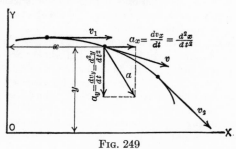

Fig. 249

Since the component, in a given direction, of the acceleration of a point is the rate of change of the component of the velocity of the point in the given direction, the axial components of acceleration (Fig. 249) are

$$a_x = \frac{dv_x}{dt} \quad \text{and} \quad a_y = \frac{dv_y}{dt}$$

And, since

$$v_x = \frac{dx}{dt} \quad \text{and} \quad v_y = \frac{dy}{dt}$$

we find that

$$a_x = \frac{d^2x}{dt^2} \quad \text{and} \quad a_y = \frac{d^2y}{dt^2}$$

In order to determine the axial components from the foregoing equations, v_x (or x) and v_y (or y) must be expressed in terms of t, unless v_x and v_y change uniformly, in which case

$$a_x = \frac{\Delta v_x}{\Delta t} = \frac{v''_x - v'_x}{t_2 - t_1} \quad \text{and} \quad a_y = \frac{\Delta v_y}{\Delta t} = \frac{v''_y - v'_y}{t_2 - t_1}$$

where v' and v'' are the velocities at the beginning and end of the time interval $\Delta t (= t_2 - t_1)$.

It is important to note that, although the component of velocity in a given direction may be zero, it does not necessarily follow that the component of acceleration of the point in that direction is zero. For example, a ball thrown horizontally from a window has no vertical velocity just as it leaves the window, that is, $v_y = 0$, but the ball has an acceleration, the vertical component of which is $a_y = g = 32.2 \text{ ft/sec}^2$. In other words, v_y is changing through its zero value at the rate of 32.2 ft/sec^2. Likewise, the velocity of the crosshead of a steam engine is zero at the end of the stroke, but its acceleration dv/dt has a large value as the velocity changes through its zero value; also a point moving on a circular path has no velocity component normal to the path, but there is a normal acceleration the magnitude of which, as shown in Art. 76, is v^2/r.

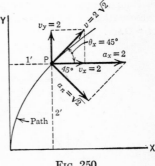

FIG. 250

Illustrative Problem

Problem 375. A particle P (Fig. 250) moves in the xy plane so that $a_x = 2 \text{ ft/sec}^2$, $a_y = 0$.

When $t = 0$, the particle is at the origin, and its velocity is 2 ft/sec in the positive y direction. Determine the equation to the path of the particle and the position of the particle when $t = 1$ sec. For this position determine the magnitude and direction of the velocity of the particle. Determine also the normal component of the acceleration and the radius of curvature of the path.

SOLUTION.

$$a_x = 2 \text{ ft/sec}^2 \qquad\qquad a_y = 0$$

$$v_x = 2t + C_1, \quad (C_1 = 0) \qquad v_y = C_3, \qquad (C_3 = 2)$$

$$x = t^2 + C_2, \quad (C_2 = 0) \qquad y = 2t + C_4, \quad (C_4 = 0)$$

The constants of integration were found from the initial conditions $x = 0$, $y = 0$, $v_x = 0$, and $v_y = 2$ ft/sec when $t = 0$. Hence, the equation to the path in parametric form is $x = t^2$, $y = 2t$. Eliminating t from the last two equations, we find the path to be the parabola $y^2 = 4x$. When $t = 1$ sec, $x = 1$ ft and $y = 2$ ft. Also $v_x = 2$ ft/sec, and $v_y = 2$ ft/sec. Hence, the velocity of the particle is $2\sqrt{2}$ ft/sec tangent to the path, as shown in Fig. 250, and $\theta_x = 45°$. The normal to the path makes an angle of $45°$ with the X axis, and hence $a_n = 2 \cos 45° = \sqrt{2}$ ft/sec^2. Therefore,

$$r = \frac{v^2}{a_n} = \frac{(2\sqrt{2})^2}{\sqrt{2}} = 5.66 \text{ ft}$$

Problems

376. A point starts at the origin and moves on the parabola $y^2 = 4x$ according to the law $v_x = \frac{1}{2}t$, where x and y are expressed in feet and t in seconds. Show in a figure the location of the point when $t = 2$ sec. Find a_x and a_y when $t = 2$ sec, and represent by vectors in the figure.

377. A ball is thrown from a room through an open window. As the ball passes over the window sill, its velocity is 30 ft/sec in a horizontal direction. What is the radius of curvature of the path of the ball at this point?   *Ans. r = 27.9 ft.*

378. If the direction of the velocity of the ball in the preceding problem as it passes over the window sill is upward at an angle of $30°$ with the horizontal, determine the radius of curvature of the path and the rate of change of speed of the ball at that instant.

379. A point starts from rest and moves in the xy plane in such a way that the x component of its acceleration is proportional to the time after starting, and the y component of its acceleration is constant and equal to 4 ft/sec^2. If the linear acceleration of the point is 5 ft/sec^2 when $t = 1$ sec, find the linear velocity when $t = 2$ sec.   *Ans. v = 10 ft/sec; $\theta_x = 53° 8'$.*

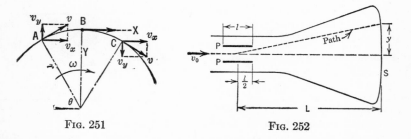

FIG. 251   FIG. 252

380. A point moves with constant speed on a circle of radius r as indicated in Fig. 251. Let the X and Y axes be chosen as indicated in the figure, and derive expressions for a_x and a_y, the rates of change in the x and y directions of the velocity, as the point moves from A to C. From these expressions find the components of the accelerations in the x and y directions when the point is at B.

381. In Fig. 252 is shown a part of a cathode-ray tube. An electron enters the space between the plates P, P with a horizontal velocity v_0. While it is between the plates, it has a constant upward acceleration a normal to the plates, and, after it leaves the plates, it has no acceleration. Determine the deflection y of the electron on the screen S. Express the answer in terms of v_0, a, l, and L.

382. A point moves along that branch of the curve $x^2 y = 4$ that lies in the first quadrant with constant speed. Determine the position of the point when the magnitudes of the x and y components of its acceleration are equal.   *Ans.* $x = 2$; $y = 1$.

383. A point moves on the curve $y^2 = 4x$ according to the law $y = 2t$ where x and y are expressed in feet and t in seconds. Find the magnitude and direction of the acceleration of the point when $t = 1$ sec. Find also the tangential and normal components of the acceleration.

Ans. $a = 2$ ft/sec^2; $\theta_x = 0$; $a_n = a_t = 1.414$ ft/sec^2.

384. A particle moves on the path $xy = 4$ according to the law $x = 2t^2$. (a) Find the x and y components of the velocity and of the acceleration when $t = 1$. (b) Determine the total acceleration by combining the components graphically. (c) Find the tangential and normal components graphically by resolving the total acceleration in the tangential and normal directions.

385. If the velocity of body C in Fig. 239 is 2 ft/sec upward when $\theta = 30°$ and is decreasing at the rate of 4 ft/sec^2, determine the linear acceleration of the center of the roller A. The length of OA is 16 in.   *Ans.* $a = 4.62$ ft/sec^2; $\theta_x = 300°$.

81   Relative motion.

In the preceding articles, the motion of a point or particle is described or defined with reference to a set of co-ordinate axes (or a body), which is assumed to be fixed in space. All bodies in the universe, however, are in motion, and therefore all motions of points or bodies are relative. In most practical problems, the earth or any set of co-ordinate axes fixed with respect to the earth may be considered to be fixed in space, and hereafter the motion of a point as defined with respect to any reference frame that is fixed with respect to the earth will be regarded as the *absolute* motion of the point. The motion of a point defined or described with respect to a reference frame that is moving with respect to the earth is called the *relative* motion of the point with respect to such a reference frame.

In the preceding paragraph the motion of a point relative to a body or reference frame is considered. In some problems, however, the motion of a point relative to another *point* is required. The motion of one point relative to another point is the motion of the one point described with reference to a set of axes which does not rotate and whose origin coincides and moves with the other point. The relation between the absolute motions of two points A and B (assumed for convenience to be moving in a plane) and the relative motion of A with respect to B may be expressed by an important theorem which may be stated in two forms as follows:

I. The absolute displacement, velocity, or acceleration of A is the geometric or vector sum of the relative displacement, velocity, or acceleration, respectively, of A with respect to B and the absolute displacement, velocity, or acceleration, respectively, of B.

II. The relative displacement, velocity, or acceleration of A with respect to B is the vector difference of the absolute displacement, velocity, or acceleration, respectively, of A and the absolute displacement, velocity, or acceleration, respectively, of B.

This theorem may be expressed in the form of equations as follows:

$$s_A = s_{A/B} \twoheadrightarrow s_B \quad \text{or} \quad s_{A/B} = s_A \rightarrow s_B$$

$$v_A = v_{A/B} \twoheadrightarrow v_B \quad \text{or} \quad v_{A/B} = v_A \rightarrow v_B$$

$$a_A = a_{A/B} \twoheadrightarrow a_B \quad \text{or} \quad a_{A/B} = a_A \rightarrow a_B$$

where s_A and s_B denote the absolute displacements of A and B, respectively, and $s_{A/B}$ denotes the relative displacement of A with respect to B, and similarly for velocities and accelerations.

It should be noted that the motion of one moving point with respect to another moving point is the motion that the one point *appears* to have to an observer moving with the other point.

RELATIVE DISPLACEMENT. As applying to displacements, the foregoing theorem is nearly self-evident. To illustrate, let A and B be two points that have the same initial position as shown in Fig. 253. Let the point A be given a displacement $s_A = AA_1$ and the point B a displacement $s_B = BB_1$. The displacement of A relative to B is its displacement relative to the co-ordinate axes X_1 and Y_1 which move with the point B and is represented by the vector $s_{A/B} = B_1A_1$. From the figure it is evident that

$$s_A = s_{A/B} \twoheadrightarrow s_B \quad \text{or} \quad s_{A/B} = s_A \rightarrow s_B' \qquad (1)$$

It is sometimes convenient when solving problems to replace Eq. 1, which is a vector equation, by two algebraic equations. Thus, from Fig. 253 it is seen that

$$x_A = x_{A/B} + x_B \quad \text{or} \quad (s_A)_x = (s_{A/B})_x + (s_B)_x$$
$$y_A = y_{A/B} + y_B \quad \text{or} \quad (s_A)_y = (s_{A/B})_y + (s_B)_y \qquad (2)$$

Equations 2 will be used later to derive the relative motion equations for velocities and for accelerations.

If the points A and B do not have the same initial position, the reasoning is changed but little, the final conclusion being the same as stated in Eq. 1 as will be evident from a study of Fig. 254.

Instead of considering the relative displacement of A with respect to B to be the vector difference of the absolute displacements of A and B, it may also be considered to be the change in the relative positions of the two points. Thus, in Fig. 254, $s_{A/B} = B_1A_1 \;+\!\!\!+\; A_1B' = B_1A_1 \rightarrow B'A_1 = B_1A_1 \rightarrow BA$. The vector B_1A_1 represents the final position of A relative to B, and BA represents the initial position of A relative to B. Therefore, the relative displacement of A with respect to B is the

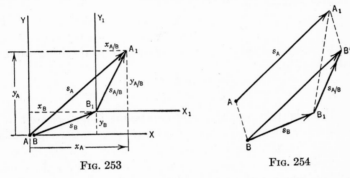

FIG. 253   FIG. 254

vector difference of the vectors that represent the final and initial positions of A with respect to B.

RELATIVE VELOCITY. If each of the terms in Eqs. 2 is differentiated with respect to time, we obtain the equations

$$(v_A)_x = (v_{A/B})_x + (v_B)_x$$
$$(v_A)_y = (v_{A/B})_y + (v_B)_y$$

(3)

By adding Eqs. 3 vectorially, we obtain

$$(v_A)_x \;+\!\!\!+\; (v_A)_y = [(v_{A/B})_x \;+\!\!\!+\; (v_{A/B})_y] \;+\!\!\!+\; [(v_B)_x \;+\!\!\!+\; (v_B)_y]$$

Hence,

$$v_A = v_{A/B} \;+\!\!\!+\; v_B \quad \text{or} \quad v_{A/B} = v_A \rightarrow v_B \qquad (4)$$

A useful interpretation of Eq. 4 makes use of an important principle of kinematics: namely, that the relative motion of two particles is not affected by any motion that they have in common. If, then, equal velocities are imposed on the motions of two particles, the relative velocity of one with respect to the other will not be changed. Further, if the velocities imposed cause the velocity of one particle to become zero, the resulting velocity of the other particle is then its velocity relative to the one. Thus, in Fig. 255 let A and B be any two moving

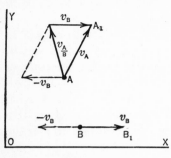

FIG. 255

points (assumed to move in a plane), let the absolute velocity v_A of A be represented by AA_1, and let BB_1 represent the absolute velocity v_B of B. Let a velocity equal to v_B but reversed in direction be given to each point. The velocity of the point B will then be zero and, hence, the resulting velocity of the point A is the velocity of A relative to B.

RELATIVE ACCELERATION. By differentiating twice with respect to time each of the terms in Eqs. 2 and adding the resulting equations vectorially, we obtain

$$a_A = a_{A/B} \nrightarrow a_B \quad \text{or} \quad a_{A/B} = a_A \rightarrow a_B \tag{5}$$

The fact that the relative motion of two points is not affected by any motion that they have in common applies to accelerations as well as to velocities. Thus, the relative acceleration of one moving point with respect to another moving point is not altered if the absolute accelerations of the two points are changed by equal amounts: that is, if an acceleration (of any magnitude and direction) be imposed on the two points.

Illustrative Problems

Problem 386. The current in a river with parallel sides is 4 mi/hr. A motor boat starting from one side keeps headed in a direction perpendicular to the sides

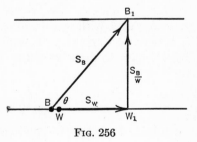

FIG. 256

and moves at a rate (relative to the water) of 6 mi/hr. If the river is 1 mi wide, what is the absolute displacement of the boat after reaching the other side?

SOLUTION. Let B (Fig. 256) represent the boat and W the water that is in contact with the boat when the boat starts. Hence the two points whose motions are to be considered are B and W. Thus,

$$s_B = s_W \nrightarrow s_{B/W}$$

The displacement of the water while the boat is moving across is

$$s_W = WW_1 = \tfrac{2}{3} \text{ mi}$$

After the boat has reached the other side, its displacement relative to the water (now at W_1) is

$$s_{B/W} = W_1B_1 = 1 \text{ mi}$$

Therefore,

$$s_B = 1 \mathbin{+\!\!\!\!+} \tfrac{2}{3} = \sqrt{(1)^2 + (\tfrac{2}{3})^2} = 1.2 \text{ mi}$$

and

$$\tan \theta = \frac{s_{B/W}}{s_W} = \frac{3}{2}; \qquad \therefore\ \theta = 56°\,20'$$

Problem 387. In the shaper mechanism shown in Fig. 257 let A be the sliding block, and let B be the point on the rocker arm O_1BM that is coincident with A at the instant. The distance OO_1 is 20 in., and θ is 30°. If $\omega = 20$ rpm, and $r = \frac{1}{2}$ ft, find v_B, the absolute velocity of B, and $v_{A/B}$, the relative velocity of A with respect to B.

SOLUTION. The two points whose motions are to be considered are the center of the block A and the point B on the rocker arm which is coincident with A. The velocities of these two points are related by the equation

$$v_A = v_{A/B} \mathbin{+\!\!\!\!+} v_B$$

Since the block A moves on a circular arc at constant speed, its velocity is given in magnitude by the equation

$$v_A = \omega r = \frac{20 \times 2\pi}{60} \times \frac{1}{2} = 1.05 \text{ ft/sec}$$

and its direction is perpendicular to r, as shown in Fig. 257. The direction of the absolute velocity of B is perpendicular to O_1BM, and its magnitude is unknown. Likewise, the direction of the velocity of A relative to B is known since it is along (parallel to) the rocker arm. By applying the foregoing equation, the magnitudes of $v_{A/B}$ and v_B are determined by the intersection of the lines that represent their directions. By scaling off the magnitudes, the following values are found:

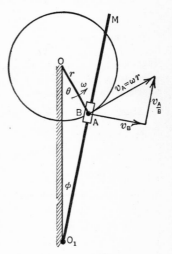

FIG. 257

$$v_{A/B} = 0.70 \text{ ft/sec} \quad \text{and} \quad v_B = 0.79 \text{ ft/sec}$$

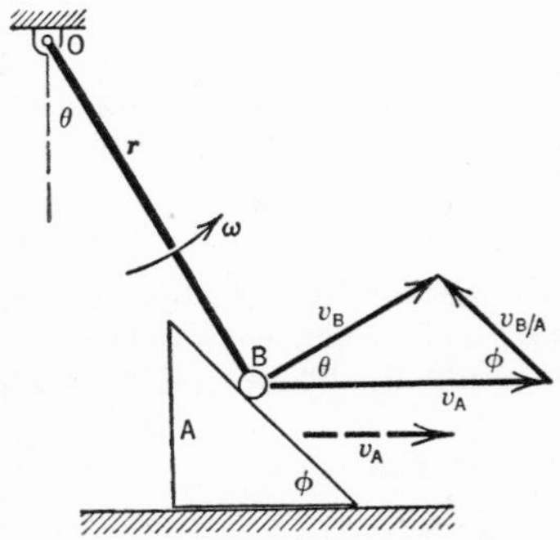

Problem 388. In Fig. 258 body A moves to the right with a constant velocity v_A causing the rod OB whose length is r to rotate about O. Determine in terms of v_A, r, ϕ, and θ the angular velocity ω of the rod.

SOLUTION. The value of ω will be found from the relation $\omega = v_B/r$. The magnitude of v_B, however, is not known. Its value may be found by considering the velocities of the two points consisting of B and a point on A. Since all points on A have the same velocity, any point on A may be considered as the second point. The velocities of these two points are related by the equation

FIG. 258

$$v_B = v_{B/A} \mathbin{+\!\!\!\!+} v_A$$

The velocity of B is perpendicular to OB and hence makes an angle θ with the horizontal. The velocity of B relative to A is parallel to the inclined surface of A and hence makes an angle ϕ with the horizontal. The velocity polygon is shown in Fig. 258. By use of the sine law, we have

$$\frac{v_B}{\sin \phi} = \frac{v_A}{\sin (180° - \theta - \phi)} \quad \text{or} \quad v_B = \frac{\sin \phi}{\sin (180° - \theta - \phi)} v_A$$

Hence,

$$\omega = \frac{v_B}{r} = \frac{\sin \phi}{\sin (180° - \theta - \phi)} \frac{v_A}{r}$$

Problem 389. An automobile A is traveling on a straight road, and another automobile B is traveling on a curve as shown in Fig. 259a. When B is in the position shown, its speed is 20 ft/sec and is increasing at the rate of 8 ft/sec². At the same time the speed of A is increasing at the rate of 10 ft/sec². Determine the acceleration of A relative to B, denoted by $a_{A/B}$.

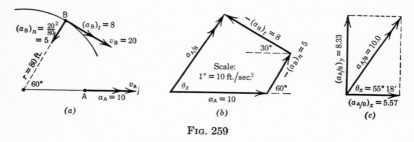

Fig. 259

GRAPHICAL SOLUTION. The accelerations of the two points (automobiles) are shown in Fig. 259a, and they are related to $a_{A/B}$ by the equation

$$a_{A/B} = a_A \rightarrow a_B = a_A \rightarrow [(a_B)_n \nrightarrow (a_B)_t]$$

$$= a_A \nrightarrow [-(a_B)_n] \nrightarrow [-(a_B)_t]$$

$$= 10 \nrightarrow 5 \nrightarrow 8$$

The acceleration polygon representing these accelerations is shown in Fig. 259b. The magnitude and direction of the relative acceleration are found by measurement to be

$$a_{A/B} = 10 \text{ ft/sec}^2; \qquad \theta_x = 55° 20'$$

ALGEBRAIC SOLUTION. The vector representing $a_{A/B}$ may be found by obtaining its x and y components as the algebraic sum of the x and y components of the other accelerations in the polygon in which $a_{A/B}$ is the resultant. Thus, as indicated in Fig. 259c,

$$(a_{A/B})_x = 10 + 5 \times 0.5 - 8 \times 0.866 = 5.57 \text{ ft/sec}^2$$

Hence,

$$(a_{A/B})_y = 5 \times 0.866 + 8 \times 0.5 = 8.33 \text{ ft/sec}^2$$

and

$$a_{A/B} = \sqrt{(5.57)^2 + (8.33)^2} = 10.0 \text{ ft/sec}^2$$

$$\theta_x = \tan^{-1} \frac{8.33}{5.77} = \tan^{-1} 1.444 = 55° 18'$$

Problems

390. Two trains move on parallel tracks with constant speeds of 45 mi/hr and 30 mi/hr. If it takes 100 sec for one train to pass the other when the trains are going in the same direction, how long will it take if the trains are going in opposite directions?

391. A car A is moving northeast on a straight road at a speed of 60 mi/hr, and at the same time another car B is moving south on a straight road at a speed of 30 mi/hr. Find the velocity of B relative to A.

Ans. $v_{B/A} = 83.9$ mi/hr; $\theta_x = 239° 39'$.

392. By use of the data of Prob. 299 and Fig. 215, find the velocity of the block A. Use the relative-motion equation for velocities.

393. The block B in Fig. 260 moves up the plane. If the distance AC increases at the rate of 4 ft/sec, determine the velocity of the push rod CD.

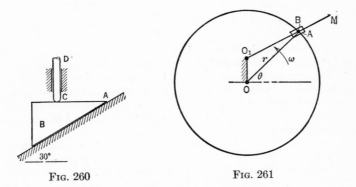

FIG. 260   FIG. 261

394. In Fig. 261 let A be a block which revolves about O at a constant angular velocity $\omega = 20$ rpm, and let B be the point on the arm O_1BM coincident with A at the instant. If $r = OA = 12$ in., $OO_1 = 4$ in., and $\theta = 45°$, find the absolute velocity of B. *Ans.* $v_B = 2.00$ ft/sec.

395. Bricks are formed from clay which is extruded through a die having a rectangular cross section. The clay is extruded horizontally with a constant velocity of 0.5 ft/sec. The bricks are cut to proper length by a wire that moves with a constant velocity of 1 ft/sec in a plane making an angle θ with the horizontal, the wire being at all times horizontal, and perpendicular to the axis of the brick. Determine the angle θ in order that the wire make a square cut on the brick.

396. A pilot flies an airplane from New York to Albany which is 150 mi north of New York. The wind is from the north, its velocity is 10 mi/hr, and the flight is made in 60 min. On another flight from New York the pilot flies with a velocity relative to the wind the same as before, but the wind is now coming from the west with a velocity of 30 mi/hr. After the pilot has flown the same length of time as before, how far and in what direction will he be from Albany?

397. An automobile travels west at 15 mi/hr, and the wind appears to the driver to come from the north. When the speed of the automobile is increased to 35 mi/hr, the wind appears to come from the northwest. Determine the absolute velocity of the wind. *Ans.* $v_W = 25$ mi/hr.

398. The recording mechanism shown in Fig. 262 consists of a plate A which moves to the left with a velocity of 2 in./sec and a pencil B attached to an arm OC that oscillates through a small arc. The length of the arm OC is long compared to the displacement of B so that the pencil may be regarded as moving on a straight line parallel to the Y axis. If the pencil moves according to the law $y = 0.2 \cos 20t$, where y is expressed in inches and t in seconds, find the velocity of the pencil relative to the plate when $t = \pi/6$ sec. Determine also with respect to the X and Y axes, which are fixed on the plate, the equation to the curve traced by the pencil on the plate. Assume $x = 0$ when $t = 0$.

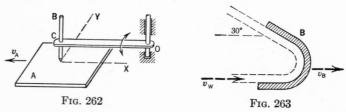

FIG. 262   FIG. 263

399. A jet of water moving with a velocity v_W of 50 ft/sec strikes a moving blade as shown in Fig. 263. The velocity v_B of the blade is 30 ft/sec in the direction of the jet. Find the magnitude and direction of the absolute velocity of the water as it leaves the blade. Assume that the velocity of the water relative to the blade remains constant in magnitude.   *Ans.* $v_W = 16.1$ ft/sec; $\theta_x = 38°\ 20'$.

400. If the acceleration of body C in Fig. 247 is 4 in./sec² downward, find the acceleration of E relative to A.

401. Two points, A and B, move clockwise on a circle whose radius is 2 ft. At a certain instant A is at the upper end of the vertical diameter and B is at the right end of the horizontal diameter. The speed of A is 2 ft/sec and is increasing at the rate of 2 ft/sec². The speed of B is 4 ft/sec and is decreasing at the rate of 8 ft/sec². Find the acceleration of A relative to B.   *Ans.* $a_{A/B} = 14.14$ ft/sec²; $\theta_x = 315°$.

402. In Prob. 401 assume that the speed of A is decreasing at the rate of 8 ft/sec² and that the speed of B is increasing at the rate of 2 ft/sec². Find the acceleration of A relative to B.

403. Two cars, A and B, are traveling in the same direction on a straight road. Car A is 600 ft behind car B, and its speed is 10 ft/sec greater than the speed of B. If A has a constant acceleration relative to B of 2 ft/sec², how long will it take for A to overtake B?

404. Two trains, A and B, travel in the same direction on parallel tracks. The speed of A is increased uniformly at the rate of 18 mi/hr/min, and the speed of B is decreased uniformly at the rate of 9 mi/hr/min. If at one instant B is traveling 15 mi/hr faster than A, find the change in the distance between the two trains in the next 30 sec.   *Ans.* 363 ft.

82 Motion of a point relative to a rotating body. Coriolis' law.

In the preceding article the motion of a point or particle relative to another point was discussed which as previously defined means the motion of the point relative to a body or reference frame which does not rotate. In some problems in kinematics, however, it is convenient to deal with the motion of a point relative to a rotating body or set of reference axes. Thus, the motion of the particle is considered to be generated by the motion of the particle along a path as the path rotates. Such problems occur in the analysis of the accelerations (and forces) involved in some types of governors for engines and motors, and in the determination of the acceleration of a fluid particle as it flows between the rotating vanes of a centrifugal pump, etc.

If a particle moves along a path as the path translates (that is, the path moves without rotating), the velocity of the particle as found in Art. 81 is the vector sum of the velocity relative to the path and the velocity of *any* point of the path. A similar statement may be made for accelerations. If, however, a particle moves along a path as the path rotates, the subsequent analysis will show that the velocity of the particle is the vector sum of the velocity relative to the path and the velocity of the point of the path only if the point of the path is chosen as the point that is *coincident* with the particle at the instant.

In general, the acceleration of a particle referred to a rotating set of axes is given by the vector sum of three component accelerations as expressed by Coriolis' law.

CORIOLIS' LAW. In Fig. 264a let P represent a particle moving along a path with a velocity v_r and an acceleration a_r relative to the path, and

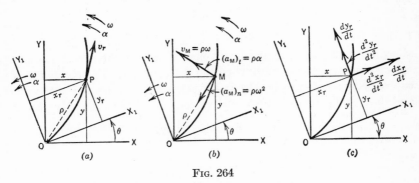

FIG. 264

at the same time let the path rotate about O with an angular velocity ω and an angular acceleration α. Let the X_1 and Y_1 axes rotate about O with the path. Thus, the motion of P relative to the path is defined by the co-ordinates x_r and y_r taken with reference to the rotating X_1 and Y_1 axes. Further, let the X and Y axes be fixed in space. Thus, the absolute motion of P is defined by the co-ordinates x and y taken with reference to the fixed X and Y axes. Let the angle θ represent the angular displacement of the path and ρ represent the distance of the particle P from O. The x and y components of the absolute displacement of P are

$$x = x_r \cos \theta - y_r \sin \theta$$
$$y = x_r \sin \theta + y_r \cos \theta$$

(1)

By differentiating with respect to time each of the terms in Eqs. 1, the components of the absolute velocity of P are found to be

$$v_x = -(x_r \sin \theta + y_r \cos \theta)\omega + \frac{dx_r}{dt} \cos \theta - \frac{dy_r}{dt} \sin \theta$$

$$v_y = (x_r \cos \theta - y_r \sin \theta)\omega + \frac{dx_r}{dt} \sin \theta + \frac{dy_r}{dt} \cos \theta$$

(2)

The right members of Eqs. 2 may be shown to represent the sum of the components of the velocity of P relative to the path and the absolute velocity of a point M of the path which is coincident with P at the instant. The velocity of the point M is equal to $\rho\omega$ (Fig. 264b), and its direction is perpendicular to OM. The x and y components of the velocity of M are

$$(v_M)_x = -y\omega = -(x_r \sin \theta + y_r \cos \theta)\omega$$

and

$$(v_M)_y = x\omega = (x_r \cos \theta - y_r \sin \theta)\,\omega$$

In Fig. 264c the path is assumed to be fixed as the particle P moves along the path and the absolute velocity of P is then the same as its velocity relative to the path when the path rotates. The components of the velocity parallel to the X_1 and Y_1 axes are as indicated in the figure and the x and y components of the velocity relative to the path are

$$(v_r)_x = \frac{dx_r}{dt} \cos \theta - \frac{dy_r}{dt} \sin \theta$$

and

$$(v_r)_y = \frac{dx_r}{dt} \sin \theta + \frac{dy_r}{dt} \cos \theta$$

Equations 2 now become

$$v_x = (v_r)_x + (v_M)_x \quad \text{and} \quad v_y = (v_r)_y + (v_M)_y$$

By adding these equations vectorially we obtain

$$v = v_r \mathrel{+\!\!\!+} v_M$$

(3)

Thus, the absolute velocity of P is the vector sum of the velocity of P relative to the path and the velocity of the point of the path which is coincident with P at the instant.

By differentiating with respect to time each of the terms of Eqs. 2, the components of the absolute acceleration of P are found to be

$$a_x = \left(\frac{d^2x_r}{dt^2}\cos\theta - \frac{d^2y_r}{dt^2}\sin\theta\right) - [(x_r\cos\theta - y_r\sin\theta)\omega^2$$
$$+ (x_r\sin\theta + y_r\cos\theta)\alpha] - 2\left(\frac{dx_r}{dt}\sin\theta + \frac{dy_r}{dt}\cos\theta\right)\omega$$

$$a_y = \left(\frac{d^2x_r}{dt^2}\sin\theta + \frac{d^2y_r}{dt^2}\cos\theta\right) - [(x_r\sin\theta + y_r\cos\theta)\omega^2$$
$$- (x_r\cos\theta - y_r\sin\theta)\alpha] + 2\left(\frac{dx_r}{dt}\cos\theta - \frac{dy_r}{dt}\sin\theta\right)\omega$$

$$(4)$$

The right members of Eqs. 4 will now be shown to represent the sum of the components of the acceleration of P relative to the path, the acceleration of M, and a supplementary acceleration.

In Fig. 264b are shown the normal and tangential components of the acceleration of M. The x and y components of the acceleration are

$$(a_M)_x = -x\omega^2 - y\alpha = -[(x_r\cos\theta - y_r\sin\theta)\omega^2$$
$$+ (x_r\sin\theta + y_r\cos\theta)\alpha]$$
$$(a_M)_y = -y\omega^2 + x\alpha = -[(x_r\sin\theta + y_r\cos\theta)\omega^2$$
$$- (x_r\cos\theta - y_r\sin\theta)\alpha]$$

By referring to Fig. 264c the x and y components of the acceleration of P relative to the path are found to be

$$(a_r)_x = \frac{d^2x_r}{dt^2}\cos\theta - \frac{d^2y_r}{dt^2}\sin\theta$$

$$(a_r)_y = \frac{d^2x_r}{dt^2}\sin\theta + \frac{d^2y_r}{dt^2}\cos\theta$$

Equations 4 may now be written

$$a_x = (a_r)_x + (a_M)_x - 2(v_r)_y\omega$$
$$a_y = (a_r)_y + (a_M)_y + 2(v_r)_x\omega$$

$$(5)$$

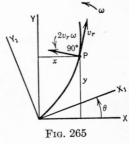

FIG. 265

The last terms of Eqs. 5 represent the x and y components of an acceleration whose magnitude is $2v_r\omega$ and whose direction is perpendicular to v_r as shown in Fig. 265. By adding Eqs. 5 vectorially, we obtain

$$\boldsymbol{a} = \boldsymbol{a}_r \mathbin{+\!\!\!+} \boldsymbol{a}_M \mathbin{+\!\!\!+} 2v_r\boldsymbol{\omega}$$

$$(6)$$

in which a_r is the acceleration the particle would have if the path were fixed and can be found from either $a_r = \dfrac{d^2 x_r}{dt^2} \leftrightarrow \dfrac{d^2 y_r}{dt^2}$ or $a_r = r\alpha' \leftrightarrow \dfrac{v_r^2}{r}$ where r is the radius of curvature of the path and α' is the angular acceleration that P would have relative to the center of curvature if the path were fixed. The component a_M is the acceleration of the point of the path coincident with the particle at the instant and can be found from $a_M = \rho\omega^2 \leftrightarrow \rho\alpha$. The component $2v_r\omega$ is a vector directed perpendicular to the vector v_r, and its sense may be found by the following rule: Apply the vector representing $2v_r\omega$ to the end of the vector representing v_r; then the sense of $2v_r\omega$ is such that, considered as a force, it would rotate the vector v_r in the sense of ω the angular velocity of the path.

If, then, a particle moves on a path as the path rotates, the acceleration of the particle is the vector sum of (1) the acceleration the particle would have if the path were fixed and the particle moved along the path with velocity v_r and acceleration a_r, (2) the acceleration of a point of the path coincident with the particle at the instant or the acceleration the particle would have if it were fixed on the path and the path rotated, and (3) $2v_r\omega$ called the Coriolis' component or the *compound supplementary acceleration*. This statement is known as *Coriolis' law*.

Illustrative Problem

Problem 405. The circular arc APB (Fig. 266a) represents the vane of a centrifugal pump, P being a particle of water. Find the acceleration of the particle P when it is 12 in. from O, the center of the shaft if, at that instant, the angular velocity of the wheel is 10 rad/sec clockwise and its angular acceleration is 50

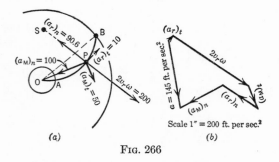

(a)

(b)

Fig. 266

rad/sec^2 clockwise. The velocity of the particle along (relative to) the vane is $v_r = 10$ ft/sec, and the tangential component of the acceleration relative to the vane is $(a_r)_t = 10$ ft/sec^2. OB makes an angle of 45° with the horizontal and is 18 in. long; OA is 3 in.; and OP is 12 in. The radius of the arc APB is $13\frac{1}{4}$ in.

SOLUTION. By Coriolis' law the total acceleration a is

$$a = a_r \mathbin{+\!\!\!\rightarrow} a_M \mathbin{+\!\!\!\rightarrow} 2v_r\omega$$

a_r and a_M are found most easily from their n and t components. Hence,

$$a = (a_r)_n \mathbin{+\!\!\!\rightarrow} (a_r)_t \mathbin{+\!\!\!\rightarrow} (a_M)_n \mathbin{+\!\!\!\rightarrow} (a_M)_t \mathbin{+\!\!\!\rightarrow} 2v_r\omega$$

$$= \frac{10^2}{13\frac{1}{4}/12} \mathbin{+\!\!\!\rightarrow} 10 \mathbin{+\!\!\!\rightarrow} 10^2 \mathbin{+\!\!\!\rightarrow} 50 \times \frac{12}{12} \mathbin{+\!\!\!\rightarrow} 2 \times 10 \times 10$$

$$= 90.6 \mathbin{+\!\!\!\rightarrow} 10 \mathbin{+\!\!\!\rightarrow} 100 \mathbin{+\!\!\!\rightarrow} 50 \mathbin{+\!\!\!\rightarrow} 200$$

each of the components being expressed in feet per second per second. The five components are shown in their proper directions in Fig. 266a, and the resultant acceleration a as found from the acceleration polygon is shown in Fig. 266b. By measuring to scale the closing line of the polygon, a is found to be 145 ft/sec² in the direction shown in Fig. 266b.

Problems

406. A rod rotates in a horizontal plane about a vertical axis through one end of the rod with a constant angular velocity of 2 rad/sec. At the same time a particle moves from the axis of rotation along the rod at a constant rate of 4 ft/sec. Find the magnitude of the linear acceleration of the particle when it is 3 ft from the axis of rotation. *Ans. a = 20 ft/sec².*

407. A freight car moves on a curved track of 300 ft radius at a constant speed of 20 ft/sec. As the car moves, a man walks forward along the top of the car with a speed relative to the car of 6 ft/sec. Determine the linear acceleration of the man.

408. Solve Prob. 431 by use of Coriolis' law.

Chapter 8

MOTION OF RIGID BODIES

83 Introduction. In the preceding chapter the motion of a point or particle and the relation between the motions of two particles have been considered. In engineering problems in general, however, the motion of bodies, not particles, must be considered. In some problems, the dimensions of the body may be small in comparison with its range of motion, and hence the body may be treated as a particle without introducing a serious error. In such problems, the methods and equations of the preceding chapter apply directly to the motion of the body. In general, however, the motion of bodies as met in engineering practice is such that the various points of a body have different motions.

The object of this chapter is to analyze certain common types of motion of a rigid body so that the displacement, velocity, and acceleration, both linear and angular, of any point in the body may be found from the methods and equations developed in the preceding chapter. The motions considered are *translation*, *rotation*, and *plane motion*.

84 Translation. *Translation* of a rigid body is a motion such that no straight line in the body changes direction: that is, each straight line remains parallel to its initial direction. Hence, all points in the body move along parallel paths and have, at any instant, the same velocity and acceleration. If the particles more on curved paths, the motion is called *curvilinear* translation, as, for example, the motion of the parallel rod of a locomotive. If the particles move on straight-line paths, the motion is called *rectilinear* translation. The body may have a uniformly or non-uniformly accelerated motion. Hence, a point in a translating body may have any of the motions treated in the preceding chapter. Furthermore, since all particles in the body have the same displacement in any time interval and have, at any instant, the same velocity and acceleration, the displacement, velocity, and acceleration of the body are described by the displacement velocity and acceleration of *any* particle of the body.

206

Problems

409. The crank OA in Fig. 267 rotates with a constant angular velocity ω of 30 rpm, causing the jointed frame $CDFE$ to oscillate. In the position shown AB and DF are horizontal and OA, CD, and EF are vertical. The length of OA is 8 in., and the length of CD and of EF is 4 ft. B is the mid-point of CD. Find the acceleration of G, the mid-point of DF, in the position shown. Note. The angular acceleration of CD is zero, a fact that may easily be proved later when the kinematics of plane motion is considered.   *Ans. $a = 4.39$ ft/sec².*

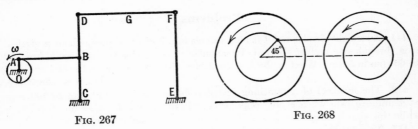

FIG. 267   FIG. 268

410. A locomotive is running on a straight track at a constant speed of 45 mi/hr. The diameter of the drivers is 5 ft, and the radius of the crank-pin circle is 15 in. What is the magnitude and the direction of the velocity and of the acceleration of the parallel rod, relative to the engine frame, when the rod is in the position shown in Fig. 268? What is the absolute velocity and the absolute acceleration for the same position? Before attempting to solve this problem, the student is advised to study Prob. 416 in which the relation between the angular velocity of a rolling wheel and the linear velocity of its center is found.

85 Rotation.

Rotation of a rigid body is a motion such that one line in the body (or body extended) remains fixed in space while all points of the body not on the line describe circular paths having centers on the fixed line. The fixed line is called the *axis of rotation*, and the plane in which the mass center of the body moves is called the *plane of motion*. The point of intersection of the axis of rotation and the plane of motion is called the *center of rotation*. It will be noted that any line parallel to the plane of motion changes direction. This motion is sometimes called a *pure rotation* in contrast to rotation in plane motion (Art. 86) in which, in general, all lines in the plane of motion change direction but no line perpendicular to the plane of motion remains fixed.

The motion of a body having rotation cannot be defined or described by stating the *linear* displacement, velocity, and acceleration of any point in the body, as was the case for translation, since all points in the body do not have the same linear motion. However, the *angular* displacements, velocities, and acceleration, respectively, about the axis of rotation, are the same for all particles in the body. Hence, the motion of a rotating rigid body may be described by the angular motion, about the axis of rotation, of any point in the body not on the axis of rotation. Thus, all the equations in the preceding chapter dealing with the angular motion of a point moving on a circular path apply to the motion of a rotating rigid body, as well as to each point in the body. The linear displacement, velocity, and acceleration of any point may be found from the equations in the preceding chapter, that deal with the linear motion of a point moving on a circular path.

Problems

411. A straight slender rod 4 ft long rotates in a horizontal plane about a vertical axis through one end of the rod. Its angular velocity changes uniformly from 10 to 60 rpm in 5 sec. What is the linear velocity of its mid-point at the end of 2 sec?

Ans. v = 6.28 ft/sec.

412. The flywheel of a punching machine fluctuates from 140 rpm to 100 rpm at a uniform rate when a hole is punched. If the flywheel makes one revolution while this change of speed takes place, how long does it take to punch the hole?

413. The flywheel of a rolling-mill engine is 14 ft in diameter. Just before the steel is fed in the rolls the speed of the flywheel is 90 rpm. As the steel enters the rolls, the speed decreases uniformly during ½ sec, before the governor can operate. If the angular acceleration (negative) of the flywheel is 20 rpm/sec, what is the speed of a point on the circumference of the wheel at the end of ½ sec? Determine the angular displacement of the wheel in ½ sec.

Ans. v = 58.6 ft/sec; θ = 0.708 rev.

Fig. 269

414. The circular disk in Fig. 269 rotates about an axis through O perpendicular to the plane of the disk. If $\omega = 2$ rad/sec and $\alpha = 3$ rad/sec^2, find the linear acceleration of A relative to P.   *Ans. $a_{A/P} = 10$ ft/sec^2; $\theta_x = 6° 52'$.*

415. If the absolute acceleration of the point P in Fig. 269 is 6 ft/sec^2 tangent to the disk, determine the magnitudes of ω and α.

86 Plane motion.

Plane motion of a rigid body is a motion such that each point in the body remains at a constant distance from a fixed plane. The motion of the connecting rod of a stationary steam engine is an example of plane motion. The wheels of a locomotive running on a straight track also have plane motion. The plane in which the mass center of the body moves is called the *plane of motion*. It is evident that a pure rotation is always a special case of plane motion, whereas a translation may or may not be a plane motion.

In plane motion, in general, a straight line in the body lying in the plane of motion changes direction, and, hence, the body rotates, but not about a fixed axis. The body, therefore, has angular motion, and its angular displacement, velocity, and acceleration are the same as that of any straight line in the body, in the plane of motion, since all such lines have the same angular motion if the body is rigid. The angular motion of the body, therefore, may be studied by means of the same equations that apply to the rotation of a rigid body about a fixed axis.

Rotation, however, is only one part of the motion of a rigid body having plane motion. Plane motion of a rigid body may be resolved into two component motions, a rotation and a translation, according to the following theorem:

> Plane motion of a rigid body, at any instant, is a combination of: (1) a pure rotation of the body, about an axis (perpendicular to the plane of motion) passing through *any* point B in the body, with an angular velocity and acceleration the same as that which the body has at the instant; and (2) a translation of the body which gives to each point the same linear velocity and acceleration that the point B has at the instant.

The point B is called the *base point*. It is evident that all points except the base point have two motions: a rotation about the base point, and a motion the same as that of the base point. From the analysis of the motion according to the above theorem, the displacement, velocity, and acceleration of any point A in the body may be found from the equations developed in Art. 81 of the preceding chapter.

To illustrate the foregoing theorem, consider the motion of the connecting rod of a steam engine (Fig. 270). Let P denote the position of

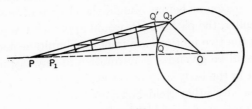

Fig. 270

the crosshead and Q that of the crank pin. When the crank moves from position OQ to position OQ_1, the connecting rod moves from position PQ to position P_1Q_1. This change of position can be given to the rod by first rotating it about P, until it becomes parallel to its new position, and then giving it a translation such that each point receives a displacement equal to PP_1. By this combination of motions the point P moves along its actual path, but any other point does not travel in its actual path. The point Q, for example, moves along the path $QQ'Q_1$ instead of its actual circular path QQ_1. However, as the change of position is made smaller and smaller, the path $QQ'Q_1$ approaches the circular path QQ_1, and, in the limit, as the two motions are generated simultaneously, each point is made to move on its actual path by successive combinations of a proper rotation and a proper translation. The rotation, at any instant, must give the body its actual angular velocity and acceleration at the instant, since the translation does not influence the angular motion of the body. The translation must give all points of the body the same motion that the base point has at the instant, since the base point receives its total motion from the translation.

By the foregoing method the rod is given a rectilinear translation, since the point P moves on a straight-line path. If, however, another base point is chosen, as, for example, the point Q, the change of position from

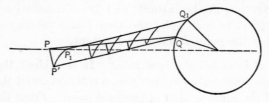

Fig. 271

PQ to P_1Q_1 may then be made by: (1) a rotation about Q (Fig. 271); and (2) a curvilinear translation giving to each point the same motion that Q has. By this combination of a rotation and a translation the point P is made to take the path $PP'P_1$ instead of its actual path PP_1. However, if we reason as before, should the change of position be made smaller and smaller, the path $PP'P_1$ would approach the path PP_1, and, in the limit, as the two motions are imposed simultaneously, each point in the body would be given its exact motion at any instant. Likewise, any other point in the body may be selected as the base point. And the plane motion of any other rigid body may be treated in like manner. Hence, a plane motion of a rigid body may be considered, at any instant, as a combination of a rotation of the body about any base point in the body, with an angular velocity and acceleration equal to the angular velocity and acceleration that the body has at the instant, and a translation of the body that gives to each point the same linear velocity and acceleration that the base point has at the instant.

When plane motion of a rigid body is analyzed as in the preceding discussion, the velocity and acceleration of any point P is obtained from the following equations (Art. 81) in which the point Q represents the base point.

$$v_P = v_{P/Q} + \!\!\!\!\rightarrow v_Q \quad \text{and} \quad a_P = a_{P/Q} + \!\!\!\!\rightarrow a_Q$$

Since any two points in a rigid body remain a fixed distance apart, the relative velocity of either point with respect to the other is perpendicular to the line joining the two points. This is not true, however, of the relative acceleration, since it is made up of a tangential and a normal component, the normal component having a direction along the line joining the two points.

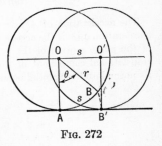

Fig. 272

Illustrative Problems

Problem 416. A circular disk of radius r rolls without slipping on a horizontal straight track. If v_O and a_O denote the linear velocity and linear acceleration of the center O of the disk, and ω and α denote the angular velocity and angular acceleration of the disk, show that $v_O = r\omega$ and $a_O = r\alpha$.

SOLUTION. The angular displacement of the disk (Fig. 272) corresponding to any linear displacement OO' (or s) of its center is the angle θ through which the radius OB turns in moving from the position OB to $O'B'$. Hence, from the figure we have

$$s = AB' = \text{arc } AB = r\theta$$

and, therefore,

$$v_O = \frac{ds}{dt} = r\frac{d\theta}{dt} = r\omega$$

and

$$a_O = \frac{d^2s}{dt^2} = r\frac{d^2\theta}{dt^2} = r\alpha$$

Problem 417. A cylinder whose radius is 2 ft (Fig. 273) rolls without slipping down an inclined plane with an angular acceleration of 6 rad/sec². At a given instant the angular velocity is 3 rad/sec. Find the linear velocity and linear acceleration of the point A at the instant.

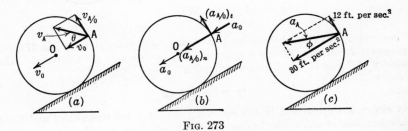

FIG. 273

SOLUTION. The velocity of O is $v_O = r\omega = 2 \times 3 = 6$ ft/sec parallel to the inclined plane. The velocity of A may be found from the equation $v_A = v_{A/O} \leftrightarrow v_O$ in which $v_{A/O} = \omega r = 6$ ft/sec perpendicular to OA, as shown in Fig. 273a, since O and A are points on a rigid body. It should be noted that $v_{A/O}$ is the velocity that A receives from the rotational component of the plane motion of the cylinder, O being used as the base point, and v_O is the velocity that A receives from the translational component of the plane motion. Hence, the magnitude and direction of the velocity are given by the equations

$$v_A = v_{A/O} \;+\!\!+ v_O = \sqrt{(6)^2 + (6)^2} = 8.48 \text{ ft/sec}$$

$$\tan \theta = \tfrac{6}{6} = 1; \qquad \therefore \; \theta = 45°$$

The acceleration of A may be found from the equation $a_A = a_{A/O} \;+\!\!+ a_O$. The acceleration $a_{A/O}$ is the acceleration given to the point A by the rotational component of the plane motion of the cylinder, and a_O is the acceleration given to A by the translational component of the plane motion. It is convenient to replace $a_{A/O}$ by its normal and tangential components as shown in Fig. 273b. Hence,

$$a_A = a_{A/O} \;+\!\!+ a_O = (a_{A/O})_n \;+\!\!+ (a_{A/O})_t \;+\!\!+ a_O$$

$$= 2 \times 9 \;+\!\!+ 2 \times 6 \;+\!\!+ 2 \times 6$$

$$= \sqrt{(30)^2 + (12)^2} = 32.3 \text{ ft/sec}^2$$

$$\tan \phi = \tfrac{12}{30} = 0.4; \qquad \therefore \; \phi = 21° 48'$$

Problem 418. A 50-hp engine has a cylinder 10 in. in diameter and a stroke of 10 in. The engine runs at a constant speed of $\omega = 300$ rpm. The ratio of the length of the connecting rod to that of the crank is 5. Find the velocity and the acceleration of the crosshead when the crank angle is 30°.

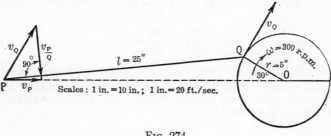

Scales: 1 in. = 10 in.; 1 in. = 20 ft./sec.

Fig. 274

SOLUTION. Let P be the crosshead and Q the crank pin. Then, in Fig. 274, PQ represents 25 in. and OQ or r represents 5 in., according to the scale used. The velocity of P may be found from the equation

$$v_P = v_{P/Q} \;+\!\!+ v_Q$$

Six elements are involved in the equation: namely, three magnitudes and three directions, four of which must be found before the equation can be used to determine the other two. The direction of the velocity of Q is perpendicular to OQ, and its magnitude is

$$v_Q = \omega r = \left(\frac{300 \times 2\pi}{60} \right) \times \frac{5}{12} = 13.1 \text{ ft/sec}$$

The direction of $v_{P/Q}$ is perpendicular to the line joining P and Q, and its magnitude is unknown. The direction of v_P is horizontal. Hence, by laying off v_Q to a convenient scale in the proper direction from P, and by drawing a line from the end of v_Q, perpendicular to the connecting rod, until it intersects a horizontal line through P, the magnitudes of $v_{P/Q}$ and v_P are determined by the intersection. By scaling off the values of $v_{P/Q}$ and v_P, the following results are found:

$$v_{P/Q} = 11.4 \text{ ft/sec} \quad \text{and} \quad v_P = 7.7 \text{ ft/sec}$$

If the plane motion of the connecting rod is thought of as a combination of a rotation and a translation, $v_{P/Q}$ is the velocity given to P by the rotation of the rod about Q, and v_Q is the velocity given to P by the translation of the rod. The two velocities produce the resultant velocity v_P.

The acceleration of P is given by the equation

$$a_P = a_{P/Q} \nrightarrow a_Q$$

For convenience, $a_{P/Q}$ will be replaced by its tangential and normal components. Hence,

$$a_P = (a_{P/Q})_t \nrightarrow (a_{P/Q})_n \nrightarrow a_Q$$

Eight elements are involved in the equation: namely, four magnitudes and four directions, six of which must be found before the graphical construction representing the equation can be completed. a_Q is directed from Q toward O, and its magnitude is

$$a_Q = \omega^2 r = \left(\frac{300 \times 2\pi}{60}\right)^2 \times \frac{5}{12} = 412 \text{ ft/sec}^2$$

a_P is known in direction, being parallel to PO (horizontal), since v_P changes in magnitude only. $(a_{P/Q})_n$ is directed from P toward Q, and its magnitude is

$$(a_{P/Q})_n = \frac{(v_{P/Q})^2}{PQ} = \frac{(11.4)^2}{\frac{25}{12}} = 62.4 \text{ ft/sec}^2$$

$(a_{P/Q})_t$ has a direction perpendicular to PQ. The two unknown elements are, therefore, the magnitudes of a_P and $(a_{P/Q})_t$.

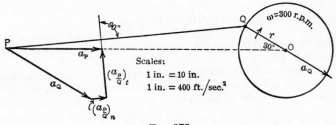

Scales:
1 in. = 10 in.
1 in. = 400 ft./sec.²

FIG. 275

In Fig. 275, starting at P, the vectors are laid off to a convenient scale. Thus a_Q and $(a_{P/Q})_n$ (both of which are completely known) are drawn, and then, from the end of $(a_{P/Q})_n$, a line is drawn that represents the direction of $(a_{P/Q})_t$; that is, it is drawn perpendicular to PQ. The intersection of this line with the line PO (which represents the direction of a_P) determines the lengths of the vectors that represent $(a_{P/Q})_t$ and a_P. By scaling off the values, the following results are obtained:

$$(a_{P/Q})_t = 200 \text{ ft/sec}^2 \quad \text{and} \quad a_P = 404 \text{ ft/sec}^2$$

Problems

419. If A and B are any two points in the plane of motion of a body that has plane motion, and C is a point midway between A and B, show that the velocity and acceleration of C may be expressed in terms of the velocities and accelerations of A and B as follows:

$$v_C = \tfrac{1}{2}(v_A \mathbin{+\!\!+} v_B) \quad \text{and} \quad a_C = \tfrac{1}{2}(a_A \mathbin{+\!\!+} a_B)$$

420. In Fig. 276, one end A of a bar AB that is 4 ft long moves downward along OM, and the other end B moves along ON. When the bar is horizontal, the velocity of A is constant and equal to 6 ft/sec. Find the linear velocity of B and the angular velocity of the bar at this instant.   *Ans.* $v_B = 3.46$ ft/sec; $\omega = 1.73$ rad/sec.

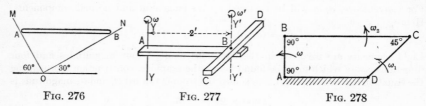

FIG. 276   FIG. 277   FIG. 278

421. The horizontal bar AB (Fig. 277) rotates about a vertical axis YY with an angular velocity of 2 rad/sec in the clockwise direction. At the same time the horizontal bar CD, which is 2 ft long, rotates with an angular velocity (relative to AB) of 1 rad/sec in the clockwise direction. If the angular velocities remain constant, how many revolutions will CD make while AB is making one revolution? If $CB = BD$, what is the magnitude of the linear velocity of C: (a) when CD is parallel to AB with C between A and B, (b) when CD is perpendicular to AB, and (c) when CD is parallel to AB with D between A and B?

422. In the four-link mechanism shown in Fig. 278, the link AD is fixed, and the angular velocity ω of the link AB is 3 rad/sec. If $AB = 1$ ft, and $BC = 3$ ft, find ω_1 and ω_2, the angular velocities of CD and BC, respectively.

Ans. $\omega_1 = 3$ rad/sec; $\omega_2 = 1$ rad/sec.

423. Find the acceleration of the mid-point of the bar AB whose motion is described in Prob. 420.

424. The disk shown in Fig. 279 rolls without slipping on a horizontal track. The diameter of the disk is 4 ft and the velocity and acceleration of the center are 8 ft/sec and 16 ft/sec², respectively, to the right. Find the velocities of the points A, B, and C.   *Ans.* $v_A = 0$; $v_B = 11.3$ ft/sec; $v_C = 16$ ft/sec.

425. The disk in Fig. 279 rolls to the right. The diameter of the disk is 4 ft, the velocity of its center is 6 ft/sec, and the angular velocity is 4 rad/sec clockwise. (These values show that the disk slips as it rolls.) Find the velocities of points A, B, and C. Find also the co-ordinates (with respect to H as the origin) of the point whose velocity is zero.

426. The angular velocity of the link AC of the four-link mechanism shown in Fig. 280 is 2 rad/sec counterclockwise. Find the linear velocity of B and the angular velocities of links BC and BD.   *Ans.* $\omega_{BC} = 4$ rad/sec; $\omega_{BD} = \tfrac{8}{3}$ rad/sec.

427. In Fig. 281 is shown a dynamic vibration absorber which is used to decrease torsional vibrations in rotating mechanisms such as the crankshaft of an internal-combustion engine. The absorber consists of a disk D to which there is pinned at A a "centrifugal pendulum" AG. If the disk rotates at a constant angular velocity ω_1, and the pendulum rotates with an angular velocity ω clockwise and angular acceleration α counterclockwise (both with respect to the disk), find the x and y components of the linear acceleration of the end G of the pendulum. The acceleration of G is needed in order to derive the differential equation of motion from which the natural frequency of vibration of the pendulum is obtained.

Ans. $(a_G)_x = r_1\omega_1{}^2 \sin\theta - r\alpha$; $(a_G)_y = -[r(\omega + \omega_1)^2 + r_1\omega_1{}^2 \cos\theta]$.

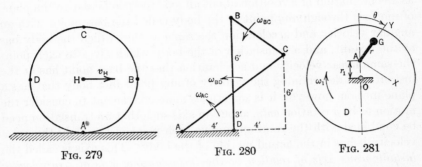

FIG. 279	FIG. 280	FIG. 281

428. Let the pendulum AG in Fig. 281 be clamped to the disk D so that its motion is pure rotation about O. If the angular velocity ω_1 of the disk and pendulum is constant and equal to 4 rad/sec, determine the linear acceleration of point G by considering the motion of AG to be a plane motion consisting of a combination of a pure rotation of AG about an axis through A and a translation of AG. Assume $\theta = 30°$, $r_1 = 4$ in., and $r = 6$ in.

429. Use the data of Prob. 424, and determine the acceleration of points A and B on the disk.

430. Use the data of Prob. 424, and find (with respect to H as the origin) the coordinates of the point on the disk whose acceleration is zero.

Ans. $x = 0.8$ ft; $y = -0.4$ ft.

431. If the angular velocities of the bars AB and CD in Fig. 277 are as stated in Prob. 421 and the bar AB has an angular acceleration of 1 rad/sec² clockwise, find the total linear accelerations of C and D when CD is perpendicular to AB as shown. Assume the angular velocity of CD relative to AB to remain constant. Note that the absolute angular velocity of CD is the sum of its angular velocity relative to AB and the angular velocity of AB. A similar statement may be made for the angular acceleration of CD.

Ans. $a_c = 11.4$ ft/sec²; $\theta_x = 142° 8'$.

432. The bar AB of the four-link mechanism shown in Fig. 278 has an angular velocity of 3 rad/sec and an angular acceleration of 2 rad/sec², both counterclockwise. Find the total linear acceleration of the point C.

433. In addition to the data given in Prob. 426, assume that ω_{AC} is increasing at the rate of 2 rad/sec², and determine the angular accelerations of BC and BD.

Ans. $\alpha_{BC} = 2$ rad/sec²; $\alpha_{BD} = 1.56$ rad/sec².

434. The lower end B of a rod AB 5 ft in length moves to the right along the positive end of the X axis, and the upper end A moves downward along the Y axis. When B is 3 ft from the origin, $v_B = 4$ ft/sec, and $a_B = 5$ ft/sec² to the right. Find the linear velocity and acceleration of A and the angular velocity and acceleration of the rod.

435. The disk shown in Fig. 279 has a diameter of 4 ft and rolls, without slipping, to the right. The angular velocity of the disk is 2 rad/sec, and the angular acceleration is 8 rad/sec² clockwise. The path described by the point B is called a cycloid. Find the components of the acceleration of B tangent and normal to its path.

Ans. $a_t = 16.97$ ft/sec²; $a_n = 5.66$ ft/sec².

87 Instantaneous center.

It was shown in the previous article that a plane motion of a rigid body may be considered, at any instant, as a combination of a rotation about an axis (perpendicular to the plane of motion) through *any* point in the body called the base point with an angular velocity and acceleration the same as that which the body has at the instant, and a translation of the body which gives to each point the same linear velocity and acceleration that the base point has at the instant. In determining the velocity of any point in a body that has a plane motion, however, it is sometimes more convenient to consider the motion to be a rotation *only*, about an axis such that no translation need be combined with the rotation to give each point of the body the same velocity it has in the actual motion of the body. This axis is called the *instantaneous axis of rotation* or the *instantaneous axis of zero velocity*. Its intersection with the plane of motion is called the *instantaneous center of rotation* or the *instantaneous center of zero velocity*.

In order to show how the instantaneous center may be located, assume A and B in Fig. 282 to be any two points in the plane of motion

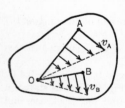

Fig. 282

whose velocities v_A and v_B are known in direction. Let lines through A and B perpendicular to v_A and v_B, respectively, intersect at O. The point O is the instantaneous center, as will now be shown. The velocity of O is the vector sum of $v_{O/A}$, the velocity of O relative to A, and v_A. Since the body is rigid, $v_{O/A}$ is perpendicular to OA, and, since v_A is also perpendicular to OA, it follows that the velocity of O, if not zero, must be perpendicular to OA. Similarly the velocity of O, considered as a point on OB, if not zero, must be perpendicular to OB. Hence, v_O is zero since it cannot be perpendicular to OA and OB at the same time. Thus, in order to locate the instantaneous center it is necessary to know the directions, only, of the velocities of any two points in the plane of motion, provided that the directions of the two velocities are not parallel.

If, then, A and O are two points in the rigid body having plane motion, A being any point, and O the instantaneous center, the velocity of A is found as follows:

$$v_A = v_{A/O} \nleftrightarrow v_O = v_{A/O} \nleftrightarrow 0 = \omega \cdot OA$$

Similarly, the velocity of B is $\omega \cdot OB$, and hence the velocities of A and B vary as their distances from the instantaneous center. Or, expressed in equational form,

$$\frac{v_A}{v_B} = \frac{\omega \cdot OA}{\omega \cdot OB} = \frac{OA}{OB}$$

If should be noted that the instantaneous center is the center of zero velocity and *not* of zero acceleration. In the case of the motion of rotation of a rigid body about a fixed axis, which is a special case of plane motion, the axis of rotation is also the instantaneous axis, and it has zero acceleration as well as zero velocity since it is at rest. In the general case of plane motion, however, the instantaneous center changes its position in the body and also in space. Although the velocity of the point in the body, coinciding with the instantaneous center at a given instant, is zero, the velocity is changing through its zero value, and hence the point has an acceleration. Therefore, in the equation

$$a_A = a_{A/O} \mathbin{+\mkern-8mu+} a_O$$

in which A is any point and O is the instantaneous center, a_O is not zero. Hence, the absolute acceleration, at any instant, of a point in a rigid body having plane motion cannot be found by considering the body to be rotating about a *fixed* axis through the instantaneous center of zero velocity, as may be done in determining the velocity of any point of the body.

Illustrative Problem

Problem 436. The four-link mechanism $ABCD$ shown in Fig. 283 has the following dimensions: $AB = 6$ in.; $BC = 3$ ft; $DC = 2$ ft; $AD = 4$ ft; $\theta = 45°$. Find the instantaneous center for the link BC. If the crank AB rotates at a constant angular velocity $\omega = 10$ rad/sec, find the angular velocities ω_2 of the link DC, and ω_3 of the link BC. Also find the linear velocity v_H of H, the mid-point of BC.

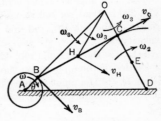

Fig. 283

SOLUTION. The instantaneous center for the link BC is O, the point of intersection of the lines AB and DC extended. By scaling off the lengths of OB, OC, and OH, the following values are found:

$$OB = 3.1 \text{ ft}, \qquad OC = 0.96 \text{ ft}, \qquad OH = 1.72 \text{ ft}$$

The velocity of B, considered as a point on AB, is

$$v_B = \omega \times AB = 10 \times \tfrac{6}{12} = 5 \text{ ft/sec}$$

Therefore, the angular velocity of B, considered as a point on BC, is

$$\omega_3 = \frac{v_B}{OB} = \frac{5}{3.1} = 1.61 \text{ rad/sec}$$

and the angular velocities, about O, of all points on BC are the same. The linear velocity of C is, therefore,

$$v_C = \omega_3 \times OC = 1.61 \times 0.96 = 1.54 \text{ ft/sec}$$

and

$$v_H = \omega_3 \times OH = 1.61 \times 1.72 = 2.77 \text{ ft/sec}$$

Therefore,

$$\omega_2 = \frac{v_C}{DC} = \frac{1.54}{2} = 0.77 \text{ rad/sec}$$

Problems

437. Use the data of Prob. 420, and find by the instantaneous-center method the angular velocity of the bar AB in Fig. 276 and the linear velocity of the mid-point of the bar.   *Ans.* $\omega = 1.732$ rad/sec; $v_P = 3.46$ ft/sec; $\theta_x = 330°$.

438. Use the data of Prob. 421, and find: (a) the velocity of the point C on the bar CD (Fig. 277) when CD is perpendicular to AB, by the method of relative motion, (b) the instantaneous center of the bar CD, and (c) the linear velocity of the point D by the instantaneous-center method.

439. Use the data of Prob. 422, and find by the instantaneous-center method the angular velocities ω_1 and ω_2 of the bars CD and BC of the four-link mechanism shown in Fig. 278. Find also the linear velocity of the mid-point of the bar BC.

Ans. $v_P = 3.35$ ft/sec; $\theta_x = 153° 30'$.

440. The angular velocity of the bar BD of the four-link mechanism shown in Fig. 280 is 2 rad/sec counterclockwise. Determine the position of the instantaneous center of the link BC, and find the angular velocities of BC and AC and the linear velocity of C.

441. Use the data of Prob. 424, and find by the instantaneous-center method the velocities of three points on the disk shown in Fig. 279 located as follows: (a) the point D, (b) the point midway between D and H, and (c) the point on the circumference of the disk midway between B and C.

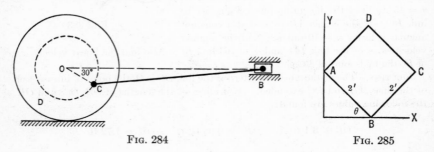

FIG. 284   FIG. 285

442. The diameter of a freight-car wheel, excluding the flange, is 33 in.; the diameter, including the flange, is 37 in. If the car is traveling at a speed of 30 mi/hr, find the velocity of the lowest point on the flange and also the velocity of the point on the flange at the forward end of the horizontal diameter of the wheel.

Ans. $v = 5.33$ ft/sec; $\theta_x = 180°$; $v = 66.1$ ft/sec; $\theta_x = 311° 40'$.

443. The diameter of the driver D of a locomotive, as shown in Fig. 284, is 5 ft, the length of the crank OC is 1.5 ft, and the length of the connecting rod CB is 8 ft. If the speed of the locomotive is 60 mi/hr, find the angular velocity of the connecting rod and the linear velocity of the crosshead B when the crank pin C is in the position shown. *Ans.* $\omega = 5.74$ rad/sec; $v = 57.3$ ft/sec.

444. In Fig. 285, $ABCD$ is a board 2 ft square. A moves downward on the Y axis with a velocity of 6 ft/sec, and B moves on the X axis. Find the velocities of C and D when $\theta = 60°$. Solve algebraically, making use of the method of instantaneous centers.

445. Find the velocities of C and D in Prob. 444 when $\theta = 30°$. Solve graphically. *Ans.* $v_C = 4.3$ ft/sec; $v_D = 6.5$ ft/sec.

Review Questions

1. Point out and correct the error in each of the following statements:

(a) The linear velocity of a point is the time rate of change of the linear displacement of the point.

(b) The total linear acceleration of a point moving on any curved path is defined as the rate of change of the speed of the point and is expressed mathematically by the equation $a = dv/dt$.

(c) If a point moves on a circular path, the velocity is tangent to the path and hence can have no component toward the center of the circle; therefore, there can be no acceleration toward the center of the circle.

(d) The angular velocity of a point moving in a plane is the same with respect to all points in the plane.

(e) In uniformly accelerated rectilinear motion, the velocity of the moving point is constant.

(f) The tangential acceleration of a point moving on a curved path is equal to the product of the angular velocity of the point with respect to the center of curvature and the radius of curvature.

(g) Simple harmonic motion of a point is a periodic motion in a straight line such that the velocity of the point is proportional to the displacement of the point from a fixed origin in the line and is directed away from the origin.

2. If a rigid bar is given a plane motion, explain why the velocity of one end relative to the other end must be in a direction perpendicular to the length of the bar. Is the acceleration of one end relative to the other end perpendicular to the bar?

3. When plane motion of a rigid body is regarded as a combination of a rotation and a translation, state what angular velocity and angular acceleration are assumed to be given to the body in the rotational motion and what linear velocity and linear acceleration are assumed in the translational motion.

4. A rigid body has a plane motion, and the directions, only, of the velocities of two points in the plane of motion are known. If the velocities of the two points are in the same direction, can the instantaneous center of the body be located? If not, what additional information is needed?

5. If a point has a rectilinear motion, is the average velocity for any displacement of the point always equal to one half of the sum of the initial and final velocities?

6. A point moves on a circular path with a constant speed. What additional information is needed in order to find the direction of the acceleration of the point at any instant?

7. If a point has a rectilinear motion and its acceleration is zero when $t = 1$ sec, $t = 2$ sec, and $t = 3$ sec, what conclusion can be drawn concerning the $(v–t)$ curve for the motion?

8. The velocity of a point that moves along a straight line is defined by the equation $v = at$. What conclusion may be drawn concerning the motion of the point?

9. Correct the error in the following statement: The linear acceleration of a point that moves along a curved path is equal to the product of the radius of curvature of the path and the angular acceleration of the point with respect to the center of curvature.

10. A rigid bar has a plane motion. At a given instant the bar is in a vertical position, and the upper end of the bar has a velocity of 10 ft/sec directed downward to the right at an angle of 45° with the horizontal. Is it possible for the lower end of the bar to have a velocity directed: (a) horizontally to the right, (b) vertically downward, (c) horizontally to the left, (d) vertically upward?

11. Which one of the following statements is correct? If a particle moves along the parabola $y^2 = ax$ with constant speed, its acceleration is: (a) in the direction of the velocity, (b) perpendicular to the velocity, (c) equal to zero.

12. A point moves along an ellipse with constant speed. At what points on the ellipse is the acceleration of the point: (a) a maximum, (b) a minimum?

PART THREE
Kinetics

Chapter 9

FORCE, MASS,
AND ACCELERATION

§ 1 Preliminary Considerations. Kinetics of a Particle

88 Introduction. *Kinetics* is that branch of mechanics which treats of the laws in accordance with which the motion of physical bodies takes place.

A *change* in the state of motion of a body always occurs when an *unbalanced* force system acts on the body, the unbalanced part (resultant) of the force system being the cause of the change in the motion. Experience teaches that the change of motion of the body is influenced both by the characteristics (Art. 5) of the resultant of the forces acting on the body and by the nature of the body itself. For example, different force systems acting, in turn, on the same body do not produce the same change of motion of the body. Similarly, the same force system applied to different bodies does not produce the same change in the motion of all of the bodies.

Although experience suggests that relations exist among the force system acting on a body, the properties of the body, and the change in the motion of the body, it required the work of many eminent men and a period of several centuries before definite and complete fundamental relations among these three factors were finally established. The laws expressing these relations were formulated by Sir Isaac Newton (1642–1727) and are known as Newton's laws of motion.

Newton's fundamental laws, however, apply directly only to the motion of a particle under the action of a single force, whereas in engineering practice the motion of a body (system of particles) under the action of a system of forces must be considered. The body may be rigid or non-rigid, and the force system acting on the body may produce any type of motion. The bodies treated hereafter, however, will, for the most part, be regarded as rigid, and the motions treated will, in general, be restricted to translation, rotation, and plane motion.

89 The general kinetics problem. In each type of motion the general character of the kinetics problem is the same; namely, a physical body is acted on by a force system that has a resultant, which causes a change in the motion of the body, and in each problem it is required to deduce, by the use of Newton's laws, the equations expressing the definite relations among (1) the resultant of the force system, (2) the kinetic properties (mass, moment of inertia, etc.) of the body, and (3) the change of motion of the body, so that the motion of a given body produced by a given force system may be determined, or the force system required to produce a given motion may be found. The equations that express these relations are called the *equations of motion* for the body.

The three elements or factors that are involved in the equations of motion of bodies may be considered briefly before stating Newton's laws and before deriving the equations that express the relations among these three factors. Change of motion is measured by acceleration, which in turn may be expressed in terms of distance, time, and velocity, as discussed in Chapter 7. The characteristics of the resultant of a force system have also been considered, in Chapter 2, and need only be reviewed briefly at this point (see next article) to show their connection with the general problem in kinetics. The property of the body (mass) that enables it to have an influence in determining its own motion, however, needs to be discussed at greater length (see Art. 91).

90   Characteristics of a force system.   The only part of a force system that influences the motion of a body is the unbalanced part (resultant) of the force system. Force systems that produce the types of motion considered in this chapter are coplanar (or may be replaced by equivalent systems that are coplanar), and, hence, the resultant of the forces is either a force or a couple (Art. 23). If the resultant is a force, the characteristics of the resultant that influence the motion of the body on which the force system acts are (1) its magnitude, (2) the position of its action line in the body, and (3) its sense (Art. 5). If, however, the resultant is a couple, the characteristics of the resultant that influence the motion of the body on which the force system acts are (1) the moment of the couple, (2) the sense of the couple, and (3) the aspect or direction of the plane of the couple (Art. 16).

The equations of motion of a body must be sufficient in number to take account of the influence of all the characteristics of the resultant of the force system. This may be done, for the types of motion considered in this chapter, by means of three equations. These three equations will contain the algebraic sum of the x components of the forces acting on the body, the algebraic sum of the y components, and the algebraic sum of the moments of the forces about some axis in the body (Art. 25).

91   Inertia and Mass. That property of a body by virtue of which a body offers resistance to a change in its motion is called *inertia*. Thus, inertia is the property that makes the body itself a factor in controlling the change of motion which occurs when the body is acted on by an unbalanced force system. Although all bodies possess the property of inertia, all bodies do not offer the same resistance to a change in their motion. That is, all bodies influence their motions according to the same law but not to the same degree. In other words, all bodies do not offer the same resistance to being accelerated at a given rate.*

The quantitative measure of the inertia of a body, that is, the resistance the body offers to being accelerated at a given rate, is called the *mass* of the body, and is found, like other properties of bodies, by experiment. This may be done as follows:

Let a given body be acted on by a single force F_1, and let the resulting acceleration be a_1. In like manner let forces F_2, F_3, etc., be applied in turn to the body, and let the resulting accelerations be a_2, a_3, etc. The results of such an experiment show that

$$\frac{F_1}{a_1} = \frac{F_2}{a_2} = \frac{F_3}{a_3} = \cdots \text{ a constant} = C \text{ (say)}$$

or, in general, if any force F applied to the body causes an acceleration a

$$\frac{F}{a} = C \tag{1}$$

Now, since C is the measure of the resistance F that the body offers to being accelerated at a rate a, it is proportional to the mass M of the body since the mass of a body is defined as a measure of the resistance the body offers to being accelerated at a given rate. Hence, $C = kM$, where k is a constant. Then Eq. 1 becomes

$$\frac{F}{a} = kM \tag{2}$$

The foregoing experiment is a verification of Newton's second law, which is stated in Art. 92, and Eq. 2 is a mathematical statement of that law. If units for F, a, and M are so chosen that k in Eq. 2 equals unity

---

* The way in which bodies resist motion is analogous to the manner in which elastic materials, such as steel, resist being stretched. Each material, within limits, resists according to the same law (stretch is proportional to stress), but some materials resist to a greater degree; that is, some materials are stiffer than others, which means that some materials require a greater force to produce a given stretch than do other materials, just as some bodies require a greater force to produce a given acceleration than do other bodies.

(as will be discussed in Art. 93), then the expression for the mass M may be written

$$M = \frac{F}{a} \tag{3}$$

Hence, if a body is acted on by a single force F which is known and the resulting acceleration a is measured, the mass of the body may be found from Eq. 3. One convenient method of applying a single force to a body is to allow the body to fall freely under the influence of its weight W (the attraction of the earth). The resulting acceleration will then be $g(32.2 \text{ ft/sec}^2)$, and hence the number of units of mass of the body may be found from its weight by the equation

$$M = \frac{W}{g}$$

It should be emphasized that the mass of a body is an invariant property of the body and is not influenced by its velocity,* acceleration, or position relative to the earth. On the other hand, the weight W of a body is defined to be the force with which the earth attracts the body, and this force is dependent on the position of the body on the earth's surface and on the height of the body above the earth's surface. In most engineering problems, however, the variation of the weight of a body is small and may be disregarded.

92 Newton's laws. Newton established his laws of motion from a study of the motion of planets. Since the dimensions of a planet are negligible in comparison with the range of its motion, Newton's laws apply directly only to a particle: that is, to a body all points of which may be considered at any instant to have the same acceleration. In most cases of motion of bodies, however, the accelerations of different particles of the body are not the same, and hence Newton's laws do not apply directly to bodies. Bodies, however, may be considered to be made up of particles, and thus Newton's laws may be extended to bodies.

Newton's laws may be stated as follows:

> First Law. If no force acts on a particle, the particle remains at rest or continues to move with uniform velocity in a straight line.
>
> Second Law. If a force acts on a particle, the particle is accelerated; the direction of the acceleration is the same as that of

---

* At very high velocities approaching the velocity of light the mass of a body increases because of relativity effects. In engineering problems, however, the velocities of bodies are such that the mass may be regarded as constant.

the force, and its magnitude is directly proportional to the force and inversely proportional to the mass of the particle.

THIRD LAW. There are mutual actions between any two particles of a system (body) such that the action of one particle on the other is collinear with and equal and opposite to that of the other on the one.

1. The first law implies that a particle has inertia; that is, it resists having its motion changed. It implies that a force must act on the particle if its motion (velocity) is changed either in direction or in magnitude: that is, if an acceleration is produced.

2. The second law is a quantitative one. It states what the magnitude and the direction of the force must be in order to produce a given acceleration of a given particle, and shows that, although a particle cannot, of itself, change its state of motion, it does nevertheless influence the change of motion caused by the force, by regulating or governing the manner in which the acceleration shall take place: namely, that it shall be always inversely proportional to the mass of the particle.

3. In the second law, it is assumed that a single particle is acted upon by a single force. But the third law brings out the fact that a single force does not exist. The special significance of the third law lies in the fact that by its use Newton's second law, which applies only to a single particle under the influence of a single force, may be extended to a system of particles (body) acted on by a system of forces.

93 Mathematical statement of Newton's second law. Units.

Newton's second law may be expressed mathematically by the equation

$$F = kma \qquad (1)$$

in which a is the acceleration of a particle of mass m, F is the single force acting on the particle, and k is a constant factor the value of which depends upon the units used to express the other quantities (F, m, and a) in the equation. In general, the mass of a body will be denoted by M and that of a particle of the body by m or dM.

It is convenient to use a system of units in which k in Eq. 1 is unity. Such a system of units is sometimes called a *kinetic system*. Thus, a kinetic system of units is one in which a unit force acting on a unit mass causes a unit acceleration. Now, in engineering problems, the units of force and acceleration are chosen arbitrarily, and hence the unit of mass is a derived unit—derived from the units of force and acceleration, since, if a kinetic system of units is used, $m = F/a = W/g$. A system of units in which the unit of mass is a derived unit is frequently called a *gravitational* system.

Thus, if one pound is chosen as the unit of force and one foot per second per second as the unit of acceleration, as is usual in engineering calculations, then, since $M = W/g$, the number of units of mass in a body is the weight of the body in pounds divided by the acceleration of gravity g in feet per second per second (32.2). Thus, a body weighing g (32.2) pounds has one unit of mass; this fact has suggested the name *g-pound* or *geepound* for this unit of mass. However, no name has gained general acceptance, although the name *slug* (from sluggishness which suggests inertia) has gained rather wide acceptance and will be employed in the subsequent pages. It is also frequently referred to as the *engineer's unit of mass*. In using a special name such as slug, it is important to keep in mind that the unit of mass is not an arbitrarily chosen unit but is derived from the units of force and acceleration.

In another system of units used considerably in electrical engineering, the units of mass, length, and time are chosen arbitrarily, and the unit of force is the derived unit. Such a system is frequently called an *absolute* system of units. If one gram is chosen as the unit of mass, one centimeter as the unit of length, and one second as the unit of time, a unit force is a force that gives an acceleration of one centimeter per second per second to a mass of one gram. This force is called a *dyne*.

94   Equations of motion for a particle. In Fig. 286, a particle of

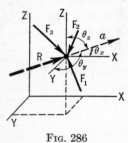

FIG. 286

mass m is acted on by any system of forces F_1, F_2, F_3, etc., which give to the particle an acceleration a. It is required to find the equations that express the relations among the forces acting on the particle, the mass of the particle, and the acceleration of the particle. Let R denote the resultant of the forces acting on the particle, and let θ_x, θ_y, θ_z denote the angles that R makes with the X, Y, and Z axes, respectively. From Newton's second law, we have $R = ma$. Multiplying each side of this equation by $\cos \theta_x$, we have

$$R \cos \theta_x = ma \cos \theta_x \quad \text{or} \quad R_x = ma_x$$

But in Chapter 2 it was found that R_x may also be expressed in terms of the forces acting on the particle by the equation $R_x = \Sigma F_x$, and hence we have $\Sigma F_x = ma_x$. Similarly, equations may be obtained by expressing in two ways the y and z components of the resultant of the forces acting on the particle. Hence the equations of motion for a particle are

$$\Sigma F_x = ma_x$$

$$\Sigma F_y = ma_y$$

$$\Sigma F_z = ma_z$$

95 Procedure in the solution of problems in kinetics. In solving problems in kinetics, it is important to follow a rather definite procedure as outlined in the following five steps. This procedure will be carried out in the solution of the problems immediately following this article, in which the bodies are treated as particles, as well as in the solution of problems involving rigid bodies having various types of motion, which will be considered later. The student should study this procedure carefully and follow it closely.

1. Determine carefully: (a) what is given in the problem and (b) what is required in the problem. The quantities involved in this step may frequently be indicated by means of an illustrative sketch. Failure to carry out this step is a common cause of difficulty in the solution of problems.

2. Draw a complete free-body diagram of the body whose motion is under consideration (see Art. 38 for discussion of free-body diagram). That is, show the body and all the forces exerted on it by other bodies. This diagram is of particular importance in determining the left-hand member of each of the equations of motion for the body.

3. Write all the equations of motion for the body, and select the axes to be used in applying these equations. These axes should be shown in the free-body diagram. Frequently, by a proper choice of axes, the problem may be solved without using all the equations of motion. As a rule, it is convenient to select one axis parallel to the acceleration of the particle and to make the positive direction of the axis agree with the sense of the acceleration. Likewise, when dealing with rotational motion, the positive direction of rotation will usually be made to agree with the sense of the angular acceleration of the body. The positive directions are chosen in this way for the purpose of making the right-hand sides of the equations of motion positive.

4. Observe whether there is a sufficient number of equations of motion to determine all the quantities desired. If there is not, write any equations in addition to the equations of motion (such as kinematics equations) that apply to the particular problem, and, if possible, solve the equations, and determine the unknown quantities.

5. If, however, there are still more unknowns than there are equations, it is usually possible, when several bodies are involved in the motion, to select another body (or group of bodies) in the system on which is acting one (or more) of the forces that acts on the first body, and to treat the motion of this second body by the foregoing procedure, and then to solve the two sets of equations simultaneously.

NOTE. In the problems that follow, the assumption is made that the bodies having the motions described may be considered to be particles without serious errors being introduced in the analysis of the motion. In the solution of the following illustrative problems, the steps in the foregoing procedure are emphasized.

Illustrative Problems

Problem 446. In Fig. 287, A and B are bodies suspended from the ends of a flexible, inextensible, weightless rope that passes over a smooth cylindrical surface. The weight of A is 40 lb, and the weight of B is 30 lb. Find the tensile stress in the rope and the acceleration of A and B.

SOLUTION. Since the cylindrical surface is frictionless and the rope is flexible, the force (stress) T in the rope has the same value on each side of the cylinder. Furthermore, since the rope does not stretch, the bodies A and B have accelerations that are equal in magnitude. The unknown force T, therefore, is a force acting on each of the two bodies. A free-body diagram of B is shown in Fig. 287, the axes being chosen in accordance with step 3 of Art. 95. There is one equation of motion only for this body, namely:

$$\Sigma F_y = ma_y \quad \text{or} \quad T - 30 = \frac{30}{32.2} a \tag{1}$$

Since there are two unknown quantities in this equation, T cannot be found. Hence, in accordance with step 5 of Art. 95 a free-body diagram of A is drawn (which also involves the force T). For this body there is also one equation of motion, namely:

$$\Sigma F_y = ma_y \quad \text{or} \quad 40 - T = \frac{40}{32.2} a \tag{2}$$

The solution of the two simultaneous equations gives the following results:

$$T = 34.3 \text{ lb} \quad \text{and} \quad a = 4.60 \text{ ft/sec}^2$$

Problem 447. A small body weighing 4 lb is attached to one end of a string 5 ft long and is made to revolve as a conical pendulum with a constant angular velocity ω, so that the string is inclined $30°$ to the vertical as shown in Fig. 288. Find the magnitudes of the tension T in the string and the linear velocity v of the body.

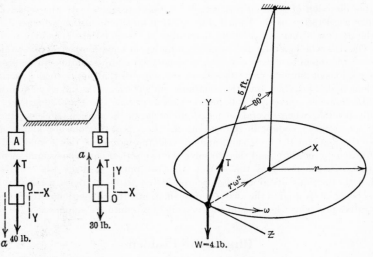

FIG. 287   FIG. 288

SOLUTION. The body moves on a circular path in a horizontal plane under the influence of two forces T and W as shown in the free-body diagram (Fig. 288). The acceleration of the body is $r\omega^2$, or v^2/r, toward the center of the circle. The equations of motion are

$$\Sigma F_x = ma_x = \frac{W}{g} r\omega^2 = \frac{W}{g}\frac{v^2}{r} \tag{1}$$

$$\Sigma F_z = ma_z = \frac{W}{g} r\alpha = 0 \quad \text{since} \quad \alpha = 0 \tag{2}$$

$$\Sigma F_y = ma_y = 0 \quad \text{since} \quad a_y = 0 \tag{3}$$

Equation 1 gives

$$T \cos 60° = \frac{4}{32.2} \times \frac{v^2}{5 \sin 30°} \tag{4}$$

Equation 3 gives

$$T \cos 30° - 4 = 0; \qquad \therefore \ T = 4.62 \text{ lb} \tag{5}$$

By substituting this value of T in Eq. 4, the value of v may be found. Thus,

$$4.62 \cos 60° = \frac{4}{32.2} \times \frac{v^2}{5 \sin 30°}$$

Hence,

$$v^2 = \frac{4.62 \times 0.5 \times 32.2 \times 5 \times 0.5}{4} = 46.3$$

Therefore,

$$v = 6.8 \text{ ft/sec}$$

Problem 448. In Fig. 289, A is a small block attached to the end of a vertical rod B whose lower end is connected to a smooth horizontal pin at O. The rod and block are given a very small displacement and then allowed to rotate about the pin at O. If the weight of the rod B is negligible, show that the velocity of A is $\sqrt{2gr}$ when B reaches a horizontal position.

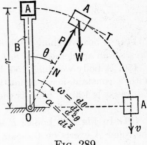

Fig. 289

SOLUTION. The only forces acting on A are its weight W and the reaction of the bar B, denoted by P. A free-body diagram of A is shown in Fig. 289. The equations of motion for A are

$$\Sigma F_t = ma_t \quad \text{or} \quad W \sin \theta = \frac{W}{g} r \frac{d^2\theta}{dt^2} \tag{1}$$

$$\Sigma F_n = ma_n \quad \text{or} \quad W \cos \theta - P = \frac{W}{g} r \left(\frac{d\theta}{dt}\right)^2 \tag{2}$$

Equation 1 gives

$$\frac{d^2\theta}{dt^2} = \frac{g}{r} \sin \theta \tag{3}$$

Multiplying each side of Eq. 3 by $d\theta/dt$, we have

$$\frac{d\theta}{dt}\frac{d^2\theta}{dt^2} = \frac{g}{r} \sin \theta \frac{d\theta}{dt} \tag{4}$$

Integrating Eq. 4 with respect to t, we obtain

$$\frac{1}{2}\left(\frac{d\theta}{dt}\right)^2 = -\frac{g}{r} \cos \theta + C$$

Since

$$\frac{d\theta}{dt} = 0 \quad \text{when} \quad \theta = 0, \qquad C = \frac{g}{r}$$

Hence,

$$\omega = \frac{d\theta}{dt} = \sqrt{\frac{2g}{r}(1 - \cos\theta)}$$

When

$$\theta = \frac{\pi}{2}, \qquad \omega = \sqrt{\frac{2g}{r}}$$

Hence,

$$v = r\omega = r\sqrt{\frac{2g}{r}} = \sqrt{2gr}$$

It will be noted that the body A would attain the same velocity if, starting from rest, it were to fall freely through a vertical distance r.

Problems

449. A box weighing 20 lb rests on the floor of an elevator. If the elevator starts up with an acceleration of 8 ft/sec², what is the pressure on the floor of the elevator?

450. A body weighing 150 lb is attached to the lower end of a rope and is lowered with a constant acceleration by means of the rope. If the greatest pull the rope can resist is 120 lb, what is the least acceleration the body can have?

Ans. $a = 6.44$ ft/sec².

451. In Fig. 239 bodies B and C are raised vertically upward by the force that the roller A exerts on the cam B. The total weight of B and C is W lb. A couple (not shown) is applied to the crank AO causing the angle θ to increase from zero to $\pi/4$ rad at a constant rate of ω rad/sec. If friction is neglected, determine the force that A exerts on B in terms of W, r, θ, and ω.

452. A pilot causes his airplane to follow a circular path in a vertical plane at a constant speed of 300 mi/hr. The radius of the circle is ½ mile. If the pilot weighs 161 lb, determine the magnitude of the force that the airplane exerts on the pilot: (a) when the airplane is at the lowest point on its circular path, and (b) 6 sec before it reaches the lowest point.

453. The shaft AB and the balls C and D (Fig. 290) rotate at a constant angular velocity of 120 rpm. The weights of C and D are 9 lb and 12 lb, respectively. Find the reactions of the bearings at A and B on the shaft when the balls are in the position shown, neglecting the weight of the shaft and also of the rods connecting the balls to the shaft. *Ans.* $R_A = 23.4$ lb; $R_B = 2.40$ lb.

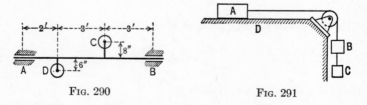

FIG. 290   FIG. 291

454. In Fig. 291, A weighs 30 lb, B weighs 20 lb, and C weighs 10 lb. The coefficient of friction for A and D is ⅓. If the weights of the cord and pulley are negligible and the pulley turns in smooth bearings, find the tension in the cord between A and B, and in the cord between B and C. Find also the acceleration of A, B, and C.

$$\text{Ans. } T_{AB} = 20 \text{ lb}; \; T_{BC} = 6.67 \text{ lb}; \; a = 10.73 \text{ ft/sec}^2.$$

455. A man weighing 150 lb stands in an elevator weighing 1850 lb. If the tension in the hoisting cable is 2600 lb, with what acceleration will the elevator ascend? What will be the pressure of the man on the floor of the elevator?

456. The block A in Fig. 215a has a weight W and slides in a horizontal slot as the oscillating arm OM rotates about O. If OM rotates from the position shown to the vertical position with a constant angular velocity ω, find in terms of W, θ, and ω the horizontal component of the force exerted on A by the pin. Neglect friction.

457. In Fig. 292, A weighs 20 lb, and B weighs 10 lb. The coefficient of friction for the surfaces of contact between A and the inclined plane is 0.1. If the weights of the cords and pulleys are negligible and the pulleys are frictionless, find the acceleration of A and the tension in the cord attached to A.

$$\text{Ans. } a = 4.68 \text{ ft/sec}^2; \; T = 5.36 \text{ lb}.$$

458. The bodies A and B (Fig. 293) and the frame on which they rest rotate about the vertical axis with a constant angular velocity of 30 rpm. The weights of A and B are 40 lb and 20 lb, respectively. Find the pressure of the stop E on B, neglecting the friction between A and B and the frame. $\quad$ *Ans.* $R_E = 15.3$ lb.

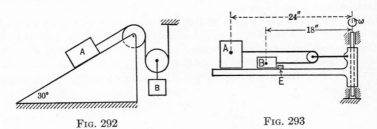

FIG. 292 $\qquad\qquad$ FIG. 293

459. A body weighing W lb rests on the floor of an elevator. When the elevator is ascending with a certain upward acceleration a, the pressure of the body on the floor of the elevator is 100 lb. When the elevator is descending with the same acceleration a downward, the pressure is 60 lb. Find W and a.

460. A wooden block weighing 16.1 lb and resting on a smooth horizontal plane is acted on by a horizontal force P of variable magnitude. If $P = 2t + 2$, where P is expressed in pounds and t in seconds, find the velocity of the body when $t = 3$ sec, if $v = 10$ ft/sec when $t = 0$. $\quad$ *Ans.* $v = 40$ ft/sec.

461. In Fig. 294, A is a small ball that weighs 4 lb, and B is a block that weighs 16 lb. A is attached to B at O by a weightless, flexible cord. A force P is applied to B, increasing very slowly until it reaches a value of 8 lb, after which it remains constant. Find the value of θ, assuming the plane on which B slides to be smooth.

462. In Fig. 295, B is a small body that starts from rest at A and slides on the surface of a smooth sphere until it leaves the surface at C. Find the angle θ.

$$\text{Ans. } \theta = \cos^{-1} \tfrac{2}{3} = 48° \, 11'.$$

463. In Fig. 296 the body A is attached to a flexible rope and is raised by winding the rope on a reel. The reel turns at a constant angular velocity of ω rad/sec. If

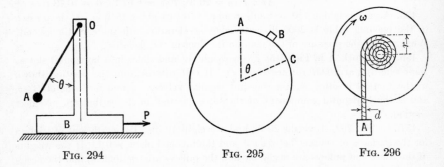

FIG. 294   FIG. 295   FIG. 296

the weight of A is W lb, the diameter of the rope is d in., and the weight of the rope is neglected, find the tension in the rope. Assume that A moves only vertically.

$$Ans. \ T = W\left(1 + \frac{\omega^2 d}{2\pi g}\right).$$

464. A 2-ton cage descending a shaft with a speed of 8 yd/sec is brought to rest with a uniform acceleration in a distance of 24 ft. What is the tension in the cable while the cage is coming to rest?

465. An automobile that weighs 3000 lb is accelerated uniformly on a level road from 10 mi/hr to 55 mi/hr in 11 sec. Calculate the frictional force exerted on the tires by the road, neglecting air resistance.   *Ans.* $F = 559$ lb.

466. In "looping the loop" (Fig. 297), show that, if friction is neglected, the minimum value of the velocity of the car when at C is $\sqrt{gd/2}$ if the car does not leave the track.

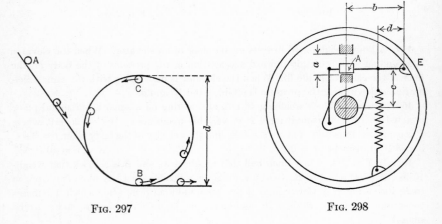

FIG. 297   FIG. 298

467. In Fig. 298 is shown one type of centrifugal shaft governor. Determine the initial tension in the spring in order that body A will not leave the inner stop until a speed of 210 rpm is reached. Assume that the weight of A is 16.1 lb, $b = 24$ in.,

$c = 8$ in., and $d = 16$ in. Also assume that the governor rotates about a vertical axis. *Ans. T = 242 lb.*

468. A man who is just strong enough to lift a 160-lb body when standing on the ground can lift only a 120-lb body from the floor of an elevator when the elevator is going up with a certain acceleration. Determine the acceleration. Determine the maximum weight of a body that the man can lift from the floor when the elevator is going down with the same acceleration.

469. The body A in Fig. 210 moves to the right with a constant velocity of 10 ft/sec, and the block B slides in a vertical slot in A. If B weighs 8 lb, find the tension in the rod OB when $\theta = 30°$. Neglect friction and the weight of the bar OB. *Ans. T = 31.3 lb.*

470. In Fig. 299, B is a smooth disk that is rotating about a vertical shaft YY with an angular velocity of 8 rad/sec, and A is a small body weighing 2 lb that is connected to the shaft by a spring. The modulus of the spring (or the spring constant) is 4 lb/in.; that is, the force required to elongate the spring 1 in. is 4 lb. Find the elongation of the spring if its unstretched length is 22 in. Assume $g = 32$ ft/sec². *Ans. e = 2 in.*

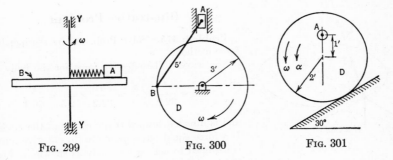

FIG. 299	FIG. 300	FIG. 301

471. The disk D in Fig. 300 rotates with a constant angular velocity $\omega = 2$ rad/sec. Body A weighs 16.1 lb and slides in a vertical slot. Determine the stress in the rigid rod AB when it is in the position shown. Neglect friction and the weight of the bar AB.

472. A small body A weighing 8.05 lb is attached by a smooth pin to the disk D shown in Fig. 301. The disk rolls without slipping down a plane inclined 30° to the horizontal. When A is vertically above the center of the disk, $\omega = 2$ rad/sec and $\alpha = 5$ rad/sec². Determine the force exerted by the pin on body A. *Ans. R_A = 6.73 lb; 120° 30′.*

473. A body which weighs 400 lb is lowered from rest by a cable a distance of 50 ft to a concrete platform. Find the minimum time necessary to lower the body if it is required that it be set on the platform without impact and if the maximum allowable tensile stress in the cable is 1000 lb.

474. A box is placed with no initial velocity on a conveyor belt which is inclined at an angle of 30° with the horizontal. The belt is moving upward with a uniform velocity of 10 ft/sec. If the coefficient of friction between the box and belt is 0.8, find the distance traveled by the box: (a) during the first second, and (b) during the first four seconds. *Ans. (a) 3.10 ft; (b) 32.0 ft.*

96 Inertia-force method for a particle. As pointed out in Art. 94, the resultant of all the forces that act on a particle having a mass

m and an acceleration a is a force having a magnitude ma and a direction the same as that of a. Furthermore, since the forces acting on a particle constitute a concurrent system, the action line of the resultant passes through the particle. Therefore, if a force equal to this resultant but of opposite sense is assumed to act on the particle in addition to the actual forces acting on the particle, the particle will be in equilibrium, and hence the equations of equilibrium may be applied to this force system. The reversed resultant (ma) force is called the *inertia force* for the particle. The resultant (ma) force is called the effective force for the particle, and hence the inertia force is sometimes called the reversed effective force. It will be observed that the introduction of the inertia force transforms the kinetics problem to an equivalent statics problem.

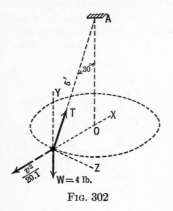

Fig. 302

Illustrative Problem

Problem 475. Solve Prob. 447 by the inertia-force method.

SOLUTION. The effective force for the body is

$$ma = \frac{4}{32.2} \times \frac{v^2}{r} = \frac{4}{32.2} \times \frac{v^2}{2.5} = \frac{v^2}{20.1}$$

and is directed toward O the center of the circle. If a force equal but opposite to the effective force is assumed to act on the body as shown in Fig. 302 in addition to T and W, the three forces would be in equilibrium, and hence the equations of equilibrium for a concurrent force system may be applied to the forces; thus,

$$\Sigma F_y = T \cos 30° - 4 = 0; \qquad \therefore \ T = 4.62 \text{ lb}$$

$$\Sigma F_x = 4.62 \sin 30° - \frac{v^2}{20.1} = 0$$

Hence,
$$v^2 = 46.4 \quad \text{or} \quad v = 6.80 \text{ ft/sec}$$

Problems

476. Solve Prob. 453 by the inertia-force method.

477. Solve Prob. 458 by the inertia-force method.

478. A body C weighing 8 lb rests upon a frame D (Fig. 303) which rotates about a vertical axis AB. When the frame is not rotating, the tension in the spring S is 15 lb. If the angular velocity of the frame is 30 rpm and the friction under C is neglected, what is the pressure against the stop at E? At what angular velocity of the frame will the body C start to move away from the stop?

479. A small body weighing 10 lb rests on an inclined surface (Fig. 304) which is revolved about a vertical axis with a constant angular velocity of 15 rpm. If the body is attached to the axis of rotation by a cord as shown in the figure, and if

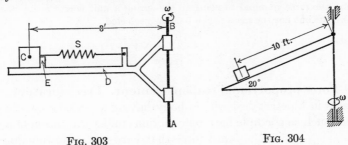

FIG. 303   FIG. 304

friction between the body and plane is neglected, find the tension T in the cord.

Ans. $T = 10.2$ lb.

480. Solve Prob. 472 by the inertia-force method.

481. A governor in Fig. 305a consists of a disk D which rests on two balls (or cylinders) each of which revolves as a conical pendulum. As the angular velocity of the disk and balls increases, the balls tend to swing farther away from the vertical axis of rotation thus raising the disk and decreasing the height h. The sensitivity of the governor is increased by loading the balls in this manner, and this type of governor is called a loaded governor. Determine the height h in terms of W, M, L, and ω where W denotes the weight and M the mass of each ball, L denotes the weight of the disk (load), and ω denotes the angular velocity of the governor. The forces which act on one of the balls with the reversed effective (inertia) force are shown in Fig. 305b.

Ans. $h = \dfrac{W + l/2}{M\omega^2}.$

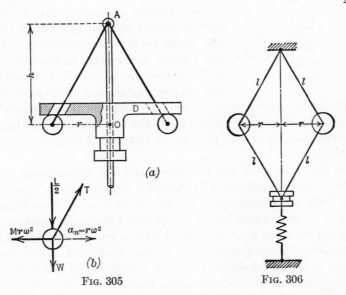

(a)

(b)

FIG. 305   FIG. 306

482. A spring-loaded governor is shown in Fig. 306. Let M be the mass of each ball, r the radius of the path of the balls, l the length of each of the four arms, and ω

the angular velocity of the balls. When the radius r is zero, the tension in the spring is T and the force required to elongate the spring a unit length is k. Show that, if the weight but not the mass of the balls be neglected,

$$\omega^2 = \frac{T + 2k(l - \sqrt{l^2 - r^2})}{M\sqrt{l^2 - r^2}}$$

97   Force proportional to displacement.   Free vibration.

Many problems in kinetics deal with a body having a periodic or vibrational motion (such as a simple harmonic motion) under the action of a result-

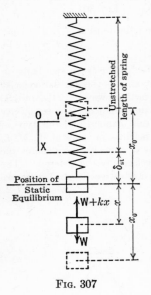

ant force that varies as some function of the displacement of the body. Such a force is usually applied to the body by means of a spring (or its equivalent), which exerts a force directly proportional to the displacement of the body. It is the purpose of this article to study briefly the periodic rectilinear motion of a body acted on by a resultant force whose magnitude is proportional to the displacement of the body from some fixed point in its path.

In Fig. 307 a small body whose weight is W is suspended from one end of a helical spring, thereby causing a displacement of the lower end of the spring equal to δ_{st} when the body and spring are in static equilibrium. A downward pull is then exerted on the body causing the displacement x_0 of the body from its equilibrium position; the pull is suddenly released, and the body undergoes a periodic (up and down) motion under the action of the earth pull (weight) and the force exerted by the spring. The main features of this periodic or vibrational motion are to be investigated.

Fig. 307

After the downward pull is released and the displacement from the position of static equilibrium has attained any value x, the forces acting on the body are as shown in Fig. 307, where k is the force required to stretch the spring a unit length and is called the *spring constant*. Thus the spring constant may be defined by the equation $k = W/\delta_{st}$. Or, in a somewhat more general form, it may be defined as the force that tends to restore the body to its initial equilibrium position divided by the corresponding displacement of the body.

If, in Fig. 307, the positive direction for x is downward, the equation of motion, $\Sigma F_x = ma_x$, may be written as follows:

$$-(W + kx) + W = \frac{W}{g} a_x = \frac{W}{g} \frac{d^2x}{dt^2} \tag{1}$$

Hence,

$$\frac{d^2x}{dt^2} = -\frac{kg}{W} x \tag{2}$$

in which kg/W is a constant. Equation 2 shows that the motion of the body is a simple harmonic motion (see Art. 75) since the acceleration is a constant times the displacement and has a direction opposite to that of the displacement. Equation 2 is the differential equation for the free or natural vibration of a particle.

It will be noted by reference to Art. 75 that the constant kg/W in Eq. 2 corresponds to ω^2 in the equation $a = d^2x/dt^2 = -\omega^2x$ which was obtained by considering a simple harmonic motion as the motion on the diameter of a circle, of the projection of a point that moves on the circle with constant angular velocity. In Art. 75 the solution of the equation $d^2x/dt^2 = -\omega^2x$ was found to be $x = r \cos \omega t$, and hence the solution of Eq. 2 is

$$x = C_1 \cos \sqrt{\frac{kg}{W}} t \tag{3}$$

in which C_1 is a constant whose value depends on the initial conditions of the motion. Thus, since the body was started in motion by giving it a displacement x_0 from its equilibrium position and then releasing it without initial velocity, we have $x = x_0$ when $t = 0$, and hence by substituting these values in Eq. 3 we find that $C_1 = x_0$. Therefore, the equation

$$x = x_0 \cos \sqrt{\frac{kg}{W}} t \tag{4}$$

expresses the relation between the displacement x and the time t for the free vibration of a particle. It is important to note that, in Eq. 4, x is measured from the equilibrium position of the body; or, in other words, the body oscillates about its equilibrium position.

The two properties or characteristics of the motion that are of particular significance are the amplitude and the period (or frequency) of the motion.

The amplitude, denoted by A, is the maximum value that x in

Eq. 4 can have. This value is x_0 since the maximum value of $\cos \sqrt{\frac{kg}{W}} t$ is unity.

The period of oscillation or of vibration, denoted by T, is the time required for the moving body to make one oscillation: that is, one complete cycle. Hence, the period of vibration is the time required for $\cos \sqrt{\dfrac{kg}{W}}\, t$ to pass through all of its values and return to the same value it had at the beginning of the period. Thus, T is the value of t in the equation $\sqrt{\dfrac{kg}{W}}\, t = 2\pi$. Hence,

$$T = 2\pi \sqrt{\frac{W}{kg}} = 2\pi \sqrt{\frac{\delta_{st}}{g}} \qquad (5)$$

It will be observed that the period of oscillation depends only on the spring constant and the weight of the body; the period varies directly as $\sqrt{W}$ and inversely as $\sqrt{k}$. For example, a stiff spring (having a large value of k) and a light weight (small value of W) will have a short period of vibration and a flexible spring, and a large weight will have a long period of vibration.

The frequency f of vibration is the number of complete cycles per unit of time, and hence

$$f = \frac{1}{T} = \frac{1}{2\pi} \sqrt{\frac{kg}{W}} = \frac{1}{2\pi} \sqrt{\frac{g}{\delta_{st}}} \qquad (6)$$

Equations 5 and 6 show that the natural period and frequency of vibration can be calculated from one measurable quantity alone: namely, the static elongation of the spring caused by the weight W of the body.

It is important to observe that the above equations apply only to free vibrations: namely, to the periodic motion of a body acted on only by its weight and a force exerted by a spring (or system of springs) such that the force is proportional to the displacement of the body and acts always to restore the position of the body to its equilibrium position. Thus, the motion of the body described by the foregoing equations does not occur in a resisting medium such as a liquid, which would produce a damped vibration rather than a free vibration. Nor is the motion a forced vibration in which an additional (periodic) force is applied to the body as it vibrates. In a forced vibration, if the period of the impressed force is the same as that of the free or natural period of vibration of the system, the theoretical amplitude of the vibration becomes exceedingly large. This condition is known as *resonance* and is, of course, to be avoided in parts of machines and structures. On the other hand, it is a condition that we often intuitively create when we wish to build up a large amplitude as, for example, in jumping on a spring board in order to execute a high dive. We create the same condition in causing a tree to fall after it has been chopped almost through at the base, by pushing repeatedly with our hand on the tree trunk with a force that has the same frequency as that of the free oscillations of the tree. Damped and forced vibrations, including the condition of resonance, are discussed briefly in Chapter 12.

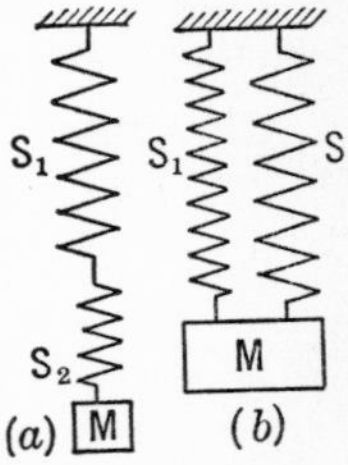

S_1 S_1 S_2

S_2 M

(a) M (b)

FIG. 308

Illustrative Problems

Problem 483. A body M is suspended from two springs, S_1 and S_2, as shown in Fig. 308. The spring constants are k_1 and k_2, respectively. In Fig. 308a the springs are in series, and in Fig. 308b the springs are in parallel. Determine in each case the equivalent spring constant: that is, the spring constant of a single spring from which the body M could be suspended and have the same period of vibration as when suspended from the two springs.

SOLUTION. (a) Assume a downward force of 1 unit to be applied to the body M in Fig. 308a. The elongations of S_1 and S_2 are $1/k_1$ and $1/k_2$, respectively. The total elongation of the two springs is $\dfrac{1}{k_1} + \dfrac{1}{k_2} = \dfrac{k_1 + k_2}{k_1 k_2}$. The force that must be applied to M to cause a total elongation of 1 unit, then, is $\dfrac{k_1 k_2}{k_1 + k_2}$. Hence, when the springs are in series, the equivalent spring constant k is

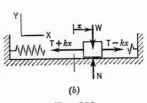

(a)

$$k = \frac{k_1 k_2}{k_1 + k_2}$$

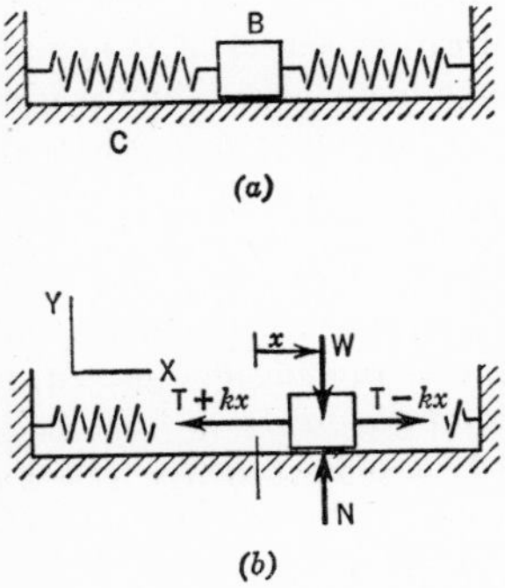

(b) Assume a downward force P is applied to the body M in Fig. 308b that will cause the springs S_1 and S_2 to elongate 1 unit. The increase in the forces in the two springs will then be numerically equal to the spring constants k_1 and k_2, respectively, and hence $P = k_1 + k_2$. Thus, when the springs are in parallel, the equivalent spring constant k is

$$k = k_1 + k_2$$

(b)

FIG. 309

Problem 484. A body B (Fig. 309a) weighing 16.1 lb is held in equilibrium by two springs in each of which there is a tensile stress of T lb. The body is displaced horizontally 2 in. from its equilibrium position and then released, causing the body to oscillate on the smooth surface C. If the spring constant for each spring is 20 lb/in., determine the frequency of oscillation of B.

SOLUTION. When the displacement of B from the equilibrium position is x in., the forces acting on B are as shown in Fig. 309b. By use of the equation of motion $\Sigma F_x = ma_x$, we have

$$T - kx - (T + kx) = \frac{W}{g} \frac{d^2x}{dt^2}$$

or

$$\frac{d^2x}{dt^2} = -\frac{2kg}{W} x$$

Since $d^2x/dt^2 = -\omega^2 x$ (Art. 75), we have

$$\omega^2 = \frac{2kg}{W} = \frac{2 \times 20 \times 32.2 \times 12}{16.1} = 960$$

and

$$\omega = 31.0 \text{ rad/sec}$$

$$\therefore f = \frac{\omega}{2\pi} = \frac{31.0}{2\pi} = 4.93 \text{ cycles/sec}$$

Problems

485. A machine that weighs 600 lb rests on a platform that weighs 200 lb. The platform and machine are supported by four springs, one at each corner of the platform, the four springs being alike. An additional downward force of 80 lb is applied at the center of the platform and compresses each spring 0.2 in. If the 80-lb force is suddenly removed, what will be the frequency and amplitude of the resulting vibratory motion, assuming that the motion of the platform is a translation only?

486. A vertical, helical spring, one end of which is attached to a fixed point, is stretched 3 in. by a body whose weight is 35 lb suspended from its lower end. The 35-lb body is lifted 3 in. so that the spring has its unstretched length and the body is then suddenly released. What will be the amplitude and frequency of the resulting motion? *Ans.* $A = 3$ in.; $f = 1.81$ cycles/sec.

487. Each of the springs on which a car is mounted carries a load of P lb and deflects vertically 2.5 in. under this load. What will be the frequency of the vertical oscillations of the car if a vertical force gives the springs an additional deflection and is then removed? *Ans.* $f = 1.98$ cycles/sec.

488. A steam pressure indicator consists of a small piston whose weight is 0.05 lb attached to a spring whose stiffness is 48 lb/in. The indicator is used to measure a variable steam pressure in the cylinder of an engine. In order that the error in the pressure recorded by the indicator when the engine is running not exceed 5 per cent, it is necessary that the natural frequency of the indicator be at least 4.58 times as great as the frequency of the fluctuations in the variable pressure. Determine the maximum frequency of the fluctuating pressure if the error in the recorded pressure is not to exceed 5 per cent.

489. A uniform bar weighing 40 lb is supported by two helical springs as shown in Fig. 310. When the bar is pulled down 2 in. from its equilibrium position and then released, the frequency of the resulting motion is 1.81 cycles/sec. What is the spring constant for each spring, assuming that the two springs are alike and that the bar has a motion of translation only? *Ans.* $k = 6.70$ lb/in.

490. A body A weighing 20 lb is supported by three springs, S_1, S_2, and S_3, as shown in Fig. 311. The spring constants are $k_1 = 20$ lb/in., $k_2 = 10$ lb/in., and $k_3 = 10$ lb/in., respectively. If the body is displaced vertically from its equilibrium position and then released, what is the frequency of the resulting motion?

491. A simple pendulum (Fig. 312) consists of a small body A of weight W lb attached to a weightless string of length l. The body (and string) is deflected a small angle θ from its vertical position and is then released. Let it be assumed that the body moves in a straight-line path since the angle θ is small. Show that the period of oscillation is $T = 2\pi\sqrt{l/g}$. *Hint:* The resultant of the forces acting on the body is approximately horizontal and equal to $P \sin \theta$ or $P\theta$ since θ is small. Also $P = W$ and $\theta = x/l$, approximately, where x is the displacement from the equilibrium position.

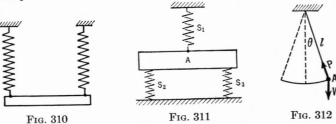

| Fig. 310 | Fig. 311 | Fig. 312 |

492. The expansion joints of a concrete highway are 42 ft apart. A two-wheeled trailer is pulled on the highway, and the expansion joints cause a series of impulses to be transmitted to the trailer. It is found that vibration of the trailer is excessive when the frequency of the impulses is equal to the natural frequency of vibration of the trailer for vertical motion. If the trailer weighs 1000 lb and is mounted on springs whose equivalent spring constant is 300 lb/in., determine the speed of the trailer in mi/hr at which excessive vibrations may be expected.

493. A body A is suspended from one end of a helical spring, and another body B is suspended from a cord that is attached to A. The static deflection of the spring due to the bodies A and B is 3 in. If the cord between A and B is cut, what will be the frequency and amplitude of the motion of A if the weight of A is four times that of B?   *Ans.* $f = 2.02$ cycles/sec; $A = 0.6$ in.

§ 2 Kinetics of Bodies

98 Introduction. Methods of analysis. As pointed out in the preceding section, the general character of a problem in kinetics of bodies may be stated as follows: A physical body is acted on by a force system that has a resultant which causes a change in the motion of the body, and relations are required among (1) the resultant of the external force system, (2) the properties of the body (mass, moment of inertia, etc.), and (3) the change in the motion of the body. For each of the types of motion of rigid bodies treated in this section, the equations that express the relations between the three factors or elements in the problem (equations of motion) are found by the same procedure or series of steps, as follows:

1. The body is considered to be composed of particles, and, from the motion of the body, the acceleration a of any particle in the body is

found, both in magnitude and in direction. This step involves the use of the facts and equations developed in the study of kinematics.

2. From the acceleration a of any particle and its mass m, the force required to produce the acceleration is found, both in magnitude and in direction, by applying Newton's second law. This force R is called the *effective force* for the particle and, in accordance with Newton's second law, may be expressed by the equation $R = ma$, the direction of R being the same as that of a. Since R is the resultant of the actual forces acting on the particle, it may also be expressed in terms of the actual forces. Thus, by expressing the resultant of the forces acting on the particle in two ways: (1) in terms of m and a and (2) in terms of the actual forces acting on the particle, the relation among the forces acting on the particle, the mass of the particle, and the acceleration of the particle may be found.

It should be noted that some (most) of the particles of a body are acted on by internal forces only (in addition to their weights), that is, by the neighboring particles of the body, and some of the particles (located where the external forces are applied to the body) are acted on by both internal and external forces.

3. The magnitude and the direction of the effective force for each particle of the body having been determined, in terms of the mass and acceleration of the particle, the resultant of the effective forces for all the particles of the body is found completely by the same methods as were used in Chapter 2 for finding the resultant of a given system of forces. The effective forces for bodies having the motions considered in this section may be assumed to form a coplanar force system. Therefore, the characteristics of the resultant of the effective forces, in general, may be expressed by writing three equations (Art. 37) involving the summations of the x components of the effective forces, of the y components of the effective forces, and of the moments of the effective forces about some axis.

4. In the preceding step, the resultant of the forces acting on all the particles is expressed in terms of the effective (ma) forces; it may also be expressed in terms of the actual forces which include all the internal forces and all the external forces. But in obtaining the summations of the x and of the y components, and of the moments of these forces, the internal forces drop out of the expressions since they occur in collinear pairs, the forces of each pair being equal and opposite (Newton's third law). Therefore,

The resultant of the effective forces for the particles of a body is identical with the resultant of the external forces which act on the body. Or,

The resultant of the effective forces for all the particles of a
body, if reversed and assumed to act on the body with the external forces, will hold the body in equilibrium.

The principle stated in these two forms is known as D'Alembert's
principle. It will be noted, therefore, that D'Alembert's principle in
the second form makes it possible to reduce a problem in kinetics to an
equivalent problem in statics by introducing a force (or forces) which
may be found completely from the motion of the body by means of the
first three steps of the foregoing outline.

99 Motion of the mass center of a system of particles. The
steps outlined in the preceding article will be used first to deduce an
important principle of kinetics, which is applicable to the motion of any
mass system (rigid or non-rigid) moving in any way, called the *principle
of the motion of the mass center.*

Let a system of particles (Fig. 313) whose masses are denoted by m',
m'', m''', etc., move in any way under the action of any force system.
The principle of the motion of the mass center expresses the relation
among the external forces acting on this mass system, the mass M of
the whole system, and the acceleration of one point in the system:

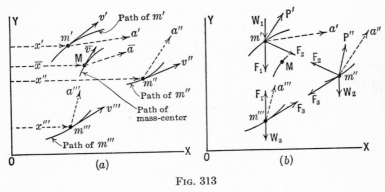

Fig. 313

namely, the mass center of the system. The principle may be deduced
as follows:

In Fig. 313a only three particles are shown, and for convenience the
particles are assumed to move in a plane. The forces that act on each
particle and give the particle its acceleration are shown in Fig. 313b.
The forces acting on any particle are external forces with respect to the
particle. Some of these forces are exerted by other particles of the
system and hence are internal forces with respect to the whole body
(such as forces F_1 and F_2 acting on the particle of mass m'); in addition,
any particle may also be acted on by forces that are external to the body.

The internal forces occur, of course, in equal, opposite, and collinear pairs. For example, in Fig. 313b the particle of mass m' is acted on by two external forces, namely, the earth pull W_1 (weight of the particle) and the force P', and by two internal forces, F_1 and F_2.

Step 1. The acceleration of each particle is here assumed to be known; a', a'', a''', etc., are the accelerations of m', m'', m''', etc.

Step 2. The resultant of the forces acting on any particle is equal to ma and acts through the particle in the direction of the acceleration a of the particle; and the component of the resultant in any direction x is ma_x, etc.

Step 3. The x component of the resultant of all the forces acting on all the particles then is

$$R_x = m'a'_x + m''a''_x + m'''a'''_x + \cdots \tag{1}$$

Step 4. The x component of the resultant of all the forces acting on all the particles may also be expressed in terms of the actual forces acting on all the particles, which are made up of forces external to the mass system and the internal actions and reactions between the particles. Hence,

$$R_x = (\Sigma F_x)_{\text{external}} + (\Sigma F_x)_{\text{internal}}$$

$$= m'a'_x + m''a''_x + m'''a'''_x + \cdots \tag{2}$$

But by Newton's third law $(\Sigma F_x)_{\text{internal}} = 0$ since the internal forces occur in pairs of equal, opposite, and collinear forces, and hence, letting ΣF_x refer to external forces only, we have

$$\Sigma F_x = m'a'_x + m''a''_x + m'''a'''_x + \cdots \tag{3}$$

To evaluate the right-hand side of this equation for any body (mass system) would, in general, be an endless task since the acceleration of each particle of the body would have to be found.

It can be proved, however, that the right-hand side of the equation is equal to the product of the mass M of the whole system and the x component of the acceleration $\bar{a}$ of the mass center of the system. In Fig. 313a the x co-ordinates of the particles are denoted by x', x'', x''', etc., and the x co-ordinate of the mass center by $\bar{x}$. From the definition of mass center we have then

$$m'x' + m''x'' + m'''x''' + \cdots = M\bar{x} \tag{4}$$

But, since the system of particles is in motion, the x co-ordinates of the particles vary with respect to time. Hence, differentiating the above equation with respect to t, we have

$$m' \frac{dx'}{dt} + m'' \frac{dx''}{dt} + m''' \frac{dx'''}{dt} + \cdots = M \frac{d\bar{x}}{dt} \qquad (5)$$

or

$$m'v'_x + m''v''_x + m'''v'''_x + \cdots = M\bar{v}_x \qquad (6)$$

This equation expresses an important principle concerning the momentum of the system of particles and will be used later in Chapter 11.

Differentiating Eq. 5 with respect to t, we obtain

$$m' \frac{d^2x'}{dt^2} + m'' \frac{d^2x''}{dt^2} + m''' \frac{d^2x'''}{dt^2} + \cdots = M \frac{d^2\bar{x}}{dt^2} \qquad (7)$$

or

$$m'a'_x + m''a''_x + m'''a'''_x + \cdots = M\bar{a}_x \qquad (8)$$

Therefore, Eq. 3 may be written

$$\Sigma F_x = M\bar{a}_x$$

In a similar way equations involving the components in the y and z directions may be found. Hence, the equations that express the relations among the external forces acting on any system of particles, the mass of the system, and the acceleration of the mass center of the system are

$$\Sigma F_x = M\bar{a}_x$$
$$\Sigma F_y = M\bar{a}_y \qquad \textbf{(9)}$$
$$\Sigma F_z = M\bar{a}_z$$

If the resultant of the external forces acting on the system of particles is a force, denoted by R, Eqs. 9 are equivalent to the single equation

$$R = M\bar{a} \qquad \textbf{(10)}$$

where M is the mass of the system and $\bar{a}$ is the acceleration of the mass center of the system.

The principle expressed either by Eqs. 9 or by Eq. 10 is sometimes called the *principle of motion of the mass center*; it simplifies the solution of many problems and is of great importance in the study of kinetics. The principle may be stated in words as follows:

If an unbalanced external force system acts on a body (whether rigid or not), the resultant of the external force system, if a force, has a magnitude that is equal to the product of the mass of the body and the acceleration of the mass center of the body, and the direction of the resultant force is the same as that of the acceleration of the mass center.

It should be noted, however, that this principle does not give any information about the action line of the resultant, but it will be found in the subsequent articles that the action line of the resultant force does *not*, in general, pass through the mass center of the body.

Translation

100   Kinetics of a translating rigid body. The equations of motion for a translating rigid body may be found by applying the four steps outlined in Art. 98. In Fig. 314a is shown a body that is assumed

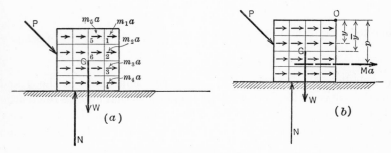

Fig. 314

to have a motion of translation when acted on by the external forces P, W, N, etc. It will further be assumed that the body is symmetrical with respect to the plane of motion and that the forces lie in the plane of motion. For convenience, the particles of which the body is composed may be regarded as small cubes.

ACCELERATION OF ANY PARTICLE. Since the body has a motion of translation, all the particles have the same acceleration a.

EFFECTIVE FORCE FOR ANY PARTICLE. By Newton's second law, the resultant of the forces (not shown) that act on any particle of mass m and give it its acceleration a is equal to ma and is in the direction of a. This resultant force is the effective force for the particle. Thus, the effective forces m_1a, m_2a, etc. (Fig. 314a) constitute a system of parallel forces.

RESULTANT OF THE EFFECTIVE FORCES. The resultant of the effective forces is a force and may be found by the methods of Chapter 2. Thus, the magnitude of the resultant is equal to $\Sigma ma = a\Sigma m = Ma$, where M is the mass of the body; and the direction of the resultant is the same as that of the acceleration a of the body. The action line may be found by use of the principle of moments (Art. 24). Thus, if y (Fig. 314b) is the distance from any point O to the effective force ma for any particle, and p is the distance from O to the action line of the resultant of the effective forces, we have

$$Ma \cdot p = \Sigma(ma \cdot y) = a\Sigma my \qquad (1)$$

or

$$p = \frac{\Sigma my}{M} = \frac{M\bar{y}}{M} = \bar{y} \qquad (2)$$

where $\bar{y}$ is the vertical distance of the mass center from O. Hence, if the body is rigid and has a motion of translation, the resultant of the effective forces passes through the mass center G of the body as shown in Fig. 315a and is not in the position shown in Fig. 314b.

Summarizing: If a rigid body has a motion of translation, the resultant of the effective forces is a force of magnitude Ma, acting through the mass center of the body in the direction of the acceleration a of the body.

RELATION BETWEEN EFFECTIVE FORCES AND EXTERNAL FORCES. Since, by D'Alembert's principle, the resultant of the external forces is identical with the resultant of the effective forces, the resultant of the external forces is also a force (R, say) of magnitude Ma in the direction of a, and it passes through the mass center (G) of the body. Since the resultant passes through G, its moment (and hence also the sum of the moments of the external forces) about G is zero. This fact may be expressed by the equation $\Sigma\bar{T} = 0$, where $\bar{T}$ denotes the moment of an external force about G. The resultant of the external forces is defined, then, by the equations

$$R = Ma$$
$$\Sigma\bar{T} = 0 \qquad (3)$$

If we let X and Y denote any two perpendicular axes in the plane of motion, each side of the first of the foregoing equations may be resolved into components in the x and y directions. Thus, $R_x = Ma_x$, and $R_y = Ma_y$. But the components of the resultant R of the external forces may also be expressed in terms of the forces. Thus, $R_x = \Sigma F_x$, and hence $\Sigma F_x = Ma_x$. Similarly, $\Sigma F_y = Ma_y$. Hence the equation $R = Ma$ may be replaced by two equations. The equations of motion, then, which express the relations between the external forces that act on the body, the mass of the body, and the acceleration of the body, may be written

$$\Sigma F_x = Ma_x$$
$$\Sigma F_y = Ma_y$$
$$\Sigma\bar{T} = 0 \qquad (4)$$

It should be noted that the first two of these equations could have been obtained directly from Eqs. 9 of Art. 99 since they apply to any type of motion.

ALTERNATIVE METHOD. INERTIA-FORCE METHOD. Since the resultant (Ma) of the effective forces (Fig. 315a) is identical with the resultant of the external forces, it is obvious that, if a force equal to Ma and having the same action line as Ma, but of opposite sense, were applied to the body in addition to the actual external forces $(P, W, N,$ etc.) as shown in Fig. 315b, the system of forces so constituted would

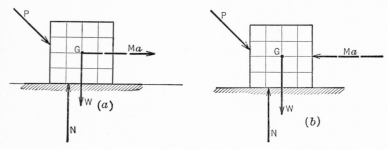

FIG. 315

hold the body in equilibrium and hence would satisfy the equations of equilibrium:

$$\Sigma F_x = 0, \qquad \Sigma F_y = 0, \qquad \Sigma M = 0$$

This additional (imaginary) force is sometimes called the *reversed effective force* or *inertia force* for the body. It is to be noted that the introduction of the inertia force has the effect of transforming the kinetics problem into an equivalent problem in statics. The advantage of using the inertia-force method lies in the fact that moments of the forces may be taken about *any* point in the plane of the forces, whereas, if Eqs. 4 are applied to the real forces that act on the body (the inertia force is not a real force acting on the body), moments must be taken about the *mass center* of the body. Methods of solution of problems by use of the equations of motion and by the inertia-force method will be illustrated in the following problems.

NOTE. In analyzing and solving problems in kinetics of bodies, the same general procedure should be followed as was outlined in Art. 95.

Illustrative Problems

Problem 494. The dimensions of block A (Fig. 316) are 3 ft by 3 ft by 5 ft, and the weight of the block is 1200 lb. The block rests on a carriage B which is given an acceleration a in the direction shown. If the friction between the block and carriage is sufficient to prevent slipping, what is the maximum acceleration that the carriage can have without causing the block to tip over?

SOLUTION. The block has a motion of translation under the action of two forces: namely, the weight W and the reaction R of the carriage. For convenience the latter force, which acts at O when the block is on the point of tipping, will be resolved into the normal pressure N and the frictional force F as indicated in the figure. The equations of motion for the block are

$$\Sigma F_x = M a_x \quad (1), \qquad \Sigma F_y = M a_y \quad (2), \qquad \Sigma \bar{T} = 0 \quad (3)$$

Since the X axis is chosen in the direction of the acceleration of the body, it follows that $a_x = a$ and $a_y = 0$. From Eqs. 1, 2, and 3 we obtain Eqs. 4, 5, and 6:

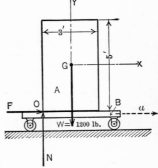

$$F = \frac{1200}{32.2} a \qquad (4)$$

$$N - 1200 = 0 \qquad (5)$$

$$\tfrac{5}{2}F - \tfrac{3}{2}N = 0 \qquad (6)$$

By solving these equations, we find

$$F = 720 \text{ lb} \quad \text{and} \quad a = 19.32 \text{ ft/sec}^2$$

Inertia-force Method. If the inertia force (reversed effective force) for the body is assumed to act on the body with the external forces, the body may be assumed to be in equilibrium (D'Alembert's principle), and hence the equations of equilibrium may be applied to the force system thus formed.

FIG. 316

The inertia force for the translating block A is

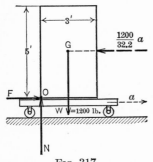

$$Ma = \frac{1200}{32.2} a$$

Its direction is opposite to that of a, and its action line passes through the mass center of the block. Therefore, the forces acting on the block as shown in Fig. 317 will hold the block in equilibrium. The unknown quantities (F, N, and a) could be found by using the three equations of equilibrium for the force system (Art. 42). However, since only the acceleration a was asked for in the problem, a single equilibrium equation ($\Sigma M_0 = 0$) is sufficient for the solution of the problem. Thus,

FIG. 317

$$\Sigma M_0 = \frac{1200}{32.2} a \times \frac{5}{2} - 1200 \times \frac{3}{2} = 0$$

$$a = \frac{3 \times 32.2}{5} = 19.32 \text{ ft/sec}^2$$

The advantage of using the inertia-force method in the solution of this problem lies in the fact that moments may be taken about any point in the plane of the

forces. Thus, if O is selected as the moment center, the unknown forces F and N
do not appear in the equation, and a is determined from the single equation, whereas
in the first method of solution it was necessary to use all three of the equations of
motion and to eliminate F and N from the three equations to determine a.

Problem 495. The parallel rod of a locomotive (Fig. 318a) weighs 400 lb. The
crank length r_1 is 15 in., and the radius r_2 of the drivers is 3 ft. If the speed of the
engine is 50 mi/hr, what is the reaction of the pin at each end of the rod when the
rod is in its lowest position?

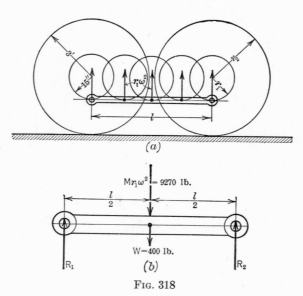

$$M r_1 \omega^2 = 9270 \text{ lb.}$$

$$W = 400 \text{ lb.}$$

(b)

Fig. 318

SOLUTION. All particles of the rod have the same acceleration at any instant.
When the rod is in its lowest position, the acceleration of each particle with reference
to the engine frame is directed vertically upwards, its value being $\omega^2 r_1$. Since the
acceleration of the engine frame is zero, the absolute acceleration of all points on the
rod is also $r_1\omega^2$ upward. The angular velocity ω of the drivers is

$$\omega = \frac{v}{r_2} = \frac{5280 \times 50}{60 \times 60} \times \frac{1}{3} = 24.4 \text{ rad/sec}$$

The resultant of the effective forces acts through the mass center, and its magnitude is

$$Ma = M\omega^2 r_1 = \frac{400}{32.2} \times (24.4)^2 \times \frac{15}{12} = 9270 \text{ lb}$$

If this resultant is reversed and assumed to act on the body with the external forces,
as shown in Fig. 318b, the forces will be in equilibrium.

It will be observed that the forces form a parallel force system. The equations
of equilibrium for a parallel force system (Art. 41) are

$$\Sigma F = 0 \quad (1), \qquad \Sigma M = 0 \quad (2)$$

Equation 1 gives

Equation 2 gives

$$R_1 + R_2 - 9270 - 400 = 0$$

$$R_1 \times l - (9270 + 400) \times \frac{l}{2} = 0$$

whence

$$R_1 = R_2 = 4840 \text{ lb}$$

Problems

496. In Prob. 494, assume the acceleration of the cart and block to be 8 ft/sec². Determine the position of the action line of the normal pressure N.

Ans. 0.880 ft from left edge.

497. A homogeneous cube each of whose edges is 1 ft long and whose weight is 64 lb slides on a rough horizontal plane when acted on by a horizontal force of 16 lb applied at a point on the vertical median line of one face of the cube and perpendicular to that face. If the coefficient of friction is ⅛, how far above the plane must the force be applied in order that the pressure of the cube on the plane be uniformly distributed?

498. The sliding door shown in Fig. 319 weighs 161 lb. If the force P is 40 lb, what is the acceleration of the door, and what are the reactions at A and B? Assume the friction of the rollers to be negligible.

Ans. $a = 8$ ft/sec²; $R_A = 67.2$ lb; $R_B = 93.8$ lb.

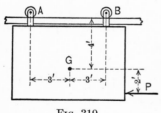

Fig. 319

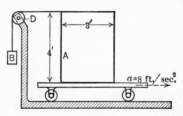

Fig. 320

499. The dimensions of body A (Fig. 320) are 3 ft by 2 ft by 4 ft, and its weight is 960 lb. Assume that the body will not slip on the carriage, and find the maximum weight that B may have without causing A to tip over when the acceleration of the carriage is 8 ft per sec². Neglect the weight of the pulley D, and assume $g = 32$ ft/sec².

500. Bodies A and B (Fig. 321) are connected by a flexible, inextensible cord that passes over a weightless, frictionless pulley C. A weighs 644 lb and the coefficient of friction between A and the plane is 0.2. What is the greatest weight B can have if A slides up the plane without overturning? Find the acceleration of A.

Ans. $W = 1340$ lb; $a = 16.2$ ft/sec².

501. In Fig. 322 a uniform bar AB weighing 64.4 lb is connected by a smooth pin at A to the frame C which weighs 128.8 lb. DB is a spring of negligible weight. When a horizontal force P is applied to the frame as shown, the system slides to the left on a smooth horizontal surface with an acceleration of 6 ft/sec². Find the magnitude of P. If the mass center of the system is 18 in. above the surface and 3 in. to the left of F, find the reactions of the surface on the frame at E and F.

Ans. $P = 36$ lb; $R_E = 53.0$ lb; $R_F = 140.2$ lb.

502. In Prob. 501 determine the tension in the spring, assuming the bar AB to be vertical when the system is moving with an acceleration of 6 ft/sec².

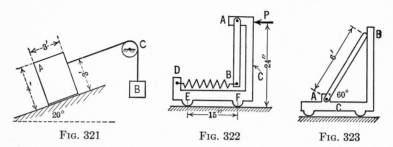

FIG. 321   FIG. 322   FIG. 323

503. In Fig. 323, AB is a uniform bar that weighs 40 lb. It is attached to the frame C by a smooth pin at A and rests against a smooth surface at B. What horizontal acceleration to the right must be given to the frame to cause the pressure on the bar at B to be zero?

504. In Fig. 324 a block has attached to it a uniform bar AC whose weight is 96.6 lb. The bar is held in a vertical position by a smooth pin at A and a flexible cord BD. If the block is moved to the right with a velocity that increases uniformly from 10 ft/sec to 50 ft/sec in 5 sec, what are the stress in the cord and the pressure of the pin at A on the bar?

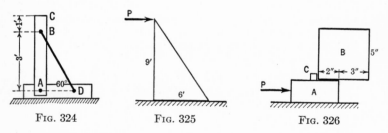

FIG. 324   FIG. 325   FIG. 326

505. The triangular prism shown in Fig. 325 is acted on by a horizontal force P as shown, whose action line is midway between the front and rear faces of the prism. If P is equal to one half of the weight of the prism and the coefficient of friction for the prism and plane is ⅓, find the distance from the left face of the prism to the action line of the resultant of the distributed normal force that the plane exerts on the prism.   *Ans.* 6 ft.

506. In Fig. 326 a horizontal force P causes a block A and a homogeneous cube B to move with a constant acceleration a. The cube B is prevented from sliding on A by a stop at C. Find the least value of a that will prevent B from overturning. If a is less than this value, will B tip forward or backward?   *Ans.* $a = 6.44$ ft/sec².

507. In Fig. 327 bodies A and B which weigh 60 lb and 40 lb, respectively, are connected by cords to a system of pulleys as shown. If the magnitude of the force P is 150 lb, find the total normal pressure between A and B. Neglect friction and the weights of the pulleys, bars, and cords.

508. In Fig. 328, A is a homogeneous rectangular block that weighs 32 lb and is connected by a pin at C to body B which weighs 64 lb, and D is a smooth roller.

Bodies A and B slide down the smooth plane inclined 30° to the horizontal. Find the magnitude and direction of the reaction of the pin at C and of the roller D on body A. Assume $g = 32$ ft/sec².

Ans. $C = 16.3$ lb; $\theta_x = 148° 20'$; $D = 15.46$ lb; $\theta_x = 90°$.

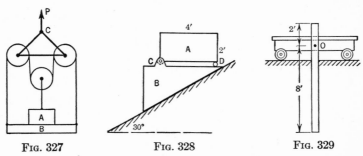

FIG. 327   FIG. 328   FIG. 329

509. In Fig. 329 the slender bar is 10 ft long and weighs 20 lb. It is attached by a smooth pin at O to a car that moves on a horizontal track. If the car moves to the right with a constant acceleration of 16.1 ft/sec², find the angle the bar will make with the vertical, and find also the horizontal and vertical components of the reaction of the pin on the bar.

510. In Prob. 499 assume that A weighs 1000 lb, B weighs 120 lb, and the acceleration of A is 8 ft/sec². Locate the action line of the normal pressure of the carriage on A. Assume $g = 32$ ft/sec².   *Ans.* 0.40 ft from left edge.

511. In Fig. 330 is shown a concrete tile that is being transported on a trailer. The tile whose outer diameter is 5 ft is held in position by two 4″ × 4″ blocks A and B. Find the maximum acceleration the trailer can have without causing the tile to roll over the block A.

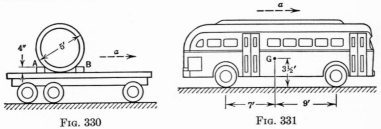

FIG. 330   FIG. 331

512. The bus shown in Fig. 331 weighs 16,000 lb. The bus has a rear wheel drive and is moving on a pavement covered with ice. If the coefficient of friction between tires and pavement is 0.2, find the maximum rate at which the velocity of the bus can increase. Assume that the weight of the wheels (whose motion is plane motion) is small compared with the weight of the rest of the bus. Use $g = 32$ ft/sec².

Ans. $a = 3.76$ ft/sec².

513. In Fig. 327 bodies A and B are connected by cords to a system of pulleys as shown. The assembly is raised or lowered by means of a cable attached at C, the tension in the cable being denoted by P. Find in terms of P, W_A, and W_B an expression for the total normal pressure between the bodies A and B. Neglect friction and the weights of the pulleys, bars, and cords.

514. A homogeneous sphere which weighs 60 lb and has a diameter of 16 in. rests on a rough horizontal plane. The coefficient of friction for the plane and sphere is ¼. The sphere is acted on by a horizontal force of 40 lb whose line of action lies in a vertical plane passing through the center of the sphere. If the sphere slides with a motion of translation, what is the distance from the horizontal plane to the action line of the force?   *Ans.* 5 in.

Rotation

101   Kinetics of a rotating rigid body. The equations of motion for a rigid body that rotates about a fixed axis may be found by the method outlined in Art. 98. But since the equations of motion of the

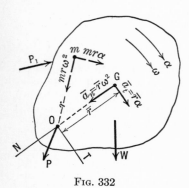

FIG. 332

mass center (Art. 99) apply to any body having any type of motion, they may be used for the motion of rotation here considered. However, it will be necessary to derive an additional equation of motion which involves the moments of the external forces that act on the body.

In applying the equations of motion of the mass center let Fig. 332 represent a rigid body that rotates about a fixed axis through O under the influence of an unbalanced force system (the weight W, the force P_1, and the reaction P of the axis). It will be assumed that the body is homogeneous and is symmetrical with respect to the plane of motion and that the forces lie in the plane of motion. Certain problems in which the forces do not lie in the plane of motion will be discussed in Art. 102. At any instant all particles of the body have the same angular velocity ω and the same angular acceleration α about the axis of rotation. The linear velocity v and the linear acceleration a of any particle, however, vary as the distance r of the particle from the axis of rotation. Let G denote the mass center of the body and $\bar{r}$ its distance from O. Furthermore, let axes ON and OT normal and tangent, respectively, to the path of the mass center be selected as axes of reference. The normal and tangential components of the acceleration $\bar{a}$ of the mass center are $\bar{a}_n = \bar{r}\omega^2$ and $\bar{a}_t = \bar{r}\alpha$ directed as shown in Fig. 332. Hence the equations of Art. 99 when applied to a rotating rigid body with axes chosen as in Fig. 332 become $\Sigma F_n = M\bar{r}\omega^2$ and $\Sigma F_t = M\bar{r}\alpha$. These two equations take account of the effect on the motion of the body of the magnitude and sense of the resultant of the external forces if the resultant is a force. But the effect of the action line of the resultant force (or the effect of the moment of the resultant couple, if the resultant is a couple) must also be included in the equations of motion. This latter effect is taken account of by means of a moment equation which is derived by use of the steps in Art. 98 as follows:

The resultant of all of the forces acting on any particle of mass m (the effective force for the particle) is ma and may be resolved into components $mr\omega^2$ and $mr\alpha$ as shown in Fig. 332. The moment about O of the effective force is $mr^2\alpha$ since the component $mr\omega^2$ passes through O. Hence, the algebraic sum of the moments of all the effective forces about the axis of rotation is equal to $\Sigma mr^2\alpha = \alpha\Sigma mr^2 = I_o\alpha$, where I_o denotes the moment of inertia of the body with respect to the axis of rotation (see Appendix for discussion of moment of inertia).

The sum of the moments of the effective forces for all the particles is equal to the sum of the moments of all the forces acting on all of the particles of the body, and these forces include all the external forces impressed on the body and all the internal forces exerted by the particles on each other. Hence we may write

$$(\Sigma T_o)_{\text{external}} + (\Sigma T_o)_{\text{internal}} = I_o\alpha$$

But $(\Sigma T_o)_{\text{internal}}$ is equal to zero since the internal forces occur in equal, opposite, and collinear pairs. Hence, letting ΣT_o denote the algebraic sum of the moments about O of the external forces only, we have $\Sigma T_o = I_o\alpha$.

Therefore, *with axes chosen as shown in Fig. 332*, the three equations of motion for a rigid body that rotates about a fixed axis are

$$\Sigma F_n = M\bar{r}\omega^2$$

$$\Sigma F_t = M\bar{r}\alpha \qquad\qquad (1)$$

$$\Sigma T_o = I_o\alpha$$

In the foregoing discussion it was assumed that the body was symmetrical with respect to the plane of motion and that the external forces were in the plane of motion. If the external forces lie in a plane other than the plane of motion, three equations of motion for rotation of a rigid body as given by Eqs. 1 are inadequate, additional equations involving moments about axes perpendicular to the axis of rotation being needed. Equations 1, however, are sufficient for most engineering problems. Certain problems in which the forces do not lie in the plane of motion will be discussed in Art. 102.

If the body rotates about an axis through the mass center, that is, if the points O and G coincide, then the right-hand members of the first two of the above equations become zero, since $\bar{r} = 0$. The directions of the N and T axes then become indeterminate, and hence any two perpendicular axes in the plane of motion may be used as reference axes. If any two such axes are denoted by X and Y, the foregoing equations become

$$\Sigma F_x = 0$$

$$\Sigma F_y = 0 \qquad (2)$$

$$\Sigma \bar{T} = \bar{I}\alpha$$

in which $\Sigma \bar{T}$ is the algebraic sum of the moments of the external forces about the axis of rotation (now through the mass center) and $\bar{I}$ is the moment of inertia of the body about the axis of rotation.

It is evident from Eqs. 2 that the resultant of the external forces acting on a body that rotates about an axis through its mass center is a couple whose moment is $\bar{I}\alpha$.

Illustrative Problems

Problem 515. Two spherical balls are connected by a light, slender, rigid rod and made to rotate in a horizontal plane about a vertical axis midway between the balls by a couple F, F in a plane perpendicular to the Y axis as shown in Fig. 333. Each sphere is 12 in. in diameter and weighs 64.4 lb. What is the moment of the couple if the rod and spheres acquire an angular velocity of 30 rpm in 4 sec, starting from rest? If one of the two forces of the couple is applied 9 in. from the axis of rotation and the other force is the reaction of the axis, what is the magnitude of each force?

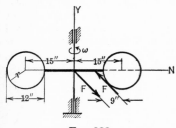

FIG. 333

SOLUTION. Since the two spheres have a motion of rotation about an axis through the mass center of the spheres, the equations of motion are

$$\Sigma F_x = 0 \quad (1), \qquad \Sigma F_y = 0 \quad (2), \qquad \Sigma \bar{T} = \bar{I}\alpha \quad (3)$$

Letting the moment of the couple be denoted by C and the mass of each sphere by M we have, from Eq. 3,

$$\Sigma \bar{T} = C = \bar{I}\alpha = 2(\tfrac{2}{5}Mr^2 + Md^2)\alpha$$

$$= 2\left[\frac{2}{5} \times \frac{64.4}{32.2} \times \left(\frac{6}{12}\right)^2 + \frac{64.4}{32.2} \times \left(\frac{15}{12}\right)^2\right]\alpha = 6.65\alpha$$

But, by definition,

$$\alpha = \frac{\omega - \omega_0}{t} = \frac{30 \times 2\pi}{60 \times 4} = 0.785 \text{ rad/sec}^2$$

Therefore,

$$C = 6.65 \times 0.785 = 5.23 \text{ lb ft}$$

But

$$C = F \times \tfrac{9}{12}; \qquad \therefore \ F = 5.23 \div \tfrac{9}{12} = 6.97 \text{ lb}$$

Problem 516. In Fig. 334a, A is a wheel and axle that weighs 320 lb, and B is a body whose weight is 32 lb that is suspended from a cord wrapped around A. If the radius of gyration of the wheel and axle with respect to the axis of rotation is 8 in. and the coefficient of friction between the axle and bearing is $\frac{1}{5}$, find the acceleration of B. Assume $g = 32$ ft/sec^2.

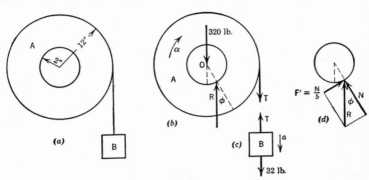

Fig. 334

SOLUTION. Figures 334b and 334c are the free-body diagrams of A and B, respectively. Since the acceleration of the mass center of A has no horizontal component, the reaction R of the bearing on the axle can have no horizontal component and hence must be vertical as shown. The action line of R makes an angle with the normal to the axle as shown in Fig. 334b equal to the angle of friction $\phi = \tan^{-1} \frac{1}{5}$. Since the radius of the wheel is 1 ft, $a = \alpha$. By use of the equations of motion, we have

For A,

$$\Sigma T_o = I_o \alpha, \qquad T - R \times \frac{1}{6} \times \frac{1}{\sqrt{26}} = \frac{40}{9} a \qquad (1)$$

$$\Sigma F_y = 0, \qquad R - 320 - T = 0 \qquad (2)$$

For B,

$$\Sigma F_y = M a_y, \qquad 32 - T = a \qquad (3)$$

Eliminating R from Eqs. 1 and 2, we obtain

$$0.967T - 10.46 = 4.44a \qquad (4)$$

Eliminating T from Eqs. 3 and 4, we have

$$a = 3.78 \text{ ft/sec}^2$$

In the foregoing solution, a considerable amount of numerical calculation is necessary in eliminating R and T from Eqs. 1, 2, and 3. A simpler solution which gives a close approximation to the correct result could be obtained by assuming the bearing reaction R to pass through the lowest point of the axle and not as shown (correctly) in Fig. 334d. The reaction would then be shown in the free-body diagram in terms of its two components, N vertically upward, and $F' = \frac{1}{5} N$ horizontally to the right. If the problem were solved by this method, it would be found that $a = 3.74$ ft/sec^2.

Problem 517. A slender uniform bar (Fig. 335a) is free to rotate in a vertical plane about a smooth pin at O. The bar is held at rest with the free end vertically above O and is then released, allowing the bar to rotate. The bar is 2 ft long and weighs 64 lb. (a) Find the angular velocity ω of the bar for any angular displacement θ. (b) Find the horizontal and vertical components of the pin reaction on the bar when $\theta = 90°$. Use $g = 32$ ft/sec^2.

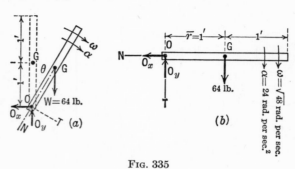

Fig. 335

SOLUTION. The forces acting on the bar when the angular displacement is θ are shown in Fig. 335a. The equations of motion for the bar are

$$\Sigma F_n = M\bar{r}\omega^2 \quad (1), \qquad \Sigma F_t = M\bar{r}\alpha \quad (2), \qquad \Sigma T_o = I_o\alpha \quad (3)$$

From Eq. 3, we have

$$64 \sin \theta = \frac{1}{3} \times \frac{64}{32} \times 4 \times \frac{d^2\theta}{dt^2}$$

Hence,

$$\frac{d^2\theta}{dt^2} = 24 \sin \theta$$

Multiplying each side of this equation by $d\theta/dt$ and then integrating the resulting equation with respect to t, we obtain

$$\frac{1}{2}\left(\frac{d\theta}{dt}\right)^2 = -24 \cos \theta + C$$

Since

$$\frac{d\theta}{dt} = 0 \quad \text{when} \quad \theta = 0, \qquad C = 24$$

Therefore,

$$\frac{d\theta}{dt} = \sqrt{48(1 - \cos \theta)}$$

When $\theta = 90°$, $\omega = d\theta/dt = \sqrt{48}$ and $\alpha = d^2\theta/dt^2 = 24$. The free-body diagram for the bar when $\theta = 90°$ is shown in Fig. 335b. Hence, from Eqs. 1 and 2, we have

$$\Sigma F_n = M\bar{r}\omega^2 \quad \text{or} \quad O_x = \tfrac{64}{32} \times 1 \times 48 \qquad \therefore O_x = 96 \text{ lb}$$

$$\Sigma F_t = M\bar{r}\alpha \quad \text{or} \quad 64 - O_y = \tfrac{64}{32} \times 1 \times 24 \qquad \therefore O_y = 16 \text{ lb}$$

Problems

518. A solid sphere 20 in. in diameter revolves with an angular velocity of 600 rpm about a fixed axis which passes through its center. What force lying in a diametral plane perpendicular to the axis and acting tangent to the surface will stop the sphere in 5 sec if friction on the axis is neglected? The weight of the sphere is 322 lb.

519. What constant twisting moment must be applied to the shaft and balls shown in Fig. 290 (Prob. 453) in order that the shaft may be given an angular velocity of 80 rpm in 4 sec, starting from rest? Treat the balls as particles, and neglect the weight of the shaft and rods.   *Ans.* 0.455 lb ft.

520. The homogeneous cylinder in Fig. 336 has a motion of pure rotation about its geometric axis under the influence of its weight, the force P, and the reaction of the plane. Find the coefficient of kinetic friction between the cylinder and plane.

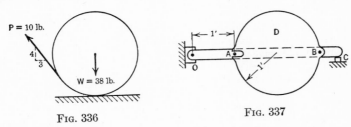

$$P = 10 \text{ lb.}$$
$$\frac{4}{3}$$
$$W = 38 \text{ lb.}$$

Fig. 336

Fig. 337

521. In Fig. 337 a homogeneous circular disk D weighing 64.4 lb is attached by smooth pins at A and B to a weightless bar OC that is free to rotate in a vertical plane about a smooth pin at O. The bar is in equilibrium in the horizontal position shown. If the support at C is suddenly removed, find the initial reactions of the pins at A and B on the disk.   *Ans.* $A = 10.74$ lb; $B = -3.58$ lb.

522. A uniform slender bar AB 6 ft long is free to rotate in a vertical plane about a smooth pin at the upper end A of the bar. When the bar is at rest in a vertical position, a horizontal force $P = 20$ lb is suddenly applied to the bar. The force P acts toward the right, and its action line is at a distance h below A. Find the initial horizontal component of the pin reaction on the bar when h is (a) 3 ft, (b) 4 ft, and (c) 5 ft.

523. The armature of an electric motor weighs W lb and has a radius of gyration of k ft. It is acted on by a torque which varies according to the equation $T = 1000/\omega$ where T is in lb ft and ω is in rad/sec. Derive an expression for the angular velocity of the armature in terms of W, k, t, and ω_0 where t is in sec and ω_0 denotes the initial angular velocity in rad/sec.

524. A homogeneous cylinder (Fig. 338) weighs 193.2 lb and has a diameter of 1 ft. The cylinder rotates with an angular velocity of 120 rpm. A frictional force is developed at the surface by the force P which causes the angular velocity to decrease uniformly to 40 rpm in 4 sec. If the coefficient of kinetic friction is 0.2, find the value of P.   *Ans.* $P = 6.28$ lb.

525. A homogeneous cylinder weighing 96.6 lb and having a radius of 2 ft rests between two smooth planes, as shown in Fig. 339. A force of 20 lb perpendicular to the axis of the cylinder is applied as shown. Find the angular acceleration of the cylinder, and the reactions R_1 and R_2 of the planes on the cylinder.

526. In Fig. 340, A is a homogeneous solid cylinder that weighs 322 lb and has a radius of 2 ft, B is a body that weighs 64.4 lb, and C is a weightless, frictionless pulley. Find the tension in the cord and the angular acceleration of the cylinder.

Ans. $T = 46$ lb; $\alpha = 4.6$ rad/sec^2.

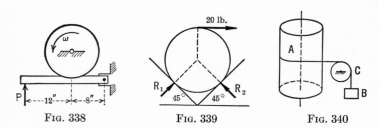

FIG. 338   FIG. 339   FIG. 340

527. An elevator weighing 3220 lb is raised by a cable wound around a hoisting drum which weighs 644 lb. The drum is 4 ft in diameter and has a radius of gyration of 1.5 ft with respect to the axis of rotation. What constant moment must be applied to the drum to give the elevator an upward acceleration of 8 ft/sec^2? Neglect friction and the weight of the cable.

528. The turntable shown in Fig. 341 rotates in a horizontal plane about a vertical axis through O. A slender bar AB which is 6 ft long is attached to the turntable by a pin at A and is prevented from sliding on the turntable by a stop at B. If at a given instant $\omega = 6$ rad/sec, at what rate must ω be decreasing in order that the pressure at the stop be zero? Assume friction to be negligible.

Ans. $\alpha = 36$ rad/sec^2.

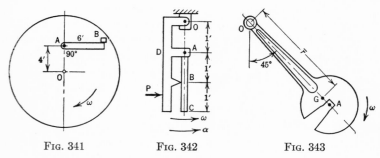

FIG. 341   FIG. 342   FIG. 343

529. The slender bar AC in Fig. 342 weighs 16.1 lb and is connected by a smooth pin at A to the body D which rotates about O. When AC is in a vertical position, $\omega = 2$ rad/sec, and the magnitude of P is such that $\alpha = 2$ rad/sec^2. Find the force exerted by the body D on the bar AC at point B.

530. The pendulum of a Charpy impact machine (Fig. 343) which is used for testing materials under rapidly applied loads is free to rotate in a vertical plane about a smooth pin at O. The weight of the pendulum is 48.3 lb, the distance from O to the mass center G is 2 ft, and the radius of gyration with respect to the axis of rotation is 2.24 ft. Find the angular acceleration of the pendulum and the horizontal and vertical components of the pin reaction when the pendulum is in the position shown if $\omega = 5$ rad/sec.

531. A homogeneous cylinder C weighing 64 lb is mounted on a horizontal axle whose axis coincides with the axis of the cylinder. A body A weighing 32 lb is suspended from one end of a cord wrapped around the cylinder, and a body B weighing 16 lb is suspended from the other end of the cord. Find the acceleration of A and B if the cord does not slip on the cylinder. Find also the tension in the part of the cord between A and C and in the part of the cord between B and C. Neglect bearing friction, and assume $g = 32$ ft/sec^2.

Ans. $a = 6.4$ ft/sec^2; $T_A = 25.6$ lb; $T_B = 19.2$ lb.

532. A homogeneous slender bar AB having a length of 4 ft and a weight of 64.4 lb lies on a smooth horizontal turntable that rotates about a vertical axis through a point O on the turntable. The ends A and B of the bar are connected to O by cords whose lengths are 5 ft and 3 ft, respectively. Find the tensions in the cords OA and OB if the turntable and bar rotate about the axis with a constant angular velocity of 4 rad/sec.

102   Second method of analysis. Inertia-force method. In some problems dealing with the rotation of a rigid body under the action of an unbalanced force system, it is convenient to assume that the resultant of the effective forces is reversed and acts on the body with the external forces, thereby forming a force system that is in equilibrium (D'Alembert's principle) and thus reducing the kinetics problem of a rotating body to an equivalent statics problem. The reversed resultant force (or resultant couple) is called the inertia force (or inertia couple) for the body. In order to use this method of solution, the resultant of the effective forces must be determined completely. This will be done (1) for a body that rotates about an axis that does not pass through its mass center and (2) for a body whose axis of rotation does pass through the mass center of the body. It will be assumed that the body is symmetrical with respect to the plane of motion and that the external forces lie in the plane of motion.

I   ROTATION ABOUT AXIS NOT THROUGH MASS CENTER. If the body rotates about an axis not through its mass center, the resultant of the effective forces (and hence also of the external forces), as found in Art. 101, is a force. The components of this resultant force parallel to the N and T axes were found to be $M\bar{r}\omega^2$ and $M\bar{r}\alpha$, respectively, as shown in Fig. 344. The action line of the resultant may be determined by finding the point where it intersects the N axis. Thus, if in Fig. 344 the resultant of the effective forces be resolved into its components $M\bar{r}\omega^2$ and $M\bar{r}\alpha$ at the point where it intersects the N axis, the distance q from this point to O may be determined from the principle of moments (Art. 14) as follows: The sum of the moments of the effective forces about O, as shown in Art. 101, is $I_o\alpha$. Further, the moment of the resultant of the effective forces is the moment of its tangential component $M\bar{r}\alpha$, only, since the normal component $M\bar{r}\omega^2$ passes through the center of rotation. Hence, the principle of moments is expressed by the equation

$$M\bar{r}\alpha \cdot q = I_o\alpha$$

And, since $I_o = Mk_o{}^2$, in which k_o is the radius of gyration of the body with respect to the axis of rotation, we may write

$$M\bar{r}\alpha \cdot q = Mk_o{}^2\alpha$$

whence

$$q = \frac{k_o{}^2}{\bar{r}}$$

Therefore, the action line of the resultant of the effective forces intersects the N axis at a distance $k_o{}^2/\bar{r}$ from the center of rotation, as shown in Fig. 344. And, since the resultant of the external forces is identical with the resultant of the effective forces, the body may be considered to be in equilibrium if the two forces, $M\bar{r}\alpha$ and $M\bar{r}\omega^2$, having the action lines as shown in Fig. 344, but *reversed in sense*, are assumed to act on

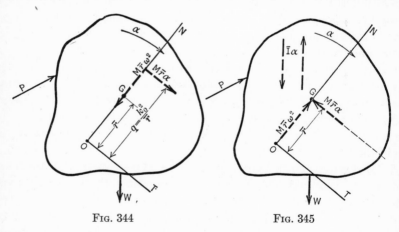

FIG. 344   FIG. 345

the body with the external forces. Hence, for the force system thus formed, we may write three equations of equilibrium.

It is sometimes more convenient to replace the resultant of the effective forces by an equal parallel force through the mass center and a couple. It can easily be shown that the moment of this couple is $\bar{I}\alpha$; thus the force $M\bar{r}\alpha$ may be resolved (Art. 19) into an equal parallel force through G and a couple whose moment is

$$M\bar{r}\alpha(q - \bar{r}) = (Mk_o{}^2 - M\bar{r}^2)\alpha = \bar{I}\alpha$$

Hence, if the inertia couple $\bar{I}\alpha$ and the inertia forces $M\bar{r}\omega^2$ and $M\bar{r}\alpha$, as shown in Fig. 345, be added to the external forces acting on the body, the body will be in equilibrium.

Centrifugal Force. The n component $M\bar{r}\omega^2$ of the inertia force for the body is called the *centrifugal force* for the body. If the body is rotating at a constant angular velocity ($\alpha = 0$), then the centrifugal force is the total inertia force for the body. The nature of this so-called force is frequently misunderstood; the centrifugal force for a body is *not an actual force* exerted on the body by some other body but is a force which, if assumed to act on the body in addition to the actual forces acting on the body, would hold the body in equilibrium, if the body is assumed to have a constant angular velocity.

II ROTATION ABOUT AXIS THROUGH MASS CENTER. If the body rotates about an axis that passes through its mass center, $\bar{r} = 0$, and hence each of the components $M\bar{r}\alpha$ and $M\bar{r}\omega^2$ of the resultant of the effective forces is zero. Therefore, the resultant is not a force. And, since the effective forces have a moment, the value of which is $\bar{I}\alpha$, the resultant is a couple of moment $\bar{I}\alpha$. The sense of the resultant couple is, of course, the same as that of α, the angular acceleration of the body. Further, since the resultant of the external forces that act on the body is identical with that of the effective forces for the body, the body may be considered to be in equilibrium if a couple having a moment equal to $\bar{I}\alpha$ and a sense opposite to that of α is assumed to act on the body with the external forces; this couple is called the inertia couple for the body. As in the preceding case, three equations of equilibrium may be written for the resulting force system.

In the foregoing discussion of Case I it was assumed that the body was symmetrical with respect to the plane of motion and that the external forces were in the plane of motion. If the external forces do not lie in the plane of motion, the foregoing discussion does not give sufficient information to enable one to locate the line of action of the inertia force. Furthermore, as pointed out in Art. 101, Eqs. 1 may be inadequate to solve such problems. However, if the body is symmetrical with respect to the plane of motion, even though the forces do not lie in the plane of motion, the inertia force $M\bar{r}\omega^2$ will pass through the mass center of the body. This fact may be shown to be true by determining the resultant of the inertia forces for the elements of mass by the method used to determine the resultant of the effective force system of a translating rigid body (see Art. 100). Hence the inertia-force method may be used to solve certain problems in which the external forces do not lie in the plane of motion. The following problem will serve to illustrate the method.

Illustrative Problems

Problem 533. A horizontal bar B (Fig. 346a) rotates with a constant angular velocity of 45 rpm about a vertical axis YY. A slender bar C, of constant cross section, having a length of 12 in. and a weight of 16 lb is attached to the rotating bar by means of a smooth pin at E, and is held in a vertical position by a weightless cord D. Find the tension in D and the magnitude of the reaction of the pin at E on the bar C.

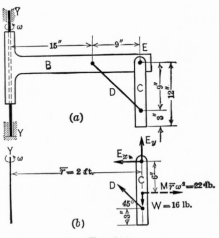

Fɪɢ. 346

Soʟᴜᴛɪᴏɴ. A free-body diagram of the bar C is shown in Fig. 346b. The bar has a motion of rotation about the vertical axis YY under the influence of three forces, W, D, and the pin pressure at E (the components of the pin pressure being denoted by E_x and E_y).

If the reversed resultant of the effective forces (inertia force) for the bar is assumed to act on the bar with W, D, E_x, and E_y, the bar may be considered to be in equilibrium. The inertia force is $M\bar{r}\omega^2$, since $\alpha = 0$ and hence $M\bar{r}\alpha = 0$. Its magnitude is

$$M\bar{r}\omega^2 = \frac{16}{32.2} \times 2 \times \left(\frac{45 \times 2\pi}{60}\right)^2 = 22.0 \text{ lb}$$

Since the bar C is symmetrical with respect to the plane of motion, the action line of $M\bar{r}\omega^2$ passes through the mass center of the bar. Thus, the forces W, D, E_x, E_y, and $M\bar{r}\omega^2$, as shown in the free-body diagram, would hold the bar in equilibrium. By using the three equations of equilibrium, we have

$$\Sigma F_x = 22 - E_x - D \cos 45° = 0$$

$$\Sigma F_y = E_y + D \cos 45° - 16 = 0$$

$$\Sigma M_E = 22 \times 6 - D \times 9 \cos 45° = 0$$

The solution of these equations gives the following results:

$$D = 20.7 \text{ lb}, \qquad E_x = 7.33 \text{ lb}, \qquad E_y = 1.33 \text{ lb}, \qquad E = 7.45 \text{ lb}$$

Problem 534. Hoop tension in flywheel. Let it be required to find the stress (often called hoop tension) in the rim of a rotating flywheel in terms of the rim velocity v and the weight of the material per unit volume. Assume that the rim is thin and that the effect of the spokes may be neglected.

SOLUTION. In Fig. 347 is represented one half of the rim of a flywheel. As the wheel rotates, each half of the rim tends to separate from the other half and is prevented from doing so by the stresses P, P which are developed in the rim. The inertia force for the half of the rim is $M\bar{r}\omega^2$, and it acts through the mass center of the half rim. And, since the inertia force is in equilibrium with the external forces (P, P) which act on the half rim, the following equation of equilibrium may be written

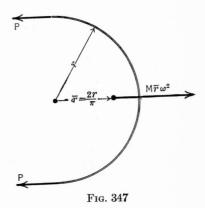

FIG. 347

$$2P = M\bar{r}\omega^2 = \frac{W}{g}\bar{r}\omega^2$$

in which W is the weight of the half rim.

If the thickness of the rim is small in comparison with the mean radius r, the mass center of the rim may be considered to coincide with the centroid of the semi-circular arc, and hence $\bar{r} = 2r/\pi$ (Prob. 783). Thus,

$$P = \frac{1}{2}\frac{W}{g} \times \frac{2r}{\pi}\omega^2 = \frac{Wr\omega^2}{g\pi}$$

The stress s (force per unit of area of the rim cross section) is $s = P/a$, in which a is the area of the cross section. Therefore,

$$s = \frac{W}{g} \times \frac{r}{\pi} \times \frac{\omega^2}{a} = \frac{\pi rak}{g} \times \frac{r}{\pi} \times \frac{\omega^2}{a} = \frac{kr^2\omega^2}{g}$$

in which k is the weight of the material per unit volume. Or, since the velocity v of the mid-points of the rim is equal to ωr, the expression for s may be written in the form

$$s = \frac{kv^2}{g}$$

The units in which s is expressed are pounds per square foot if k is expressed in pounds per cubic foot, r in feet, g in feet per second per second, and ω in radians per second. It will be noted, therefore, that the stress s developed in the rim of a rotating wheel, if the rim is thin and the effect of the spokes is neglected, varies directly as the square of the linear speed of the rim.

Problem 535. Superelevation of railroad track. When a locomotive or car travels around a curve on a level track, a horizontal force (called flange pressure) is exerted on the flange of the wheels by the rails. Let it be required to find the distance (called superelevation) that the outer rail must be raised above the inner rail to reduce the flange pressure to zero. This superelevation may be expressed in terms of the speed of the car, the radius of the curve, and the distance between the rails.

SOLUTION. In Fig. 348, the pressures of the rails are R_1 and R_2, θ being such an angle that the flange pressure is zero when the car is moving with a certain speed v. The resultant of R_1 and R_2 will be denoted by R. W is the weight of the car, and r is the radius of the curve around which the car is traveling. Since the mass center of the car travels in a horizontal plane, the inertia force $Mr\omega^2$ is horizontal. The dimensions of the car are small compared to the radius of the curve, and hence the car may be treated as a particle; thus, the inertia force and the force R may be assumed to pass through the mass center G of the car as shown. The forces W, $Mr\omega^2$, and R form a concurrent force system in equilibrium, and we may write

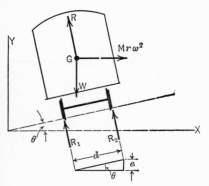

FIG. 348

$$\Sigma F_x = 0, \quad \text{or} \quad R \sin \theta = \frac{W}{g} \frac{v^2}{r}$$

$$\Sigma F_y = 0, \quad \text{or} \quad R \cos \theta = W$$

And, by dividing the first of these equations by the second, the equation obtained is $\tan \theta = v^2/gr$. For small angles the sine and the tangent of the angle are approximately the same and $\sin \theta = e/d$, in which d is the distance between the action lines of the rail pressures (usually taken as 4.9 ft). Therefore, $\tan \theta = e/d = v^2/gr$. Hence, if v is expressed in feet per second, g in feet per second per second, and d and r in feet, the superelevation (in feet) is found from the equation

$$e = \frac{v^2 d}{gr}$$

In order to indicate common values of the superelevation, the values used on one particular steam railroad are given in the following table:

SUPERELEVATION OF OUTER RAIL IN INCHES

Degree * of Curve	Speed in Miles per Hour			
	30	45	60	75
1	$\frac{3}{8}$	$1\frac{1}{8}$	2	$3\frac{1}{8}$
2	$\frac{7}{8}$	$2\frac{1}{8}$	4	$6\frac{1}{2}$
3	$1\frac{1}{4}$	$3\frac{1}{8}$	6	$9\frac{3}{4}$
4	$1\frac{5}{8}$	$4\frac{1}{4}$	8	
5	2	$5\frac{1}{4}$		

* A one-degree curve is a curve (circle) in which a 100-ft chord is subtended by a central angle of one degree. In a two-degree curve a chord of 100 ft is subtended by a central angle of two degrees, and so on.

Problems

536. Solve Prob. 522 by the inertia-force method.

537. The radius of a railroad curve is 2640 ft. What must be the superelevation of the outer rail in order to make the flange pressure zero when the speed of a car around the curve is 60 mi/hr? *Ans. e = 5.36 in.*

538. Solve Prob. 532 by the inertia-force method.

539. In Fig. 349, A represents a frame which revolves about a vertical axis at a constant angular velocity $\omega = 30$ rpm. A bar B is attached to the frame at E by means of a smooth pin. At the end of B a spherical ball C is fastened. B weighs 16 lb and is 16 in. long. C weighs 8 lb and is 4 in. in diameter. Find the reaction of the pin at E and of the frame at F, on the bar. Assume $g = 32$ ft/sec^2.

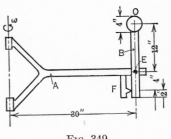

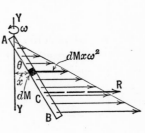

FIG. 349 FIG. 350

540. A uniform bar AB (Fig. 350) of length l and mass M rotates about a vertical axis YY with a constant angular velocity ω. The inertia force for any element of mass dM is $dMx\omega^2$ as indicated. Find the magnitude and line of action of the inertia force R for the bar in terms of M, l, θ, and ω. Find also the horizontal and vertical components of the reaction of the axis on the bar.

Ans. $R = \frac{1}{2}Ml\omega^2 \sin\theta$; $AC = \frac{2}{3}l$; $A_x = -\frac{1}{2}Ml\omega^2 \sin\theta$; $A_y = Mg$.

541. A homogeneous door of constant thickness is 8 ft high and 4 ft wide. The door swings on two hinges which are placed 1 ft from the ends of a vertical edge. When the door swings with a certain constant angular velocity, the horizontal component of the reaction at the lower hinge is zero. Find this velocity.

Ans. $\omega = 3.28$ rad/sec.

542. A disk rotates in a horizontal plane about a vertical axis through its center with a constant angular velocity of 30 rpm. A vertical bar which weighs 20 lb and is 3 ft long is pivoted at its lower end to the disk at a point 4 ft from the axis of rotation of the disk. The bar is prevented from rotating about its lower end by a cord which is attached to the upper end of the bar and to the center of rotation of the disk. Find the tension in the cord.

543. A door of constant cross section is 3 ft wide and weighs 32.2 lb/ft of width. It swings on its hinges so that its outer edge has a speed of 8 ft/sec. Find the force applied perpendicularly to the door at the outer edge to bring it to rest in a distance of 1 ft. What is the total horizontal reaction of the hinges perpendicular to the door while the force is acting?

544. A homogeneous cylinder having a diameter of 2 in. and a height of 3 in. rests on end on a circular disk that rotates with a constant angular velocity of 4 rad/sec in a horizontal plane about a vertical axis. If the cylinder does not slip but is on the point of overturning, find the distance between the axis of the cylinder and the axis of rotation of the disk. *Ans.* 16.1 in.

545. The center of gravity of a flywheel weighing 8000 lb is 0.144 in. from the axis of rotation. The flywheel is midway between bearings and is rotating at 300 rpm. If bearing friction is negligible, find the reaction at each bearing: (*a*) when the center of gravity is vertically above the axis of rotation and (*b*) when it is vertically below. Assume $g = 32$ ft/sec^2.

546. A common rule limits the peripheral speed of cast-iron flywheels or pulleys to 6000 ft/min (sometimes stated 1 mi/min). Calculate the tensile unit stress in the rim corresponding to this speed, assuming that the effect of the spokes may be neglected. Assume the weight of cast iron to be 450 lb/cu ft. *Ans.* 970 lb/sq in.

547. Calculate the greatest number of revolutions per minute at which a thin cast-iron hoop 2 ft in diameter can rotate without bursting. Assume that the maximum tensile strength of the cast iron is 20,000 lb/sq in. and that the material weighs 450 lb/cu ft.

103 Center of percussion. The point P (Fig. 351) on the N axis, through which the resultant of the effective forces for a rotating rigid body acts, is called the center of percussion of the body with respect to

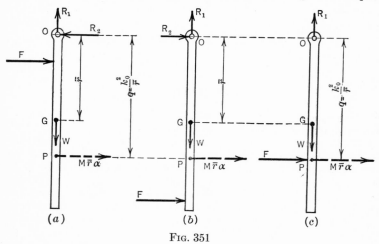

Fig. 351

the given axis of rotation. Hence, the center of percussion is a point on a line joining the center of rotation and the mass center, at a distance q from the center of rotation, such that $q = k_o^2/\bar{r}$ (Art 102), in which k_o is the radius of gyration of the body about the axis of rotation and $\bar{r}$ is the distance from the axis of rotation to the mass center of the body.

The physical significance of the center of percussion is suggested in the following illustration. Let a bar (Fig. 351) of weight W be free to rotate about a horizontal axis when a horizontal force F is suddenly applied to it. If the force F is applied above the center of percussion, as shown in Fig. 351*a*, the horizontal reaction R_2 of the axis of rotation acts towards the left and becomes larger as the force F is applied closer to the axis of rotation. If the bar is struck below the center of percussion, the reaction R_2 acts towards the right, as shown in Fig. 351b. And, if the bar is struck so that the center of percussion is on the action line of the force, as in Fig. 351c, the horizontal reaction at O is zero, since the action line at F is collinear with the action line of the tangential component $M\bar{r}\alpha$ of the resultant of the effective forces. It will be noted that the resultant of F and R_2, in each case, is collinear with $M\bar{r}\alpha$, since the component of the resultant of the external forces in any direction is identical with the component of the resultant of the effective forces in the same direction; that is, if $M\bar{r}\alpha$ were reversed and applied to the body as an external force, it would hold F and R_2 in equilibrium.

An excellent illustration of the effect of varying the position of the force F is found in batting a baseball. If the ball strikes the bat at the center of percussion (about three-fourths the length of the bat from the end, assuming the axis of rotation at the hands) no reaction perpendicular to the bat is experienced by the batter. If, however, the ball strikes the bat near the end or near the hands, the batter experiences a painful stinging of the hands as a result of the reaction perpendicular to the bat.

Problems

548. The pendulum of the impact-testing machine described in Prob. 530 is released from an inclined position, and, when it reaches the vertical position, the edge A strikes a test specimen. The pendulum is designed so that, when it strikes the specimen, the horizontal component of the reaction at the bearing O is zero. Find the distance from the bearing to the striking edge of the pendulum.

549. A slender uniform bar AB that weighs 20 lb and is 3 ft long is held in equilibrium in a horizontal position by a smooth horizontal pin at the left end A of the bar and a support under the right end B. A force $P = 20$ lb is suddenly applied vertically upward at a point 2 ft from A. Find the vertical component of the reaction of the pin at A. *Ans.* $R_A = 5$ lb.

550. A steel plate 3 ft square weighing 96.6 lb is held in equilibrium in a vertical plane by a smooth horizontal pin at the upper left corner O and a support under the lower right corner, two of the edges being vertical. A horizontal force $P = 180$ lb is suddenly applied to the plate. The force acts to the right, and its action line passes through the center of percussion (with respect to O). Find the horizontal and vertical components of the pin reaction at O.

Plane Motion

104 Kinetics of plane motion of a rigid body. It will be assumed that the body is symmetrical with respect to the plane of motion and that the external forces lie in the plane of motion. For these conditions there will be three equations of motion as explained in Art. 90. Two of the equations may be taken directly from Art. 99: namely, $\Sigma F_x = M\bar{a}_x$ and $\Sigma F_y = M\bar{a}_y$, which were found to apply to any mass system having any type of motion. The third equation must involve the moments of the forces and will here be derived by applying the steps discussed in Art. 98.

In Fig. 352, is shown a rigid body that is given a plane motion by a system of unbalanced external forces that act on it. At any instant, the body has an angular velocity ω and an angular acceleration α. Since

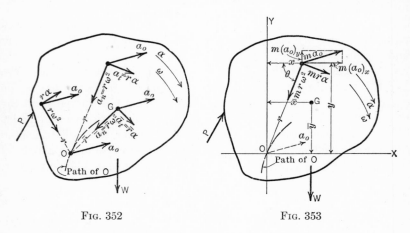

FIG. 352   FIG. 353

the body is rigid, the particles of which the body is composed all have the same angular velocity ω and the same angular acceleration α about any axis perpendicular to the plane of motion. The linear velocity and linear acceleration of any particle, however, vary with the position of the particle in the body.

As shown in Art. 86, a plane motion of a rigid body may be considered, at any instant, as a combination of a pure rotation about an axis perpendicular to the plane of motion of the body through any point O in the plane of motion, which gives to the body the same angular velocity ω and angular acceleration α that the body has at the instant, and a translation of the body which gives to each particle the same linear velocity and acceleration that the point O has at the instant. Thus, the motion of any particle of the body is made up of two component motions, (1) a rotation about O and (2) a motion identical with that of O. Hence, the acceleration of any particle at a distance r from O has a normal component $a_n = r\omega^2$ and a tangential component $a_t = r\alpha$, resulting from the rotation of the body about O, and also an acceleration a_o, the same as that of O, resulting from the translation of the body. If now each of these components of the acceleration of the particle is multiplied by the mass of the particle, the components of the effective force for the particle are obtained and are shown in Fig. 353. For convenience ma_o will be resolved into its two components $m(a_o)_x$ and $m(a_o)_y$ as shown in Fig. 353.

The algebraic sum of the moments of the effective forces about O

$$= \Sigma m r \alpha \cdot r + \Sigma m(a_o)_x y - \Sigma m(a_o)_y x$$

$$= \alpha \Sigma m r^2 + (a_o)_x \Sigma m y - (a_o)_y \Sigma m x$$

$$= I_o \alpha + M \bar{y}(a_o)_x - M \bar{x}(a_o)_y \qquad (1)$$

But the algebraic sum of the moments of the effective forces for all of the particles can also be expressed in terms of the actual forces which include all of the external forces and all of the internal forces (actions and reactions between the particles). Hence,

$$(\Sigma T_o)_{\text{external}} + (\Sigma T_o)_{\text{internal}} = I_o \alpha + M \bar{y}(a_o)_x - M \bar{x}(a_o)_y \qquad (2)$$

But, according to Newton's third law, the internal forces occur in pairs of equal, opposite, and collinear forces, and hence $(\Sigma T_o)_{\text{internal}} = 0$. Therefore, if ΣT_o refers to external forces only, the above equation becomes

$$\Sigma T_o = I_o \alpha + M \bar{y}(a_o)_x - M \bar{x}(a_o)_y \qquad (3)$$

As already noted, the center O about which the assumed rotation takes place and about which the moments of the forces are taken may be any point in the plane of motion of the body. Thus, if the mass center is selected for the center about which moments are taken, that is, if O coincides with G (Fig. 353), then in Eq. 3 $\bar{x}$ and $\bar{y}$ are zero, a_o becomes $\bar{a}$, I_o becomes $\bar{I}$, and ΣT_o becomes $\Sigma \bar{T}$. Hence, the right-hand member of Eq. 3 reduces to one term, $\bar{I}\alpha$. Thus the equations of motion for a rigid body having plane motion may be written

$$\Sigma F_x = M\bar{a}_x$$

$$\Sigma F_y = M\bar{a}_y \qquad (4)$$

$$\Sigma \bar{T} = \bar{I}\alpha$$

It may be noted further that Eq. 3 reduces to $\Sigma T_o = I_o \alpha$, not only if O coincides with G, but also if O is a point whose acceleration is zero, or if O is a point whose acceleration is toward (or away from) G, since in this case the quantity $M\bar{y}(a_o)_x - M\bar{x}(a_o)_y$ in Eq. 3 is zero, which may be proved by assuming in Fig. 353 that a_o is along the line OG and selecting OG as the X axis, in which case it will be found that the last two terms in Eq. 3 vanish.

Illustrative Problems

Problem 551. In Fig. 354 a homogeneous cylinder having a radius of 2 ft and a weight of W lb rests on a horizontal plane for which the coefficient of friction is $\frac{1}{10}$. The cylinder is acted on by a horizontal force of $\frac{1}{2}W$ lb whose action line is at a distance h from the plane. If $h = 2$ ft as shown in Fig. 354, find the linear acceleration of the center of the cylinder and the angular acceleration of the cylinder.

SOLUTION. It is not known whether the cylinder will roll without slipping or will slip as it rolls. It will first be assumed that the cylinder rolls to the right without slipping but that slipping is impending, in which case $\bar{a} = r\alpha$ and $F' = \mu N = \mu W$, where μ is the coefficient of friction. Since the acceleration of point O is toward the mass center if the cylinder rolls without slipping, we can use the equation $\Sigma T_o = I_o\alpha$. By use of the equations of motion, we have

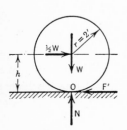

FIG. 354

$$\Sigma F_x = M\bar{a}_x, \qquad \frac{1}{2}W - \mu W = \frac{W}{g}\bar{a} \qquad (1)$$

$$\Sigma T_o = I_o\alpha, \qquad \frac{1}{2}Wr = \frac{3}{2}\frac{W}{g}r^2\alpha = \frac{3}{2}\frac{W}{g}r\bar{a} \qquad (2)$$

Eliminating $\bar{a}$ from Eqs. 1 and 2, we find $\mu = \frac{1}{6}$; and, substituting this value of μ in Eq. 1, we find $\bar{a} = \frac{1}{3}g$. Since the least value of μ that will permit the cylinder to roll without slipping is $\frac{1}{6}$ and the value of μ specified is $\frac{1}{10}$, the cylinder will slip, and hence the acceleration of the center is not $\frac{1}{3}g$, nor is $\bar{a} = r\alpha$. But, since the cylinder slips, $F' = \frac{1}{10}W$. Using this value of F', we may write the equations of motion as follows:

$$\Sigma F_x = M\bar{a}_x, \qquad \frac{1}{2}W - \frac{1}{10}W = \frac{W}{g}\bar{a} \qquad (3)$$

$$\Sigma \overline{T} = \overline{I}\alpha, \qquad \frac{1}{10}Wr = \frac{1}{2}\frac{W}{g}r^2\alpha \qquad (4)$$

From Eqs. 3 and 4, we find

$$\bar{a} = \tfrac{2}{5}g = 12.88 \text{ ft/sec}^2; \qquad \alpha = \frac{2g}{10r} = \frac{2g}{10 \times 2} = 3.22 \text{ rad/sec}^2$$

Problem 552. A uniform bar AB (Fig. 355a) which weighs 40 lb and is 4 ft long rests in a vertical plane with its upper end B on a smooth vertical wall and

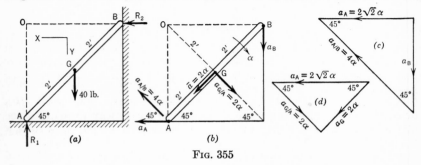

FIG. 355

its lower end A on a smooth horizontal surface. The bar is in equilibrium in the position shown when acted on by a horizontal force (not shown) applied at A. If the force is suddenly withdrawn, find the initial angular acceleration of the bar and the reactions R_1 and R_2 at A and B, respectively. Assume $g = 32$ ft/sec².

SOLUTION. Before using the equations of motion, we must find the linear acceleration of the mass center G of the bar. Considering the points A and B, we have, from the principle of relative motion,

$$a_A = a_{A/B} \nrightarrow a_B$$

Since $\omega = 0$, $a_{A/B}$ is equal to 4α in the direction shown in Fig. 355b. From the acceleration polygon in Fig. 355c it is seen that $a_A = 2\sqrt{2}\alpha$. Considering points A and G, we have

$$a_G = a_{G/A} \nrightarrow a_A$$

From the acceleration polygon in Fig. 355d, it is seen that $a_G = \bar{a} = 2\alpha$ downward to the left at an angle of 45° with the horizontal. Taking the X and Y axes as shown in Fig. 355a, we may write the equations of motion as follows:

$$\Sigma F_x = M\bar{a}_x, \qquad R_2 = \tfrac{40}{32} \times \sqrt{2}\alpha \qquad (1)$$

$$\Sigma F_y = M\bar{a}_y, \qquad 40 - R_1 = \tfrac{40}{32} \times \sqrt{2}\alpha \qquad (2)$$

$$\Sigma \bar{T} = \bar{I}\alpha, \qquad \sqrt{2}R_1 - \sqrt{2}R_2 = \tfrac{1}{12} \times \tfrac{40}{32} \times 16\alpha = \tfrac{5}{3}\alpha \qquad (3)$$

Solving the three equations, we find

$$\alpha = 6\sqrt{2} = 8.48 \text{ rad/sec}^2, \qquad R_1 = 25 \text{ lb}, \qquad R_2 = 15 \text{ lb}$$

Second Method. Another method for finding α in this problem, and one which is frequently useful in treating initial motions will now be considered. Assume that a body is formed by rigidly connecting a thin triangular plate AOB to the bar AB (Fig. 355b). It can easily be shown that the acceleration of the point O of the body is zero; that is, O is the center of zero acceleration of the body. Hence, using the equation of motion $\Sigma T_o = I_o\alpha$, we have

$$\Sigma T_o = 40 \times \sqrt{2} = (\tfrac{1}{12} \times \tfrac{40}{32} \times 16 + \tfrac{40}{32} \times 4)\alpha = \tfrac{20}{3}\alpha$$

Whence, $\alpha = 6\sqrt{2} = 8.48$ rad/sec², and R_1 and R_2 may be found from Eqs. 1 and 2 as in the previous solution.

Problems

553. A homogeneous solid sphere rolls without slipping down a rough plane which is inclined at an angle θ with the horizontal. Show that the acceleration of the center of the sphere is $\tfrac{5}{7}g \sin \theta$, and that the ratio of the friction to the normal pressure must be not less than $\tfrac{2}{7} \tan \theta$ to prevent the sphere from slipping.

554. Assume in Prob. 553 the body to be a homogeneous cylinder instead of a sphere. Show that the acceleration of the mass center is $\tfrac{2}{3}g \sin \theta$, and that the least coefficient of friction that will permit the cylinder to roll without slipping is $\tfrac{1}{3} \tan \theta$.

555. A hollow cylinder weighing 161 lb rolls, without slipping, on a horizontal plane when acted on by a horizontal force of 41 lb whose action line passes through the mass center of the cylinder and is perpendicular to its axis. If the acceleration of the mass center is 5 ft/sec², find, in terms of the outer radius r, the radius of gyration of the cylinder with respect to its axis. Also find the frictional force developed.

Ans. $k = 0.8r$; $F = 16$ lb.

556. A homogeneous cylinder is placed on the horizontal floor of a car so that it is free to roll in the direction of the track. The friction is sufficient to prevent slipping. If the car is given an acceleration of 6 ft/sec² in the direction of the track, what will be the acceleration of the center of the cylinder relative to the track?

Ans. $a = 2$ ft/sec².

557. Two homogeneous circular disks, A and B (Fig. 356), weighing 32.2 lb and 128.8 lb, respectively, are keyed together. The force P causes A to roll without slipping on a horizontal track. If $P = 54$ lb, find the magnitude and direction of the acceleration of the center of the disks.

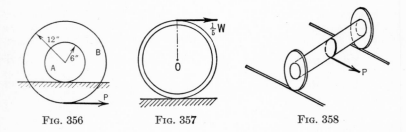

FIG. 356   FIG. 357   FIG. 358

558. A thin cylinder whose thickness may be neglected weighs W lb. It rolls, without slipping, on a horizontal surface when acted on by a horizontal force of $\frac{1}{5}W$ lb applied to the top, as shown in Fig. 357. Find the acceleration of the center of the cylinder, and the frictional force exerted by the plane on the cylinder.

Ans. $a = 6.44$ ft/sec²; $F = 0$.

559. Two solid cylindrical disks are keyed to an axle as shown in Fig. 358. A string is wrapped around the axle in its central plane, and a force P is exerted by the string in a direction parallel to the plane on which the disks roll (without slipping) and tangent to the under surface of the axle. Each disk weighs 16.1 lb and is 2 ft in diameter. The axle is 6 in. in diameter and weighs 64.4 lb. The magnitude of the force P is 19 lb. Will the disks and axle roll forward or backward? Find the acceleration of the central axis of the disks and axle.   *Ans.* $a = 4$ ft/sec².

560. If the string in the preceding problem is wrapped around the axle in the opposite direction so that the force P is tangent to the top of the axle, what is the acceleration of the central axis of the disks and axle?

561. Let the string in Prob. 559 be wrapped around the axle as shown in Fig. 358 and a force $P = 19$ lb be exerted by the string in a direction making an angle θ with the horizontal. Find the angular acceleration of the disks and axle in terms of θ. If the value of θ is such that the line of action of the force P intersects the horizontal line passing through the points of contact of the disks and plane, show that the angular acceleration will be zero.

562. In Fig. 359, AC is a uniform slender bar that weighs 64.4 lb and is attached to a disk by means of a smooth pin at A. The bar is prevented from turning relative to the disk by a peg at B. The disk rolls on a horizontal plane without slipping, and, when AC is in the position shown, $\omega = 2$ rad/sec and $\alpha = 2$ rad/sec² in the direction indicated. Find the force exerted by the peg B on the bar.

Ans. $R_B = 20$ lb.

563. The uniform bar AC in Fig. 360 which weighs 64.4 lb is connected by smooth pins to a block A and at B to a bar BD which is pin-connected at D. A force P is applied to A holding the bar AC in equilibrium in the position shown. If the force P is suddenly removed, find the initial reactions of the pins at A and B on the bar AC. Neglect the weights of the block A and the bar BD and friction on A.

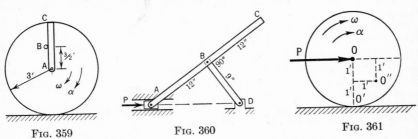

Fig. 359   Fig. 360   Fig. 361

564. A circular disk (Fig. 361) weighs 80.5 lb and is 4 ft in diameter. The disk rolls without slipping to the right on a straight horizontal track. The angular velocity of the disk is 2 rad/sec, and the angular acceleration is 4 rad/sec². [Find the horizontal force P required to produce this motion. Solve in three ways, using the points O, O', and O'' as moment centers in the moment equation. The acceleration of O' is toward the mass center, and the acceleration of O'' is zero.

Ans. $P = 30$ lb.

565. Assume in Prob. 551 that $h = 3$ ft. Find the angular acceleration of the cylinder and the linear acceleration of the mass center.

566. Assume in Prob. 551 that $h = 4$ ft. Find the angular acceleration of the cylinder and the linear acceleration of the mass center.

Ans. $\alpha = 12.88$ rad/sec²; $a = 19.32$ ft/sec².

567. A homogeneous sphere weighing W lb rests on a rough horizontal plane for which the coefficient of friction is $\frac{1}{10}$. The sphere is acted on by a horizontal force of $\frac{1}{2}W$ lb whose action line is at a distance x above the plane. If the radius of the sphere is 10 in., find the value of x if the sphere has a motion of translation.

568. If the coefficient of friction in the preceding problem were zero, find the value of x that would cause the sphere to roll without slipping. *Ans. $x = 14$ in.*

569. A two-wheeled cart (Fig. 362) weighs 360 lb including the weight of the wheels; the weight of each disk wheel is 60 lb, and the diameter is 4 ft. If the force

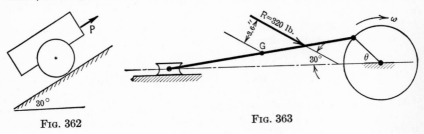

Fig. 362   Fig. 363

$P = 240$ lb and the coefficient of friction between the wheels and the inclined surface is sufficient to prevent slipping, determine the force that the axle exerts on each wheel and the linear acceleration of the body of the cart. Neglect axle friction.

570. The resultant R of all forces acting on the connecting rod (Fig. 363) is 320 lb, and its action line is located as shown. If the connecting rod is 30 in. long and weighs 80 lb, what are the linear acceleration of the mass center of the rod and the angular acceleration of the rod, if the rod is assumed to be of constant cross section?

Ans. $\bar{a} = 129$ ft/sec^2; $\alpha = 74.2$ rad/sec^2.

571. A uniform bar is 6 ft long and weighs 48 lb. It rests on a smooth horizontal surface. The bar is acted on by a suddenly applied horizontal force P whose action line passes through one end of the bar and makes an angle of 30° with the bar. If $P = 24$ lb, find the initial angular acceleration of the bar and the linear acceleration of the mass center.

572. A solid sphere having a radius of 8 in. and a weight of 161 lb is made to roll up a rough inclined plane (Fig. 364) by means of a flexible cord, one end of which is attached to an axis through the center of the sphere. The cord passes over a smooth peg and has attached to its other end a suspended body B which weighs 128.8 lb. Find the acceleration of the body B and the tension in the cord.

Ans. $a = 4.39$ ft/sec^2; $T = 111.2$ lb.

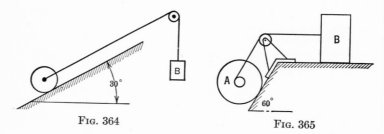

FIG. 364   FIG. 365

573. In Fig. 365, A is a body consisting of two cylindrical disks having a radius of 8 in. connected by an axle having a radius of 2 in. (similar to the arrangement in Fig. 358). The weight of A is 48 lb, and the radius of gyration about the axis of the axle is 5 in. A cord wrapped around the axle passes over a smooth, weightless pulley and is attached to a body B that weighs 60 lb. The coefficient of friction between B and the horizontal plane is 0.2. If A rolls, without slipping, down the inclined plane, find the tension in the cord and the acceleration of B.

Ans. $T = 24.4$ lb; $a = 6.66$ ft/sec^2.

574. A homogeneous sphere whose weight is 80.5 lb and radius is 2 ft moves to the right on a horizontal plane when acted on by one or more forces in addition to its weight and the reaction of the plane. If the acceleration of the mass center is 12 ft/sec^2 to the right and the angular acceleration is 5 rad/sec^2 counterclockwise, determine completely the resultant of all external forces acting on the sphere.

Review Questions

1. Complete the following statement: The equations of motion for a body are the equations expressing the relations among the following three factors or quantities:

2. Define: (*a*) weight of a body, and (*b*) mass of a body.

3. Is the following definition correct? The engineer's unit of mass, called a slug, is the mass of a body that is given an acceleration of 1 ft/sec^2 by a 1-lb force.

4. What is the weight of a body having a mass of 1 slug? How many units of mass (slugs) in a body weighing W lb?

5. State Newton's second law of motion.

When attempting to compare the weights of two small bodies (pebbles, say) a person instinctively jounces or shakes the bodies in his hands. Why does this enable the person to obtain a better estimate of the relative weights than he could by merely supporting the bodies in his hands?

6. In analyzing the motion of a body by use of Newton's laws of motion, why is the body considered to be made up of particles? Define effective force for a particle.

7. State Newton's third law of motion.

Let A and B be two bodies between which there are mutual actions; if A is a freely falling body and its weight is one of the two (mutual) actions, what body is B?

8. Explain briefly the four steps followed in obtaining the equations of motion for a body.

9. Point out and correct the error in the following statement: The principle of motion of the mass center states that, if the resultant of all the external forces acting on any body is a force, its magnitude is equal to the product of the mass of the body and the acceleration of the mass center $\bar{a}$ of the body, and it acts through the mass center in the direction of $\bar{a}$.

10. (a) State D'Alembert's principle. (b) Define inertia force for a body. (c) Explain the inertia-force method of solving kinetics problems. (d) What is meant by the term "centrifugal force"; is it an actual force exerted by one body on another body?

11. Specify the magnitude, sense, and action line of the inertia force for a translating rigid body of mass M having an acceleration a.

12. If a rigid body rotates about a fixed axis with an angular acceleration, under what conditions will the resultant of the external forces acting on the body be: (a) a force, (b) a couple?

13. A rigid body rotates about a fixed axis that does not pass through the mass center of the body. What is the distance from the center of rotation to the point where the resultant of the effective forces (and hence also the external forces) intersects the N axis?

14. A rigid body has plane motion: (a) If the acceleration $\bar{a}$ of the mass center is zero and the angular acceleration α of the body is not zero, what can be said about the resultant of the forces acting on the body? (b) If α is zero and $\bar{a}$ is not zero, what can be said?

15. If the mass of a body whose weight is 20 lb be arbitrarily selected as the unit of mass, and an acceleration of 8.05 ft/sec^2 be selected as the unit of acceleration, what is the magnitude (in pounds) of the force that must be used as the unit of force in order that the system of units constitute a kinetic system.

16. A body rests on the floor of an elevator that is moving upward with a certain acceleration. Is the weight of the body the same as it would be if the elevator were were moving downward with the same acceleration?

Chapter 10

WORK AND ENERGY

105 Introduction. In the preceding chapter the relations among force, mass, and acceleration were developed from Newton's laws of motion and applied to the motion of bodies under the action of unbalanced forces. As already noted, the quantities involved *directly* in Newton's laws are force, mass, and acceleration. But acceleration involves the quantities, velocity, distance, and time. In many problems in engineering, it is convenient to use certain other quantities, the more important of which are: work, power, energy, impulse, and momentum. The expression for each of these quantities is a combination of some of the six quantities (force, mass, acceleration, velocity, distance, and time) that are involved in Newton's laws of motion. Thus, force and distance combine to measure work; force, distance, and time combine to measure power; mass and velocity combine to measure momentum and kinetic energy; force and time combine to measure impulse, etc. Although the conceptions of these quantities are largely a result of our experience with physical phenomena, the exact relations between them, as expressed in certain principles to be developed in the following pages, are based on Newton's laws.

The present chapter is devoted to a discussion of the meaning and use of work, of energy, and of certain principles that express relations between these two quantities. Although no fundamental physical laws other than Newton's laws of motion are used in developing the principles of work and energy, nevertheless, the method of analysis that makes use of work and energy possesses certain advantages over the method that makes use directly of force, mass, and acceleration, even in certain types of problems that involve only rigid bodies having rather simple types of motion such as translation, rotation, and plane motion. And, in dealing with non-rigid bodies having unordered motion, that is, motion in which the particles of the mass system (body) do not follow definite known paths, the principles of energy are of particular importance. In fact, the study of the behavior of non-rigid bodies in general, such as water, steam, gas, and air, is largely based on the principles of energy, and, hence, these principles play an important part in hydraulics, aerodynamics, thermodynamics, etc.

§1 Work and Power

106 Work defined. A force does work on a body if the body on which the force acts moves so that the displacement of the point of application of the force has a component in the direction of the force. The amount of work done by a constant force whose point of application has a rectilinear displacement is the product of the force and the component of the displacement of its application point in the direction of the force. The work may also be expressed as the product of the rectangular component of the force in the direction of the displacement of its application point and the displacement. The component of the force in the direction of the displacement of its application point is often called the *working component*. And the component of the displacement in the direction of the force is called the *effective displacement*.

107 Algebraic expressions for work done by a force. The mathematical expression for the work w done by a force F in a displacement s of its application point depends on the way the force varies during the displacement. Several important special cases are considered here.

I. The force is constant in magnitude and in direction and agrees in direction with the displacement as, for example, the force exerted in lifting a body vertically upward with a constant acceleration. The amount of work done is

$$w = F \cdot s$$

II. The force is constant in magnitude and in direction but does not

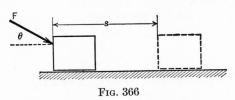

Fig. 366

agree in direction with the displacement (Fig. 366). The amount of work done is

$$w = F \cos \theta \cdot s = F_t \cdot s$$

in which $F \cos \theta$ is denoted by F_t since $F \cos \theta$ is tangent to the path of the point of application.

III. The force varies in magnitude but not in direction, and the direction agrees with that of the displacement, as, for example, the force exerted in compressing a helical spring or the steam pressure against the piston of a steam engine after cut-off. Thus, in compressing a spring, the force corresponding to any position s is F (Fig. 367), and this force may be assumed to remain constant in an infinitesimal displacement ds. Hence, according to Case I, the workdone by the force

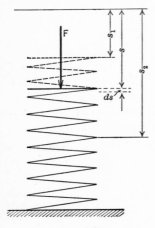

F in the displacement ds is $dw = F \, ds$, and the total work done on the spring, as F varies from its initial to its final value, is

$$w = \int_{s_1}^{s_2} F \, ds = F_{\text{avg}} \cdot \Delta s$$

where F_{avg} is the *space-average* value of the force in the displacement Δs or $s_2 - s_1$. In order to evaluate the integral by the method of calculus, F must be expressed in terms of s. That is, the manner in which F varies with s must be known.

IV. The force varies in magnitude and in direction, as, for example, the pressure of the connecting rod on the crank pin of an engine (Fig. 368). The expression for the

Fig. 367

work done by the force is found by the same method as was used in Case III except that the tangential component of the force must be used. Hence,

$$w = \int_{s_1}^{s_2} F_t \, ds \tag{1}$$

This expression applies for a displacement along any curved path. But, when the displacement takes place on a circular path of radius r, the

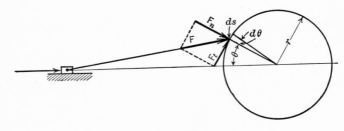

Fig. 368

elemental displacement ds is expressed by the equation $ds = r \, d\theta$. Hence,

$$w = \int_{s_1}^{s_2} F_t \, ds = \int_{s_1}^{s_2} F_t r \, d\theta = \int_{\theta_1}^{\theta_2} T \, d\theta$$

in which T is the torque or moment of the force about the center of the circular path. And, if the torque remains constant during an angular displacement $\theta = \theta_2 - \theta_1$,

$$w = T \int_{\theta_1}^{\theta_2} d\theta = T(\theta_2 - \theta_1) = T \cdot \theta$$

Thus, in one revolution, the work done by the force F having a moment T about the center of the circular path is $w = T \cdot 2\pi$. And, if n revolutions occur per unit of time, the work done per unit of time is $w = T \cdot 2\pi n$.

108 Work done by a couple. In Fig. 369 the couple whose moment is $F \cdot 2r$ turns through an angle $d\theta$ during which displacement the forces F of the couple may be assumed to be constant. The work done by the forces of the couple is $2F\,ds$ or $2Fr\,d\theta$. But $F \cdot 2r$ is the moment of the couple. Therefore, the work done by the couple in the angular displacement $d\theta$ is the product of the moment T of the couple and the angular displacement $d\theta$ of the couple. Further, if the angular displacement of the couple is $\theta = \theta_2 - \theta_1$, the work done is

$$w = \int_{\theta_1}^{\theta_2} T\,d\theta$$

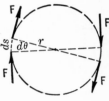

Fɪɢ. 369

If the moment of the couple remains constant during the angular displacement θ, the work done by the couple is $w = T\theta$.

109 Work a scalar quantity. Sign and units of work. Work is a scalar quantity. Thus the work done by one force may be added (algebraically) to the work done by another force, regardless of the directions of the forces or of the displacements of their points of application. And the work done on one body of a system may be added (algebraically) to the work done on the other bodies of the system in order to obtain the total work done on the system, regardless of the manner in which the bodies move.

It is convenient to regard the work done by a force as having sign. Work is positive when the working component of the force and the displacement of its application point agree in sense, and work is negative when the working component and the displacement are opposite in sense. Thus, a force that retards the motion of a body does negative work on the body.

The unit of work is the work done by a unit force acting through a unit distance and hence depends on the units used for force and distance. Thus, the more common units for work in the gravitational (engineer's) system of units are the foot pound, inch pound, meter kilogram, etc. No one-term names are given to the units of work in the gravitational system of units. The common units of work in the absolute system of units are the dyne centimeter, which is called an erg, and the joule, which is 10^7 ergs. For large units of work the horsepower-hour and the kilowatt-hour are used. For a definition of these units see Art. 112.

110 Graphical representation and calculation of work. In calculating the work done by a variable force, by use of the equation $w = \int_{s_1}^{s_2} F_t \, ds$, the working component F_t of the force must be expressed in terms of the displacement s. If it is impossible to express F_t in terms of s, or if, when possible, the expression for F_t is complex and difficult to use, the relation between F_t and s may be expressed graphically by means of a graph or curve, and the work done may be found from the graphical diagram as follows: If values of F_t and s are plotted on a pair of rectangular axes for all positions of the application point of the force F, the curve joining the plotted points is called a tangential-force-space $(F_t\text{–}s)$ curve (Fig. 370). In most problems, only a sufficient number of values of F_t are plotted to make it possible to draw a reliable $F_t\text{–}s$ curve, values of F_t being plotted more frequently when the value of F_t is

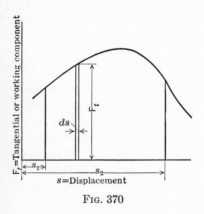

changing the more rapidly. In the foregoing equation $F_t \, ds$ represents an elemental part of the area (Fig. 370) between the $F_t\text{–}s$ curve and the s axis. And the total area under the $F_t\text{–}s$ curve between any two ordinates corresponding to abscissas s_1 and s_2 is

$$\text{Area} = \int_{s_1}^{s_2} F_t \, ds$$

Fig. 370

Therefore, the work done by a force in any displacement s is represented by the area under the tangential-force-space curve between the ordinates at s_1 and s_2. This diagram is called a work diagram. In determining the amount of work represented by the work diagram, the scales used in plotting the $F_t\text{–}s$ curve must be considered. Thus, if ordinates are plotted to a scale of 1 in. = 50 lb and abscissas to the scale of 1 in. = 5 ft, each square inch of area under the $F_t\text{–}s$ curve represents 250 ft lb of work.

Since the area of a work diagram equals the product of the average ordinate and the base, the work done by a force equals the (space) average value of the tangential (working) component of the force and the length of the path described by the point of application.

The area of the work diagram may be found by means of a planimeter or by dividing the area into small strips and applying Simpson's rule. Or, in some cases, less exact methods may be employed in estimating the area.

111   Work done on a body by a force system.   So far, the work done on a body by a single force or by a couple has been considered.   In general, however, a body is acted on by a force system, and, in order to find the work done on the body in any displacement, the work done by the whole force system must be found.   The work done by a force system is the algebraic sum of the works done by the forces of the system.   For a concurrent force system acting on a particle or for a force system acting on a translating rigid body in which the displacements of the points of application of the forces and the displacement of the point of application of the resultant (assumed to be a fixed point on the body) are equal, the work done by the force system is equal to the work done by the resultant.   However, in general, the work done by a force system cannot be found from the work done by the resultant of the force system. Thus if two equal, opposite, and collinear forces F, F be applied at the ends of a helical spring causing the spring to stretch as the magnitude of the forces F, F increases, the work done by the forces in stretching the spring is the product of the average value of F and the increase in the length of the spring, although the resultant of the two forces F, F is at all times equal to zero.

If the spring in the foregoing discussion be replaced by a rigid stationary bar and two equal, opposite, and collinear forces F, F be applied along the axis of the bar, it is obvious that the work done by the two forces is zero, regardless of the manner in which the magnitude of the two equal forces may vary during the time they act on the bar, since the point of application of each force does not move.   If the rigid bar is moved in any way while the two equal, opposite, and collinear forces are acting on it, it can likewise be shown that the work done by the forces is zero.   Hence, an important fact may be stated as follows:

> The work done by two forces which at all times are equal, opposite, and collinear is zero, provided that the distance between the points of application of the forces remains constant.

This statement will be found to be of particular importance in the discussion of the principle of work and energy for a rigid body (Art. 121). For a rigid body the distance between any two particles of the body remains constant, and, by Newton's third law, the forces that the two particles exert on each other are equal, opposite, and collinear, and hence the work done by each such pair of forces in any displacement of the body is zero. Therefore in any displacement of a rigid body the work done by the internal forces is zero.

Although it is not *always* possible to find the work done by a force system acting on a body by finding the work done by the resultant of the system, it is *sometimes* possible to do so. Thus, the work done by the earth pulls on the particles of a body (weights of the particles) in any displacement of the body is found to be equal to the work done by the resultant of the weights of the particles: that is, by the weight of the body if it is assumed that the point of application of the resultant is the center of gravity of the body. This may be formally stated as follows:

> The work done by the weight of a body in any displacement of the body is equal to the product of the weight of the body and the vertical component of displacement of the center of gravity of the body.

Illustrative Problems

Problem 575. A helical spring (Fig. 371) having a modulus of 200 lb/in. is compressed $s = 4$ in. by an axial load. How much work is done by the (variable) load in compressing the spring?

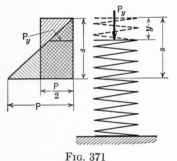

FIG. 371

SOLUTION. If P_y denotes the force corresponding to any compression y of the spring, then, from Case III, Art. 107, we have

$$w = \int_0^s P_y \, dy$$

But

$$P_y = 200y$$

Hence,

$$w = \int_0^s 200y \, dy = \frac{200s^2}{2} = \frac{200(4)^2}{2} \quad (\text{when } s = 4)$$

$$= 1600 \text{ in lb}$$

The expression $w = 200s^2/2$ may be written:

$$w = \frac{200s}{2} \times s = \frac{P}{2} \times s = \text{area of triangular work diagram}$$

= average force times total displacement

= area of rectangular diagram having the same area as the triangular diagram

Problem 576. The component F_t of the crank-pin pressure F in Fig. 368 is called the tangential effort. The tangential-effort diagram for a steam engine (similar to Fig. 372) is drawn to the following scales: 1 in. of ordinate = 24 lb/sq in. of piston area and 1 in. of abscissa = a 30° arc of the crank-pin circle. The area under the curve is found to be 11.5 sq in. Find the work done on the crank pin per square inch of the piston area per stroke (one-half revolution), if the crank length is 7.5 in. Also find the total work done per stroke, the diameter of the piston being 14 in.

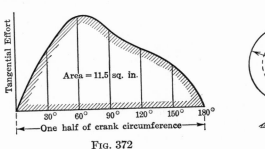

Fig. 372

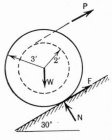

Fig. 373

Solution. A 30° arc of the crank-pin circle = 3.92 in. 1 sq in. of the work diagram = 24 × 3.92 = 94.2 in lb. Work done per stroke per square inch of piston = 94.2 × 11.5 = 1083 in lb = 90.2 ft lb.

$$\text{Total work per stroke} = 90.2 \times \frac{\pi \times (14)^2}{4} = 13,900 \text{ ft lb}$$

Problem 577. A homogeneous cylinder that weighs 80 lb is made to roll up an inclined plane (Fig. 373) by means of a force P applied to a string wrapped around a groove in the central plane of the cylinder. If $P = 40$ lb, and the cylinder rolls without slipping 10 ft up the plane, find the work done by the external forces that act on the cylinder.

Solution. The forces acting on the cylinder as shown in Fig. 373 are the weight W, the force P, the normal force N, and the frictional force F. The work done by the weight W is equal to the product of the weight and the vertical component of the displacement of the center of gravity of the cylinder. Thus,

$$w_W = -80 \times 10 \sin 30° = -400 \text{ ft lb}$$

The work done by the force P is the product of the force P and the displacement of the end of the cord. Thus,

$$w_P = 40 \times \tfrac{5}{3} \times 10 = 667 \text{ ft lb}$$

Since the cylinder rolls without slipping, the forces N and F do no work.* Hence,

* In order to show that the forces F and N do no work, consider a constant force of Q lb whose point of application on a body moves in the direction of the force with a velocity of v ft/sec. The rate at which work is being done by the force is Qv ft lb/sec. If $v = 0$, the rate at which work is being done is zero. In the foregoing problem, the velocity of the point of the cylinder in contact with the plane (the point of the cylinder on which the forces F and N act) is zero. Hence, for all positions of the cylinder, the rate at which work is being done by the two forces is zero. Therefore, the work done by each of the forces in any displacement of the cylinder is zero. If the cylinder slips as it rolls up the plane, the point of the cylinder on which the forces F and N act will have a velocity parallel to the plane. Hence, the frictional force F will do work since the point of application moves in a direction parallel to the force; however, the normal force N will do no work since the point of application moves perpendicular to N.

the total work done on the cylinder is

$$w = -400 + 667 = 267 \text{ ft lb}$$

Problems

578. A rope which weighs 1.5 lb per foot is wound around a drum with 500 ft of the rope hanging vertically from the drum. How many foot pounds of work must be done to wind up 200 ft of the rope? *Ans. w = 120,000 ft lb.*

579. An automobile that weighs 3500 lb coasts a distance of 400 ft up a grade of 1 ft in 50 ft. The tractive resistance parallel to the road (due to air resistance, rolling resistance, etc.) is 0.08 of the weight of the automobile. Find the total work done on the automobile while it is traveling the 400 ft. *Ans. w = −140,000 ft lb.*

580. How much work in ft tons is done by the draw-bar pull of an engine in pulling a train of 40 cars, each weighing 40 tons, at a constant speed of 30 mi/hr up a 1 per cent grade a distance of 1 mi? Assume the train resistance (due to air resistance, rolling resistance, etc.) to be 8 lb/ton of weight.

581. A box weighing 80 lb is pulled up an inclined plane that makes an angle of 30° with the horizontal by a force P of 60 lb. If P makes an angle of 30° with the plane and the coefficient of friction between the box and plane is $\frac{1}{8}$, find the work done by each force acting on the box in moving it 20 ft. Find also the total work done on the box in the same displacement. *Ans. Total w = 141 ft lb.*

582. A uniform bar AB in Fig. 374 is rigidly attached to a disk D. The disk and bar each weigh 10 lb, and a couple whose moment $C = 100 \cos \theta$ lb ft acts on the disk as shown. The force system acting on the disk and bar causes the disk to roll without slipping on the horizontal surface. Find the total work done on the disk and bar in a displacement in which the angle θ increases from 30° to 60°.

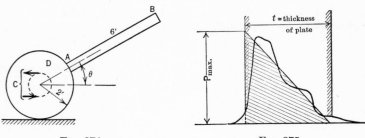

Fɪɢ. 374   Fɪɢ. 375

583. In the design of punching machines (see Fig. 396) it is important to know how much work is done in punching a hole in a plate. Tests show that the work diagram for steel is approximately of the form shown by the heavy curved line in Fig. 375. This diagram may be assumed, without serious error, to be equal to the triangular work diagram in which the maximum pressure P corresponds to a shearing strength in the steel plate of 50,000 lb/sq in. Find the work done in punching a 1-in. hole in a $\frac{5}{8}$-in. steel plate. *Ans. w = 30,700 in. lb.*

584. The steam-indicator card (Fig. 376) is drawn to the following scales: 1 in. of ordinate = 100 lb/sq in. and 1 in. of abscissa = 5 in. of the stroke of the piston. The area of the indicator card is found to be 2.5 sq in., and the length of the diagram is 3 in. (stroke = 15 in.). The diameter of the piston is 12 in. Find the work done per stroke by the steam on the piston. What is the average steam pressure in pounds per square inch (mean effective pressure) that will do the same amount of work?

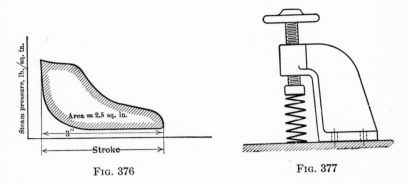

Fig. 376   Fig. 377

585. The screw of the bracket clamp (Fig. 377) moves vertically 1 in. when the hand wheel is turned 6 revolutions. A helical spring having a modulus of 200 lb/in. is compressed by turning the hand wheel. The average frictional moment of the screw is 20 in. lb. What is the average turning moment applied to the hand wheel in compressing the spring 3 in.? *Ans.* $T = 27.96$ lb in.

586. A standpipe 60 ft high and 6 ft in diameter is filled with water that is pumped from a pond whose level is 60 ft below the bottom of the standpipe. The frictional resistance of the water in passing through the pipe is equivalent to an additional lift of 10 ft. Determine the work done by the pump in filling the standpipe; assume the weight of water to be 62.4 lb/ft³. *Ans.* $w = 10,600,000$ ft lb.

587. In Fig. 378 the body A is moved along a smooth horizontal plane by means of a constant force $P = 10$ lb applied at the end of a cord connected to A and passing over a small smooth peg B. Find the work done on A by the cord while A is displaced 10 ft.

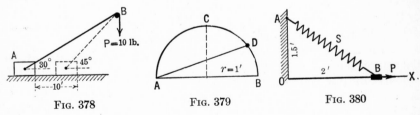

Fig. 378   Fig. 379   Fig. 380

588. In Fig. 379, D is a small body that slides on the semi-circular track BCA. AD is an elastic spring attached to the track at A. The unstretched length of the spring is 1 ft, and the modulus of the spring is 100 lb/ft. Find the work done on D by the spring as D moves from B to C. *Ans.* $w = 41.4$ ft lb.

589. A spring S (Fig. 380) is attached at A to a fixed vertical plane and to a block B that slides on a smooth horizontal rod OX. The unstretched length of the spring is 1.5 ft, and the modulus of the spring is 120 lb/ft. How much work is done by the spring on B as B is moved 2 ft from O by the force P?

590. Two blocks, A and B, in Fig. 381 are connected by a spring whose unstretched length is 4 ft and whose modulus is 120 lb/ft. How much work is done on the spring as the blocks are moved from the position indicated by the dotted line to the position shown in the figure?   *Ans.* $w = 141.1$ ft lb.

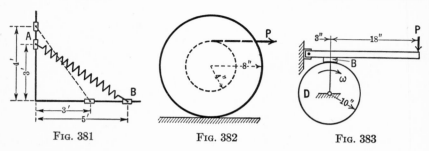

FIG. 381   FIG. 382   FIG. 383

591. A cylinder having a radius of 8 in. has a groove of 4-in. radius cut in its mid-section (Fig. 382). A string is wrapped around the cylinder in the groove, and a horizontal force P of 10 lb is applied to the end of the string. The cylinder rolls without slipping on the horizontal surface. Find the work done on the cylinder while its center travels a distance of 8 ft.

592. In Fig. 383 the force P applied at the end of a brake lever is 20 lb. The coefficient of friction for the brake shoe B and drum D is $\frac{1}{4}$. The drum is rotating when the brake is applied. Find the work done on the drum while it makes 10 revolutions. Assume that the friction of the drum axle in its bearing is negligible.

                                        Ans. $w = -1833$ ft lb.

112 Power defined. The term *power* as used in mechanics is defined as the rate of doing work. The use or function of many machines depends upon the rate at which they do work as well as upon the amount of work performed. Thus, some machines such as electric generators and steam engines are rated in terms of the power they are able to develop under specified conditions of service.

If the rate of doing work is constant, the power P developed may be defined by the expression $P = w/t$, in which w is the work done in time t. If the rate of doing work varies, the power at any instant may be defined by the expression $P = dw/dt$.

UNITS OF POWER. Power, like work, is a scalar quantity. The unit of power may be any unit of work per unit of time. Thus, in the gravitational system of units, the foot pound per second (ft lb/sec) and kilogram meter per second are common units, whereas, in the absolute system, the dyne centimeter per second (erg/sec) or joule per second are in common use. In many problems in engineering, however, it is more convenient to use a larger unit of power. In the gravitational system of units these larger units are the British or American horsepower (hp) and the *force de cheval* or Continental horsepower. They are defined as follows:

One British or American horsepower $= 550$ ft lb/sec

$$= 33{,}000 \text{ ft lb/min}$$

One Continental horsepower $= 75$ kilogram meters per second

$$= 4500 \text{ kilogram meters per minute}$$

And in the absolute system, the larger units are the watt and kilowatt, which are defined as follows:

$$\text{One watt} = 10^7 \text{ ergs/sec}$$

$$\text{One kilowatt} = 1000 \text{ watts}$$

They may be converted into British horsepower by means of the relations

$$\text{One horsepower} = 746 \text{ watts}$$

$$\text{One kilowatt} = 1.34 \text{ horsepower}$$

And, for approximate computations, it is convenient to use 1 horse-power $= \frac{3}{4}$ kilowatt or 1 kilowatt $= \frac{4}{3}$ horsepower.

For expressing very large quantities of work, the units used are the horsepower-hour (hp-hr) and the kilowatt-hour (kw-hr). A horsepower-hour is the work done in one hour at a constant rate of one horsepower. Thus:

$$\text{One horsepower-hour} = 33{,}000 \times 60 = 1{,}980{,}000 \text{ ft lb}$$

Similarly,

$$\text{One kilowatt-hour} = 1.34 \times 1{,}980{,}000 = 2{,}650{,}000 \text{ ft lb}$$

113 Special equations for power. If a force F remains constant in a given displacement of its application point and acts in the direction of the displacement, as, for example, the draw-bar pull of a locomotive, the work done in one unit of time is Fv, in which v is the velocity of the application point: that is, the distance moved through in one unit of time. Hence, if F is expressed in pounds and v in feet per second, the horsepower developed by the force (or the body exerting the force) is

$$hp = \frac{Fv}{550}$$

If the velocity varies, the above equation expresses the horsepower at the instant the velocity is v. If the force does not act in the direction of the displacement of its application point, the working component of the force must be used in the above equation. And, if the force agrees in direction with the displacement but varies in magnitude, as, for example, the pressure of the steam against the piston of a steam engine or the tangential effort against the crank pin, then the value of F (or F_t) at any instant may be used to obtain the power at that instant. However, the average power during a given cycle (or many cycles) of operations is generally more useful than the instantaneous power. Thus, for a steam engine, the average horsepower is expressed by

$$hp = \frac{2Plan}{33,000}$$

in which P is the mean effective pressure (lb/sq in.), a is the piston area (sq in.), l is the length of stroke (ft), and n is the number of revolutions per minute (rpm). This expression is derived from the fact that Pa is the average force (lb) which acts through a distance $l \cdot 2n$ (ft) per minute, the number of strokes per minute being $2n$ in a double-acting engine, and hence the work (ft lb) done per minute (power) is $Pa \cdot l \cdot 2n$ and the horsepower is as given.

If a couple having a constant moment T acts through a given angular displacement of θ radians, the work done is $T \cdot \theta$ (Art. 108). And, if the couple turns through ω radians per unit of time, the work done per unit of time is $T\omega$. Hence, if the moment of the couple is expressed in pound feet and ω in radians per second, the horsepower developed by the couple is

$$hp = \frac{T\omega}{550}$$

If the angular velocity is not constant, the above equation expresses the horsepower at the instant at which the velocity is ω. But in many problems the average horsepower during a given cycle of operations is of more use than the instantaneous value.

Problems

593. Niagara Falls is approximately 200 ft high, and the rate of discharge of water over the falls is about 280,000 cu ft per sec. Compute the horsepower that could be developed if no energy were lost.

594. A locomotive exerts a constant draw-bar pull of 25,000 lb while increasing the speed of a train uniformly from 30 to 60 mi/hr. What horsepower does the engine develop: (a) at the beginning of the period, (b) at the end of the period? (c) What is the average horsepower during the period?

Ans. (a) 2000 hp; (b) 4000 hp; (c) 3000 hp.

595. A man in turning the crank on the winch of a crane was found to exert the forces shown in Fig. 384 at the positions indicated. Plot (free-hand) carefully a tangential-effort diagram, the crank (radius) being 12 in. long. Estimate from the diagram the mean tangential effort, and calculate the mean horsepower developed by the man, assuming that he turns the crank at a constant speed of 45 rpm.

596. Two pulleys are keyed to the same shaft 10 ft apart. One pulley is driven by a belt from an engine. The other pulley is belted to and drives a machine. If the first (driving) pulley received 2 hp from its belt, what torque is transmitted to the shaft (and driven pulley), if it is assumed that the shaft rotates at a constant speed of 180 rpm?

Ans. 58.4 lb ft.

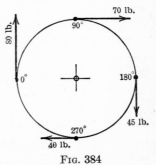

FIG. 384

597. A pump driven by a 10-hp motor discharges 200,000 cu ft of water from one reservoir to another (higher) reservoir whose water level is 20 ft above that of the lower reservoir. If the over-all efficiency of the whole installation is 80 per cent, how long does it take to pump the water?

598. What indicated horsepower will the engine referred to in Prob. 584 develop if it operates at a constant speed of 250 rpm and is double acting?   *Ans.* 178 hp.

599. A generator develops 500 kw and delivers 420 kw to a machine shop. A price of 4 cents per kilowatt-hour is paid. Does the machine shop pay for power or for work? What is the cost to the machine shop per day of 8 hours?

600. A certain machine requires 3 hp for its operation. If the machine is in use 8 hr per day, how many foot pounds of work are delivered to the machine in one day?

601. If the efficiency of the pump referred to in Prob. 586 is 60 per cent and the time required to fill the standpipe is 30 min, what horsepower must be delivered to the pump?

602. In Prob. 580 what horsepower is developed by the draw-bar pull of the engine?   *Ans.* 3580 hp.

§ 2   Energy

114   Energy defined. It is difficult to define energy so that it has physical meaning for all of its uses in the study of mechanical phenomena. It is however closely associated with work, and for the use of energy in this chapter it may be defined in terms of work. Thus the *energy* of a body is the capacity of the body for doing work. Work may be considered to be done by forces as in the preceding section, or, since forces are exerted by bodies, work may also be considered to be done by the bodies that exert the forces, the work being done by virtue of the energy that the bodies possess. A body may have the capacity to do work (possess energy) by virtue of a variety of conditions or states of the body. Thus, energy may be classified as mechanical energy, heat or thermal energy, chemical energy, electric energy, etc., depending on the state or condition of the body as a result of which it is capable of doing work. Our knowledge of all the conditions that render bodies capable of doing work is far from complete, but experience shows that any of the forms of energy may, under the proper conditions, be transformed into other forms.

Mechanical energy is of particular importance in connection with the kinetics of bodies and is therefore considered further in the following pages. The other forms of energy are discussed briefly in Art. 119. Mechanical energy is divided into *potential energy*, or energy of position or configuration, and *kinetic energy* or energy of motion.

From the definition of energy it follows that energy, like work, is a scalar quantity. Thus, the energy of any mass system is the sum of the energies of the various particles of the system, regardless of the directions of motion of the particles.

The units of energy are the same as the units of work discussed in the preceding section.

115 Potential energy. The potential energy of a body or mass system is the capacity of the body for doing work by virtue of the configuration of the body, that is, the relative positions of the particles of the body. Thus, a compressed spring and the compressed steam in a boiler are capable of doing work by virtue of the relative positions (configuration) of their particles. Likewise, a system of bodies may possess potential energy by virtue of the relative positions of the bodies. Thus, the water above a mill dam is said to possess potential energy since it is capable of driving a water wheel by virtue of its relative position with respect to the water wheel. Strictly speaking, however, the energy is possessed not by the water alone but by the system consisting of the earth and the water. But, since the earth is usually regarded as being fixed, it is convenient to regard the water as possessing the energy.

The potential energy of a mass system may be defined quantitatively as the amount of work the mass system is capable of doing against external forces, in passing from the given position or configuration to some standard position or configuration, assuming that no other change in the state or condition of the mass system takes place. This definition, however, does not lead to a definite quantity for the potential energy of the mass system for a given configuration, unless the work done by the mass system depends only on the initial and final configuration of the mass system and not at all on the paths described by the parts of the system while coming to the standard state. Mass systems for which this condition is fulfilled are called conservative mass systems, and the force system that acts on such a mass system while its potential state changes is called a conservative force system.* The properties of a conservative system are treated further in Art. 122.

The most common example of a non-conservative system is that in which the mass system does work against frictional forces. Conservative mass systems occur frequently in engineering problems. A common example of a conservative system is that of the earth and an elevated body (whether rigid or not). The work done by the weight of the body in any displacement is equal to the earth pull (weight) of the body times the vertical displacement of the center of gravity of the body (Art. 111), regardless of the intermediate positions occupied by the body in moving from one position to another position. Another example is that of an elastic body, for, if the body is elastic, the energy possessed by the body when in a given strained condition, that is, for a given configuration of its particles, is the same, regardless of the relative displacements of the particles which occurred while being put in the given strained condition. The standard configuration may be arbitrarily chosen, but, for convenience, it is so chosen that the potential energy of the body is positive or zero. Thus, in the example of the earth and an elevated body the earth is considered fixed, and the standard configuration occurs when the body is in contact with the earth at a standard elevation.

Problems

603. A helical spring whose weight is 10 lb and whose modulus is 100 lb per in. is compressed 3 in. at sea level by applying forces to its ends by means of a clamp. What is its potential energy, considering its unstrained condition at sea level as the standard configuration? If this compressed spring is now taken to the top of a tower 100 ft above sea level, what will be the potential energy of the spring?

604. A flexible, weightless cord passes over a fixed cylinder whose axis is horizontal. From each end of the cord a body is suspended; one body weighs 20 lb, and the other weighs 30 lb. The standard configuration of the system consisting of the cord and two bodies will be assumed to occur when the bodies are at the same level. What will be the potential energy of the system if the configuration is changed by allowing the 30-lb body to descend 3 ft and the 20-lb body to ascend the same distance?   *Ans.* $E_p = -30$ ft lb.

605. A body B weighing 80 lb is attached by a flexible string to a spring S (Fig. 385). The pulley over which the string passes is weightless and frictionless. The spring has a modulus of 40 lb/in. If a force P of 50 lb is gradually applied to B, what is the change in the

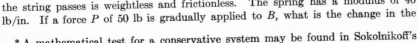

FIG. 385

---

* A mathematical test for a conservative system may be found in Sokolnikoff's *Higher Mathematics for Engineers and Physicists,* pp. 166–189.

potential energy: (a) of the spring, and (b) of the spring and body B considered as one system?   *Ans.* (a) $\Delta E_p = 131$ in. lb; (b) $\Delta E_p = 31.2$ in. lb.

606. Water is supplied to a Pelton water wheel from a lake whose surface is 600 ft above the wheel. The water striking the blades of the wheel discharges through a nozzle, the amount of water discharged per second being 3.5 cu ft. The wheel drives an electric generator. If 10 per cent of the energy of the water flowing through the conduit is lost and if the efficiencies of the water wheel and generator are 80 per cent and 90 per cent, respectively, how much power (in kilowatts) is delivered to the switchboard?

116   Kinetic energy.   The kinetic energy of a body is its capacity for doing work as a result of its motion. Thus, by virtue of its kinetic energy, a body is capable of doing work against forces that change its motion. For example, a jet of water does work on a tangential water wheel; a steam forging hammer does work on the material that is deformed by the hammer; the rotating flywheel on a punching machine does work in punching the hole in the metal plate, etc.

The kinetic energy of a body at any instant may be defined quantitatively as the amount of work that the body is capable of doing against forces which destroy its motion: that is, which bring it to a state of rest. The expression for the kinetic energy of a body (mass system) should, therefore, contain a quantity (velocity) which is a measure of the motion of the body and also a quantity (mass, moment of inertia, etc.) which is a measure of the (kinetic) property of the body that has an influence in governing its change of motion. The "velocity of a mass system," however, is, in general, an indefinite and meaningless phrase since in general the velocities of the various parts of a system are not the same. Hence, an expression for the kinetic energy of a particle is first obtained and, since energy is a scalar quantity, the kinetic energy of a system of particles (mass system) is the arithmetic sum of the kinetic energies of the particles. However, the expression for the kinetic energy of a particle is of considerable importance in itself since in many problems a physical body may be regarded as a particle without introducing serious errors.

117   Kinetic energy of a particle.   In Fig. 386 let P be a particle of mass m in a body (assumed rigid for convenience only) which moves so that P travels from position P' to P'', along the path shown, while its velocity decreases from v at P' to zero at P'' as the particle does work against the forces acting on it. The work done on the particle by the forces (which form a concurrent system) is equal to the work done by their resultant R (see Art. 111). Or, $w = \int_{s_1}^{s_2} R_t \, ds$. But, by definition, the kinetic energy E_k of the particle is the work that the particle does against the forces. Hence, the defining equation for the kinetic energy

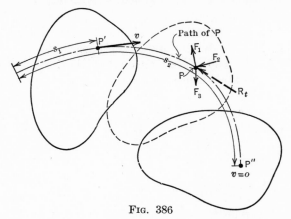

Fig. 386

of a particle is

$$E_k = -w = -\int_{s_1}^{s_2} R_t \, ds$$

This expression may be transformed so that E_k is expressed in terms of m and v by means of the following relations:

$$R_t = ma_t, \qquad a_t = \frac{dv}{dt}, \quad \text{and} \quad \frac{ds}{dt} = v$$

Thus,

$$E_k = -\int_{s_1}^{s_2} R_t \, ds = -\int_{s_1}^{s_2} ma_t \, ds = -\int_{s_1}^{s_2} m \frac{dv}{dt} \, ds$$

$$= -\int_{s_1}^{s_2} m \frac{ds}{dt} \, dv = -\int_{v}^{0} mv \, dv = \frac{1}{2} mv^2$$

Therefore, the kinetic energy of a particle of mass m having a velocity v is equal to $\frac{1}{2}mv^2$. That is,

$$E_k = \frac{1}{2} mv^2 = \frac{1}{2} \frac{W}{g} v^2$$

UNITS. If W is expressed in pounds, g in feet per second per second, and v in feet per second, E_k will be expressed in foot pounds. Thus, energy is expressed in the same units as is work.

118 Kinetic energy of a body. Since energy is a scalar quantity, the kinetic energy of a body (whether rigid or not) is the arithmetic sum of the kinetic energies of its particles. Hence, for any mass system,

$$E_k = \Sigma \tfrac{1}{2}mv^2$$

It is convenient, however, to express the kinetic energy of a *rigid* body in terms of the mass (or some other kinetic property such as moment of inertia) of the *whole* body, and either the linear velocity of some particular point in the body (as, for example, the mass center) or the angular velocity of the whole body. Thus, for rigid bodies having the special motions of translation, rotation, and plane motion, the expressions for the kinetic energy are found as follows:

I TRANSLATION OF A RIGID BODY. All parts of the body have the same velocity at any instant whether the motion is rectilinear translation or curvilinear translation; that is, v in the preceding equation is constant. Hence,

$$E_k = \Sigma \tfrac{1}{2}mv^2 = \tfrac{1}{2}v^2 \Sigma m$$

But Σm is the mass of the body and may be denoted by M. Therefore,

$$E_k = \tfrac{1}{2}Mv^2$$

II ROTATION OF A RIGID BODY. The angular velocities of all particles are the same at any instant; that is, the angular velocity ω of any particle with respect to the center of rotation is the angular velocity of

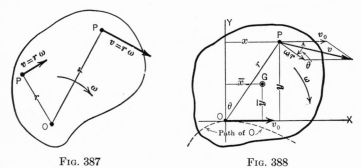

FIG. 387   FIG. 388

the body. The linear velocity v of any particle P of mass m, at a distance r from the axis of rotation O (Fig. 387), is equal to $r\omega$. Hence, the kinetic energy of the body is

$$E_k = \Sigma \tfrac{1}{2}mv^2 = \tfrac{1}{2}\Sigma m(\omega r)^2 = \tfrac{1}{2}\omega^2 \Sigma mr^2$$

But Σmr^2 is the moment of inertia of the body with respect to the axis of rotation and is denoted by I_o. Thus, $I_o = \Sigma mr^2$. Therefore,

$$E_k = \tfrac{1}{2}I_o\omega^2$$

III PLANE MOTION OF A RIGID BODY. As shown in Art. 86, the motion of the body at any instant may be considered to be a combination of a rotation about an axis through any point O in the plane of motion with the angular velocity ω of the body and a translation defined by the motion of O. Hence, the velocity v of any particle P of mass m (Fig. 388) is the resultant of the velocity ωr which P is given by the rotation about O, and the velocity v_o which is given to all particles by the translation. And, since the body is rigid, the velocity ωr has a direction perpendicular to r. Thus,

$$v^2 = (\omega r)^2 + v_o{}^2 + 2v_o\omega r \cos \theta$$

In Fig. 388, let O be the origin, and, for simplicity, let the X axis have the same direction as v_o. The kinetic energy of the body may then be found in terms of the mass of the whole body, the angular velocity of the body, and the linear velocity of one point (in this case the point O) in the body as follows:

$$E_k = \Sigma\tfrac{1}{2}mv^2 = \tfrac{1}{2}\Sigma m(\omega^2 r^2 + v_o{}^2 + 2v_o\omega r \cos \theta)$$

$$= \tfrac{1}{2}\Sigma m\omega^2 r^2 + \tfrac{1}{2}\Sigma mv_o{}^2 + \Sigma mv_o\omega r \cos \theta$$

$$= \tfrac{1}{2}\omega^2\Sigma mr^2 + \tfrac{1}{2}v_o{}^2\Sigma m + \omega v_o\Sigma mr \cos \theta$$

But Σmr^2 is the moment of inertia of the body with respect to the axis through O from which r is measured. Thus, $\Sigma mr^2 = I_o$. Further, $r \cos \theta = y$, whence $\Sigma mr \cos \theta = \Sigma my = M\bar{y}$, in which M is the mass of the body and $\bar{y}$ is the distance of the mass center from the X axis. Therefore,

$$E_k = \tfrac{1}{2}I_o\omega^2 + \tfrac{1}{2}Mv_o{}^2 + M\bar{y}\omega v_o \tag{1}$$

provided that the directions of the X and Y axes and ω are chosen as in Fig. 388. Since the point O is any point in the plane of motion, it may be chosen at the mass center; that is, the motion of the body may be resolved into a rotation about an axis through the mass center and a translation defined by the motion of the mass center. If the point O is taken as the mass center, then, $\bar{y} = 0$, I_o becomes $\bar{I}$, and v_o becomes $\bar{v}$. Hence, the kinetic energy is given by the expression

$$E_k = \tfrac{1}{2}\bar{I}\omega^2 + \tfrac{1}{2}M\bar{v}^2 \tag{2}$$

It is important to note that, although plane motion of a rigid body may be resolved, at any instant, into a rotation about an axis through *any* point in the plane of motion and a simultaneous translation defined by the motion of that point, it does *not* follow that the kinetic energy of the body at the given instant is the kinetic energy due to the rotation plus the kinetic energy due to the translation, *unless* the assumed rotation is about an axis through the mass center of the body and the translation is defined by the motion of the mass center.

ALTERNATIVE METHOD. Plane motion of a rigid body may be considered to be a pure rotation about the instantaneous axis of rotation

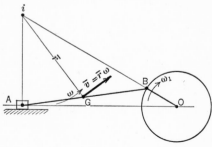

FIG. 389

(Art 87), and hence, if O in Eq. 1 is taken as the instantaneous center i, v_o becomes zero, and I_o becomes I_i, and thus the expression for E_k becomes

$$E_k = \tfrac{1}{2} I_i \omega^2 \tag{3}$$

This expression for E_k may be shown to be equivalent to the expression in Eq. 2. Thus, the E_k of the connecting rod shown in Fig. 389 is

$$E_k = \tfrac{1}{2} I_i \omega^2 = \tfrac{1}{2}(\bar{I} + M\bar{r}^2)\omega^2 = \tfrac{1}{2}\bar{I}\omega^2 + \tfrac{1}{2}M\bar{v}^2$$

Problems

607. A slender rod which is 3 ft long rotates about an axis through one end at a constant speed of 60 rpm. The rod weighs 50 lb. Find the kinetic energy of the rod.

Ans. $E_k = 92$ ft lb.

608. Two spherical bodies each weighing 20 lb are connected by a slender rod and revolve at 90 rpm in a horizontal plane about a vertical axis located midway between the two bodies. The center of each ball is 6 in. from the axis. The diameter of each ball is 4 in. The weight of the rod is 6 lb. Find the kinetic energy of the rotating system of bodies.

609. The homogeneous cylinder C in Fig. 390 weighs 64 lb, and its angular velocity at a given instant is 4 rad/sec. Bodies A and B weighing 16 lb and 8 lb, respectively, are attached to the ends of a cord which passes over the cylinder. If the cord does not slip on the cylinder, determine the kinetic energy of the three bodies at the given instant. Use $g = 32$ ft/sec^2. *Ans.* $E_K = 56$ ft lb.

610. The rod BCD (Fig. 391) is caused to oscillate by the crank OA and connecting rod AC. The crank is 4 in. long and rotates at 180 rpm. What is the kinetic energy of the rod BCD and the small body E in the position shown? The rod is of uniform cross section and weighs 20 lb, and E weighs 4 lb. *Ans.* $E_K = 13.03$ ft lb.

611. In Fig. 392, AB is a uniform slender bar that weighs 48.3 lb and is rigidly connected to a disk D by pins at A and B. The disk rolls without slipping on a horizontal surface with a constant angular velocity of 30 rpm. Find the kinetic energy of the bar when it is in the position shown and also when it is in its lowest position.

612. A car weighing 1400 lb is mounted on four cylindrical disk wheels, each of which weighs 100 lb, the total weight of car and wheels being 1800 lb. The diameter of each wheel is 18 in. When the car is traveling on a straight track at 30 mi/hr,

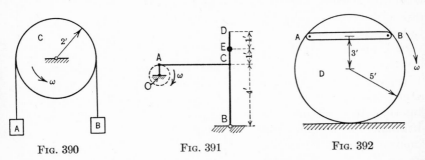

FIG. 390   FIG. 391   FIG. 392

what is the ratio of the kinetic energy of the wheels alone to the kinetic energy of the car and wheels? Disregard the weight of the axles.   *Ans.* Ratio = 3/10.

613. The winding drum of a mine hoist is 14 ft in diameter, its radius of gyration is 6 ft, and its weight is 7 tons. A cage weighing 6 tons is raised by it. When the cage is rising at the rate of 35 ft/sec, what is the kinetic energy of the system?

614. A homogeneous sphere weighing 64.4 lb rolls without slipping on a horizontal surface. The velocity of the center of the sphere is 10 ft/sec. Determine the kinetic energy of the sphere by making use, in addition to the other necessary quantities, of the moment of inertia of the sphere about an axis through: (*a*) the lower end of the vertical diameter, (*b*) the mass center, (*c*) the upper end of the vertical diameter, and (*d*) the forward end of a horizontal diameter.   *Ans.* $E_K = 140$ ft lb.

119 Non-mechanical energy.

Experience shows that some bodies are capable of doing work (possess energy) by virtue of certain states or conditions of their parts, the nature of which is not definitely enough known to make it possible to determine their energy by the methods used in the preceding articles. Energy that cannot be determined directly as potential or kinetic energy is called *non-mechanical* energy. Thus, heat or thermal energy, chemical energy, and electric energy are forms of non-mechanical energy.

A body is capable of doing work by reason of its heated state or condition since by giving up its heat it may do work, under favorable conditions, as in the case of steam in the cylinder of a steam engine. Energy possessed by a body by virtue of its heated state is called heat or thermal energy.

Certain bodies are capable of doing work by reason of their chemical state or condition. Thus, carbon (coal) and oxygen combine and produce heat which may in turn do work. Energy possessed by bodies due to the state of their chemical elements is called chemical energy.

Some bodies are capable of doing work by virtue of their electrical state or condition. Thus, a copper wire on an armature moving in a field of force may develop electric current which in turn may do work in driving a motor. Or, a charged condenser may do work as its electrical condition changes, etc. Energy that arises out of the electrical conditions of bodies is called electric energy.

Any one of these, so-called, special forms of energy may be converted, under favorable conditions, into mechanical energy, and there is considerable evidence to indicate that all energy is mechanical energy. Thus, according to this view, the heat energy of a body could be determined as kinetic energy if the motions of the individual particles were known. And certain forms of chemical and electric energy could be determined as potential energy if the molecular forces were definitely known. Therefore, the energy possessed by bodies by virtue of special states of their molecular structure are considered as non-mechanical forms of energy, not because these special forms are necessarily different from mechanical energy, but because the energy cannot be determined directly as mechanical energy and, therefore, has to be transformed into mechanical energy and then measured. Thus, one unit of heat energy, the British thermal unit (Btu), has a definite mechanical equivalent which carefully made experiments have shown to be

$$1 \text{ Btu} = 778 \text{ ft lb}$$

However, the lack of knowledge of the molecular structure and conditions by virtue of which bodies possess energy does not prevent the application of certain principles of energy to such conditions. In fact, the outstanding feature concerning energy is that certain general principles of energy, such as principles of the conservation of energy and of degradation of energy, are the basis upon which our knowledge of the behavior of non-rigid bodies, in general, is built, and thus they furnish a method of approach to problems for which the principles of force, mass, and acceleration are inadequate. They are of special importance, therefore, in the study of hydraulics, thermodynamics, electrodynamics, physical chemistry, etc.

In the following section certain principles concerning mechanical energy are developed and applied to the motion of bodies (mainly rigid) in which the motions of the particles are definitely known. And, even though the principles of force, mass, and acceleration may be used for many of the problems considered, nevertheless, it will be noted that even for rigid bodies the principles of work and energy are of great importance in many kinetics problems as met in engineering practice.

§ 3   Principle of Work and Energy

120   Preliminary.   As stated in Art. 89, in order to deal with the main problem in kinetics, a relation is found among the forces acting on the body, the kinetic properties (mass, moment of inertia, etc.) of the body, and the change of motion (involving acceleration, velocity, distance, etc.) of the body.   This may be done by determining the relation between the work done by the forces acting on the body and the kinetic energy of the body, since work and kinetic energy involve quantities in terms of which the three factors in the kinetics problem are expressed.   And since, in general, the motions of all particles of a body are not the same, the principle of work and kinetic energy will be developed for a particle first and then extended to the motion of a body.   However, as already noted, in many problems the body may be regarded as a particle without serious errors being introduced.

121   Principle of work and kinetic energy.   I   For a Particle. In Fig. 393 let A' and A'' be two positions of a body, the motion of which changes due to the unbalanced forces (F_1, F_2, F_3, and F_4) which

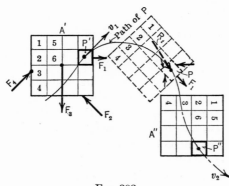

Fig. 393

act on it.   The body is assumed, for convenience, to be composed of small cubes rigidly attached (glued together), each cube being regarded as a particle of the body.   Let P be one of the particles which describes the path shown in the figure as the particle moves from P' to P'' while its velocity changes from v_1 to v_2, owing to the unbalanced (concurrent) forces that act on it.   Let the resultant R of the forces acting on P be resolved into components R_t tangent to the path and R_n (not shown in Fig. 393) normal to the path.   It will be noted that some of the particles (cubes) have their velocities changed (are accelerated) by forces exerted only by other particles of the body (internal forces) whereas other particles are acted on both by internal and by external forces.

The work done by the forces acting on the particle as it moves along its path from P' to P'' is $w = \int_{s_1}^{s_2} R_t \, ds$, but $R_t \, ds$ may be expressed in terms of the mass m and velocity v of the particle by means of the relations:

$$R_t = ma_t \quad \text{and} \quad a_t = \frac{dv}{dt} = v\frac{dv}{ds}$$

Hence,

$$w = \int_{s_1}^{s_2} R_t \, ds = \int_{s_1}^{s_2} mv\frac{dv}{ds}\, ds = \int_{v_1}^{v_2} mv \, dv$$

$$= \tfrac{1}{2}mv_2{}^2 - \tfrac{1}{2}mv_1{}^2$$

$$= \Delta E_k = \text{change in kinetic energy of the particle}$$

Therefore, the work done by the forces acting on a particle of a body (whether rigid or not) during any displacement is equal to the change in the kinetic energy of the particle in the same displacement.

Or, expressed in the form of an equation,

$$w = \Delta E_k = \tfrac{1}{2}mv_2{}^2 - \tfrac{1}{2}mv_1{}^2$$

II FOR A SYSTEM OF PARTICLES. The principle of work and kinetic energy for a system of particles (body) may now be derived. Since work and energy are scalar quantities, the work done on a body is the algebraic sum of the work done on all the particles. And the change in the kinetic energy of the body is the algebraic sum of the changes in the kinetic energies of all the particles. But the work done by all the forces acting on all the particles equals the work done by the external forces that act on the body (w_e) plus the work done by the internal forces of the body (w_i). Thus, by writing the foregoing equation for each particle and adding both sides of the equations, the resulting equation is

$$w_e + w_i = \tfrac{1}{2}\Sigma mv_2{}^2 - \tfrac{1}{2}\Sigma mv_1{}^2 = \Delta E_k$$

That is, the work done on a system of particles (whether rigid or not) by all of the external and internal forces in any displacement of the system is equal to the change in the kinetic energy of the system in the same displacement.

III FOR A RIGID BODY. The principle may now be expressed for the special case of a rigid body, for, as pointed out in Art. 111, the internal forces in any mass system occur in pairs of equal, opposite, and collinear forces whether the body is rigid or not, but the work done by these forces is zero, only if the application points of each pair of forces remain a fixed distance apart, which is the case in a rigid body. Hence, for a rigid body, $w_i = 0$. Therefore,

$$w_e = \Delta E_k$$

That is, the work done by the external forces acting on a rigid body in any displacement is equal to the change in the kinetic energy of the body in the same displacement.

Although an absolutely rigid body does not exist in nature, in kinetics problems the work done by the external forces in causing the relative displacements of the particles in physical bodies is usually negligible in comparison with the work done by the forces in causing the displacement of the body as a whole.

Application of Principle to Special Cases of Motion of Rigid Bodies. By making use of the expressions developed in Art. 118, the principle of work and kinetic energy may be expressed for important special cases of motion of *rigid* bodies as follows:

I   Translation.

$$w_e = \tfrac{1}{2}M(v_2{}^2 - v_1{}^2)$$

II   Rotation.

$$w_e = \tfrac{1}{2}I_o(\omega_2{}^2 - \omega_1{}^2)$$

III   Plane Motion.

$$w_e = \tfrac{1}{2}M(\bar{v}_2{}^2 - \bar{v}_1{}^2) + \tfrac{1}{2}I(\omega_2{}^2 - \omega_1{}^2)$$

Units. If the pound, foot, and second be arbitrarily selected as the units of force, length, and time, respectively, as is usually done in the engineer's system of units (Art. 93), w_e will be expressed in foot pounds, and kinetic energy will likewise be expressed in foot pounds, the mass of the body ($M = W/g$) being expressed in slugs.

Illustrative Problems

Problem 615. An engine capable of exerting a maximum draw-bar pull of 51,000 lb is used on a certain railroad having small grades to draw freight trains having a maximum weight of 2000 tons, the average weight of a freight car with its cargo being about 45 tons. The train resistance per ton of weight varies with the car weight and with the speed. If an average value of 8 lb/ton is used and the engine

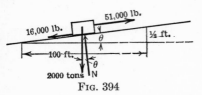

FIG. 394

pulls a 2000-ton train while going up a ½ per cent grade, how far will the train travel while its velocity is increasing from 15 to 30 mi/hr? How long will it take?

SOLUTION. The forces acting on the train are shown in the free-body diagram (Fig. 394). The angle θ (exaggerated in the diagram) for a ½ per cent grade is so small that tan θ may be considered to be equal to sin θ. Hence, sin θ = $\frac{1}{200}$.

$$w_e = \Delta E_k = \tfrac{1}{2}M(v_2{}^2 - v_1{}^2)$$

$$\left(51,000 - 16,000 - \frac{2000 \times 2000}{200}\right) s = \frac{1}{2}\frac{2000 \times 2000}{32.2}(\overline{44}^2 - \overline{22}^2)$$

$$15,000\ s = 62,200 \times 1452, \qquad \therefore\ s = 6020\ \text{ft}$$

But

$$s = \frac{v_1 + v_2}{2} \times t, \qquad \therefore\ 6020 = \frac{22 + 44}{2} \times t$$

whence

$$t = 182.5\ \text{sec} = 3.04\ \text{min}$$

Problem 616. In Fig. 395 a homogeneous cylinder A is connected by a cord passing over a homogeneous cylinder C to the body B. Each cylinder weighs 16 lb and has a radius of r ft. The weight of B is 32 lb. Find the velocity v of the body B after it has descended 6 ft from rest, if A rolls without slipping and the cord does not slip on C. Neglect axle friction on C, and assume $g = 32$ ft/sec².

SOLUTION. *First Method.* The problem may be solved by considering each of the bodies A, B, and C as a free body and expressing for each body the fact that the work done by the external forces acting on the body is equal to the change in kinetic energy of the body in the given displacement. The velocity of the mass center of A (which is equal to the velocity v of

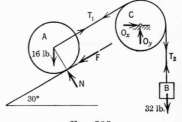

FIG. 395

B) is equal to $r\omega$. The force N does no work on A, and, since A rolls without slipping, the frictional force F does no work. Using the equation $w_e = \Delta E_k$, we have

For A,
$$(T_1 - 8)6 = \tfrac{1}{2} \times \tfrac{16}{32} \times v^2 + \tfrac{1}{2}(\tfrac{1}{2} \times \tfrac{16}{32} \times r^2)\omega^2 = \tfrac{12}{32}v^2$$

For B,
$$(32 - T_2)6 = \tfrac{1}{2} \times \tfrac{32}{32} \times v^2 = \tfrac{16}{32}v^2$$

For C,
$$(T_2 - T_1)6 = \tfrac{1}{2}(\tfrac{1}{2} \times \tfrac{16}{32} \times r^2)\omega^2 = \tfrac{4}{32}v^2$$

Adding the two sides of these equations, we have

$$(32 - 8)6 = v^2$$

or

$$v^2 = 144 \quad \text{and} \quad v = 12\ \text{ft/sec}$$

Second Method. Instead of the principle of work and kinetic energy being applied to each of the three bodies, A, B, and C, as in the foregoing solution, the entire system consisting of the three bodies and the cord could be considered as one body. Although each of the three bodies is a rigid body, the system considered as a whole is not rigid, and for a non-rigid mass system the work done by all forces (both external and internal) is equal to the change in kinetic energy of the system. In the system here considered the work of the internal forces is zero (it will be left to the student to explain why this is true), and hence the only work done on the system is that done by the weight of B (192 ft lb) and that done by the weight of A (-48 ft lb). Hence the total work done on the system is $192 - 48 = 144$ ft lb, which is equal to the total change of kinetic energy of the system which as found in the first solution is v^2. Hence, $v^2 = 144$, and $v = 12$ ft/sec.

Problem 617. The punching and shearing machine shown in Fig. 396 has a capacity for punching a 2½-in. hole in a ½-in. steel plate. The pinion shaft (and flywheel) is driven at 220 rpm from a countershaft by means of a belt drive to the tight pulley on the pinion shaft. Each operation of punching a hole (punching cycle) causes a fluctuation (decrease) in the speed of the flywheel. The "coefficient of speed fluctuation" is 0.8; that is, the speed of the flywheel decreases 20 per cent in each punching cycle. If the work done in punching the hole is all supplied by the flywheel, what moment of inertia should the flywheel have? What is the moment of

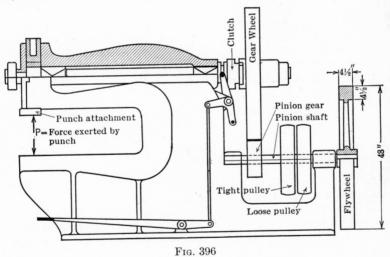

Fɪɢ. 396

inertia of the flywheel on the machine as actually designed (as shown in Fig. 396), neglecting the material in the hub and spokes? If the difference in the belt tensions, $T_2 - T_1$, is 286 lb, and the pinion shaft turns through an angle of 230° while the hole is being punched, how much work is done on the shaft (and flywheel) by the belt while the hole is being punched? The diameter of the pulley is 22 in.

Soʟᴜᴛɪᴏɴ. The maximum value of the force P required to punch the hole, using 50,000 lb/sq in. for the ultimate shearing strength of the material of the plate, we find to be

$$P = \pi dt \times 50,000$$

$$= \pi \times \tfrac{5}{2} \times \tfrac{1}{2} \times 50,000 = 196,200 \text{ lb}$$

By assuming a triangular work diagram (see Prob. 583), we obtain the work done in punching the hole as follows:

$$w = \frac{P}{2} \times \frac{1}{2} = \frac{196,200}{4} = 49,100 \text{ in. lb} = 4090 \text{ ft lb}$$

which is supplied by the flywheel. For the flywheel we have then

$$w_e = \Delta E_k = \frac{1}{2}\bar{I}(\omega_2{}^2 - \omega_1{}^2)$$

$$4090 = \frac{1}{2}\bar{I}\left[\left(\frac{220 \times 2\pi}{60}\right)^2 - \left(0.8 \times \frac{220 \times 2\pi}{60}\right)^2\right] = 95.5\bar{I}$$

whence

$$\bar{I} = 42.8 \text{ slug ft}^2$$

Hence, the moment of inertia of the flywheel should be 42.8 slug ft^2 in order that the speed be decreased not more than 20 per cent. If the flywheel is assumed to be made of cast iron which weighs 450 lb/cu ft, the moment of inertia of the flywheel as actually designed, neglecting hub and spokes, may be found as follows:

$$\bar{I} = \frac{1}{2}M(r_2{}^2 + r_1{}^2) \qquad \text{(see Prob. 915.)}$$

$$= \frac{1}{2} \times \frac{\pi}{32.2}\left[2^2 - \left(\frac{19.5}{12}\right)^2\right] \times \frac{4.5}{12} \times 450 \times \left[2^2 + \left(\frac{19.5}{12}\right)^2\right]$$

$$= \frac{1}{2}\frac{\pi}{32.2} \times 1.36 \times 0.375 \times 450 \times 6.64 = 74.3 \text{ slug ft}^2$$

The work done on the flywheel while the hole is being punched is

$$w = \Sigma T \cdot \theta = 286 \times \frac{11}{12} \times 230 \times \frac{\pi}{180} = 1050 \text{ ft lb}$$

Problems

618. A bullet fired with a velocity of 1000 ft/sec penetrates a block of wood to a depth of 6 in. If the bullet were fired through a board of the same wood 3 in. thick, find its velocity after passing through the board. Assume the resistance of the wood to the bullet to be constant.   *Ans. v* = **707** ft/sec.

619. A body weighing 80 lb is projected along a rough horizontal plane with a velocity of 8 ft/sec. It comes to rest in a distance of 4 ft. Find the coefficient of kinetic friction.

620. Solve Prob. 448 by making use of the principle of work and energy.

621. The pendulum of the impact-testing machine described in Prob. 530 is released from rest from a position such that it swings through an angle of 160° before it reaches the vertical position. When it reaches the vertical position, the edge *A* strikes a test specimen. If the distance *OA* is 30 in., find the velocity of the edge *A* immediately before it strikes the specimen. If the pendulum swings through an angle of 100° (the angle of rise) after striking the specimen, how much energy is absorbed by the specimen? Neglect friction.

622. An automobile that weighs *W* lb is moving at the rate of 30 mi/hr when it comes to the foot of a hill. Power is then shut off. The slope of the hill is 1 ft in

50 ft. How far will the machine coast up the hill if the total tractive resistance (parallel to the road) is $0.09W$? *Ans. $s = 273$ ft.*

623. A box slides from rest 10 ft down a plane inclined 30° to the horizontal. After reaching the bottom of the plane, the box moves on a horizontal floor. If the coefficient of friction between the box and plane and between the box and floor is $\frac{1}{5}$, how far will the box move on the floor before coming to rest?

624. A bullet that weighs 1 oz is moving with a velocity of 2000 ft/sec when it strikes a plank normally and passes through it. The velocity on leaving the plank is 1000 ft/sec. If the average resistance to penetration is 5000 lb, how thick is the plank? *Ans. $t = 6.99$ in.*

625. A body B (Fig. 397) that weighs W lb falls from rest through a distance h of 3.5 ft and strikes a helical spring whose modulus is 40 lb/in. If the maximum compression s of the spring is 6 in., what is the value of W? Find the velocity of B when the spring has been compressed 3 in.

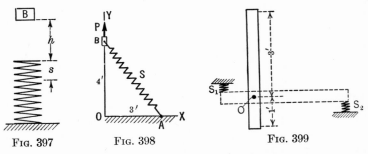

FIG. 397   FIG. 398   FIG. 399

626. A block B (Fig. 398) that weighs 16.1 lb slides without friction along a vertical rod OY. A spring S, whose unstretched length is 3 ft, is attached to B and to the stationary plane OX at A as shown. If a constant vertical force P of 50 lb is exerted on B, what will be the velocity of B after a displacement of 4 ft, assuming that B starts from rest at O? The modulus of the spring is 30 lb/ft.
Ans. $v = 17.4$ ft/sec.

627. The vertical bar in Fig. 399 is 4 ft long and weighs 50 lb. The bar is displaced slightly from the position shown and rotates about O. When it comes to a horizontal position, it strikes the two springs shown and continues to rotate until the spring S_1 is compressed 1 in. The springs have the same modulus. Find the modulus of the springs. Assume the bar to be rigid and of constant cross section.

628. A hollow cylinder whose outer radius is r and whose radius of gyration with respect to its geometrical axis is $\sqrt{\frac{3}{4}}r$ starts from rest and rolls without slipping down a plane inclined 30° to the horizontal. Find the velocity of the center of the cylinder when the cylinder has rolled 3.5 ft. *Ans. 8.02 ft/sec.*

629. A simple pendulum consists of a cord of length l and a bob (assumed to be a particle) of weight W. If the velocity of the bob is zero when the cord makes an angle θ with the vertical, find in terms of l and θ the velocity v of the bob when in its lowest position. Find v if $l = 4$ ft and $\theta = 60°$.

630. In Fig. 400, AB is a uniform slender bar that weighs 40 lb, BO is a rigid bar of negligible weight, and C is a homogeneous cylinder that weighs 40 lb and rolls without slipping on a horizontal plane. If the system is allowed to move from rest from the position shown, find the angular velocity of AB when it has rotated through an angle of: (a) 30°, and (b) 60°.

631. The hand-operated screw press shown in Fig. 401 is used for embossing, lettering dies, punching thin plates, etc. The diameter of the screw is $2\frac{1}{2}$ in. The screw has triple threads with a pitch of $2\frac{1}{2}$ in. Each ball weighs 100 lb, and the diameter of each ball is 9 in. If the balls are revolved at 60 rpm, what is the maximum

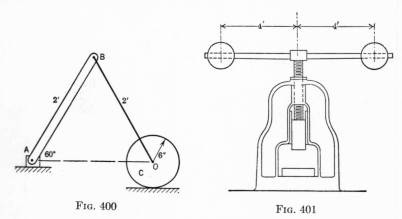

FIG. 400   FIG. 401

size (diameter) of hole that can be punched in a $\frac{1}{4}$-in. steel plate, assuming the shearing strength of the steel to be 45,000 lb/sq in. and the efficiency of the screw to be 15 per cent. Also assume the work diagram for punching the hole to be triangular. (See Prob. 583.) Assume $g = 32$ ft/sec².   *Ans. d* = 0.804 in.

632. A shearing machine has 3 hp delivered to it by the belt. Every two seconds an operation occurs that requires 0.8 of all the energy supplied during the two seconds; the other 0.2 of the energy is required to overcome the friction of the machine. During each operation the speed of the flywheel decreases from 120 to 90 rpm. If it is assumed that the work done in shearing is done by the flywheel, what should be the moment of inertia of the flywheel? If the weight of the flywheel is 400 lb, what is its radius of gyration?

633. A generator driven by a hydraulic turbine has a speed of 600 rpm and delivers 1000 hp. An additional load of 200 hp is put on the generator. If 2 sec elapse before the governor can act, what must be the moment of inertia of the rotating parts in order that the decrease in speed shall be 2 per cent?

634. In Fig. 402 a uniform slender bar AB which weighs 96.6 lb rotates about a smooth pin B. Body D weighs 161 lb and is suspended from a cord which passes over a smooth peg C and is attached to the end A of the bar. If the velocity of D is zero when AB is horizontal, find the velocity of D when AB has rotated 90°.
          Ans. v = 12.9 ft/sec.

635. In Fig. 403 the uniform slender bars AB, BC, and CD weigh 20 lb, 40 lb, and 20 lb, respectively. The bars are connected by smooth pins at A, B, C, and D. If the system is allowed to move from rest from the position shown, what will be the angular velocity of AB when it has rotated 90°?

636. Two homogeneous cylindrical wood disks shown in Fig. 404 are connected by smooth pins to a steel bar AB. Each disk weighs 8 lb, and the bar weighs 16 lb. If the system starts from rest, find the velocity of the center of each disk after traveling a distance of 80 ft. Assume that the disks roll without slipping.
          Ans. v = 45.4 ft/sec.

637. A train weighing 2200 tons is drawn on a horizontal track by an engine whose draw-bar pull varies with the speed so that it always develops 500 hp. How many seconds does it take to pull the train 972 ft starting from rest? How much

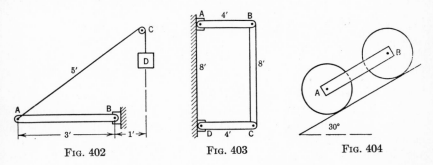

FIG. 402   FIG. 403   FIG. 404

work is done on the train by the draw-bar pull? Neglect train resistance, and assume $g = 32$ ft/sec^2.   *Ans. t* = 81 sec; *w* = 22,300,000 ft lb.

638. In Fig. 405 the force P compresses the spring B 2 in. The spring constant for B is 240 lb/in., body A weighs 10 lb, and the coefficient of friction between A and the plane is $\frac{1}{10}$. The force P is suddenly removed, and body A slides 9.75 ft when it hits spring C and compresses it 3 in. Find the spring constant for C.

                                                                Ans. k = 80 lb/in.

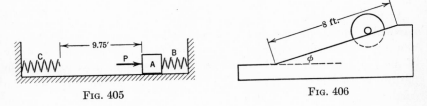

FIG. 405   FIG. 406

639. A solid disk 16 in. in diameter is mounted on a shaft 4 in. in diameter (Fig. 406). The shaft rolls, without slipping, on two inclined tracks. The disk weighs 120 lb, and the weight of the shaft may be neglected. The angle of inclination ϕ is $\sin^{-1} \frac{1}{4}$, and the incline is 8 ft long. If the disk starts from rest at the top, what will be the velocity of its center at the bottom of the incline?

640. A car weighing 966 lb is mounted on four cylindrical disk wheels. Each wheel weighs 161 lb and has a diameter of 4 ft. (The total weight of the car and wheels is 1610 lb.) If the car travels on a straight horizontal track with a velocity of 15 ft/sec, what force parallel to the track is required to stop the car in a distance of 25 ft? Assume that the wheels do not slip.   *Ans. P* = 270 lb.

641. The work done by a punching machine (Fig. 396) in punching a hole through a steel plate is 450 ft lb. The speed of the flywheel at the beginning of the operation is 120 rpm. Find the speed at the end of the operation, assuming that no energy is supplied to the machine while the hold is being punched and that the moment of inertia of the flywheel is 10 slug ft^2.

642. A hollow steel cylinder has an outside radius of 1 ft and an inside radius of 6 in. The cylinder rolls with its axis horizontal and without slipping up a plane, making an angle of 30° with the horizontal. If the initial velocity of the mass center of the cylinder is 10 ft/sec up the plane, what will be the velocity of the mass center when it has reached a position 20 ft down the plane from the initial position?

643. A solid sphere is 2 ft in diameter and weighs 100 lb. It rolls without slipping down the inside of a thin-walled hollow cylinder whose radius is 6 ft, the axis of the cylinder being horizontal. In its initial position the line from the center of the sphere perpendicular to the axis of the cylinder makes an angle of 60° with the vertical. If the sphere starts from rest, find its kinetic energy and the velocity of its center when it is in its lowest position.   *Ans.* $E_k = 250$ ft lb; $\bar{v} = 10.7$ ft/sec.

122 Conservation of energy.

One of the greatest achievements of the nineteenth century was the recognition and statement of the principle of the conservation of energy. Like Newton's laws of motion, it is an inductive generalization from observation of, and experience with, physical phenomena. The principle states that, in any change of the state or condition of an isolated material system, the total amount of energy of the system remains constant. By an isolated system is meant one in which there is no transfer of energy to or from bodies that are external to the system. Thus, the distribution of energy within the isolated system may be altered and the various forms of energy changed into other forms, but the total amount of energy remains constant. Or, as sometimes stated, energy may be transformed or transferred but cannot be created or destroyed.

As noted in Art. 119, the principle of conservation of energy is of particular importance in the study of material systems which possess non-mechanical energy, although it is also of much value in the study of mechanical energy. Although an isolated system does not exist in nature, certain systems approach closely thereto, as, for example, the earth and a falling body, provided that the action (and reaction) between the earth and body is large compared with the resistance of the air and the attractions of other bodies on the falling body.

In the restricted problems dealt with in this book in which mechanical energy only is considered, the principle of conservation of energy as applied to a *conservative mass system* (Art. 115) states that

$$E_p + E_k = \text{constant}$$

or

$$\Delta E_p + \Delta E_k = 0$$

That is, in any displacement of a conservation mass system, the change in the potential energy of the system plus the change in kinetic energy of the system is equal to zero.

It should be emphasized that the foregoing equations apply only to a conservative mass system: that is, one in which the work done by the mass system depends only on the initial and final configuration of the mass system and not on the paths described by the particles of the system.

If the mass system is not conservative, the transformation of energy within the system from potential to kinetic (or vice-versa) is accompanied by an increase in other forms of energy such as heat energy, and, although the total energy remains constant, the mechanical (potential and kinetic) energy does not remain constant. The relations between potential and kinetic energy for conservative systems, only, are considered herein.

The following illustrative problem could be solved by the principle of work and kinetic energy (Art. 121); it is important, however, to observe the application of the principle expressing the relation between the potential and kinetic energy for conservative systems.

Illustrative Problem

Problem 644. A simple pendulum (Fig. 407) consists of a cord having a length r of 4 ft and a bob (assumed to be a particle) having a weight W of 6 lb. The pendulum is displaced an angle θ of 60° and released from rest in that position. Determine the velocity v of the bob when it reaches its lowest position. Neglect air resistance.

SOLUTION. The tension T in the string does no work, and friction (air resistance) is neglected. Thus, the earth and bob may be treated as a conservative system. Hence,

$$\Delta E_p + \Delta E_k = 0$$

$$-Wh + \tfrac{1}{2}mv^2 = 0,$$

or

$$-6(4 - 4\cos 60°) + \frac{1}{2}\frac{6}{32.2}v^2 = 0,$$

hence,

$$v = 11.36 \text{ ft/sec}$$

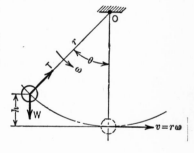

FIG. 407

Problems

645. Solve Prob. 625 by use of the principle of conservation of energy.

646. Solve Prob. 627 by use of the principle of conservation of energy.

647. The homogeneous cylinder C in Fig. 390 weighs 64 lb, and bodies A and B weighing 16 lb and 8 lb, respectively, are attached to the ends of a cord which passes over the cylinder. If the system is released from rest and the cord does not slip on the cylinder, determine the velocity of A when it has moved 1 ft from its initial position. Neglect friction at the axis of the cylinder. Use $g = 32$ ft/sec².

Ans. $v = 3.02$ ft/sec.

648. Solve Prob. 630 by use of the principle of conservation of energy.

649. Solve Prob. 634 by use of the principle of conservation of energy.

§ 4 Efficiency.   Dissipation of Energy

123 Efficiency defined. The efficiency of a machine, as, for example, a steam engine, an electric motor, a chain hoist, or a jackscrew, is the ratio of the energy output of the machine in a given period of time to the energy input in the same period, provided that no energy is stored in the machine which becomes available at a later period. By input is meant the amount of energy received by the machine, a portion of which is transformed or transmitted into the work for which the machine is designed. The work done or energy delivered by the machine is called the output. Thus, denoting efficiency by e, we have

$$e = \frac{\text{energy output}}{\text{energy input}} \quad \text{or} \quad e = \frac{\text{power output}}{\text{power input}}$$

As already noted, in the transformation and transference of energy (which is the main function of many machines), some of the energy always takes the form of a lower grade of energy (heat energy) and thereby becomes unavailable for the particular process for which the machine is used. The amount of energy that thus miscarries or leaks out in the process is spoken of by various names, such as lost energy (or lost work), energy leak, dissipated energy. Since dissipation of energy occurs with every physical process, the output is always less than the input, and, therefore, the efficiency is always less than unity.

The efficiency as defined above is the over-all efficiency of the machine. Certain parts of the machine, however, may have their individual efficiencies; and the over-all efficiency is the product of the efficiencies of the several elements of the machine.

124 Dissipation of energy. The work done against frictional forces is the most frequent cause of dissipation of energy in machines. Energy dissipated in doing work against frictional forces is transformed into heat energy. Electrical resistance in connection with electric machinery also causes a loss of available energy by developing heat. The work done against friction is, in some machines, a necessary evil to be reduced to a minimum, as in prime movers, bearings, teeth of gears, whereas, in other machines or machine elements, the main object of the machine is to dissipate all the energy received by the machine, as in friction brakes and absorption dynamometers.

125 A simple dynamometer. Prony brake. A simple dynamometer, commonly called a prony brake, is shown in Fig. 408. A is a flanged pulley keyed to a rotating shaft. The power transmitted by the shaft is not only dissipated or absorbed but is also measured by the brake. B, B are bearing blocks against which the pulley develops a frictional resistance, the magnitude of which is varied by adjusting the nuts C, C. D is the frame or beam with its end E resting on the platform of a weighing scale. When the pulley is running, the beam develops an additional pressure on the platform, due to the friction of the pulley on the bearing blocks. The work lost in friction and the power developed by the shaft may be found as follows:

It will be assumed that the scales are adjusted to read zero when the beam rests on the platform and the pulley is not running. Thus, the scale reading is a measure of the pressure P at E due to the friction developed on the bearing blocks when the pulley is running. Since the

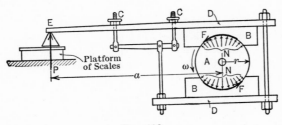

FIG. 408

brake frame is in equilibrium under the action of the forces, N, P, and F (F denotes the total frictional force on the two blocks), the sum of the moments of P and F about the axis of the shaft must equal zero, or

$$Fr = Pa$$

and the work done by the frictional moment Fr in 1 sec is

$$w_f = Fr\omega = Pa\omega$$

in which ω is expressed in radians per second. And, since $\omega = 2\pi n/60$ where n is the number of revolutions per minute (rpm) of the shaft and pulley, the expression for w_f becomes

$$w_f = \frac{2\pi Pan}{60} = \frac{\pi Pan}{30}$$

If P is expressed in pounds and a in feet, then w_f will be expressed in foot pounds, and the horsepower developed by the frictional moment (and hence by the shaft) is

$$hp = \frac{\pi Pan}{30 \times 550} = \frac{\pi Pan}{16,500}$$

This expression may be simplified if the dynamometer is constructed so that a has a special value. It should be remembered that the scale reading should not be used for the value of P unless the scales are adjusted to read zero when the pulley is not running.

Problems

650. What force is required to raise a load W of 300 lb by means of the differential chain hoist shown in Fig. 103 if e = 30 per cent, r_2 = 4 in., and r_1 = 8 in.?

Ans. F = 250 lb.

651. In a test of a jackscrew (see Fig. 192) with a screw 1.5 in. in diameter and a pitch of $\frac{1}{3}$ in., it was found that a pull of 80 lb at the end of a 15-in. lever was required to raise a load of 2400 lb when no lubricant was used, and a pull of 60 lb when an oil lubricant was used. What is the efficiency of the jack for each case?

Ans. e = 10.6 per cent; *e* = 14.1 per cent.

652. The band brake described in Prob. 272 allows a certain load to lower at a constant speed such that the brake sheaves rotate at 180 rpm, in a counterclockwise direction. What horsepower is absorbed by the brake?

653. An automobile when traveling at a speed of 50 mi/hr delivers to the transmission shaft 60 hp. If the efficiency in transmitting the power from the engine to the rear wheels is 80 per cent, what is the propelling force (tractive effort) developed?

Ans. F = 360 lb.

654. A jet of water 2 in. in diameter having a velocity of 120 ft/sec impinges against the buckets of a tangential water wheel. If the efficiency of the wheel is 90 per cent, what horsepower is delivered by the wheel? Assume the weight of water to be 62.4 lb/cu ft.

655. In the band brake shown in Fig. 409 the scale S indicates a force of 100 lb when P = 20 lb and when the drum D is rotating at 150 rpm. What horsepower is being developed by the motor that turns the shaft on which the drum is keyed?

Ans. 0.571 hp.

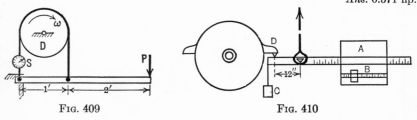

FIG. 409   FIG. 410

656. Figure 410 represents one form of a dynamometer. A cast-iron disk keyed to the shaft rotates inside the drum as the shaft turns. The disk rotates in a watertight compartment between two copper plates that are attached to the drum, and pressure of the copper plates against the disk is produced by water from the city mains which fills the spaces between the copper plates and the ends of the drum. The narrow spaces between the disk and the copper plates are filled with oil. As the shaft (and disk) rotates, the drum (due to the friction developed on the copper plates) tends to turn, causing a pressure at D on the scale beam, which is balanced by the poise weights A and B. The weight of A and B together is 150 lb, and that of B alone is 4 lb. The divisions on the large scale are 1 in., and those on the small scale are 0.4 in. When both A and B are set at zero on the scales, they are just balanced by the weight of C. If, in order to maintain balance when the disk is rotating, A is set at the ninth division and B is set at the third division, what is the pressure of the dynamometer on the scale beam at D, and what horsepower is developed by the shaft when rotating at 240 rpm? The distance from the center of the shaft to D is 18 in. *Ans.* **7.73** hp.

Review Questions

1. Define work done by any force: (*a*) in words, (*b*) as a mathematical expression. Write an expression for the work done by a couple in terms of the moment of the couple.

2. Define kinetic energy of a particle: (*a*) in words, (*b*) as a mathematical expression. Show that this mathematical expression leads to the expression $\frac{1}{2}mv^2$ for the kinetic energy of the particle. If the engineer's system of units is used, what are the units of m and v, and of $\frac{1}{2}mv^2$?

3. Point out and correct the errors in the following demonstration that the kinetic energy of a rotating rigid body is $\frac{1}{2}I_0\omega^2$: E_k for a particle is $\frac{1}{2}mv^2$. Therefore, E_k for the whole body is $\frac{1}{2}Mv^2$. But $v = r\omega$. Hence, $\frac{1}{2}Mv^2 = \frac{1}{2}Mr^2\omega^2$. But $Mr^2 = I_0$; therefore, $E_k = \frac{1}{2}I_0\omega^2$.

4. If the kinetic energy of a rigid body having plane motion is expressed as the sum of two terms $(\frac{1}{2}Mv_0^2 + \frac{1}{2}I_0\omega^2)$, what point in the body must be selected as the point O?

5. The following equation expresses the principle of work and kinetic energy as applying to a non-rigid mass system: $w_e + w_i = \Delta E_k$. Explain why w_i becomes zero for a rigid body. State in words the principle of work and kinetic energy for a rigid body.

6. State the conditions to which the equation $w_e = \frac{1}{2}M(v_2^2 - v_1^2)$ applies.

7. A mass system consists of two particles each having a mass m. If one particle moves vertically upward with a velocity v and the other particle moves vertically downward with a velocity v, will the kinetic energy of the system be equal to: (*a*) mv^2, or (*b*) zero?

8. A box lies on the bed of a truck which accelerates on a horizontal pavement. If the box does not slip on the bed of the truck, will the work done by the frictional force that the truck exerts on the box be positive or will it be negative? If the brakes of the truck are applied and the box slides forward on the bed of the truck, will the work done by the frictional force acting on the box be positive, or will it be negative?

9. The motion of a rigid body is plane motion. If the kinetic energy of the body is equal to $\frac{1}{2}I_0\omega^2$, what can be said about the point O?

10. Is the following statement correct? If a body weighing 2 tons is raised from the floor of a building by means of a crane and placed on a platform which is 10 ft above the floor, the total work done on the body by all the external forces is zero.

Chapter 11

IMPULSE AND MOMENTUM

126 Preliminary. In Art. 105, the statements were made that impulse is a quantity that involves force and time and that momentum is a quantity that involves mass and velocity. And the fact was noted that the use of these quantities in the analysis of the motion of bodies requires no fundamental laws in addition to Newton's laws of motion. However, methods that make use of impulse and momentum offer advantages, in certain types of problems, over the methods of work and energy (Chapter 10) and of force, mass, and acceleration (Chapter 9).

In determining the effect of forces on the motion of bodies, thus far, by the method of force, mass, and acceleration and by the method of work and energy, it has been assumed that the forces have acted on bodies (mainly rigid bodies) during a definite (comparatively large) interval of time, and, when the forces were not constant, the manner in which they varied during the period was assumed to be known. To such conditions the methods of impulse and momentum also apply, and in many cases offer a simpler method of solution than the methods previously discussed. Forces sometimes act, however, for a very short and indefinite interval of time during which the value of the force at any instant is not known. These forces may, nevertheless, produce very appreciable changes in the motion of the body. Such forces are called *impulsive forces*. The principles of impulse and momentum are of special value when the motion of bodies under the action of impulsive forces is considered. The bodies upon which impulsive forces act deform under the excessive pressures produced, and hence, in determining the motions of bodies under the influence of impulsive forces, the bodies cannot always be assumed to be rigid without appreciable errors being introduced. As examples of impulsive forces the following may be mentioned: the force exerted on a projectile due to the explosion of the powder, the action of one billiard ball on another, the force exerted by the ram of a pile driver on the pile, the pressure between two railway cars when making a flying coupling, the action of a steam jet on the blades of a high-speed steam turbine, the pressure exerted by the water in a pipe line on a valve which is closed suddenly.

The purpose of the present chapter is to make clear the meaning of impulse and of momentum, to develop certain principles which express relations between these quantities, and to apply these principles to problems in kinetics.

§ 1   Impulse

127   Impulse and impact defined.   The impulse of a constant force is defined as the product of the force and the time interval during which the force acts.   Thus, if the impulse of a force be denoted by Q, the impulse of a force F is defined by the equation

$$Q = F \cdot \Delta t$$

provided that the force remains constant during the time interval Δt. If the force varies in magnitude but not in direction, the impulse for an indefinitely short period of time dt, is $F \cdot dt$, and, for a time interval $\Delta t = t_2 - t_1$, the impulse is

$$Q = \int_{t_1}^{t_2} F \, dt$$

In order to evaluate this integral by the method of calculus, F must be expressed in terms of t.   The impulse of a force that acts on a body during a very short (indefinite) interval of time is also given by the foregoing expression, but, as noted in the preceding article, the impulsive force cannot be expressed in terms of t, since its law of variation is not known, and hence the impulse cannot be determined directly but is found in terms of the change of momentum of the body on which the force acts, as is discussed in the subsequent pages.

The impulse of an impulsive force is sometimes called an *impact*; that is, an impact is a sudden impulse.   The term impact, however, is also frequently used as descriptive of the act of collision of bodies.   In some problems it is convenient to estimate the time interval of the impulsive force and to express the impact as the product of an average value of the force and an assumed or estimated time interval $\Delta t = t_2 - t_1$.   Thus,

$$Q = \int_{t_1}^{t_2} F \, dt = F_{\text{avg}} \cdot \Delta t$$

in which F_{avg} denotes the *time-average* value of the impulsive force which is assumed to act during the time interval Δt.   The impulse of a force frequently is called *linear* impulse in contrast to the moment of the impulse which is called *angular* impulse (see Art. 129).

UNITS.   The unit of an impulse is a combination of a unit of force and of time and, hence, is a compound unit.   The unit of impulse has no special name. In the gravitational or engineer's system of units (Art. 93) if the pound is selected as the unit of force and the second as the unit of time, the unit of impulse is the pound second (lb sec).

128   Components of linear impulse. The impulse of a force, like the force itself, is a directed or vector quantity, the sense and action line of the impulse being the same as that of the force. An impulse of a force, therefore, may be resolved into components and may have a moment with respect to a point or a line. The component, in any direction, of the impulse of a *constant* force is the product of the component of the force in the given direction and the time interval Δt during which the force acts. That is,

$$Q_x = F_x \cdot \Delta t; \qquad Q_y = F_y \cdot \Delta t, \quad \text{etc.}$$

And, if the force varies in magnitude or in direction during the time interval $\Delta t = t_2 - t_1$, the components of the impulse are

$$Q_x = \int_{t_1}^{t_2} F_x \, dt; \qquad Q_y = \int_{t_1}^{t_2} F_y \, dt, \quad \text{etc.}$$

LINEAR IMPULSE OF A FORCE SYSTEM. The linear impulse, in any direction, of a force system is the algebraic sum of the components, in the given direction, of the impulses of the forces of the system. Thus, for a force system in which the forces are constant, the linear impulse of the force system in any direction x, is

$$Q_x = \Sigma F_x \cdot \Delta t$$

Or, if the forces of the system vary during the interval $\Delta t = t_2 - t_1$, then,

$$Q_x = \Sigma \int_{t_1}^{t_2} F_x \, dt$$

129   Moment of impulse. Angular impulse. The moment of the impulse of a *constant* force about any point or axis is the product of the moment T of the force about the given point or axis and the time interval Δt during which the force acts. The moment of the impulse of a force is also called the *angular impulse* of the force. Thus, if the angular impulse of a force be denoted by L, the angular impulse of a constant force with respect to an axis O is defined by the equation

$$L_o = T_o \cdot \Delta t$$

in which T_o is the moment of the force with respect to the axis O. And, if the force varies in magnitude during the time interval $\Delta t = t_2 - t_1$, the moment of the impulse is expressed by the equation

$$L_o = \int_{t_1}^{t_2} T_o \, dt$$

UNITS. In the gravitational system of units, if the units of force, time, and length are the pound, second, and foot, respectively, the unit of angular impulse is the pound-second-foot (lb sec ft).

ANGULAR IMPULSE OF A FORCE SYSTEM. The angular impulse of a force system about any axis is the algebraic sum of the angular impulses of the forces of the system about the given axis. Thus, if the forces of the system are constant, the angular impulse of the system about the axis O is

$$L_o = \Sigma T_o \, \Delta t$$

And, if the forces vary, the angular impulse of the force system about the axis O, for the time interval $\Delta t = t_2 - t_1$, is expressed by the equation

$$L_o = \Sigma \int_{t_1}^{t_2} T_o \, dt$$

Problems

657. A car coasting on a straight track is brought to rest by bumping into a spring bumper. From a study of the change in the velocity of the car it is found that the impulse of the force exerted on the car by the spring while being compressed is 100,000 lb sec. If the time consumed in compressing the spring is $\frac{1}{2}$ sec, what is the time-average value of the force exerted by the spring?

658. A body weighing 40 lb slides down an inclined plane in 4 sec. The plane makes an angle of 60° with the horizontal. If the coefficient of friction is 0.3, find the component of the linear impulse of the force system acting on the body parallel to the plane.   *Ans.* $Q_x = 114.5$ lb sec.

659. A particle is acted on by a horizontal force whose magnitude increases at a uniform rate from zero to P lb in t sec. Determine in terms of P and t the linear impulse of the force during the time interval of t sec.

660. A vibrating body is acted on by a force which varies as a function of time according to the equation $P = 10 \cos 2\pi t$ where P is in lb and t in sec. Find the linear impulse of the force during the time interval from $t = 0$ to $t = \frac{1}{4}$ sec.

661. A train having a weight of 2000 tons travels up a $\frac{1}{2}$ per cent grade. The draw-bar pull of the engine is 40,000 lb, and the train resistance (due to air resistance, rolling resistance, etc.) is 8 lb/ton of weight. If it takes 2 min to travel up the grade, find the linear impulse of the force system acting on the train for the 2-min interval.

662. The linear impulse of the total pressure of the steam on the piston of a steam engine is 4200 lb sec. The diameter of the cylinder is 14 in., and the engine runs at 240 rpm. Find the average (time-average) pressure (in pounds per square inch) of the steam against the piston during one stroke.   *Ans.* $p = 218$ lb/in.^{2}

663. A force acts on a body along a fixed straight line, the magnitude and sense of the force being indicated by the ordinate to the graph shown in Fig. 411. Find the impulse of the force for the period of 4 sec. Find the impulse for the first three seconds.

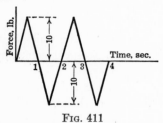

Fig. 411

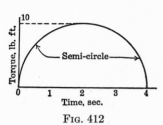

Fig. 412

664. The torque-time curve for a couple that acts on a body is a semi-circle as shown in Fig. 412. What is the angular impulse of the couple for a period of 4 sec? What is the angular impulse for the first three seconds?

665. A disk is keyed to a shaft, and the moment T exerted by the shaft on the disk varies according to the law $T = 3t^2 - 4t$, where T is expressed in pound feet and t in seconds. Find the angular impulse of the shaft on the disk in the interval $t = 0$ to $t = 4$ sec.   *Ans.* $L = 32$ lb sec ft.

666. A constant frictional moment of 200 lb ft is applied to a rotating drum by means of a band brake (see Fig. 195). If the moment decreases the angular velocity of the drum uniformly from 90 rpm to 10 rpm while the drum makes 40 revolutions, find the angular impulse of the band brake on the drum.   *Ans.* 9600 lb ft sec.

§ 2 Momentum

130 Momentum of a particle defined. The momentum of a moving particle, at any instant, is defined as the product of the mass of the particle and its velocity at the instant. Thus, if momentum be denoted by U, the momentum of a particle of mass m moving with velocity v is defined by the equation

$$U = mv$$

Momentum, like velocity, is a directed or vector quantity. Furthermore, momentum is represented by a localized vector; that is, it has a definite position line; the direction of the momentum of a particle is the same as that of the velocity of the particle, and its position line passes through the particle.

The momentum of a particle frequently is called *linear* momentum in contrast to the moment of momentum of the particle which is called *angular* momentum.

Units. The unit of momentum is a combination of a unit of mass and a unit of time, and hence is a compound unit. The unit of momentum has no special name. In the gravitational or engineer's system of units, the unit of mass is a derived unit called a slug, as explained in Art. 93, derived from the units of force, length, and time; hence, the unit of momentum is also a derived unit. Thus, if the pound, foot, and second are chosen for the units of force, length, and time, respectively, the unit of momentum is expressed by

$$1 \text{ unit of mass} \times 1 \text{ unit of velocity} = \frac{1 \text{ lb} \times 1 \text{ sec}^2}{1 \text{ ft}} \times \frac{1 \text{ ft}}{1 \text{ sec}} = 1 \text{ lb sec}$$

It will be observed, therefore, that momentum is expressed in the same fundamental units as is impulse.

131 Components of momentum. Angular momentum. Since the momentum of a particle is a vector quantity, it may be resolved into components, and like any localized vector it has a moment with respect to any point, the moment being de-fined as the product of the magnitude of the momentum and the perpen-dicular distance from the position line of the momentum vector to the point or moment center. The moment of the momentum of a particle is also called the *angular momentum* of the particle and will be denoted by H. The components of the momen-tum of a particle of mass m moving with velocity v (Fig. 413), and the angular momentum of the particle with respect to the point O are expressed by the equations:

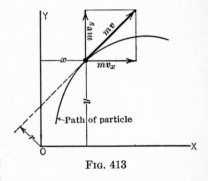

FIG. 413

$$U_x = (mv)_x = mv_x; \qquad U_y = (mv)_y = mv_y$$

$$H_0 = mv \cdot r, \quad \text{or} \quad H_0 = mv_x \cdot y - mv_y \cdot x$$

The latter expression states that the angular momentum of a particle equals the algebraic sum of the moments of the components of the momentum of the particle. In Fig. 413 the positive direction for the moment of linear momentum is considered to be the clockwise direction; however, the positive direction may be arbitrarily selected.

From the expression mvr it is evident that the units of angular mo-mentum are $\text{slug} \cdot \dfrac{\text{feet}}{\text{seconds}} \text{ feet} = \dfrac{\text{slug-feet}^2}{\text{seconds}}$, or, if m is expressed in its fundamental units, then the units of mvr are pound foot seconds, which are the same as those of angular impulse.

132 Linear momentum of a body. The component of the linear momentum, in any direction, of any body (mass system) is the algebraic sum of the components in the given direction of the momentums of the particles of the body. In general, the momentums of the particles of a body vary in magnitude and in direction. It was shown in Art. 99, however, that the linear momentum of the whole body may be found from the mass of the whole body and the velocity of the mass center of the body. Likewise the component, in the x direction, of the linear momentum of the mass system (Art. 99) is

$$U_x = m'v'_x + m''v''_x + m'''v'''_x + \cdots = M\bar{v}_x$$

A similar equation may be written for the y component. Thus, for any mass system we may write

$$U_x = M\bar{v}_x; \quad U_y = M\bar{v}_y; \quad \text{and} \quad U = M\bar{v}$$

That is, the linear momentum of any moving mass system is the product of the mass of the whole system and the velocity of the mass center of the system, and its direction agrees with that of the velocity of the mass center.

It should be noted, however, that the linear momentum vector does *not*, in general, pass through the mass center of the mass system. If, however, the mass system is a *rigid* body that has a motion of *translation*, then the linear momentum vector passes through the mass center of the body. (The proof is left to the student; see Art. 100 for method of proof.)

A general expression could also be obtained for the moment of the linear momentum (angular momentum) of any mass system having any motion, but it will be found more desirable to derive expressions that apply only to rigid bodies having the special motions of rotation and plane motion, as is done in the following articles.

133 Angular momentum of a rotating rigid body. Let Fig. 414 represent a rigid body rotating about a fixed axis through O with an angular velocity ω. The linear velocity of any particle of the body at a distance r from the axis of rotation is $r\omega$, and the linear momentum of the particle of mass m is mv or $mr\omega$ perpendicular to r. Therefore, the moment of momentum of the particle about the axis of rotation is

$$mv \cdot r = mr\omega \cdot r = mr^2\omega$$

and the algebraic sum of the moments of the momentums of all the particles about the same axis is

$$H_o = \Sigma mr^2\omega = \omega\Sigma mr^2$$

whence

$$\boldsymbol{H_o = I_o\omega}$$

in which I_o is the moment of inertia of the body about the axis of rotation.

POSITION OF THE LINEAR-MOMENTUM VECTOR. The distance q from the center of rotation O to the linear-momentum vector $M\bar{v}$ for a rotating

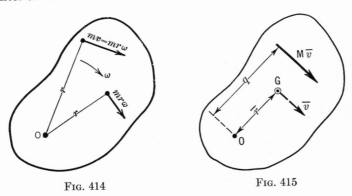

FIG. 414   FIG. 415

rigid body (Fig. 415) may be found by use of the principle of moments (Art. 14) as follows:

$$M\bar{v}q = I_o\omega = Mk_o^2\,\frac{\bar{v}}{\bar{r}}, \quad \text{whence} \quad q = \frac{k_o^2}{\bar{r}}$$

in which k_o is the radius of gyration of the body about the axis of rotation.

134 Angular momentum of a rigid body having plane motion. Since a plane motion of a rigid body may be considered as a combination of a rotation and a translation (Art. 86), the velocity of any particle P (Fig. 416) is the resultant of a velocity $r\omega$ due to the rotation of the body with angular velocity ω about an axis through any point O perpendicular to the plane of motion, and the velocity v_o due to the translation which gives to each particle the velocity v_o of the point O. Therefore, the components of the momentum of the particle P are $mr\omega$ and mv_o as shown in Fig. 416. And, if $m(v_o)_x$ and $m(v_o)_y$ denote the x and y components of mv_o, then the angular momentum of the particle with respect to the axis through O is

$$mr\omega\cdot r + m(v_o)_x\cdot y - m(v_o)_y\cdot x$$

and the angular momentum for the whole body with respect to the axis through O is

$$H_o = \Sigma mr^2\omega + \Sigma m(v_o)_x y - \Sigma m(v_o)_y x$$

$$= \omega \Sigma mr^2 + (v_o)_x \Sigma my - (v_o)_y \Sigma mx$$

$$= I_o\omega + (v_o)_x M\overline{y} - (v_o)_y M\overline{x} \qquad (1)$$

where the directions of the X and Y axes and ω are taken as shown in Fig. 416. If the point O is taken as the mass center G of the body, the above expression reduces to

$$\overline{H} = \overline{I}\omega \qquad (2)$$

since $\overline{y}$ and $\overline{x}$ are then equal to zero and I_o becomes $\overline{I}$.

It is important to note that, although plane motion of a rigid body may be considered as a rotation about an axis through any point O in

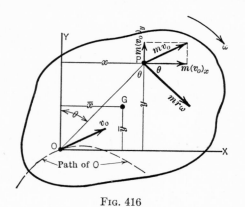

Fig. 416

the plane of motion, combined with a translation, Eq. 1 shows that the angular momentum of the body about the axis through O is not equal to $I_o\omega$ unless O is chosen as one of the three following points:

1. The mass center of the body, in which case the expression for the angular momentum in Eq. 1 reduces to $I_o\omega$ (or $\overline{I}\omega$), since $\overline{x}$ and $\overline{y}$ are zero as already noted.

2. The instantaneous center of zero velocity, in which case the expression reduces to $I_o\omega$ since v_o is then zero.

3. A point whose velocity is directed toward (or away from) the mass center. To prove this, let v_o in Fig. 416 be directed toward G, and, for convenience, let the X axis be coincident with v_o. The resulting expression for the angular momentum then becomes $I_o\omega$.

POSITION OF THE LINEAR-MOMENTUM VECTOR. The distance q of the linear-momentum vector $M\overline{v}$ from O in Fig. 416 when O has any one of the three positions specified in the foregoing paragraph may be found, as in the case of pure rotation, from the principle of moments. Thus,

$$M\bar{v}q = I_o\omega = Mk_o{}^2\omega. \quad \text{Hence,} \quad q = \frac{k_o{}^2\omega}{\bar{v}}$$

in which k_o is the radius of gyration of the body about the axis through O.

Problems

667. A small body (particle) weighing 8 lb is attached to one end of a string and is made to revolve as a conical pendulum (see Fig. 288). If the body revolves at a distance of 30 in. from the axis with an angular velocity of 90 rpm, find: (a) the magnitude of the linear momentum of the body, (b) the angular momentum of the body with respect to the axis of rotation.

Ans. $U = 5.85$ lb sec; $H = 14.64$ lb sec ft.

668. A slender rod rotates in a horizontal plane about a vertical axis through one end of the rod. If the rod is 3 ft long, weighs 5 lb per foot, and rotates at 120 rpm, find its angular momentum about the axis of rotation.

669. Determine the linear momentum of the rod described in the preceding problem, and find the position of the momentum vector.

670. Two small bodies, A and B (Fig. 417), move on a circle whose radius is 2 ft. When they are in the positions shown, the velocity of A is 40 ft/sec, and the x component of the momentum of the system consisting of the two bodies is 5 lb sec. The weight of A is 5 lb, and that of B is 10 lb. What is the velocity of B?

Ans. $v = 5.52$ ft/sec.

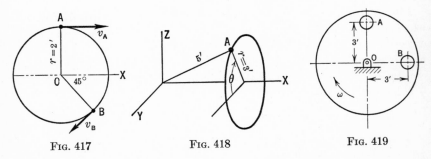

FIG. 417   FIG. 418   FIG. 419

671. A small body A in Fig. 418 weighs 4 lb and is made to rotate clockwise with a constant angular velocity of 60 rpm in a circular path in a plane parallel to the yz plane. Calculate the angular momentum of the body with respect to the Z axis in terms of θ, where θ is measured from a line parallel to the Y axis. Draw (freehand) a curve showing approximately the variation of the angular momentum with θ.

672. In Fig. 419 two small bodies, A and B, weigh 8.05 lb each and are attached to a disk of negligible weight which rotates with an angular velocity of 4 rad/sec. Find the angular momentum of the system with respect to the axis of rotation. Find the magnitude of the linear momentum and the position of the momentum vector.

Ans. $H_0 = 18$ lb sec ft; $U = 4.24$ lb sec; $q = 4.24$ ft.

673. A door of uniform thickness and 4 ft in width swings about a vertical axis through one edge with an angular velocity of 2 rad/sec. The door weighs 96.6 lb. Find the angular momentum of the door about the axis of rotation. Also find the magnitude of the linear momentum and the position of the momentum vector.

674. A solid cylinder weighing 128.8 lb rolls, without slipping, down an inclined plane. The linear velocity of the mass center of the cylinder at a given instant is 40 ft/sec. The diameter of the cylinder is 18 in. Find the angular momentum of the cylinder: (a) about an axis through the mass center perpendicular to the plane of motion, (b) about the instantaneous axis of rotation.

Ans. (a) $\bar{H} = 60$ lb sec ft; (b) $H_o = 180$ lb sec ft.

675. A homogeneous cylinder weighs 322 lb and has a radius of 1 ft. The cylinder rolls, without slipping, on a horizontal plane. If the kinetic energy of the cylinder is 480 ft lb, what is the angular momentum about an axis through the center of the cylinder perpendicular to the plane of motion? Find the linear momentum of the cylinder and the position of the momentum vector.

§ 3   Principles of Impulse and Momentum

135   Preliminary. In order to determine the effect of a force system on the motion of a body, that is, in order to treat the usual problem in kinetics, by means of the quantities impulse and momentum, the relations that exist between the impulse of the force system and the momentum of the body on which the force system acts must be established. These relations are expressed by means of two principles: namely, (1) the principle of linear impulse and linear momentum, and (2) the principle of angular impulse and angular momentum.

136   Principle of linear impulse and linear momentum. It was stated in Art. 99 that the algebraic sum of the components, in a given direction, of the external forces acting on any body (whether rigid or not) is equal to the mass of the body times the component of the acceleration of the mass center of the body in the given direction. That is, if x denotes any direction,

$$\Sigma F_x = M\bar{a}_x = M\frac{d\bar{v}_x}{dt} = \frac{d}{dt}(M\bar{v}_x) \tag{1}$$

And, by integrating this equation, the following equation which expresses the principle of linear impulse and linear momentum is obtained

$$\int_{t_1}^{t_2} \Sigma F_x\, dt = \int_{\bar{v}'_x}^{\bar{v}''_x} d(M\bar{v}_x)$$

or

$$\Sigma \int_{t_1}^{t_2} F_x\, dt = M\bar{v}''_x - M\bar{v}'_x \tag{2}$$

in which $\bar{v}''_x$ and $\bar{v}'_x$ are the x components of the velocity of the mass center of the body at the end and at the beginning, respectively, of the time interval $t_2 - t_1$. The principle of linear impulse and linear momentum then, as expressed in Eq. 2, may be stated in words as follows:

> The algebraic sum of the components, in any direction, of the impulses of the external forces acting on a body during any time interval is equal to the change in the component of the linear momentum of the body in the same direction during the same interval of time,

or, stated in the form of an equation,

$$Q_x = \Delta U_x \tag{3}$$

in which x represents any direction.

It should be noted also that Eq. 1 expresses an important principle which may be stated in words as follows:

> The algebraic sum of the components, in any direction, of the external forces acting on any body is equal to the rate of change of the component of the linear momentum of the body in the same direction.

137 Principle of angular impulse and angular momentum.
The relation between the angular impulse of the forces acting on a body and the angular momentum of the body will now be found for *rigid* bodies having a motion of rotation or a plane motion.

ROTATION OF A RIGID BODY. It was shown in Art. 101 that, if a rigid body rotates about a fixed axis, the algebraic sum of the moments of the external forces about the axis of rotation is equal to the product of the moment of inertia of the body about the axis of rotation and the angular acceleration of the body. That is,

$$\Sigma T_o = I_o\alpha = I_o\frac{d\omega}{dt} = \frac{d}{dt}(I_o\omega) \tag{1}$$

By integrating this equation, the following equation, which expresses the principle of angular impulse and angular momentum for a rigid body rotating about a fixed axis, is obtained:

$$\int_{t_1}^{t_2}\Sigma T_o \, dt = \int_{\omega_1}^{\omega_2}d(I_o\omega)$$

or

$$\Sigma\int_{t_1}^{t_2}T_o \, dt = I_o\omega_2 - I_o\omega_1 \tag{2}$$

in which ω_1 and ω_2 are the angular velocities of the body at the beginning and end, respectively, of the time interval $t_2 - t_1$.

The principle expressed by Eq. 2 may be stated as follows:

> The algebraic sum of the angular impulses of the external forces acting on a rotating rigid body, about the axis of rotation, for any time interval, is equal to the change of angular momentum of the body about the same axis in the same interval of time.

Or, stated in the form of an equation,

$$L_o = \Delta H_o \tag{3}$$

It should be noted also that Eq. 1 expresses an important principle which may be stated in words as follows:

> The algebraic sum of the moments of the forces acting on a rotating rigid body about the axis of rotation is equal to the rate of change of the angular momentum of the body about the same axis.

PLANE MOTION OF A RIGID BODY. It was shown in Art. 104 that the equation $\Sigma T_o = I_o \alpha$ also applies to a rigid body having plane motion, provided that the point O is the mass center of the body. Therefore, Eqs. 2 and 3 apply also to a rigid body having plane motion, provided that O is the mass center of the body. Thus, the equation $L_o = \Delta H_o$ becomes $\overline{L} = \Delta \overline{H}$, and, if the forces acting on the rigid body are constant, this may be written

$$\Sigma \overline{T} \cdot \Delta t = \overline{I}(\omega_2 - \omega_1)$$

It may be shown (the proof will not be given here) that the equation $L_o = \Delta H_o$ is not restricted to the case where O coincides with the mass center of the body but may be used where O is (1) any fixed point in the plane of motion, (2) any moving point in the plane of motion provided the velocity of the mass center of the body is zero, and (3) a moving point in the plane of motion whose velocity agrees in direction with the velocity of the mass center of the body.

138   Method of analysis of the motion of a body by means of impulse and momentum. It was noted in Art. 98 that, in the analysis of the motion of any body under the action of an unbalanced force system, relations must be found that involve (1) the forces acting on the body, (2) the kinetic properties of the body, and (3) the kinematic properties of the motion of the body (linear and angular velocity or acceleration, etc.).

These three factors are involved in the principles of impulse and momentum. And, as noted in Art. 90, in the analysis of the motion of a body that has a plane motion, three equations are needed. Two of these equations are obtained by expressing the principle of linear impulse and linear momentum with reference to any two rectangular axes in the plane of motion, and the third equation is obtained by expressing the principle of angular impulse and angular momentum with reference to an axis perpendicular to the plane of motion. Thus, in terms of the symbols already defined, the three equations may be written as follows:

$$Q_x = \Delta U_x, \qquad Q_y = \Delta U_y, \qquad L_o = \Delta H_o$$

The particular forms of the expressions for the above quantities depend upon the type of forces (whether constant or variable, etc.), the kind of body (whether rigid, etc.), and the type of motion (whether translation, rotation, or plane motion).

Illustrative Problems

Problem 676. A cylindrical jet of water $1\frac{1}{2}$ in. in diameter strikes a moving blade as shown in Fig. 420. The velocity of the jet before reaching the blade is 80 ft/sec, and the velocity of the blade is 30 ft/sec in the direction of the velocity of the jet. Find the horizontal and vertical components of the pressure of the water on the blade (or blade on the water). Neglect friction between the water and the blade, and assume that the only force acting on the water while it is in contact with the blade is the pressure of the blade.

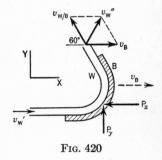

FIG. 420

SOLUTION. Let P_x and P_y be the unknown horizontal and vertical pressures exerted by the blade on the water, these pressures being considered as the cause of the change in the momentum of the water. The principle of impulse and momentum states that

$$Q_x = \Delta U_x \quad \text{or} \quad \Sigma F_x \cdot \Delta t = M(v''_x - v'_x) \quad (1)$$

$$Q_y = \Delta U_y \quad \text{or} \quad \Sigma F_y \cdot \Delta t = M(v''_y - v'_y) \quad (2)$$

The final velocity of the water may be found by applying the equation $v''_W = v_{W/B} +\!\!\!\!\!\rightarrow v_B$. Since friction between the water and the blade is negligible, $v_{W/B}$ remains constant in magnitude and is equal to $80 - 30 = 50$ ft/sec. From the vector diagram in Fig. 420, $(v''_W)_x = v_B - v_{W/B} \cos 60° = 30 - 50 \times 0.5 = 5$ ft/sec, and $(v''_W)_y = v_{W/B} \sin 60° = 50 \times 0.866 = 43.3$ ft/sec.

Let Δt be taken as any convenient time interval (1 sec, say). Then M is the mass of the water upon which the blade acts in 1 sec: that is, the mass of a tube of water $1\frac{1}{2}$ in. in diameter and $80 - 30 = 50$ ft long. Assuming the weight of water to be 62.4 lb/cu ft, we have:

From Eq. 1,
$$-P_x \cdot 1 = \frac{\pi(1.5)^2 \times 50 \times 62.4}{4 \times 144 \times 32.2}(5 - 80)$$

Hence,
$$P_x = 1.189 \times 75 = 89.2 \text{ lb}$$

From Eq. 2,
$$P_y \cdot 1 = 1.189(43.3 - 0) \quad \text{and} \quad P_y = 51.5 \text{ lb}$$

Problem 677. A cylinder weighing W lb and having a radius of r ft rolls, without slipping, up a plane, making an angle of 30° with the horizontal. A force of $\frac{4}{5}W$ lb perpendicular to the axis of the cylinder is exerted on the cylinder by means of cords wrapped around short cylindrical projections on the ends of the cylinder as shown in Fig. 421. The radius of the projections is $\frac{1}{2}r$. What is the velocity $\bar{v}$ of the center of the cylinder 4 sec after starting from rest?

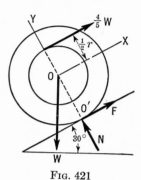

FIG. 421

SOLUTION. The free-body diagram of the cylinder is shown in Fig. 421. From the principles of impulse and momentum we have

$$\Sigma F_x \cdot \Delta t = M(\bar{v}''_x - \bar{v}'_x) \quad \text{or} \quad \left(\frac{4}{5}W - \frac{1}{2}W + F\right)4 = \frac{W}{g}\bar{v} \tag{1}$$

$$\Sigma F_y \cdot \Delta t = M(\bar{v}''_y - \bar{v}'_y) \quad \text{or} \quad (N - 0.866W)4 = 0 \tag{2}$$

$$\Sigma \bar{T} \cdot \Delta t = \bar{I}(\omega_2 - \omega_1) \quad \text{or} \quad \left(\frac{4}{5}W \cdot \frac{1}{2}r - Fr\right)4 = \frac{1}{2}\frac{W}{g}r^2\omega_2 \tag{3}$$

From Eq. 3,

$$F = \frac{2}{5}W - \frac{1}{8}\frac{W}{g}\bar{v}, \quad \text{since} \quad r\omega_2 = \bar{v}$$

Substituting this value of F in Eq. 1 and solving, we find

$$\bar{v} = \tfrac{28}{15}g = 60.1 \text{ ft/sec}$$

Problem 678. The wheel in Fig. 422 is rotating with an angular velocity of 120 rpm when the brake shoe A is applied. The force P is increased gradually from 0 to 20 lb in 5 sec and then gradually decreased to 0 again as indicated in the force-time diagram in Fig. 422b. Find the angular velocity of the wheel at the end of 10 sec. The weight of the wheel is 322 lb, its radius of gyration is 1.5 ft, and the coefficient of friction μ for the wheel and brake shoe is 0.3.

SOLUTION. From the principle of angular impulse and momentum, we have

$$\int T \, dt = \Delta(I\omega)$$

where T is the torque acting on the wheel at any time t. From the free-body diagram

of the wheel (Fig. 422c) we see that the frictional force $F = \mu N$ at any instant is
1.2P, the value of the normal pressure N being found by considering the equilibrium

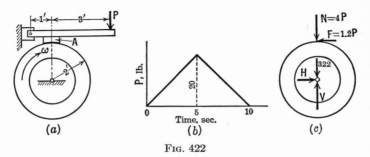

(a) (b) (c)

FIG. 422

of the bar on which P is acting. Hence, the torque $T = Fr = 2.4P$. But $P = 4t$.
Therefore,

$$2\int_0^5 T\, dt = 2\int_0^5 2.4 \times 4t\, dt = \frac{322}{32.2}\left(\frac{3}{2}\right)^2(4\pi - \omega_2)$$

$$19.2\left[\frac{t^2}{2}\right]_0^5 = \frac{90}{4}(4\pi - \omega_2)$$

$$\frac{19.2 \times 25}{2} = \frac{90}{4}(4\pi - \omega_2)$$

Hence,

$$\omega_2 = 1.90 \text{ rad/sec} = 18.15 \text{ rpm}$$

Problems

679. A jet of water 2 in. in diameter has a velocity of 40 ft/sec in a horizontal
direction. If the jet impinges normally against a fixed vertical plane, what is the
pressure of the water on the plane?

680. Solve Prob. 518 by use of the principles of impulse and momentum.

681. A 5½-oz baseball moving horizontally with a velocity of 150 ft/sec is struck
by a bat and is deflected 135° from its original direction as indicated in Fig. 423.
If the speed of the ball as it leaves the bat is 130 ft/sec, compute the horizontal and

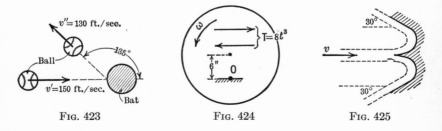

FIG. 423 FIG. 424 FIG. 425

vertical components of the impulse of the bat on the ball. Assuming that the time
of contact is $\frac{1}{50}$ sec, determine the average value of the force during the impact.

Ans. $Q_x = 2.58$ lb sec; $Q_y = 0.98$ lb sec; $F_{\text{avg}} = 138$ lb.

682. A homogeneous cylindrical disk (Fig. 424) weighs 128.8 lb and has a radius of 1 ft. It is mounted so that it rotates in a horizontal plane about a smooth vertical axis at O. A couple of variable moment $T = 8t^3$ is applied to the disk, T being expressed in lb ft and t in sec. If the initial value of ω is 6 rad/sec, how long will it take the disk to come to rest?

683. A horizontal stream of water whose cross-sectional area is 2 sq in. strikes a fixed blade as shown in Fig. 425. The velocity of the water is 150 ft/sec before striking the blade, and is 120 ft/sec after striking the blade. Find: (a) the horizontal force exerted on the blade, and (b) the per cent loss in the kinetic energy of the water.

Ans. (a) $P = 1026$ lb; (b) 36 per cent.

684. Solve Prob. 524 by use of the principles of impulse and momentum.

685. A certain machine gun fires 350 bullets per minute. If each bullet weighs 0.1 lb and the muzzle velocity of the bullets is 2200 ft/sec, what is the average reaction of the gun against its support? Neglect the reaction due to the discharged gases.   *Ans.* 39.8 lb.

686. The table of a planing machine together with the material bolted on it weighs 5 tons. Find the time required to change its velocity from 20 ft/min (cutting stroke) to 40 ft/min in the opposite direction (return stroke) if the average force of the pinion on the rack while the velocity is being changed is 180 lb.

687. Water flows in a straight pipe with a velocity of 12 ft/sec. The pipe is 4 ft in diameter and 2 mi long. Calculate the linear momentum of the water. What would be the effect of closing a valve quickly if the valve is near the discharge end of the pipe? What is the time of closing the valve if the average additional pressure due to closing is 20 lb/sq in.?   *Ans.* $U = 3,090,000$ lb sec; $t = 85.4$ sec.

688. A horizontal stream of water having a velocity of 30 ft/sec strikes a moving blade as shown in Fig. 426. The velocity u of the blade is 10 ft/sec in the direction of the velocity of the water. The diameter of the stream is ¾ in. Assume that the friction of the water on the blade is negligible, and find: (a) the horizontal force exerted on the blade, and (b) the per cent loss in kinetic energy of the water.

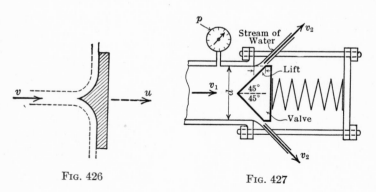

Fig. 426   Fig. 427

689. In the relief valve shown in Fig. 427 the discharge area is assumed to be equal to the circumference of the pipe times the lift of the valve times cos 45°. The rate of discharge of the water is 2 cu ft/sec. The diameter d of the pipe is 8 in. The "lift" is 0.25 in. The pressure p in the pipe is 30 lb/sq in. Find the force exerted by the spring on the valve. *Hint:* The force causing the change in the horizontal component of the momentum of the water from Mv_1 to $Mv_2 \cos 45°$ is the difference between the pressure on a cross section of the water in the pipe and the force exerted by the spring. *Ans. P = 1355 lb.*

690. A shell which weighs 800 lb is fired with an initial velocity of 1600 ft/sec from a gun weighing 160,000 lb. What will be the maximum velocity of recoil of the gun? How far will the gun recoil if a constant resistance of 18,000 lb begins to act immediately after the explosion? *Ans. v = 8 ft/sec; s = 8.83 ft.*

691. The rotating parts of a horizontal-shaft turbine weigh 20 tons and have a radius of gyration of 2 ft. It takes 10 min for the turbine to come to rest from a speed of 55 rpm under the influence of journal friction alone. The shaft is 10 in. in diameter. What is the average coefficient of friction?

692. A locomotive scoops water from a track pan by means of a tender water scoop while it travels at 60 mph. The track pan is 2400 ft long, and the scoop is in contact with the water for a distance of 1700 ft. If the scoop delivers 950 gal of water into the tank, what additional force of traction must the locomotive apply to keep its velocity constant? *Ans. F = 1120 lb.*

693. A cylindrical jet of water 1 in. in diameter impinges on a fixed blade which is inclined at an angle of 30° with the direction of the jet as shown in Fig. 428. The velocity of the jet is 30 ft/sec. Find the horizontal and vertical components of the pressure of the water on the blade (or blade on the water). Assume that the magnitude of the velocity of the jet is not changed by the action of the blade. Also assume that the only force acting on the water while it is in contact with the blade is the pressure of the blade.

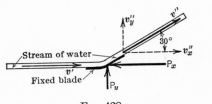

FIG. 428

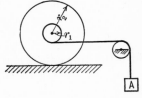

FIG. 429

694. The weight of A in Fig. 429 is 20 lb. The string attached to A passes over a smooth peg and wraps around a drum of radius $r_1 = 5$ in. attached to a wheel having a radius $r_2 = 18$ in. The radius of gyration of wheel and drum is 15 in. The wheel rolls without slipping. How many seconds are required for A to acquire a velocity of 10 ft/sec, starting from rest? The weight of the wheel and drum is 64.4 lb. *Ans. t = 3.56 sec.*

695. The two homogeneous disks, A and B, in Fig. 356 weigh 32.2 lb and 128.8 lb, respectively, and are keyed together (see Prob. 557). If $P = 54$ lb and the disks are at rest when $t = 0$, find: (a) the velocity of the center of the disks when $t = 2$ sec, and (b) the acceleration of the center of the disks.

696. A cylinder weighing 96.6 lb and having a radius of 6 in. is mounted on a horizontal axle whose axis coincides with the axis of the cylinder. A body weighing 32.2 lb is suspended from a cord wrapped around the cylinder. If the body is allowed to descend from rest, what will its velocity be at the end of 2 sec? Neglect bearing friction. *Ans. v = 25.8 ft/sec.*

139   Conservation of momentum. I Linear Momentum. As already noted, the principle of linear impulse and linear momentum for the motion of any mass system under the action of an unbalanced external force system is expressed by the equation

$$Q_x = \Delta(M\bar{v}_x)$$

in which x represents any direction.   If the resultant of the forces which act on the body has no component in the x direction, the impulse of the force system in the x direction will be zero, and hence $\Delta(M\bar{v}_x)$ will be equal to zero.   Thus,

$$M\bar{v}_x = \text{a constant}$$

That is, if the resultant of the external forces which act on a body has no component in a given direction, the component of the linear momentum of the body in the given direction remains constant.

This statement expresses the principle of conservation of linear momentum.

II   Angular Momentum. As already noted, the principle of angular impulse and angular momentum for the motion of any rigid body under the action of an unbalanced external force system is expressed by the equation

$$L_o = \Delta H_o$$

provided that the axis O is the axis of rotation for a rotating rigid body or is the mass center for a rigid body having plane motion.   If the resultant of the external forces which act on the body has no moment about a given axis O, the angular impulse of the forces about the same axis will be zero, and hence ΔH_o will be equal to zero.   Thus,

$$H_o = \text{a constant}$$

That is, if the resultant of the external forces which act on a body has no moment about a given axis, the angular momentum of the body with respect to that axis remains constant.

This statement expresses the principle of the conservation of angular momentum.

It was shown in Arts. 133 and 134 that the angular momentum H_o of a body about an axis O is expressed by $I_o\omega$ if one of the following conditions is satisfied: (1) The body is rigid and rotates about a fixed axis, the O axis being the axis of rotation; (2) the body is rigid and has a plane motion and the point O is the mass center of the body.   Furthermore, $I_o\omega$ also expresses the angular momentum of a non-rigid mass system that rotates about a fixed axis, provided that all parts of the mass system have the same angular velocity. Thus, if a rod rotates about a fixed axis as bodies slide radially outward (or inward) along the rod, the mass system is not rigid, but the angular momentum of the system about the axis O of rotation is $I_o\omega$.

Therefore, the principle of conservation of angular momentum *when the foregoing conditions are satisfied*, may be expressed as follows:

$$I_o\omega = \text{a constant}$$

Thus, if I_o decreases, ω must increase, and vice-versa. For example, a gymnast who leaves the swinging trapeze at the top of a circus tent with a relatively small angular velocity ω (his body being extended) may increase his angular velocity and make several complete turns in mid-air by "doubling up" as he descends in a vertical plane. His moment of inertia is thereby decreased, and his angular velocity is increased a sufficient amount to keep $I_o\omega$ constant since no external turning moment acts on him while he is descending.

Illustrative Problems

Problem 697. The weight of the parts of a 3-in. field gun (Fig. 430) that move during recoil is 950 lb. The weight of the projectile is 15 lb, and that of the powder charge is 1.5 lb. The muzzle velocity is 1700 ft/sec. Determine the velocity of free recoil at the time the projectile reaches the end of barrel, assuming that the projectile leaves the gun with a horizontal velocity.

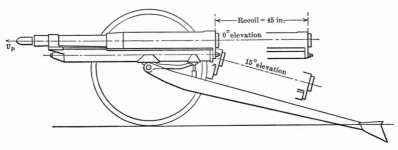

Fig. 430

SOLUTION. Three bodies are to be considered: the projectile, the powder charge, and the recoiling parts of the gun. Since the recoil is free, no horizontal external forces are acting on these three bodies while the projectile is reaching the muzzle of the gun, and hence the linear momentum of the system remains constant. That is, the momentum of the projectile plus the momentum of the gases is equal to the momentum of the recoiling parts. Thus,

$$M_p v_p + M_g \bar{v}_g = M_r v_r$$

The gases (and unburned powder) form a non-rigid body, and hence the velocity $\bar{v}_g$, of the mass center, must be used. It is usually assumed that $\bar{v}_g$ is one half of the velocity of the projectile. Thus, using weights instead of masses since they are proportional, we have

$$15 \times 1700 + 1.5 \times \tfrac{1700}{2} = 950\, v_r$$

Hence,

$$v_r = \frac{25{,}500 + 1275}{950} = 28.1 \text{ ft/sec}$$

The velocity of free recoil as the projectile reaches the muzzle of the gun is about 0.7 of the maximum velocity of free recoil. The bore is filled with gases for a short interval after the projectile leaves the gun, and these gases continue to exert pressure on the breech and thus to increase the velocity of recoil.

Problem 698. A 2-oz bullet moving with a velocity of 1000 ft/sec strikes, centrally, a block of wood which is moving with a velocity of 40 ft/sec on a smooth horizontal plane in a direction opposite to that of the bullet. If the block of wood in which the bullet imbeds itself weighs 15 lb, what is the resulting velocity of the block and bullet? What proportion of the kinetic energy of the bullet and block of wood is lost?

SOLUTION. Since the horizontal component of the resultant of the external forces which act on the mass system is zero, the horizontal component of the linear momentum of the mass system remains constant. That is, the linear momentum of the bullet and block of wood before impact is equal to their linear momentum after impact. Whence

$$\frac{0.125}{32.2} \times 1000 - \frac{15}{32.2} \times 40 = \frac{15 + 0.125}{32.2}\, v$$

in which the linear momentum is considered to be positive when in the direction of the initial velocity of the bullet. Hence,

$$v = \frac{125\text{–}600}{15.12} = -31.4 \text{ ft/sec}$$

Thus the block and bullet will have a resulting velocity of 31.4 ft/sec and will move in the direction of the initial velocity of the block.

Energy Loss. The initial kinetic energy of the bullet and block of wood is

$$E_k = \frac{1}{2}\frac{0.125}{32.2} \times (1000)^2 + \frac{1}{2}\frac{15}{32.2} \times (40)^2 = \frac{149{,}000}{64.4} \text{ ft lb}$$

The final kinetic energy of the bullet and block of wood is

$$E_k = \frac{1}{2}\frac{15.12}{32.2} \times (31.4)^2 = \frac{14{,}910}{64.4} \text{ ft lb}$$

The proportion of the kinetic energy lost is

$$\frac{149{,}000 - 14{,}910}{149{,}000} = 0.900$$

Thus it is seen that, although the principle of conservation of linear momentum applies to the mass system, and the linear momentum remains constant, the principle of conservation of mechanical energy does not apply (see Art. 122) since about

$\%_0$ of the kinetic energy is lost or dissipated during the impact, mainly in the form of heat energy.

Problems

699. Two similar pulleys are running loose on a shaft. One has an angular velocity of 10 rpm and the other a velocity of 20 rpm in the opposite direction. They are suddenly coupled together by means of a friction clutch. What will be the angular velocity of the pulleys after the clutch has ceased to slip? What proportion of the kinetic energy is lost?

700. A disk D and a small body A (Fig. 431) are rotating at 60 rpm about the axis YY. The body A is attached to a string that passes through a small hole at the center of the disk. The distance r of A from the axis of rotation is 24 in., and the weight of A is 8 lb. The top surface of the disk is smooth. If by pulling on the string r is decreased to 8 in., what will be the angular velocity of A?

Ans. $\omega = 540$ rpm.

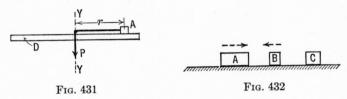

FIG. 431   FIG. 432

701. Three bodies, A, B, and C (Fig. 432), whose weights are 20 lb, 10 lb, and 20 lb, respectively, rest on a smooth horizontal surface. If A is given a velocity of 20 ft/sec to the right and B a velocity of 10 ft/sec to the left and C remains at rest until A and B come into contact with it, what will be the final velocity of the three bodies if it is assumed that after coming into contact they remain in contact?

702. A projectile which weighs 64 lb is fired from a gun with an initial velocity of 1000 ft/sec, making an angle of 60° with the horizontal. When it reaches its greatest height, it explodes, and one third of the projectile falls vertically downward with no initial velocity. If the remainder of the projectile remains intact, how far apart will the two pieces lie when they reach the ground? Assume the ground to be horizontal. *Ans.* 20,200 ft.

703. A bullet weighing 1 oz and moving horizontally with a velocity of 2000 ft/sec strikes centrally a wooden sphere weighing 99 oz that is suspended vertically by a cord, the distance from the point of suspension to the center of the sphere being 4 ft. With what velocity will the sphere (and imbedded bullet) start moving after the impact? How far will the sphere rise vertically above its initial position?

704. Two spherical balls (Fig. 433) connected by a rod rotate about a vertical axis with an angular velocity ω of 30 rpm. Each ball weighs 200 lb and is 1 ft in diameter. The rod also weighs 200 lb. A man weighing 161 lb jumps vertically and catches hold of the bar at A. What is the angular velocity of the system after the man catches hold of the bar? *Ans.* $\omega = 2.88$ rad/sec.

705. In Fig. 434, A is a disk keyed to the vertical shaft and rotating with it at 30 rpm. The disk B is not keyed to the shaft and is not rotating. If the disk B is allowed to slide down the shaft until it comes in contact with the disk A, what will be the angular velocity of the two disks after slipping between the disks has ceased? Each disk is 4 ft in diameter and weighs 161 lb. Neglect the mass of the axle. What frictional moment is exerted on B by A if slipping between the disks occurs for 2 sec? What percentage of the energy of the system is lost?

Ans. $\omega = 1.57$ rad/sec; $T = 7.85$ lb ft; loss = 50 per cent.

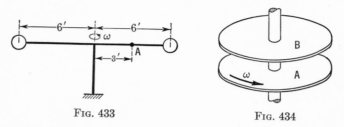

FIG. 433   FIG. 434

706. A man weighing 150 lb jumps into the center of a boat that weighs 200 lb. He lands in the boat with a velocity having a horizontal component of 10 ft/sec. The boat is drifting with a velocity of 5 ft/sec in the same direction. Neglect the resistance of the water, and find the resulting velocity of the boat and man. If it takes ½ sec for the boat to acquire this resulting velocity, what is the average value of the horizontal force exerted by the man on the boat?

707. A tank partly filled with water rests on a flat-topped car. The car and tank are moving along a straight track at 15 mi/hr when a stone weighing 200 lb is dropped vertically into the water. The weight of the car is 400 lb, and that of the tank and water is 300 lb. Neglect the friction of the car on the track and find the velocity of the car after the stone has been dropped in the water. If the tank slides on the car for ½ sec before coming to rest relative to the car, what is the average value of the horizontal force that is exerted by the car on the tank while the velocity of the tank (and car) is being changed?

708. In Fig. 435, A and B are two sprocket wheels mounted on horizontal axles which rest in smooth bearings. Each wheel weighs 20 lb and has a diameter of 4 ft and a radius of gyration of 1.5 ft. A body C weighing 10 lb hangs from a light inextensible chain which passes over the two wheels as shown. C descends from rest, and 2 sec elapse before the slack in the chain is taken up. If the weight of the chain is neglected, what will be the angular velocity of the two wheels immediately after the 2-sec period? Assume that the body C is detached from the chain just as the chain between the pulleys becomes taut. *Ans.* $\omega = 7.57$ rad/sec.

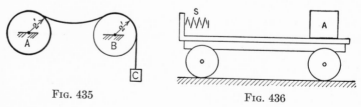

FIG. 435   FIG. 436

709. In Fig. 436 block A weighs 40 lb and slides on the bed of a truck until it hits a spring S whose spring constant is 80 lb/in. The body of the truck weighs 160 lb, and the wheels have negligible weight. If the truck is at rest and the velocity of A is 10 ft/sec before A hits the spring, find the maximum compression of the spring. Neglect friction.

710. A block of wood weighing 20 lb is suspended by a long string. The block is swinging with a velocity of 40 ft/sec through its lowest position when a bullet weighing 0.1 lb and moving with a horizontal velocity of 2000 ft/sec strikes the block and is imbedded in it. What will be the velocity of the block and bullet: (a) if the velocities of the block and bullet before impact are parallel but opposite in sense? (b) if the velocities are parallel and have the same sense? (c) if the velocities are at right angles?   *Ans.* (a) $v = 29.8$ ft/sec; (b) $v = 49.7$ ft/sec; (c) $v = 41.0$ ft/sec.

140 Impact. The equations of Art. 138 which express the principles of impulse and momentum apply to the motion of bodies, whether the bodies move under the action of impulsive forces or of forces that act during a finite time interval. In fact, as stated in Art. 126, the principles of impulse and momentum are particularly well adapted to the solution of kinetics problems that involve sudden impulses.

The effect of impulsive forces on the motion of a body, in most problems, is so large in comparison with the effect of the other forces which act on the body that the effect of the other forces on the motion of the body, while the impact lasts, may be neglected. The only details of the change in the motion of a body that can be determined, when the change in the motion is caused by impulsive forces, are the initial and final velocities of the body. For the distance traveled during the impact is indefinitely small; the time interval is also indefinitely small, and hence the acceleration produced is indefinitely large, since the change in velocity is a finite quantity. Thus, the distance, time, and acceleration are indeterminate. There is, however, a definite (appreciable) change in the velocity, although, as just noted, the manner in which the velocity changes during the period of the impact is unknown, and only the initial and final values of the velocity can be determined. Therefore, the momentum of the body at the beginning and at the end of the impact period are definite quantities, and, since these quantities are involved in the principles of impulse and momentum, problems that involve impulsive forces yield to this method of solution although the impulse of the impulsive forces is used and not the forces themselves.

DIRECT CENTRAL IMPACT. If two bodies collide and the velocity of each is directed normal to the striking surfaces, the impact is said to be *direct*. If two bodies collide in such a way that the action line of the pressures exerted by the bodies on each other is directed along the line connecting the mass centers of the two bodies, the impact is said to be *central*.

The period of impact may be divided into two parts: (1) the time of deformation during which the impulsive force is increasing to its maximum value as the two bodies deform, and (2) the time of restitution during which the bodies are separating and partially recovering from the deformation. If the two bodies were perfectly elastic, the period of deformation would be equal to the period of restitution, and the velocity of separation would be equal to the velocity of approach. But, all bodies are more or less inelastic, and hence the velocity of separation is always somewhat less than the velocity of approach.

COEFFICIENT OF RESTITUTION. For direct central impact of two bodies, the ratio of the relative velocity of separation to the relative velocity of approach is defined as the *coefficient of restitution*. Thus, if the velocities before impact are denoted by v_1 and v_2 and after impact by v'_1 and v'_2 and if e denotes the coefficient of restitution, the value of e is defined by the following equation:

$$e = -\frac{v'_2 - v'_1}{v_2 - v_1} \quad \text{or} \quad v'_2 - v'_1 = -e(v_2 - v_1) \tag{1}$$

In order to have a positive value of e, the negative sign before the fraction representing the ratio of the relative velocities is necessary, since the relative velocities before and after impact are of opposite sign; that is, if v_2 is greater than v_1 and $v_2 - v_1$ is positive, then v'_1 will be greater than v'_2 and $v'_2 - v'_1$ will be negative.

Experiments show that the value of the coefficient of restitution for two spheres in central direct impact depends only on the materials of the two spheres, provided the velocity of approach is not high enough to cause considerable inelastic deformation of the spheres. It is generally assumed that the value of e as found for two spheres of any two materials is the same for other bodies of the same materials, whether the impact is central and direct or not. But, if the impact is not central and direct, the components of the velocities normal to the impact surfaces must be used in Eq. 1 instead of the total velocities. Although the coefficient of restitution is a useful concept, it is not adequate for the solution of many problems in impact because of the assumption of oversimplified conditions and of uncertainty of the value to use for a given set of conditions.

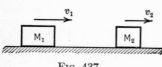

FIG. 437

141 Impact of two translating bodies. DIRECT CENTRAL IMPACT. In Fig. 437 are represented two translating bodies which collide with direct central impact. It is assumed that the values of

$$M_1, \quad M_2, \quad v_1, \quad v_2, \quad \text{and} \quad e$$

are known, and it is required to find the values of

$$v, \quad v'_1, \quad v'_2, \quad \int_0^{t_d} P_d \, dt \quad \text{or} \quad (P_d)_{\text{avg}} \cdot t_d \quad \text{and} \quad \int_{t_d}^{t} P_r \, dt \quad \text{or} \quad (P_r)_{\text{avg}} \cdot t_r$$

where v is the velocity of the bodies at the end of the deformation period t_d, v'_1 and v'_2 are the velocities of the bodies after the impact, and t_r is the restitution period.

Evidently five equations must be found from which the five unknown quantities may be determined. The five equations may be found as follows: From the principle of conservation of linear momentum Eqs. 1 and 2 below are obtained. Thus,

$$M_1 v_1 + M_2 v_2 = (M_1 + M_2)v \quad \text{for the period } t_d \tag{1}$$

$$(M_1 + M_2)v = M_1 v'_1 + M_2 v'_2 \quad \text{for the period } t_r \tag{2}$$

And, from Art. 140,

$$v'_1 - v'_2 = -e(v_1 - v_2) \tag{3}$$

From these three equations the values of v, v'_1, and v'_2 may be found. The impulses for the periods t_d and t_r may now be found by applying the principle of linear impulse and momentum for the periods t_d and t_r, which leads to the following equations:

$$\int_0^{t_d} P_d \, dt = -M_1(v - v_1) = M_2(v - v_2) \tag{4}$$

$$\int_{t_d}^{t} P_r \, dt = -M_1(v'_1 - v) = M_2(v'_2 - v) \tag{5}$$

Problems

711. A freight car weighing 40 tons and traveling at a speed of 20 mi/hr on a straight track overtakes another car weighing 30 tons and traveling on the same track in the same direction at a speed of 10 mi/hr. If the value of e is 0.2, find the velocity of each car after impact and the impulse of each car on the other both for the time of deformation and for the time of restitution.

712. A body weighing 40 lb moving to the right collides with a 30-lb body moving to the left. The speed of each body is 15 ft/sec. The impact of the two bodies is direct and central. If the coefficient of restitution is 0.6, find: (a) the velocity of each body after impact, (b) the velocity of each body at the end of the deformation period.

713. A sphere which is at rest is struck directly by another sphere having the same mass and diameter. The velocity of the center of the latter is 30 ft/sec. If the coefficient of restitution is 0.5, find the velocities of the centers of the spheres after impact. *Ans.* $v'_1 = 7.5$ ft/sec; $v'_2 = 22.5$ ft/sec.

714. A ball drops from rest 16 ft and strikes a horizontal rigid steel plate. If the ball rebounds 9 ft, what is the coefficient of restitution? *Ans.* $e = 0.75$.

715. A falling weight of 1200 lb is used to drive a pile into the ground. If the weight of the pile is 800 lb and the weight is dropped 18 ft, what will be the depth of penetration of the pile, assuming an average resistance to penetration of 30,000 lb? Assume the impact between the weight and pile to be perfectly inelastic ($e = 0$).

142   The gyroscope. THE PROBLEM DEFINED. Gyroscopic motion occurs whenever a body rotates about an axis in the body as the axis (and body) is turned about a second axis, provided that the two axes are not parallel. Thus, the wheels of a locomotive when rounding a curve, or the screw propeller of a ship when the ship is pitching in a rough sea, are given gyroscopic motion. The forces that act on the body in giving it gyroscopic motion may be of considerable importance since under certain conditions they are very undesirable, as, for example, the forces exerted on the propeller of an airplane when making a sharp turn. On the other hand, the gyroscope is sometimes used to introduce desirable forces, as, for example, in reducing the rolling of ships.

The gyroscope here considered is a body symmetrical with respect to one of three rectangular axes about which the body rotates or spins with constant angular velocity ω and at the same time turns about one of the other axes with constant angular velocity Ω. The problem to be considered is that of determining the forces that must act on the disk or its axles (axle reactions) in order to maintain this gyroscopic motion.

ANGULAR MOMENTUM A VECTOR QUANTITY. In the foregoing articles the magnitude, only, of the angular momentum of a body was assumed to change. However, in expressing the principle of angular impulse and angular momentum for a body which moves so that its plane of motion changes in direction (such as the propeller of an airplane when making a turn), the angular momentum of the body must be considered as a quantity having direction as well as magnitude; that is, it must be considered to be a vector quantity. The angular momentum of a body may be represented by a vector drawn (1) perpendicular to the plane of motion of the body to indicate the direction of the plane of motion, (2) of such length that it represents, to some scale, the magnitude of the angular momentum, and (3) with the sense of rotation indicated by an arrow which points in the direction along the vector in which a right-handed screw would advance if given the same sense of rotation as that of the body. Thus, if a disk (Fig. 438) rotates with angular velocity ω_1 about the axis OZ, its angular momentum ($H_1 = I\omega_1$) about the axis of rotation is represented completely by the vector OB. It will be noted that the vector representing the angular momentum may change in length only, in direction only, or both in length and in direction. Thus,

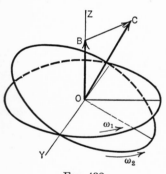

FIG. 438

in Fig. 438, if the disk is rotated about the axis OY to a new position, and at the same time the angular velocity about the OZ axis is increased to ω_2, the vector representing the angular momentum ($H_2 = I\omega_2$) of the disk is OC. Furthermore, the change in the angular momentum of a body is represented completely by the change in the angular momentum vector. Thus, in Fig. 438 the change in the angular momentum of the disk is represented by the vector BC.

THE GYROSCOPIC COUPLE. In Fig. 439a is represented a disk or wheel which rotates with a constant angular velocity ω about its axis

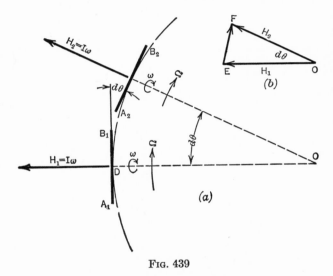

FIG. 439

(axle) OD as it rolls round a curved track with a constant angular velocity Ω and hence has gyroscopic motion. It will be observed that the angular velocity of the disk about an axis through D perpendicular to the paper is also equal to Ω. At a given instant, the disk is in the position A_1B_1, and its angular momentum H_1 is equal to $I\omega$. After an interval of time dt the disk is in the position A_2B_2, and its angular momentum is H_2, the magnitude of which is also equal to $I\omega$. That is, the angular momentum of the disk ($I\omega$) has changed in direction, only, during the time interval dt.*

The change in the angular momentum of the disk from H_1 to H_2 is represented by the vector EF (Fig. 439b) which connects the ends of the vectors H_1 and H_2. Since the angle $d\theta$ is small (greatly exaggerated

* The disk has an angular momentum with respect to an axis perpendicular to the paper; however the magnitude and direction of this angular momentum do not change as the disk rolls round the track.

in Fig. 439b), the length of EF, that is, the magnitude of the change in the angular momentum, is

$$EF = H_1\, d\theta = H_2\, d\theta = I\omega\, d\theta$$

and the limiting direction of the vector EF as $d\theta$ becomes indefinitely small is perpendicular to H_1. The rate of change of the angular momentum, then, is

$$\frac{I\omega\, d\theta}{dt} = I\omega\Omega$$

and the direction of the vector which represents this rate of change of the angular momentum is also perpendicular to H_1. A torque or couple is required to produce the change in the angular momentum of the disk; the moment of the couple is equal to the rate of change of the angular momentum of the disk; the plane in which it acts is perpendicular to the vector which represents the rate of change of the angular momentum; and the sense of rotation of the couple is such that it would cause a right-handed screw to progress (in the direction of the arrow) along the vector which represents the rate of change of the angular momentum.

Therefore, a couple C must act on the disk in a plane perpendicular to the plane of the disk and to the plane of the paper, with a clockwise sense of rotation (as viewed from behind), the magnitude of the couple being

$$C = I\omega\Omega$$

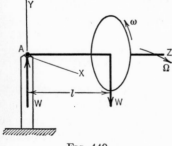

FIG. 440

This couple is called the *gyroscopic couple*. The angular velocity Ω which is maintained by the couple is called the *velocity of precession*, and the corresponding axis is called the *axis of precession*. The axis about which the couple $I\omega\Omega$ tends to rotate the disk is called the *torque axis*.

The determination of the sense of rotation about the axis of precession will be illustrated in the following example. In Fig. 440 a circular disk of weight W is mounted on a horizontal axle which is free to rotate about a vertical axis. The disk has an angular velocity ω with respect to the Z axis (the spin axis) and the couple having a moment Wl causes the disk (and Z axis) to rotate with an angular velocity Ω about the Y axis (the axis of precession). The angular velocity ω is clockwise when viewed from the positive end of the Z axis, and hence the angular momentum of the disk is in the negative z direction. Since the sense of rotation of the couple is clockwise when viewed from the positive end of the X axis (the torque axis), the vector representing the rate of change in angular momentum must be in the negative x direction. Thus, the sense of rotation about the axis of precession (Y axis) must be clockwise when viewed from the positive end of the Y axis. Thus, it is seen that the sense of rotation about the axis of precession is in accordance with the following rule:

> The sense of precession is such as to turn the vector representing the angular momentum of the disk toward the vector representing the gyroscopic couple.

The forces of a gyroscopic couple frequently cause considerable pressure on the axle of a rotating body, and the sense of the couple must be in accordance with the foregoing rule. This explains, for example, why a heavy rotating flywheel or armature on board a ship, with its axle horizontal and athwartship, will offer no more resistance to the rolling of the ship than when it is not rotating. The bearing of the axles, however, must exert a large couple $C = I\omega\Omega$ in a horizontal plane which tends to "nose" the ship around; Ω here represents the angular velocity of roll.

In the foregoing discussion it was assumed that the motion of the gyroscope was known, and it was required to determine the forces that must act on the gyroscope to maintain its steady state of motion. A detailed analysis of the effect on the motion of a gyroscope of a change in the gyroscopic couple which produces a transient motion will not be given here; however, the following observations will be made.

If in Fig. 440 an external couple is applied in a horizontal plane to retard the precession, the couple will cause a change in the angular momentum such that the vector representing the rate of change will be in the positive y direction. Thus, in accordance with the rule for the sense of precession, the disk and axle will fall. However, if an external couple is applied in a horizontal plane to increase or hurry the precession, the disk and axle (Fig. 440) will rise. This principle is employed in the Brennan monorail car, the precession being hurried by the rolling of the axle of the revolving flywheels, on a shelf attached to the side of the car. This principle is also used in the "active type" of gyroscope for stabilizing ships. In this type the precession is hurried by means of a precession engine which acts after the ship has rolled a very small amount, thus producing a gyroscopic righting couple sufficient to extinguish the roll. Since the roll is checked in its incipiency, only a small amount of work is done. The stresses produced in the hull of the ship are also small for the same reason, and hence the weight and displacement of the active type of gyroscope likewise may be small.

Illustrative Problem

Problem 716. The flywheel of an engine on a ship weighs 6000 lb and has a radius of gyration of 3.75 ft. It is mounted on a horizontal axle which is parallel to the longitudinal axis of the ship, and has a speed of 400 rpm clockwise when viewed from the rear. Find the gyroscopic couple when the ship is turning to the left with an angular velocity of 0.1 rad/sec. What are the axle reactions if the distance between the centers of bearings is 4 ft?

SOLUTION. The moment of inertia of the flywheel about the axis of spin is

$$I = \frac{6000}{32.2} \times (3.75)^2 = 2620 \text{ slug ft}^2 \quad \text{and} \quad \omega = \frac{400 \times 2\pi}{60} = 41.9 \text{ rad/sec}$$

Hence, the gyrocopic couple is

$$I\omega\Omega = 2620 \times 41.9 \times 0.1 = 10,980 \text{ lb ft}$$

The forces constituting the gyroscopic couple are the axle reactions, and, in accordance with the rule stated in Art. 142, the reaction at the forward bearing is downward and that at the rear bearing is upward. Since the distance between centers of bearings is 4 ft, the magnitude of each of these reactions is $10,980 \div 4 = 2745$ lb. The effect of the gyroscopic motion, then, is to increase the reaction at the rear bearing and to decrease it at the forward bearing. The reaction at each bearing due to the weight of the flywheel is 3000 lb. Hence, the resultant reaction at the rear bearing is $3000 + 2745 = 5745$ lb, and that at the forward bearing is $3000 - 2745 = 255$ lb.

Problems

717. A disk 4 ft in diameter (Fig. 441) rolls on a circular track having a radius of 10 ft. The center of the disk has a velocity of 20 ft/sec. The disk is attached

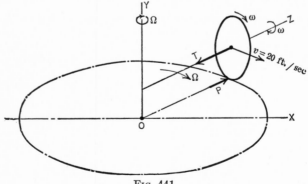

FIG. 441

to the central axis OY by means of a rod which is collinear with the Z axis about which the disk turns. The disk has a flange similar to that on a car wheel. If the weight of the disk is 450 lb, find the tension T in the rod and the pressure P of the track against the flange of the wheel. *Ans.* $T = 838$ lb; $P = 279$ lb.

718. A circular disk is mounted on a horizontal axle which is free to rotate about a vertical axis as shown in Fig. 440, the distance from the center of the disk to the vertical axis being 2 ft. The radius of the disk is 6 in., and its weight is 10 lb. If the disk rotates about the horizontal axle with a speed of 300 rpm, with what velocity will it rotate about the vertical axis? *Ans.* $\Omega = 157$ rpm.

719. In Fig. 442 each of the disks A and B weighs 32.2 lb and has a radius of gyration of 0.8 ft. The disks turn on a horizontal shaft with an angular velocity $\omega = 1200$ rpm as the shaft rotates about a vertical post with an angular velocity

Fig. 442

$\Omega = 0.5$ rad/sec. Determine the magnitude of the couple that the horizontal shaft exerts on the post. Will the upper end of the post bend toward the disk A or the disk B?

720. The propeller of an airplane rotates clockwise when viewed from the rear. If the airplane turns to the right when moving in a horizontal plane, what will be the effect on the airplane of the gyroscopic couple?

721. The flywheel of an automobile engine is mounted on a horizontal axle parallel to the longitudinal axis of the automobile. The flywheel rotates counterclockwise when viewed from the rear. What will be the effect of the gyroscopic couple on: (a) the axle reactions of the flywheel, (b) the pressures of the wheels on the road?

Review Questions

1. Define linear impulse of a force: (a) in words, (b) as a mathematical expression. Is impulse a vector quantity?

2. What is another name for angular impulse of a force? What are the units of angular impulse?

3. Is the linear momentum of a particle a vector quantity? State in words the meaning of $(mv)_x$. What are the units of linear momentum?

4. What is another name for moment of momentum of a particle? What are the units of moment of momentum?

5. Prove that $\Sigma(mv)_x = M\bar{v}_x$, and state in words the meaning of the equation.

6. Where in the body is the position line of the linear momentum vector $M\bar{v}$: (a) for a translating rigid body, (b) for a rotating rigid body?

7. Point out, and correct, the errors in the following demonstration that the angular momentum of a rotating rigid body is $I_o\omega$: The linear momentum of the body is $M\bar{v}$, and the angular momentum of the body about the axis of rotation O is $M\bar{v}\bar{r}$. But $\bar{v} = \bar{r}\omega$, and hence $H_o = M\bar{r}^2\omega$. Thus, $H_o = I_o\omega$, since $M\bar{r}^2 = I_o$.

8. Start with the equation $\Sigma F_x = M\bar{a}_x$, and derive the equation expressing the principle of linear impulse and linear momentum for any mass system acted on by constant forces.

9. State the principle of conservation of linear momentum and the principle of conservation of angular momentum.

10. Define coefficient of restitution. Is the coefficient of restitution ever negative?

11. Define gyroscopic couple. State a rule for determining the sense of rotation of a gyroscope about the axis of precession.

12. When an automobile is rounding a curve at high speed, the gyroscopic motion of the wheels causes a couple to act on the axles of the automobile. Will this couple tend to stabilize the automobile or to overturn it?

PART FOUR

*Special Topics**

* Each topic or chapter is self-contained and may be studied without reference to the preceding topics in Part Four. The topics treated in Part Four are somewhat more advanced than those discussed in Parts One, Two, and Three, but no additional principles are employed.

Chapter 12

MECHANICAL VIBRATIONS

143 Introduction. A mechanical vibration as met in most engineering problems is a periodic motion, usually of small amplitude, which repeats itself in a definite time interval called the *period* of the vibration; each repetition of the motion is called a *cycle*, and the number of cycles per unit of time is called the *frequency* of vibration.

The prevention of vibration in machine parts and structural members is important in eliminating excessive wear, in reducing repeated stresses that are likely to cause the failure of a member by a progressive fracture called a fatigue failure, and in reducing objectionable noise.   On the other hand, vibrations are sometimes desirable as in the production of musical sounds, in vibration machines for the determination of endurance limits for repeated stresses of materials, in the handling of powdered materials which are likely to pack, in tamping concrete mixtures, etc.

The simplest type of a vibration is a harmonic motion: that is, one for which the displacement may be expressed as a sine or cosine function. Although not all vibrations of bodies are harmonic motions, most vibrations may be considered to be harmonic especially if the displacements are small.   Simple harmonic motion of a particle (in which the particle has rectilinear motion) was discussed in Arts. 75 and 97, and the student is advised to read these articles again before proceeding with the next article in which a simple harmonic motion will be analyzed in somewhat greater detail.

A motion, such as a harmonic motion, that can be described in terms of a single co-ordinate is said to have *one degree of freedom*.   The vibrations considered here are restricted to this class of motions.

144 Free vibrations. Consider the motion of a small rigid body of mass m and weight W (Fig. 443) suspended by an elastic weightless spring from a rigid support.   The *spring constant* or *modulus of the spring* (that is, the force required to deflect the end of the spring a unit distance) will be denoted by k, and the static deflection of the end of the spring due to the weight W will be denoted by δ_{st}; hence $k = W/\delta_{st}$.   It is assumed that the body is free to move only along a vertical line which will here be taken as the X axis, x being regarded as positive when measured *downward* from the position of static equilibrium of the body. Let the body be given some initial displacement x_o, and, as it is released, let it be given an initial velocity v_o. The body will then oscillate or vibrate with an amplitude A; the forces acting on the body when it has

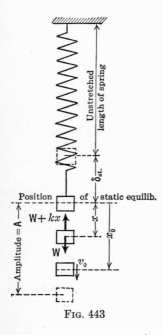

any displacement x are shown in Fig. 443, and, by applying the equation of motion $\Sigma F_x = ma_x$ to the body, we obtain

$$W - (W + kx) = ma_x \quad \text{or} \quad \frac{d^2x}{dt^2} = -\frac{k}{m}x \quad (1)$$

This equation is the defining equation for a simple harmonic motion (Art. 75). Replacing the constant k/m, for convenience, by p^2 and noting that $W = k\delta_{st}$, we have

$$p^2 = \frac{k}{m} = \frac{kg}{W} = \frac{g}{\delta_{st}} \quad (2)$$

Hence Eq. 1 may be written

$$\frac{d^2x}{dt^2} = -p^2x \quad (3)$$

Fig. 443

The value of x that satisfies Eq. 3 must be a function of t whose second derivative with respect to t is equal to the original function multiplied by $-p^2$. The functions $x = B \cos pt$ and $x = C \sin pt$ (where B and C are constants) satisfy the equation, as does also their sum. Hence, the general solution to Eq. 3 is

$$x = B \cos pt + C \sin pt \quad (4)$$

where B and C may be regarded as constants of integration whose values depend on the initial conditions of the motion. The velocity of the body at any instant during the oscillation may be found by differentiating Eq. 4. Thus,

$$v = \frac{dx}{dt} = -Bp \sin pt + Cp \cos pt \quad (5)$$

If the initial conditions of the motion are known, the values of B and C can now be found. For example, let it be assumed that, when $t = 0$, the displacement $x = x_o$ and that the body has an initial velocity $v = v_o$ in the positive (downward) direction. Substituting these values in Eqs.

4 and 5, we find that $B = x_o$, and $C = v_o/p$. Thus, Eq. 4 becomes

$$x = x_o \cos pt + \frac{v_o}{p} \sin pt \qquad (6)$$

A useful interpretation of Eq. 6 may be made by representing the displacement x as the projection, on the diameter of a circle, of a rotating vector. Thus, in Fig. 444, assume that the vectors $B = x_o$ and $C = v_o/p$, which are at right angles to each other, rotate about O with an angular velocity p, called the *natural circular frequency* of vibration, and assume also that the vector A which is the resultant of vectors B and C also rotates about O with angular velocity p. It will be noted that the projection of A on the X axis is $x = B \cos pt + C \sin pt$. The angle that the vector A makes with the X axis is $pt - \phi$ where ϕ is the angle between the vectors B and A. Thus,

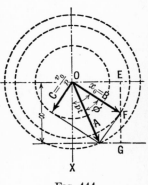

Fig. 444

$$x = B \cos pt + C \sin pt = A \cos (pt - \phi) \qquad (7)$$

where

$$A = \sqrt{B^2 + C^2} = \sqrt{x_o{}^2 + \left(\frac{v_o}{p}\right)^2} = \text{the amplitude of motion} \qquad (8)$$

and

$$\tan \phi = \frac{C}{B} = \frac{v_o}{px_o} \qquad (9)$$

By plotting the x projections of the vectors B and C as ordinates and time as abscissas, the curves shown as B and C in Fig. 445 are obtained. The displacement x at any time t is obtained by adding algebraically the corresponding ordinates to these two curves, and is plotted as the ordinate to the curve denoted as A in Fig. 445.

Because of the difference in the directions of the vectors in Fig. 444, their maximum projections on the X axis do not occur at the same time t. Thus, the maximum value of the displacement x, which is represented by the maximum ordinate to the curve A, occurs at a time ϕ/p after the ordinate in curve B attains its maximum value. The angle ϕ is called the *phase angle*.

It will be observed that the simple harmonic motion defined by Eq. 6 or Eq. 7 may be regarded as the resultant of two simple harmonic motions $x = x_o \cos pt$ and $x = v_o/p \sin pt$, which have the same frequency but different amplitudes, and which differ in phase by 90°.

Equations 6 and 7 and Fig. 445 show that the oscillatory motion repeats itself whenever the angle pt changes through 2π radians. There-

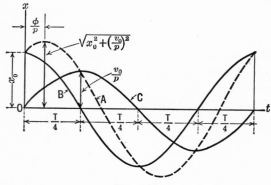

FIG. 445

fore, the time interval T for each cycle of motion (the period) is $2\pi/p$. Thus,

$$T = \frac{2\pi}{p} = 2\pi \sqrt{\frac{W}{kg}} = 2\pi \sqrt{\frac{\delta_{st}}{g}} \qquad (10)$$

The number of cycles per second, called the *frequency f* is then

$$f = \frac{1}{T} = \frac{p}{2\pi} = \frac{1}{2\pi} \sqrt{\frac{kg}{W}} = \frac{1}{2\pi} \sqrt{\frac{g}{\delta_{st}}} \qquad (11)$$

By substituting $g = 386$ in./sec^2 and expressing δ_{st} in inches, we have

$$f = \frac{1}{2\pi} \sqrt{\frac{g}{\delta_{st}}} = 3.127 \sqrt{\frac{1}{\delta_{st}}} \text{ cycles per second} \qquad (12)$$

Equations 10 and 11 show that the period and frequency of free vibration of a body depend only on the weight of the body and the stiffness of the spring, and are not affected by the initial conditions of the motion. These equations will be found to be applicable to periodic motions of widely different arrangements of elastic members. In other words, Fig. 443 is a conventionalized diagram that can be used with small error to replace many actual motions of bodies that vibrate with small amplitudes.

The motion described in the foregoing paragraphs is called a *free* vibration; once started, it continues at constant frequency and amplitude without the aid of externally applied driving or exciting forces. *Damped free vibrations* in which frictional forces cause the amplitude of the motion to decrease with time are discussed in Art. 148. *Forced vibrations* which are maintained by an exciting force that may vary with any frequency are discussed in Art. 149.

SPRING CONSTANT. In a system of vibrating elastic bodies, such as shown in Fig. 446, the vibration of one of the bodies, body M for example, is frequently reduced for convenience to the simple case treated in the preceding discussion by assuming that the body is caused to vibrate with equal frequency by an equivalent spring attached to the body as in Fig. 443. The constant for the equivalent spring is obtained from the spring constants of the several elastic bodies of the system. For this purpose a some-what more comprehensive definition of spring constant is needed than that used in connection with Fig. 443. The con-stant of an equivalent spring for any body of a system is the force acting on

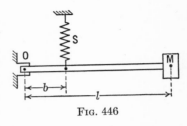

FIG. 446

the body tending to restore it to its equilibrium position when its displacement from the equilibrium position is unity.

To find the equivalent spring constant for M in Fig. 446, let a vertical force F be applied to the body that will give it a displacement Δ. Since F is equal (but opposite) to the restoring force, it is equal to the equiva-lent spring constant when Δ is unity. Thus, the equivalent spring constant is equal to the ratio F/Δ. It will be assumed that OM is a weightless, rigid bar and that its angular displacement is small. The force in the spring S when F is acting on M is found from equilibrium to be lF/b. The corresponding deflection of the spring S is lF/bk, where k is the constant of the spring S. From geometry the displacement of M is found to be l/b times the deflection of the spring. Hence, $\Delta = \left(\dfrac{l}{b}\right)^2 \dfrac{F}{k}$, and the equivalent spring constant is

$$k_e = \frac{F}{\Delta} = \left(\frac{b}{l}\right)^2 k$$

From Eq. 11 the frequency of the vibration is found to be

$$f = \frac{1}{2\pi} \frac{b}{l} \sqrt{\frac{kg}{W}}$$

If the mass of the rod OM is not negligible, the foregoing method of solution cannot be conveniently used. The solution may be conveniently obtained, however, by deriving the differential equation of motion for the rod and obtaining from it the natural frequency. This method will be illustrated in Prob. 735. The method that makes use of the equivalent spring constant may be used in determining the natural frequency of vibration in the following problems.

Illustrative Problem

Problem 722. A body M weighing 150 lb falls from a height h of 1.5 in. (Fig. 447) upon a helical spring, the modulus of which is 200 lb/in. If the body remains attached to the upper end of the spring: (a) determine the frequency of the resulting free vibration; (b) write an equation for the displacement of the vibrating body, assuming that $t = 0$ at the instant the weight makes contact with the spring; (c) determine the amplitude of motion, and the maximum shortening s of the spring that occurs during the vibration.

FIG. 447

SOLUTION. (a) From Eq. 2, the natural circular frequency is

$$p = \sqrt{\frac{kg}{W}} = \sqrt{\frac{200 \times 386}{150}} = 22.7 \text{ rad/sec}$$

and, from Eq. 11, the frequency of vibration is

$$f = \frac{p}{2\pi} = \frac{22.7}{6.28} = 3.61 \text{ cycles per sec}$$

(b) At the instant the weight makes contact with the spring, the initial conditions for the motion are

$$x_o = -\delta_{st} = -\tfrac{150}{200} = -0.75 \text{ in.}$$

$$v_o = \sqrt{2gh} = \sqrt{2 \times 386 \times 1.5} = 34 \text{ in./sec}$$

in which the origin of co-ordinates is at the position of static equilibrium of the body. Hence, from Eq. 6, the displacement at any time t is

$$x = x_o \cos pt + \frac{v_o}{p} \sin pt = -0.75 \cos 22.7t + 1.5 \sin 22.7t$$

(c) From Eq. 8, the amplitude of motion is

$$A = \sqrt{x_o^2 + \left(\frac{v_o}{p}\right)^2} = \sqrt{(0.75)^2 + (1.5)^2} = 1.68 \text{ in.}$$

Therefore, the weight vibrates with an amplitude of 1.68 in. about the position of equilibrium, and the maximum shortening s of the spring is

$$s = A + \delta_{st} = 1.68 + 0.75 = 2.43 \text{ in.}$$

Problems

723. A helical spring when supporting a body whose weight is 400 lb deflects 1 in. If the weight is increased to 1600 lb and is displaced from its equilibrium position and then released so that it can vibrate freely, what will be the period of vibration?

724. The motor in Fig. 448 weighs 1000 lb and is mounted on four springs, each having a modulus of 2000 lb/in. Calculate the natural frequency with which the motor will vibrate if given a vertical displacement from its equilibrium position and then released. *Ans.* $f = 8.85$ cycles per sec.

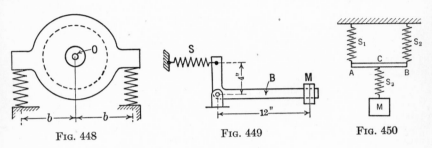

FIG. 448	FIG. 449	FIG. 450

725. In Fig. 449 the body M weighs 40 lb, and the weight of the bell crank B is negligible. The modulus of the spring S is 20 lb/in. Calculate the equivalent spring constant, and determine the frequency of vibration of the system.
Ans. $k = 2.22$ lb/in.; $f = 0.74$ cycles per sec.

726. In Fig. 450 a body M whose weight is W is suspended from a system of springs as shown. The upper end C of the spring S_3 is attached to the mid-point of a rigid bar AB of negligible weight and is free to rotate in a vertical plane. The spring constants for S_1, S_2, and S_3 are k_1, k_2, and k_3, respectively. Show that the equivalent spring constant for the system is

$$\frac{4k_1k_2k_3}{k_2k_3 + k_1k_3 + 4k_1k_2},$$ and determine the natural frequency of vibration

of the body M for small vertical displacements.

727. Assume that the body in Fig. 443 is raised by a force until the length of the spring is the same as its unstretched length and that the force is then suddenly removed. Write an expression for the displacement x in terms of δ_{st} and the time t after the force is removed. Show that the maximum elongation of the spring is twice as great as the static elongation caused by the weight of the body.

728. An elevator weighing 10 tons is slowly lowered by a cable whose cross-sectional area is 1.5 sq in. and whose modulus of elasticity is 20×10^6 lb/in.[2] When the length of the cable is 112 ft, the hoisting drum FIG. 451 is suddenly stopped. If the mass of the cable is neglected, find the frequency of vibration of the cage. NOTE. The stretch of a bar or cable caused by a static axial force W, as found in texts on strength of materials, is $e = Wl/aE$, in which a is the cross-sectional area of the cable, l is the length of the cable, and E is the modulus of elasticity of the cable. *Ans.* $f = 3.3$ cycles per sec.

729. The body M in Fig. 451 weighs 8 lb. It is given a small vertical displacement from its equilibrium position and then released. The constant for each of the springs is 30 lb/in. Calculate the frequency of the vibration of M, neglecting the mass of the springs. *Ans.* $f = 8.56$ cycles per sec.

730. A body M whose weight is W lb is attached to a system of springs (similar to the arrangement in Fig. 450) whose equivalent spring constant is k_e lb/in. The natural frequency of the body is found by measurement to be 90 cycles per min (cpm). When a 2-lb body is attached to M, its natural frequency is reduced to 60 cpm. Determine the weight of M and the equivalent spring constant.

731. A cantilever beam of constant cross section (Fig. 452) when supporting a body M of weight W at its free end deflects elastically an amount $\delta_{st} = \dfrac{1}{3} \dfrac{W l^3}{EI}$ (see any text on strength of materials) in which E is the tensile modulus of elasticity of the material of the beam and I is the moment of inertia of the cross section of the beam with respect to its horizontal centroidal axis. Show that the period of vibration of M, if the mass of the beam is negligible, is $T = 2\pi \sqrt{W l^3 / 3EIg}$. If the mass of the beam is *not* negligible, it can be shown that only a very small error is introduced in obtaining the period of vibration by neglecting the mass of the beam and assuming that $\frac{1}{4}$ of the mass (and weight) of the beam is added to that of the body M. If the weight of the beam is $\frac{1}{2}W$, what error (in per cent) is introduced by neglecting the weight of the beam?

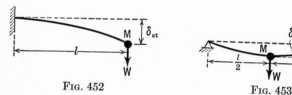

Fig. 452   Fig. 453

732. A simple beam of constant cross section (Fig. 453) when supporting a body M of weight W at the center of the span deflects elastically an amount $\delta_{st} = \dfrac{1}{48} \dfrac{W l^3}{EI}$. (See Prob. 731 for meaning of E and I.) Assume that the mass of the beam is negligible compared to that of M, and show that the frequency of vibration of M is $f = \dfrac{1}{2\pi} \sqrt{\dfrac{48EIg}{W l^3}}$. If the mass of the beam is *not* negligible, it can be shown that only a very small error is introduced in obtaining the period (or frequency) of vibration by neglecting the mass of the beam and assuming that $\frac{1}{2}$ of the mass (and weight) of the beam is added to that of the body M. If the weight of the beam is $\frac{1}{4}W$, what error (in per cent) is introduced by neglecting the weight of the beam?

733. In Fig. 452 let the body M be suspended from the end of the beam by means of a coiled spring whose constant is k. Find the equivalent spring constant for the system; the spring constant for the beam may be obtained by using the expression for δ_{st} in Prob. 731. Neglect the weight of the beam.

Ans. $k_e = \dfrac{3EIk}{3EI + kl^3}$.

734. A frequency-measuring instrument known as Frahm's tachometer, consists of a number of reeds, each of which is clamped at one end and has a small body attached at the other end. If the instrument is placed on a vibrating machine whose frequency is approximately equal to the natural frequency of one of the reeds, that reed will vibrate with considerable amplitude. It is desired to construct a tachometer whose reeds have frequencies varying from 20 cycles per sec (cps) to 30 cps in steps of 1 cps. It is found that, if a small body of weight W is attached to a reed 5 in. long and made of a certain spring steel, its natural frequency is 20 cps. Determine the lengths of the other reeds if it is assumed that the bodies attached to the ends of the reeds have equal weights and that the reeds are made from the same strip of spring steel. Neglect the weight of the reed. (See Prob. 731 for the period of vibration.)

145 Simple pendulum. As a simple application of a free vibration, let it be required to find the period of vibration of small amplitude of a simple pendulum consisting of a particle C (Fig. 454) suspended by a weightless cord of length l from the point O, and allowed to swing in a vertical plane along the path $B'B$. Using the equation of motion $\Sigma T_o = I_o \alpha$, we have

$$-Wl \sin \theta = \frac{W}{g} l^2 \frac{d^2\theta}{dt^2} \quad (13)$$

and, since $\sin \theta = \theta$ approximately, when θ is small, the last equation may be written

$$\frac{d^2\theta}{dt^2} = -\frac{g}{l}\theta \qquad (14)$$

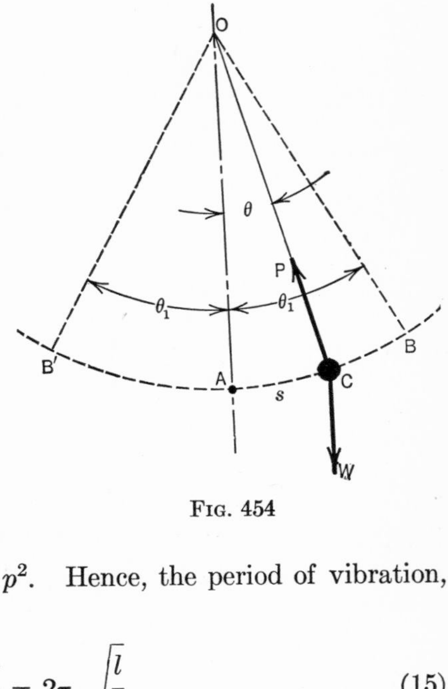

FIG. 454

This equation has the same form as Eq. 3 when g/l is replaced by p^2. Hence, the period of vibration, if the amplitude is small, is

$$T = \frac{2\pi}{p} = 2\pi \sqrt{\frac{l}{g}} \qquad (15)$$

If the amplitude θ_1 is not sufficiently small to permit the assumption that $\sin \theta = \theta$, it can be shown that the period is

$$T = 2\pi \sqrt{\frac{l}{g}} \left[1 + \left(\frac{1}{2}\right)^2 b^2 + \left(\frac{1\cdot 3}{2\cdot 4}\right)^2 b^4 + \left(\frac{1\cdot 3\cdot 5}{2\cdot 4\cdot 6}\right)^2 b^6 + \cdots \right] \quad (16)$$

where $b = \sin (\theta_1/2)$.

146 Compound pendulum. A physical body of finite dimensions (in contrast to a particle) which oscillates or swings about a horizontal axis is called a compound pendulum. Figure 455 represents a section of such a pendulum that is free to oscillate about a horizontal axis through O. Let it be required to find the period of vibration for oscillations of small amplitude. Using the equation of motion $\Sigma T_o = I_o \alpha$, we have

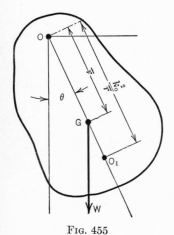

$$-W\bar{r}\sin\theta = \frac{W}{g}k_o{}^2\frac{d^2\theta}{dt^2} \qquad (17)$$

or, if θ is small,

$$\frac{d^2\theta}{dt^2} = -\frac{g\bar{r}}{k_o{}^2}\theta \qquad (18)$$

where k_o is the radius of gyration of the pendulum about the axis of rotation. The last equation is the same in form as Eq. 3 if $g\bar{r}/k_o{}^2$ is replaced by p^2. Hence, the period of the compound pendulum for oscillations of small amplitude is

Fig. 455

$$T = \frac{2\pi}{p} = 2\pi\sqrt{\frac{k_o{}^2}{g\bar{r}}} \qquad (19)$$

By comparing Eqs. 15 and 19, it is seen that for small amplitudes the period of oscillation of a compound pendulum will be the same as that of a simple pendulum if the length l of the simple pendulum is equal to $k_o{}^2/\bar{r}$ of the compound pendulum. The point O_1 in Fig. 455 is called the *center of oscillation*. It will be noted that the center of oscillation is also the center of percussion (Art. 93). Furthermore, it can be shown that the center of oscillation may be made the center of rotation without changing the period of oscillation. That is, in a compound pendulum the centers of oscillation and suspension are interchangeable.

147   Free torsional vibration. As another application of Eq. 6, let it be required to find the period of vibration (or of oscillation of small amplitude) of a torsional pendulum. In Fig. 456 a disk is rigidly attached to the slender cylindrical rod or shaft of length l. If the disk is given an angular displacement θ_1, and is then released, the disk will oscillate under the influence of the torque exerted by the rod. The torque is proportional to the angular displacement, provided that the elastic strength of the material is not exceeded, and is opposite in sense to θ. Thus, using the equation of motion $\Sigma T_o = I_o \alpha$, we have

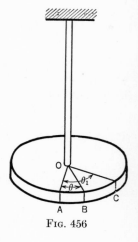

Fig. 456

$$-k\theta = I_o \frac{d^2\theta}{dt^2} \quad \text{or} \quad \frac{d^2\theta}{dt^2} = -\frac{k}{I_o}\theta \qquad (20)$$

where k is the torsional spring constant, or the torque required to produce a unit angle of twist of the rod or shaft to which the disk is attached. Equation 20 is also the equation of motion for free torsional vibrations of many machine parts such as rotors or flywheels in cases where the mass of the shaft is relatively small. Equation 20 has the same form as Eq. 1. Thus, the solution is of the same form as Eq. 6, and hence the angular displacement at any time is given by the equation

$$\theta = \theta_o \cos pt + \frac{\omega_o}{p} \sin pt \qquad (21)$$

in which $p = \sqrt{\dfrac{k}{I_o}}$, θ_o is the initial angular displacement, and ω_o is the initial angular velocity of the disk or the value of ω when $t = 0$.

The period of oscillation therefore is

$$T = \frac{2\pi}{p} = 2\pi \sqrt{\frac{I_o}{k}} \qquad (22)$$

The torsional spring constant for a cylindrical rod or shaft, as given in books on strength of materials is

$$k = \frac{\pi d^4 G}{32l} \qquad (23)$$

where d is the diameter of the rod, G is the shearing modulus of elasticity of the material of the shaft, and l is the length of the rod. For a cylindrical disk $I_o = \dfrac{1}{2}\dfrac{W}{g}r^2$ where r is the radius of the disk, and, hence,

$$T = 2\pi \sqrt{\frac{16Wr^2l}{\pi g d^4 G}} \qquad (24)$$

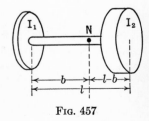

Fig. 457

Two Bodies Connected by Shaft. Nodal Point. When two heavy masses such as the rotors of a large motor and generator are connected by a relatively small shaft as shown in Fig. 457, torsional vibrations of the system will result if the shaft is given a twist by turning the rotors in opposite directions and then releasing them. Since, after release, there are no external torques acting on the system, the principle of conservation of angular momentum (Art. 139) may be applied. Thus, if I_1 and I_2 are the moments of inertia of the two rotors and ω_1 and ω_2 are their angular velocities at any time, we have

$$I_1\omega_1 + I_2\omega_2 = 0 \quad \text{or} \quad \omega_1 = -\omega_2\frac{I_2}{I_1} \tag{25}$$

Hence, the two bodies rotate in opposite directions during the vibration since their angular velocities are of opposite sign, and there must be a section N (called the nodal section), of the shaft that remains stationary. Thus, the motion of each body may be considered as that of a torsional pendulum on a shaft which is fixed at N, and the position of this nodal section can be determined since the periods of oscillation for the two parts of the system are equal. From Eq. 22 the period is

$$T = 2\pi\sqrt{\frac{I_1}{k_1}} = 2\pi\sqrt{\frac{I_2}{k_2}} \tag{26}$$

where k_1 and k_2 are the torsional spring constants of the two parts of the shaft as divided by the point N. Therefore $k_2/k_1 = I_2/I_1$, and, by substituting the values of k from Eq. 23, this equation becomes

$$\frac{b}{l-b} = \frac{I_2}{I_1} \quad \text{whence} \quad b = \frac{I_2l}{I_1 + I_2} \tag{27}$$

By using this value of b for the length of the shaft in Eq. 23 and substituting the resulting value of k_1 in Eq. 26, we find the period of free torsional vibration for the system in Fig. 457 to be

$$T = 2\pi\sqrt{\frac{32lI_1I_2}{\pi d^4G(I_1 + I_2)}} = 2\pi\sqrt{\frac{I_1I_2l}{JG(I_1 + I_2)}} \tag{28}$$

where J is the polar moment of inertia of the area of the cross section of the shaft about the axis of the shaft.

Illustrative Problem

Problem 735. Body M in Fig. 446 is a small body whose weight is W, and it is attached to the end of a slender rigid bar OM whose weight is W_1. The constant for the spring S is k. Determine the natural frequency of vibration of the system for small angular displacements about the axis of rotation O.

SOLUTION. When the system is in its equilibrium position, the force in the spring is found by use of the equation of equilibrium $\Sigma M_o = 0$ to be $\dfrac{l}{2b}W_1 + \dfrac{l}{b}W$. If the bar and body M are given a small angular displacement θ from their equilibrium position, the increase in length of the spring is $b\theta$, and the force is increased to $\dfrac{l}{2b} W_1 + \dfrac{l}{b} W + kb\theta$. Thus, the forces acting on the bar and body M for a small angular displacement θ are as shown in Fig. 458. Using the equation of motion,

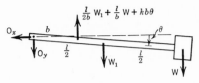

Fig. 458

$\Sigma T_o = I_o \alpha$, and considering the positive direction to be the direction of the angular displacement θ, we have

$$-kb^2\theta - \frac{l}{2} W_1 - lW + \frac{l}{2} W_1 + lW = \left(\frac{1}{3}\frac{W_1}{g} l^2 + \frac{W}{g} l^2\right) \frac{d^2\theta}{dt^2}$$

or

$$\frac{d^2\theta}{dt^2} = -\frac{kb^2}{\dfrac{l^2}{g}\left(\dfrac{W_1}{3} + W\right)}\, \theta$$

This equation has the same form as Eq. 3; hence,

$$p^2 = \frac{kb^2}{\dfrac{l^2}{g}\left(\dfrac{W_1}{3} + W\right)} \quad \text{and} \quad f = \frac{p}{2\pi} = \frac{1}{2\pi}\frac{b}{l}\sqrt{\frac{kg}{\dfrac{W_1}{3} + W}}$$

Problems

736. The disk in Fig. 456 has a weight of 32.2 lb and a radius of 6 in. A torque of 4000 lb in. gives the steel rod to which the disk is attached an angle of twist of 0.04 radian, which is the maximum angle of twist the rod can sustain without having its elastic limit exceeded. What will be the frequency of oscillation of the disk? Assume the motion of the disk is started by twisting it through an angle less than 0.04 radian and then releasing it without initial velocity. Neglect the mass of the rod. *Ans.* $f = 41.1$ cycles per sec.

737. A small body of mass m and weight W is attached to the center of a tightly stretched weightless elastic wire of length $2l$ (Fig. 459) in which there is a stress S. If the mass is displaced laterally a small distance and then released, show by use of the equation of motion, $\Sigma F_x = ma_x$, that the body has a simple harmonic motion, and determine the period of vibration. Assume that the increase in stress in the wire due to a small lateral displacement is small in comparison with S and may therefore be neglected.

Ans. $T = 2\pi\sqrt{\dfrac{Wl}{2gS}}.$

738. A steel pendulum consists of a circular disk 10 in. in diameter and 1 in. thick, and a rectangular bar 30 in. long, 3 in. wide, and 1 in. thick, as shown in

Fig. 460. If the pendulum oscillates about a horizontal axis through O, what is the period of oscillation?   *Ans.* $T = 1.75$ sec.

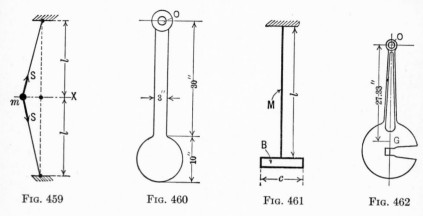

FIG. 459   FIG. 460   FIG. 461   FIG. 462

739. In Fig. 461 a disk B of unknown moment of inertia is suspended from a weightless wire M. A couple whose plane is horizontal and whose moment is 0.85 lb in. is applied to the disk, thus causing the wire to twist 10°. If the couple is released, the disk is observed to oscillate and to require 80 sec for 50 complete cycles of oscillation. Determine the moment of inertia of the disk.

740. The pendulum (Fig. 462) of a Charpy impact machine, which is used for testing materials under rapidly applied loads, weighs 50.5 lb, and the distance of the center of gravity from the axis of rotation, as determined by balancing, is found to be 27.33 in. When allowed to vibrate about the axis of rotation, the pendulum is observed to make 35 complete oscillations in 61 sec. Find the moment of inertia of the pendulum with respect to the axis of rotation.   *Ans.* $I = 8.85$ slug ft².

741. The connecting rod of a steam engine weighs 300 lb, and the distance of the center of gravity from the crank pin is found (by balancing) to be 50 in. When suspended from the crank-pin end and allowed to vibrate as a compound pendulum, it is found to make 30 complete oscillations in 75 sec. Determine the moment of inertia of the rod with respect to the axis of the crank pin and also with respect to a parallel axis through the center of gravity.

                               Ans. $I = 198$ slug ft²; $\bar{I} = 36.5$ slug ft².

742. Derive the differential equation of motion for the centrifugal pendulum of the dynamic vibration absorber described in Prob. 427, and determine the natural frequency of vibration. Assume the angular displacements of the pendulum relative to the disk to be small and the mass of the pendulum to be concentrated at G.

743. Liquid is placed in a U-shaped glass tube (Fig. 463), the total length of the liquid column being l. Pressure is applied to one side of the column, depressing it as shown, and the pressure is then suddenly released, allowing the column of liquid to oscillate. Assume friction to be negligible, and show by applying the equation of motion, $\Sigma F_x = ma_x$, to the liquid that $\dfrac{d^2x}{dt^2} = -\dfrac{2g}{l}x$ and that, therefore, the period of vibration is $T = 2\pi\sqrt{l/2g}$.

744. A body M whose weight is W (Fig. 464) is suspended from a cylindrical rotor by means of an inextensible cable. The rotor has a moment of inertia I about its axis of rotation O. The motion of the rotor is restrained by the spring S whose modulus is k. If M is given a small downward displacement and then is released,

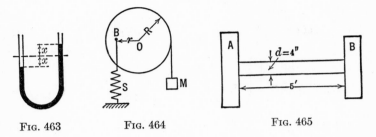

FIG. 463   FIG. 464   FIG. 465

determine, by use of the equation of motion, $\Sigma T_o = I_o \alpha$, the period of vibration.

$$Ans.\ T = 2\pi \sqrt{\frac{I_o + \dfrac{W}{g} R^2}{kr^2}}.$$

745. A Diesel engine whose flywheel and other rotating parts, represented by A in Fig. 465, have a combined moment of inertia of 600 slug ft^2, drives a generator whose rotor, represented by B, has a moment of inertia of 100 slug ft^2. The steel shaft connecting the engine to the generator is 4 in. in diameter and 5 ft long. The shearing modulus of elasticity of steel is $G = 12 \times 10^6$ lb/in.^{2} Neglecting the mass of the shaft, calculate the natural frequency of torsional vibration of the system.

$$Ans.\ f = 11.1 \text{ cycles per sec.}$$

746. A rectangular block floats in water with a depth of immersion d. The cross-sectional area of the block parallel to the water surface is A, and the weight of water per unit volume is w. If the block is given a small vertical displacement of y from its equilibrium position and then released, it will oscillate. If the inertia and friction of the water are neglected, show by applying the equation of motion, $\Sigma F_y = ma_y$, that $\dfrac{d^2y}{dt^2} = -\dfrac{g}{d} y$ and, hence, that the frequency of the oscillation is $f = \dfrac{1}{2\pi} \sqrt{\dfrac{g}{d}}$. In this problem the water is the spring; what is the spring constant?

747. The motor in Fig. 448 is supported by coil springs placed under the four corners of the motor frame. The variable torque on the motor produces a small rocking (angular) vibration of the motor in its supports; the axis of vibration may be assumed for small vibrations to be the same as the axis of rotation O of the motor. If the spring constant for each of the four springs is k and the moment of inertia of the motor and frame about O is I_o, show that the natural frequency of the angular vibration is $f = \dfrac{1}{\pi} \sqrt{\dfrac{kb^2}{I_o}}$.

748. Determine the frequency of vibration of the pendulum in Fig. 466 which consists of a stiff weightless bar of length l and a small body M whose weight is W. The spring constant for each of the two springs S, S, is k.

$$Ans.\ f = \frac{1}{2\pi} \sqrt{\frac{g}{l} + \frac{2b^2kg}{l^2W}}.$$

749. Assume the mass of the rigid bar AB in Fig. 467 to be negligible and the spring constant for the spring S to be k. Calculate: (a) the natural frequency of vibration of the system, and (b) the equivalent spring constant k_e for the system.

$$Ans. \ (a) \ f = \frac{1}{2\pi} \frac{b}{l-b} \sqrt{\frac{kg}{W}} \ ; \ (b) \ k_e = k \left(\frac{b}{l-b}\right)^2.$$

750. A simple pendulum 4 ft long swings through an angle of 60° (that is, $\theta_1 = 30°$). Find the period of oscillation: (a) by the approximate method, and (b) by the exact method.   *Ans.* (a) $T = 2.21$ sec; (b) $T = 2.25$ sec.

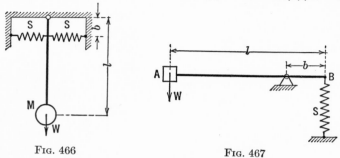

FIG. 466   FIG. 467

751. Find the length of a uniform slender bar having a period of oscillation of 1 sec when allowed to swing as a compound pendulum about an axis through one end of the bar.   *Ans.* $l = 1.22$ ft.

752. The moment of inertia of a body may be found experimentally by allowing the body to oscillate as a compound pendulum and observing the period of oscillation. Show from Eq. 19 that

$$I_o = \frac{WT^2\bar{r}}{4\pi^2}$$

in which I_o is the moment of inertia of the body about the center of oscillation, T is the period of a complete oscillation of the body, and $\bar{r}$ is the distance from the center of oscillation to the mass center of the body.

148   Free vibration with viscous damping. Free vibrations, that is, vibrations that are not maintained by driving or exciting forces, gradually die out because of the damping due to frictional resistance encountered during motion. In the analysis of vibration problems, the damping force developed is usually assumed to be proportional to the velocity of the body and is expressed as $-c \dfrac{dx}{dt}$, where c is called the damping coefficient. Thus, the frictional forces are assumed to be of the type developed by the viscosity of the oil in a dashpot; if a proper damping coefficient is assumed, this assumption usually yields satisfactory results even though other types of friction may be damping the motion.

If a frictional force equal to $-c \dfrac{dx}{dt}$ is added to the force system shown in Fig. 443, the force system will be as shown in Fig. 468, and the equation of motion for the resulting damped free vibration may be written as follows:

$$\Sigma F_x = ma_x$$

$$W - (W + kx) - c\frac{dx}{dt} = \frac{W}{g}\frac{d^2x}{dt^2}$$

which may be written

$$\frac{d^2x}{dt^2} + 2n\frac{dx}{dt} + p^2x = 0 \tag{29}$$

where

$$p^2 = \frac{kg}{W} \quad \text{and} \quad 2n = \frac{cg}{W} = \frac{c}{m}$$

An inspection of this equation indicates (as is shown below) that x must be such a function of t that each successive derivative of x with respect to t is equal to the original function times a constant. In a study of differential equations, it is found that the function $x = Ce^{st}$ satisfies this condition, where C and s are unknown constants to be determined from the initial conditions of the motion and e is the base of natural logarithms. It is important to note that the nature of this function of t depends on whether s is real or imaginary. If s is a negative real number and the displacement x has its maximum value when $t = 0$, then x will decrease and approach zero as the time t increases. If s is an imaginary number (or the sum of a real and an imaginary number), the displacement x will alternate from positive to negative values; that is, the motion of the body will be an oscillatory motion. The truth of these statements is easily shown. Thus, if $x = Ce^{st}$,

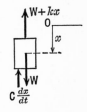

Fig. 468

$$\frac{dx}{dt} = Cse^{st} \quad \text{and} \quad \frac{d^2x}{dt^2} = Cs^2e^{st}$$

Hence, if these values of x, $\dfrac{dx}{dt}$, and $\dfrac{d^2x}{dt^2}$ are substituted in Eq. 29, the equation becomes

$$(s^2 + 2ns + p^2)Ce^{st} = 0 \tag{30}$$

and, hence, the function $x = Ce^{st}$ satisfies Eq. 29 if the conditions of the motion are such that

$$s^2 + 2ns + p^2 = 0 \tag{31}$$

Thus, there are two values of s that yield a solution of Eq. 29, namely:

$$s_1 = -n + \sqrt{n^2 - p^2} \quad \text{and} \quad s_2 = -n - \sqrt{n^2 - p^2}$$

The general solution of Eq. 29 then is

$$x = C_1 e^{s_1 t} + C_2 e^{s_2 t} \tag{32}$$

The damping of the motion, in accordance with this equation, results in two different types of motion, depending on whether n is greater than p or less than p.

For n greater than p. If $n > p$, the solution (Eq. 32) does not contain any terms that vary periodically with time. Hence, the frictional resistance is so large that the body when displaced does not vibrate, but gradually creeps back to the equilibrium position. When this condition exists, the motion is said to be *overdamped*.

If $n = p$ the body is said to have *critical damping* in which case $c/2m = \sqrt{k/m}$ and $c = 2\sqrt{km}$. This value of c is called the critical coefficient of viscous damping. For this condition $s_1 = s_2 = -n$, and Eq. 32 becomes $x = C_3 e^{-nt}$, which is not a general solution of Eq. 29, since it may be verified, by substitution in the differential Eq. 29, that $x = C_4 t e^{-nt}$ is also a solution. Hence, the general solution of Eq. 29 when the damping is critical is

$$x = C_3 e^{-nt} + C_4 t e^{-nt} = (C_3 + C_4 t)e^{-nt}$$

Critical damping has the particular significance that it represents the limiting damping above which the body gradually creeps back to the equilibrium position. The amount of damping present in a vibrating system is usually measured in terms of the critical damping as given by the ratio $c/2\sqrt{km} = n/p$ which is called the *damping factor*.

For n less than p. If $n < p$, the expressions for s_1 and s_2 become complex numbers and may be written

$$s_1 = -n + i\sqrt{p^2 - n^2} = -n + iq$$

and

$$s_2 = -n - i\sqrt{p^2 - n^2} = -n - iq \tag{33}$$

where

$$i = \sqrt{-1} \quad \text{and} \quad q = \sqrt{p^2 - n^2}$$

Thus,

$$x = C_1 e^{(-n+iq)t} + C_2 e^{(-n-iq)t} = e^{-nt}(C_1 e^{iqt} + C_2 e^{-iqt}) \tag{34}$$

By substituting in Eq. 34 the following mathematical relations, given in texts on calculus and trigonometry,

$$e^{iqt} = \cos qt + i \sin qt, \quad \text{and} \quad e^{-iqt} = \cos qt - i \sin qt$$

and simplifying, we obtain the equation

$$x = e^{-nt}(B \cos qt + D \sin qt) \tag{35}$$

in which B and D are constants such that $B = C_1 + C_2$ and $D = i(C_1 - C_2)$, and they are determined from the initial conditions of motion. The expression in parentheses is a periodic function of the same form as Eq. 4 for a free vibration without damping. Hence, it represents a vibratory motion with a period

$$T = \frac{2\pi}{q} = \frac{2\pi}{\sqrt{p^2 - n^2}} = \frac{2\pi}{p} \cdot \frac{1}{\sqrt{1 - \left(\dfrac{n}{p}\right)^2}} \tag{36}$$

For the majority of cases of vibratory motion the damping factor n/p is less than 0.2, and it will be observed that for these cases the period of the damped free vibration is practically the same as the period of un-damped free vibrations. If the initial conditions of the motion are such that $x = x_o$ and $v = 0$ when $t = 0$, Eq. 35 is found, by evaluating the constants B and D, to reduce to

$$x = e^{-nt}(x_o \cos qt) \tag{37}$$

The relation between x and t in Eq. 37 is represented graphically by the curve in Fig. 469.

The value of the factor e^{-nt} in Eq. 37 gradually decreases with time, and, hence, the amplitude of each successive oscillation is decreased in

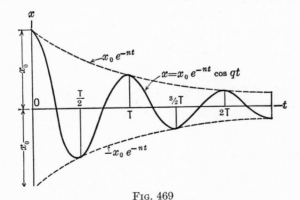

FIG. 469

the ratio e^{nT} to 1 where $T = 2\pi/q$ is the period of oscillation. This may be shown as follows: If x_r denotes the amplitude and t the time at the end of r complete cycles and x_{r+1} the amplitude at the end of $r + 1$ cycles, we have

$$x_r = e^{-nt}x_o \cos qt$$

$$x_{r+1} = e^{-n(t+T)}x_o \cos q\left(t + \frac{2\pi}{q}\right) = e^{-n(t+T)}(x_o \cos qt)$$

Hence,

$$\frac{x_r}{x_{r+1}} = \frac{e^{-nt}}{e^{-n(t+T)}} = e^{nT}$$

The logarithm, to base e, of this ratio is $nT = \dfrac{cg}{2W} \cdot \dfrac{2\pi}{q} = \dfrac{\pi c}{mq}$ and is

called the *logarithmic decrement*. The logarithmic decrement is equal to the difference in the logarithms of two consecutive amplitudes of the motion and measures the rate of decay of a damped free vibration.

It is seen that the ratio of consecutive amplitudes of a damped free vibration remains constant. Thus, if two consecutive amplitudes are 1.0 in. and 0.80 in., then the next amplitude will be 0.64 in., etc.

Illustrative Problem

Problem 753. In Fig. 470 is shown a body M of weight W connected to a spring S whose constant is 40 lb/in. M is also connected by a rod to a piston that moves in a dashpot B that is filled with a viscous fluid. The damping force due to the fluid resistance varies directly as the velocity of M and is equal to 50 lb when $v = 2$ ft/sec. The combined weight of M, the rod, and the piston is 100 lb. Find: (a) the damping coefficient, (b) the period of vibration, and (c) the logarithmic decrement.

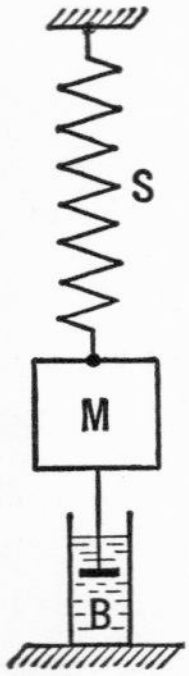

SOLUTION.   (a) The damping coefficient is

$$c = \frac{50 \text{ lb}}{2 \times 12 \text{ in./sec}} = 2.08 \text{ lb sec/in.}$$

(b) The natural circular frequency is

$$p = \sqrt{\frac{kg}{W}} = \sqrt{\frac{40 \text{ lb/in.} \times 386 \text{ in./sec}^2}{100 \text{ lb}}} = 12.4 \text{ rad/sec}$$

Hence,

$$n = \frac{cg}{2W} = \frac{2.08 \text{ lb sec/in.} \times 386 \text{ in./sec}^2}{2 \times 100 \text{ lb}} = 4.02 \text{ rad/sec}$$

Therefore,

$$q = \sqrt{p^2 - n^2} = \sqrt{(12.4)^2 - (4.02)^2} = 11.8 \text{ rad/sec}$$

and

$$T = \frac{2\pi}{q} = \frac{2 \times 3.142}{11.8} = 0.532 \text{ sec}$$

FIG. 470

(c) The logarithmic decrement is

$$nT = 4.02 \times 0.532 = 2.15$$

Problems

754. If the initial amplitude of the motion described in Prob. 753 is 4 in., what is the amplitude at the end of one complete cycle? *Ans. x = 0.47 in.*

755. Use the data of Prob. 753, and determine the least value of the damping coefficient that will cause an overdamped condition in the motion and hence will prevent a periodic motion. Find also the corresponding value of the damping force when $v = 2$ ft/sec. *Ans. c = 6.43 lb sec/in.; F = 154 lb.*

756. Assume in Prob. 753 that the damping force is 20 lb when $v = 2$ ft/sec and that the other data are unchanged. Find the period of vibration and the logarithmic decrement. *Ans. T = 0.507 sec; nT = 0.815.*

757. A body which has free vibration with viscous damping vibrates with a damped frequency of 10 cps. Determine the damping factor n/p if after an elapse of 4 sec the amplitude of vibration is reduced to 0.6 of its initial value.

758. In Fig. 470 the combined weight W of M, the rod, and the piston is 100 lb, and the constant of the spring S is 40 lb/in. If the viscous fluid in the dashpot is such that two consecutive amplitudes of vibration of the body M are 0.12 in. and 0.10 in., determine the coefficient of viscous damping for the dashpot.
Ans. c = 0.187 lb sec/in.

759. The weight of the moving parts of the field gun in Fig. 430 is 950 lb, and the recoil distance is 45 in. Assume that the barrel of the gun recoils against a spring whose constant is 8000 lb/ft and at the end of the recoil engages a dashpot that allows the barrel to return to its initial position in the minimum time without oscillation. Determine the critical coefficient of viscous damping for the dashpot.

149 Forced vibrations without damping.

The amplitude of a *free* vibration of a body depends only on the starting conditions, whereas a *forced* vibration, which is maintained by an alternating exciting force, has a frequency and an amplitude that are influenced by the frequency and amplitude of the exciting force. A slight eccentricity or lack of balance in rotating machinery may cause exciting forces that develop vibrations of large amplitude.

Two ways in which forced vibrations may be developed are shown in the conventionalized systems in Figs. 471b and 471d; namely, (I) a force P that varies harmonically with time may be applied directly to the body N of mass m and weight W, as indicated in Fig. 471b, or (II) the upper end of the spring may be moved vertically with a reciprocating displacement y that is assumed to vary harmonically with time, as indicated in Fig. 471d. The resulting free-body diagrams for the body N for the two cases are also shown in Figs. 471c and 471e.

Case I. The conditions assumed in Case I, for example, could be produced by attaching to an elastic beam (Fig. 471a), a rotor that revolves with an angular velocity ω and that has an unbalanced mass M at a distance r from the axis of rotation, thus causing a rotating unbalanced (centrifugal) force equal to $Mr\omega^2 = P_o$, the vertical component of which is $P_o \cos \omega t$. In this expression of the alternating or exciting force, P_o is the amplitude of the exciting force, and ω is its circular frequency, which in this case is the angular velocity of the rotor. The equation of motion, $\Sigma F_x = ma_x$, for N (Fig. 471b) then may be written

$$W - (W + kx) + P_o \cos \omega t = m \frac{d^2x}{dt^2} \tag{38}$$

This equation may be written

$$\frac{d^2x}{dt^2} + p^2x = \frac{P_o}{m} \cos \omega t \tag{39}$$

in which $k/m = p^2$.

Case II. Before Eq. 39 is solved, Case II will be considered. If the displacement x in Fig. 471e is measured from the position of static

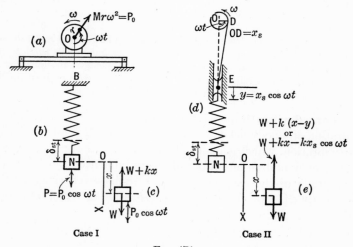

FIG. 471

equilibrium of the body N when the crosshead E is in its middle position, it will be noted that any additional extension of the spring is equal to the difference $(x - y)$ of the displacements of its two ends. The spring force acting on the body N is therefore $W + k(x - y)$. The equation of motion then becomes

$$W - [W + k(x - y)] = m \frac{d^2x}{dt^2}$$

Hence,

$$m \frac{d^2x}{dt^2} + kx = ky = kx_s \cos \omega t$$

or

$$\frac{d^2x}{dt^2} + p^2x = \frac{kx_s}{m}\cos \omega t \tag{40}$$

in which x_s is the maximum value of y: that is, the amplitude of motion of the crosshead. This equation is of the same form as Eq. 39, and the two equations are identical if $x_s = P_o/k$. It should be noted that the expression $P_o/k = x_s$ may be interpreted as the static elongation of the spring which would be produced in Case I by a load P_o. If this substitution is made, Eqs. 39 and 40 are identical.

It is convenient to visualize the forced vibration of the body N as being composed of a combination of a free vibration of the type discussed in Art. 144, plus a new motion caused by the exciting force. Let it be assumed, therefore, that the displacement $x = x_1 + x_2$, where x_1 is the displacement produced by the free vibration and is independent of the exciting force, and x_2 is the additional displacement caused by the exciting force. With this substitution we may assume Eq. 39 to be made up of two parts:

(a)
$$\frac{d^2x_1}{dt^2} + p^2x_1 = 0 \tag{41}$$

(b)
$$\frac{d^2x_2}{dt^2} + p^2x_2 = \frac{P_o}{m}\cos \omega t \tag{42}$$

These expressions, when added, give an equation that is equivalent to the original equation. It will be noted that Eq. 41 is of the same form as Eq. 3, and hence the solution for x_1 is of the same form as Eq. 4. Therefore,

$$x_1 = B \cos pt + C \sin pt \tag{43}$$

It is obvious that a function $x_2 = A \cos \omega t$ will satisfy Eq. 42 if the constant A (the amplitude) is properly selected. Substituting this function in Eq. 42, we have

$$-A\omega^2 \cos \omega t + p^2A \cos \omega t = \frac{P_o}{m}\cos \omega t$$

or

$$A(p^2 - \omega^2) = \frac{P_o}{m}$$

Therefore,

$$A = \frac{P_o}{m(p^2 - \omega^2)} = \frac{P_o}{\dfrac{k}{p^2}(p^2 - \omega^2)} = \frac{P_o}{k}\frac{1}{1 - \dfrac{\omega^2}{p^2}} \tag{44}$$

Thus, a solution for the forced vibration becomes

$$x_2 = A \cos \omega t = \frac{P_o}{k} \frac{1}{1 - \dfrac{\omega^2}{p^2}} \cos \omega t = x_s \frac{1}{1 - \dfrac{\omega^2}{p^2}} \cos \omega t \qquad (45)$$

in which $x_s = P_o/k$. Hence, the complete solution of Eq. 39 is found by combining Eqs. 43 and 45. Thus,

$$x = x_1 + x_2 = B \cos pt + C \sin pt + \frac{x_s}{1 - \dfrac{\omega^2}{p^2}} \cos \omega t \qquad (46)$$

and it can be verified, by substitution, that this solution satisfies Eq. 39 and Eq. 40.

STEADY-STATE FORCED VIBRATION. In most practical applications the free vibration represented by the expression $B \cos pt + C \sin pt$ in Eq. 46 is transient in nature, being gradually damped out by frictional resistances if the exciting force maintains a constant frequency and amplitude. Thus, the final, or *steady-state*, forced vibration which the body performs is represented by the solution for x_2 in Eq. 45. Thus, it is seen that the displacement x for a steady-state forced vibration is a cosine function whose amplitude depends on the ratio of the impressed circular frequency ω, of the disturbing force, to the natural circular frequency p for free vibration of the system. The maximum value of x (that is, the amplitude of the forced vibration) is $x_s \dfrac{1}{1 - (\omega/p)^2}$. Denoting this amplitude by A, we have then

$$A = x_s \frac{1}{1 - (\omega/p)^2} = x_s \frac{1}{1 - (f_1/f)^2} \qquad (47)$$

where $f_1 = \omega/2\pi = $ frequency of the exciting force in cycles per second; likewise $f = p/2\pi$. The ratio f_1/f of the frequency of the exciting force to the natural frequency of the system is called the frequency ratio. The ratio $\dfrac{1}{1 - (f_1/f)^2}$ may be interpreted as a *magnification factor*; for example, the force P_o if statically applied would produce a displacement x_s, but, when the alternating force varies with a frequency ω, the actual amplitude A of motion is increased in proportion to this magnification factor. Similarly, for the case of Fig. 471d, if the crank arm OD is revolved very slowly, the body N moves through the same displacement x_s as the upper end of the spring; but, when OD revolves with the angular velocity ω, the forced amplitude A of motion of the body is x_s times the magnification factor.

By plotting a curve showing values of the magnification factor as a function of the frequency ratio ω/p, as shown in Fig. 472, a complete picture of the amplitudes developed for steady-state undamped forced vibrations is obtained. It will be noted that, if the exciting force alternates slowly (ω/p smaller than $\frac{1}{2}$), the amplitudes of motion are only slightly larger than would be obtained if the force were applied

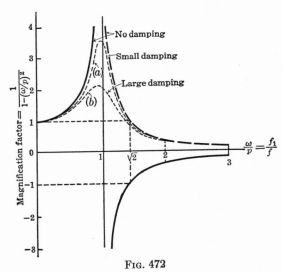

Fig. 472

statically (that is, A/x_s approaches unity). However, for values of ω/p in the neighborhood of unity, the numerical value of the magnification factor is very large, and, hence, the amplitudes of the forced vibration become dangerously large. When the impressed frequency ω coincides with the natural frequency p of free vibration, the system is said to be in *resonance*, and this is a condition that must usually be avoided in moving machine parts.

The speed of rotation of a shaft and the rotor attached to it at which resonance occurs is frequently called the *critical speed* for the shaft. In general, it is important to know the critical speed of a rotating member so that the speed of operation can be maintained either considerably above or below this dangerous (critical) speed, or so that the member can be designed for an operating speed that will not be too near to the critical speed.

For values of ω/p greater than one, the values of A/x_s become negative, and the exciting force is said to be 180° out of phase with the displacement. Physically this means that the exciting force is pushing upward with its maximum value when the body N is in its lowest position, and the force is always of opposite sense to the displacement. Usually this phase relationship is not of great interest, and the magnitude (but not the sign) of the magnification factor may be represented by the ordinate to the dashed line in Fig. 472.

For frequency ratios of ω/p greater than $\sqrt{2}$, the amplitude of forced vibration becomes *less* than would be obtained if P_o were applied statically. In fact, for ratios of ω/p greater than 10, the mass practically stands still in space (its amplitude of motion being less than about 1 per cent of x_s).

DAMPED FORCED VIBRATIONS. If Eqs. 38 to 47 were modified to take into consideration the small damping forces that are always present in actual machines or structures, the magnification factors obtained would differ somewhat from those obtained from Eq. 47 in which damping is neglected. The two dotted curves a and b in Fig. 472 show the values of magnification factor that would be obtained for a relatively small and for a relatively large viscous damping coefficient, respectively. The addition of damping does not appreciably affect the amplitudes of motion except near resonance, and the resonant frequency remains practically unchanged. Hence, Eq. 47 will also yield satisfactory results for most cases of damped forced vibrations in which the damping is relatively small.

TORSIONAL FORCED VIBRATIONS. Equations the same as the foregoing equations may be found for *torsional* forced vibrations, except that force is replaced by torque, mass by moment of inertia of mass, and linear displacements, velocities, and accelerations by angular displacements, velocities, and accelerations.

NON-HARMONIC EXCITING FORCES. In many problems in vibration the exciting force is not harmonic (cannot be expressed as a single sine or cosine function) but is an irregular periodic function of time. The engine torque of a 4-cycle Diesel engine, for example, is periodic but non-harmonic. Any periodic function of frequency ω, however, may be represented as the sum of a series of sine (or cosine) terms of frequency ω, 2ω, 3ω, etc., of a form such as $A_0 + A_1 \sin (\omega t + \phi_1) + A_2 \sin (\omega t + \phi_2) + \cdots$. Such a series is known as a Fourier series. The harmonic function of lowest frequency ω is called the fundamental or first harmonic, and the other harmonic functions are called higher harmonics. Thus, it is seen that there is a number of possibilities for resonance to occur when the exciting force is non-harmonic since, if the frequency of any of the harmonics of the force is approximately equal to the resonant frequency, a large amplitude of displacement would result unless the amplitude of that harmonic of the force is small. Fortunately the amplitudes of the higher harmonics of most exciting forces are small, and there is usually enough damping present in the vibrating system to prevent large amplitudes at resonance for these harmonics.

150 Vibration reduction. The engineering problem relating to vibration is frequently that of reducing a forced vibration. There are several methods of reducing vibrations, based on the principles discussed in the preceding articles, the more important being:

1. Removal of the exciting force, by balancing.
2. Tuning to avoid resonance.
3. Damping, usually by introducing frictional forces.
4. Isolation, by introducing elastic supports.

1. BALANCING. A brief discussion of methods of balancing rotating masses is given in the following chapter. There are several widely used machines for determining the dynamic unbalance of rotating parts and the masses that must be added to produce balance, and hence to remove (or greatly reduce) the exciting force.

2. TUNING. In order that large amplitudes of vibration may be avoided, machines are frequently designed so that they do not operate at or near the critical speed, the critical speed of a rotating body being identical to its natural frequency of free vibration. This process is called tuning. If the operating speed of a member is at or near the critical or resonant speed, even for a supposedly balanced member, a slight exciting force caused by deviations from assumed conditions will build up large amplitudes of motion. If a member is found to be operating near the resonant speed it may be detuned (I) by changing the frequency of the exciting forces through (a) a change in the speed of rotation, or (b) a change in the number of forced impulses per revolution of the member, as for example a change in the number of jets in a turbine; or (II) by changing the natural frequency of the member by adjusting the relative stiffness and masses of the moving parts.

3. DAMPING. If the operating speeds of an apparatus or machine that is subjected to forced vibrations involve a wide range including the resonant speed, damping (caused by introducing frictional forces) is frequently useful in reducing the amplitudes that would occur near the resonant speed. Damping has only a small effect on amplitudes except near the resonant speed. This is indicated in Fig. 472 by the decrease in the magnification factor for a damped forced vibration; the decrease in amplitude produced by the addition of a damping force of considerable magnitude is appreciable only in the neighborhood of the resonant frequency. An automobile that must operate over a wide range of

speeds and conditions of road is equipped with shock absorbers as friction dampers which limit the amplitude of resonant vibrations of the body of the car (sprung weight) induced by road irregularities. Damping caused by the friction in built-up leaf springs as the leaves slip against each other when the spring oscillates plays an important part in reducing the amplitude of resonant vibration of railroad cars on their springs.

On the other hand, the automobile engine is mounted on springs of relatively low modulus, so that the operating speed of the engine is very much above the speed of natural vibration of the assembly of the engine and springs, and hence damping is not needed since resonance does not occur. This method of avoiding resonance is called isolation of the vibration.

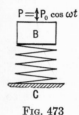

$P = \updownarrow P_o \cos \omega t$

B

C

Fig. 473

4. ISOLATION. When the exciting forces in a forced vibration of a body cannot be eliminated, it is necessary to resort to some method of isolating the vibration so that the periodic force reaction on the foundations or supporting frame is reduced. The usual method of isolation is to use some form of elastic suspension of the vibrating body. The term *transmissibility* is used to denote the ratio of the maximum force actually transmitted to the support through the spring (which is k times the stretch of the spring) to the maximum force that would be transmitted to the support with no elastic suspension; this latter value may be thought of as the amplitude of the exciting force.

The simplest type of spring suspension is indicated in Fig. 473 in which a body B, whose weight is W, is supported by a spring and is given an up and down forced vibration of amplitude A and frequency f_1. The transmissibility ϵ of such an undamped isolation mechanism is

$$\epsilon = \frac{\text{max. spring force}}{\text{max. exciting force}} = \frac{kA}{P_o} = \frac{k\left[\dfrac{P_o}{k} \cdot \dfrac{1}{1 - (f_1/f)^2} \right]}{P_o}$$

$$= \frac{1}{1 - (f_1/f)^2} = \frac{1}{1 - (\omega/p)^2}$$

where f is the natural frequency of vibration for vertical motion of the body B. It will be observed that ϵ is the same as the magnification factor for undamped forced vibration, shown in Fig. 472. In obtaining a value of ϵ its algebraic sign may be neglected, the minus sign merely indicating that the force transmitted to the support is out of phase with the exciting force. It is evident that, to be effective, ϵ must be less than unity, and experience shows that in most cases ϵ should not be greater than $\frac{1}{10}$, which means that f should be from $\frac{1}{3}$ to $\frac{1}{4}$ of f_1. If the constant k of the springs is such that the frequency ratio f_1/f is less than $\sqrt{2}$, the transmissibility ϵ will be greater than 1 (see Fig. 472). Thus, if the springs that support a machine are too stiff, it would be better to remove them and bolt the machine to its foundation.

Hence, if the body B (Fig. 473) represents a machine subjected to a forced vibration, which we desire to isolate by preventing the exciting forces from being trasmitted to the supporting structure, Fig. 472 indicates that the ratio $\omega/p = f_1/f$ should be made as large as possible, thus making the amplitude of motion approach zero. This is usually accomplished by using a very flexible elastic mounting (spring with a small value of k), in order to make the natural frequency, $p = \sqrt{kg/W}$, small compared to ω.

Similarly, to isolate delicate instruments from vibrations which may be present in the framework of a building, they may be placed on a heavy table that is suspended from the ceiling by flexible springs which deflect several inches under the weight of the table. For example, if the elongation of the springs is 2.44 in., the natural frequency of the system is

$$ f = 3.127 \sqrt{\frac{1}{\delta_{st}}} = \frac{3.127}{\sqrt{2.44}} = 2.0 \text{ cycles per sec} $$

Hence, if the impressed frequency of the vibration of the building is about 20 cycles per second, the magnification factor or transmissibility becomes

$$ \frac{1}{1 - (f_1/f)^2} = \frac{1}{1 - (\frac{20}{2})^2} = \frac{1}{99} $$

indicating that the amplitude of motion transmitted to the table is approximately 1 per cent of that present in the building.

Illustrative Problem

Problem 760. An automobile has main (helical) springs that are compressed 6 in. by the weight of the body of the car. If the axles of the wheels of the automobile are clamped to a test platform and the platform is given a vertical harmonic motion having an amplitude of 1 in. and a frequency of 1 cycle per second, determine the amplitude of the motion of the body of the car. Assume that there are no shock absorbers and hence that the vibration takes place without damping. Find also the maximum shortening of the spring.

SOLUTION. The frequency of the free vibration is $f = \dfrac{1}{2\pi} \sqrt{\dfrac{g}{\delta_{st}}} = \dfrac{1}{2\pi} \sqrt{\dfrac{386}{6}} = 1.28$

cycles per sec. Since $x_s = 1$ in. and $f_1 = 1$ cycle per sec, the amplitude A of the forced vibration is

$$A = x_s \frac{1}{1 - (f_1/f)^2} = 1 \times \frac{1}{1 - (1/1.28)^2} = \frac{1}{1 - 0.610} = 2.56 \text{ in.}$$

Since the frequency of the impressed motion is below the resonant frequency, the motion of the axles is in phase with the motion of the body of the car, and hence the change in the length of the spring is $2.56 - 1 = 1.56$ in. The maximum shortening of the spring therefore is $1.56 + 6 = 7.56$ in.

Problems

761. In Prob. 760 assume that the body of the car weighs 2400 lb and that the axles of the car are acted on by forces, the resultant of which is a vertical force that varies harmonically and has a maximum value of 40 lb. If the length of each cycle is 3 sec, what is the amplitude of the forced vibration?   *Ans.* $A = 0.107$ in.

762. A horizontal shaft rotates in bearings at its ends and has keyed to it at the center of its length a disk whose center of mass is 0.01 in. from the axis of the bearings. The weight of the disk is 193 lb, and that of the shaft may be assumed to be negligible. It is found that a static force of 2000 lb deflects the shaft and disk 0.1 in. (a) Calculate the resonant (or critical) speed of rotation of the shaft. (b) If the speed of rotation is one-half the resonant speed, calculate the amplitude of the steady state forced vibration.   *Ans.* (a) $\omega = 200$ rad/sec $= 1910$ rpm; (b) $A = \frac{1}{300}$ in.

763. A motor weighing 40 lb is mounted at the center of a simple beam as shown in Fig. 471a. The static elastic deflection of the beam caused by the weight of the motor is 0.01 in. A small body M weighing 0.11 lb is attached to the rotor at a distance r of 4 in. from the shaft. Assuming the weight of the beam to be negligible, determine the amplitude of the forced vibration of the motor when running at 1800 rpm.   *Ans.* $A = 0.123$ in.

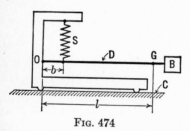

Fig. 474

764. In Fig. 474 is shown a device for measuring the vibrations of ships. Such a device is called a vibrometer. The vibrometer has a period of free vibration of 2 sec and is rigidly attached to a body C that has a vertical harmonic vibration with a frequency of 1 cycle per sec. If the amplitude of the motion of the body B relative to the frame of the vibrometer is 0.5 in., find the amplitude of motion of C. (*Hint:* The instrument is operating above its resonant frequency, and hence the amplitude of the motion of B relative to the frame is the sum of the true amplitude of B and the amplitude of C.)   *Ans.* $A_c = \frac{3}{8}$ in.

765. A refrigerator motor and compressor weighs 60 lb and is supported by springs whose equivalent spring constant is k. If the compressor operates at 600 rpm, determine the value of k in lb/in. in order that only 10 per cent of the shaking force produced by the compressor be transmitted to the supporting structure.

766. A radio which weighs 40 lb is located in an airplane cabin which is found to vibrate with an amplitude of 0.006 in. when the speed of the engine is 2000 rpm.

If the radio is supported by springs, determine the equivalent spring constant necessary to reduce the amplitude of displacement of the radio to 0.0004 in.

767. A centrifugal pump is driven by a 25-cycle induction motor. The shaft connecting the motor to the pump is 2 in. in diameter and is 10.5 in. long. It is made of steel whose shearing modulus of elasticity G is 12,000,000 lb per sq in. The moment of inertia of the motor rotor is 20 lb in. sec^2, and the moment of inertia of the pump may be assumed to be large so that the node N (see Fig. 457) for torsional vibration is located at the pump. The driving torque of the motor varies from zero to 6000 lb in. at a frequency equal to twice the frequency of the line current. Thus, at any time t the driving torque of the motor is $T = 3000 + 3000 \cos 2\pi \cdot 50t$. The maximum shearing stress in the shaft is given by the equation $s = 16T/\pi d^3$, where T is the torque in the shaft and d is the diameter of the shaft (see any textbook on strength of materials). Determine the maximum shearing stress in the shaft, and show that this stress would be *decreased* if a shaft $1\frac{1}{2}$ in. in diameter is used.

768. The main driving wheels of a locomotive are overbalanced by an excess counterweight of 400 lb in the wheel at a distance of 15 in. from the axis of rotation. A vertical vibration of the wheel is possible between the locomotive spring (whose stiffness is 15,000 lb/in.) and the track which may be assumed to have a stiffness of 140,000 lb/in. The wheel has a diameter of 72 in. and a total weight (including counterweight) of 8000 lb. Determine the forward speed of the locomotive at which a resonant forced vibration of the wheel would occur. What would be the amplitude of the vertical vibration of the wheel when running at 90 miles per hour? Assume that the wheel does not leave the track.

Ans. v = 177 mi/hr; A = 0.262 in.

769. A motor generator set weighing 2000 lb is mounted on four identical rubber pads placed under the corners of the frame. The speed of the motor is 1200 rpm. Determine the maximum allowable spring constant for each pad if the difference in the maximum and minimum values of the force transmitted through the pads to the building is not to exceed $\frac{1}{3}$ of the double amplitude of the vertical force impressed on the set by dynamic unbalance of the rotor.

Ans. k = 5120 lb/in.

Chapter 13

BALANCING

151 Need for balancing. A moving part of a machine, as a rule, has either a reciprocating motion similar to that of the crosshead of a steam engine or a motion of rotation such as that of the crankshaft of an automobile engine or the rotor of an electric motor. In any case, if the moving parts are accelerated, forces must be supplied to produce the accelerations. If the moving parts are not balanced, the accelerating forces which act on the moving masses are transmitted to them from the stationary parts of the machine such as the bearings and the machine frame. Likewise the moving parts exert equal and opposite forces on the frame of the machine or structure. These forces are frequently called inertia or shaking forces or kinetic loads. These accelerating and shaking forces may cause serious trouble, such as vibrations in automobiles and turbines; defective commutations in electric machinery; heavy bearing pressures which cause undue wear; defective work with grinding disks and high-speed drilling machines; and defective lubrication. It is of great importance, therefore, to neutralize or balance these forces properly in various types of machines.

The moving parts of a machine may be (1) in static or standing balance or (2) in dynamic or running balance. Standing balance exists if the forces that act on the parts, when the parts are not moving, are in equilibrium, regardless of the positions in which the parts are placed. Dynamic balancing consists in distributing the moving masses, or in introducing additional masses, so that the shaking forces exerted by the masses of the moving system on the stationary parts of the machine are in equilibrium among themselves and hence exert no resultant force on the stationary parts of the machine. The complete balancing of a machine, however, is not always practicable or possible.

The method of balancing rotating masses, only, is discussed here. Furthermore, the shaft on which the rotating parts are mounted is assumed to be rigid. If the elastic deflection of the shaft is considered, the rotating masses could be in balance only for one speed of the shaft. For methods of balancing reciprocating masses and for an excellent

discussion of the whole subject of the balancing of engines see Dalby's
Balancing of Engines.

152   Balancing of rotating masses.   The inertia forces or kinetic
loads exerted by the unbalanced rotating masses on the foundations or
other stationary parts of machines may be treated, in general: (1) as a
system of centrifugal forces or (2) as a system of centrifugal couples, or
(3) as a combination of the two systems.

A SINGLE ROTATING MASS.   CENTRIFUGAL FORCE.   If a shaft (Fig.
475a) rotates at an angular velocity ω and carries a single mass M_1, the
center of gravity of which is at the distance r_1 from the axis of rotation,
the shaft will be subjected to a kinetic load (which is equal to the

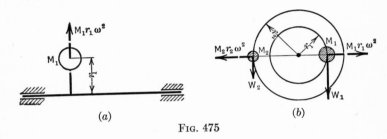

(a)   (b)

FIG. 475

centrifugal force of mass M) of magnitude $M_1 r_1 \omega^2$.   This kinetic load
causes the shaft to exert forces on the bearings which in turn are transmitted to the machine frame.   The reactions at the bearings may be
eliminated by balancing the rotating mass.   This may be done by the
addition of a single mass M_2 diametrically opposite to M_1 (Fig. 475b), the
center of gravity of M_2 being at a distance r_2 from the axis of rotation,
such that

$$M_1 r_1 \omega^2 = M_2 r_2 \omega^2 \quad \text{or} \quad \frac{W_1}{g} r_1 \omega^2 = \frac{W_2}{g} r_2 \omega^2$$

But, since ω^2/g is a common factor, the conditions for running or dynamic
balance may be expressed by the equation

$$W_1 r_1 = W_2 r_2$$

It is evident from Fig. 475b that this equation expresses the condition for standing balance also.   Thus, a shop method of obtaining
approximate running balance with a rotating member, in which the
material is substantially in a plane of rotation such as a disk, a pulley,
or a flywheel, consists in drilling out material on the heavy side or adding
material on the light side until standing balance is obtained.

Two Rotating Masses.   Centrifugal Couple.   If a shaft carries two rotating masses, M_1 and M_2, in different planes of rotation but in the same axial plane (Fig. 476) and, further, if the centrifugal forces $M_1 r_1 \omega^2$ and $M_2 r_2 \omega^2$ exerted on the shaft by the two masses are equal, the shaft is subjected to an unbalanced centrifugal couple which is resisted by an equal couple exerted by the bearings. Or, if the two rotating masses are to be balanced, two additional masses, M_3 and M_4, must be introduced in the same axial plane (Fig. 476) such that the centrifugal couple $M_3 r_3 \omega^2 b$ or $M_4 r_4 \omega^2 b$ which they exert on the shaft is equal and opposite to the centrifugal couple of M_1 and M_2.   Hence,

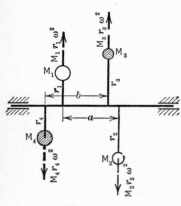

Fig. 476

$$M_1 r_1 \omega^2 a = M_3 r_3 \omega^2 b \quad \text{or} \quad M_2 r_2 \omega^2 a = M_4 r_4 \omega^2 b$$

And, as before, omitting the common factor ω^2/g, we may write

$$W_1 r_1 a = W_3 r_3 b, \quad \text{etc.}$$

It will be noted that the shaft when carrying only the two masses, M_1 and M_2, is in standing balance but not in running balance.

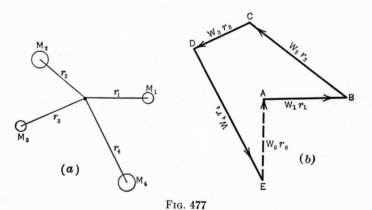

Fig. 477

153   Several masses in a single plane of rotation.   If several masses, M_1, M_2, M_3, etc., lie in the same transverse plane (Fig. 477a), the shaft is subjected to the centrifugal forces

$$M_1 r_1 \omega^2, \quad M_2 r_2 \omega^2, \quad M_3 r_3 \omega^2, \quad \text{etc.}$$

which form a concurrent system of forces.

The condition that such a force system shall balance is that the force polygon shall close. That is, the vectors representing the forces $M_1 r_1 \omega^2$, $M_2 r_2 \omega^2$, $M_3 r_3 \omega^2$, etc., if laid off in succession, each in its proper direction, shall form a closed polygon. Or, since $Mr\omega^2$ may be written $\dfrac{W}{g} r\omega^2$ and since $\dfrac{\omega^2}{g}$ is a factor common to the expression for each force, the products $W_1 r_1$, $W_2 r_2$, etc., may be used instead of the actual forces. Thus, let the four masses as shown in Fig. 477a be a system of masses that rotate in a transverse plane. Suppose that the products $W_1 r_1$, $W_2 r_2$, $W_3 r_3$, and $W_4 r_4$ when laid off as vectors (Fig. 477b) do not form a closed polygon. It is evident then that the four masses are not in running balance. In order to balance the system of masses, a mass M_o must be added at a distance r_o such that the product $W_o r_o$ is represented both in magnitude and in direction by the closing side EA of the vector polygon. By assuming a convenient value for r_o, a value of M_o may be found. The gap EA may be closed, however, by two or more vectors from which two or more masses may be found that will balance the system.

154 Masses in different transverse planes.

In Fig. 478 let the masses M_1 and M_2 be connected with the shaft at A and B, respectively, and through some point O of the shaft let a transverse plane, called a reference

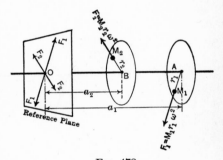

Fig. 478

plane, be chosen. The mass M_1 exerts a kinetic load F_1 on the shaft such that
$$F_1 = M_1 r_1 \omega^2$$

Now at O let two equal and opposite forces be introduced, each equal and parallel to F_1. The force F_1 at A and the equal opposite force at O form a couple C_1 the moment of which is

$$C_1 = M_1 r_1 \omega^2 a_1$$

Thus, the single force F_1 at A is replaced by an equal parallel force at O and the couple C_1. In like manner the single force, $F_2 = M_2 r_2 \omega^2$, at B may be replaced by the equal parallel force F_2 in the reference plane and a couple, $C_2 = M_2 r_2 \omega^2 a_2$.

Thus, the kinetic loads on a shaft exerted by a system of rotating masses may be reduced to a system of concurrent forces in an arbitrarily chosen reference plane and a system of couples which lie in different axial planes. The resultant of the system of concurrent forces, if not balanced, is a single force in the reference plane, and the resultant of the system of couples, if not balanced, is a single couple in some axial plane. Hence, in general, the system of kinetic loads, if not balanced, may be reduced to a single force and a couple. The moment of the couple will, of course, depend on the position chosen for the reference plane.

The conditions then that must be fulfilled to have a system of rotating masses in equilibrium are:

1. The resultant of the system of concurrent forces must be zero. That is, the force polygon for the forces in the reference plane must close.
2. The resultant of the system of couples must be zero. That is, the couple polygon must close.

These conditions may be satisfied by the addition of two rotating masses in different transverse planes. Thus, let the shaft (Fig. 479)

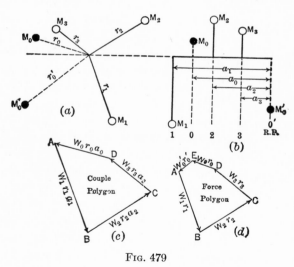

Fig. 479

carry an unbalanced system of rotating masses M_1, M_2, and M_3, and let the two balancing masses be denoted by M_o and M'_o. Let the transverse planes in which these balancing masses are to lie be chosen arbitrarily, but let the plane of one of the masses be chosen as the reference plane. The plane of mass M'_o will here be selected as the reference plane. Let a_o, a_1, a_2, and a_3 denote the respective distances of the masses M_o, M_1, M_2, and M_3 from the reference plane. The couples $W_1 r_1 a_1$, $W_2 r_2 a_2$, etc., may now be calculated (the common factor ω^2/g is omitted in each term for simplicity). The only unknown couple is $W_o r_o a_o$, since the couple $W'_o r'_o a'_o$ is zero, owing to the fact that the reference plane was chosen as the plane of M'_o, which makes a'_o equal to zero. If the vectors that represent the known couples as the sides of a polygon are laid off (see Art. 18), the closing side determines both the moment of the unknown couple $W_o r_o a_o$ and the axial plane in which it lies. By assigning any convenient value to the moment arm a_o, the product $W_o r_o$ may be found, and, by assuming a convenient value for r_o, W_o may be determined and placed in the plane indicated by the closing vector of the couple polygon. Thus, by the addition of the couple $W_o r_o a_o$, condition 2 is satisfied.

Condition 1 may now be satisfied as follows: The kinetic load due to the added mass M_o is replaced by a force in the reference plane and the couple $W_o r_o a_o$ as was done for the kinetic loads due to the original masses. Now, if the products $W_1 r_1$, $W_2 r_2$, etc. (including $W_o r_o$), are laid off as the sides of a polygon, the closing side gives the magnitude and the direction of a product $W'_o r'_o$ for a body W'_o which must be added in the reference plane to balance the system of concurrent forces in the reference plane and thereby satisfy condition 1. By choosing a convenient value for r'_o, the mass M'_o may be determined, and the direction of the closing side of the polygon gives the direction of M'_o from the axis of the shaft.

If the couple polygon is formed by drawing the couple vectors perpendicular to the planes of the couples, as explained in Art. 18, and then is turned through $90°$, it will be the same as the polygon formed by drawing the couple vectors according to the following rule: Draw the couple vectors parallel to the respective crank directions: outwards for masses on one side of the reference plane, inwards towards the axis for masses on the opposite side of the reference plane. The vectors of the force polygon are drawn, of course, from the axis outwards parallel to the radii to the masses. This method of balancing masses in transverse planes will be illustrated in Prob. 770.

155 Balancing of an elongated rotor. In the foregoing articles it was assumed that small bodies of known weights were attached by weightless rods to a rigid shaft, and the method of balancing was discussed. However, it is frequently necessary to obtain a running or dynamic balance for an elongated rotor: that is, one in which the mass is distributed longitudinally forming a cylinder such as is shown diagrammatically in Fig. 480. The rotor may not be homogeneous, and the distribution of mass may be unknown. In other words, the rotor cannot be conveniently replaced by a system of known masses located in different planes.

A shop method of obtaining a static balance for such a rotor consists of placing the axles of the rotor on parallel bars and allowing it to seek a position of equilibrium. Material may then be removed by drilling on the heavy side in any transverse plane (usually the ends of the rotor),

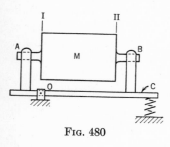

Fig. 480

or material may be added to the light side in any transverse plane until static balance is obtained.

Although an elongated rotor may be balanced statically by adding weights in a single transverse plane, it is necessary, in general, to balance dynamically by adding weights in two transverse planes. Furthermore, the mass center of the rotor may coincide with its geometric center, and, although it is said to be in static balance, it may not be in dynamic balance. The reasons for this may be made clear by referring to Fig. 476 in which the rotating body, consisting of the shaft and masses M_1 and M_2, may have its mass center coincident with the geometric center of the shaft and yet not be in dynamic balance, since there will exist an unbalanced centrifugal couple in a longitudinal plane.

One method that may be used to obtain a running balance of an elongated rotor is based on the theory of a forced vibration of a body without damping (Art. 149). Let it be assumed that the rotor M in Fig. 480 is to be balanced by adding (or subtracting) weights in planes I and II. Let the rotor be mounted in bearings at A and B which are rigidly attached to a horizontal plate C. The plate C is free to rotate in a vertical plane about a pin O which is located in plane I. If the rotor needs a balancing weight in plane II, the assembly will oscillate about the pin O when the rotor is given an angular velocity.

In Art. 149 it was found that, if a body is vibrating below resonance, the displacement is in phase with the shaking force. It follows that, if the angular velocity of the rotor is less than the natural frequency of the assembly, the right end of the plate will move up when the shaking force is up; the shaking force acting on the plate C being the unbalanced centrifugal force for the rotor.

Thus, if chalk is held above the rotor, it will scribe a line on the "heavy" side of the rotor, and material should be removed from this

side or added to the opposite side until a balance is obtained for plane
II. In a similar manner the necessary balancing weights for plane I
may be determined by placing the pivot O in plane II and scribing a line
on the left end of the rotor. When the balancing weights for planes I
and II have been added (or subtracted), the rotor will be completely
balanced.

Illustrative Problem

Problem 770. Three weights, W_1, W_2, and W_3 (Fig. 481), which revolve in the
planes 1, 2, and 3 are to be balanced by the addition of two weights. Plane 1 is
chosen as the plane of one of the weights (W_o), and the plane of the other weight

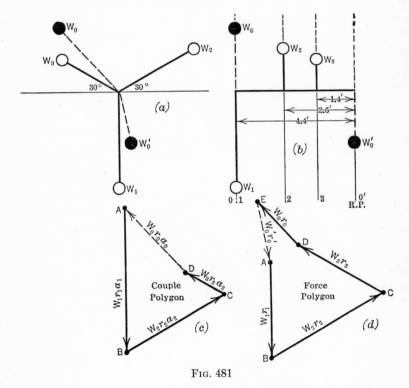

Fig. 481

(W'_o) will arbitrarily be taken 1.4 ft to the right of plane 3 and will be selected as
the reference plane. It is required to determine values of W_o and W'_o and the lengths
and directions of the corresponding radii for kinetic balance. The accompanying
table gives the values of the weights, the lengths and directions of the radii, and the
distances from the reference plane.

SOLUTION. From the given data, the values of the products Wr and Wra for the
known weights are calculated and entered in the last two columns of the table. The
couple polygon is then drawn as shown in Fig. 481c. AB is laid off in the direc-

tion of W_1 outward from the shaft, and its length represents to scale the value of the product $W_1r_1a_1$ which is 79.2. Next BC is laid off in the direction of W_2 such that its length represents to the same scale $W_2r_2a_2$ (62.4). Similarly CD is laid

Plane	Weight W (lb)	Radius r (in.)	Angle θ	Distance from R.P. a (ft)	Wr (lb in.)	Wra (lb in. ft)
1	2	9	270°	4.4	18	79.2
2	3	8	30°	2.6	24	62.4
3	3	6	150°	1.4	18	25.2
O	(1.36)	(8)	....	4.4	(10.9)	(48.0)
O' (R.P.)	(2.28)	(5)	....	0	(11.4)	....

off to represent $W_3r_3a_3$ (25.2). The closing side DA of the polygon represents the product $W_or_oa_o$ due to the balancing weight W_o in plane 1 (or O). This product is found by measuring to be 48.0. Hence,

$$W_or_o = \frac{48.0}{4.4} = 10.9 \text{ lb in.}$$

This product is now entered in the column of the table with the other Wr products. The addition of the weight W_o in the plane 1 at the distance r_o reduces the resultant couple to zero. There are left, however, the forces in the reference plane, including the force corresponding to the product W_or_o just found, and these forces will, in general, not be balanced. Now, if the vectors corresponding to these Wr products are laid off in order as in Fig. 481d, the closing vector EA represents the product $W'_or'_o$ which by measurement is found to be 11.4. If the values of W_or_o and $W'_or'_o$ are divided by assumed values of r_o and r'_o (8 in. and 5 in., respectively), we obtain the values, $W_o = 1.36$ and $W'_o = 2.28$. Hence, if weights of 1.36 lb and 2.28 lb are placed in planes O and O' at radial distances 8 in. and 5 in., respectively, as indicated in Fig. 481, the system will be in kinetic balance.

Problems

771. Five bodies are attached to a disk which revolves with constant angular velocity. In the accompanying table are given the weights of the bodies, the angles that the radii from the mass centers to the axis of rotation make with the X axis, and the lengths of the radii to the mass centers. The angles θ are measured counterclockwise from the X axis.

W	θ	r
5 lb	45°	18 in.
6 lb	120°	15 in.
10 lb	150°	12 in.
4 lb	240°	12 in.
6 lb	315°	18 in.

Determine sufficient data for kinetic balance of the system of bodies:

(a) By the addition of a single weight placed 2 ft from the axis of rotation.

(b) By the addition of two weights, one of 2 lb placed on the Y axis, and the other of 2.25 lb placed 2 ft from the axis of rotation.

772. Four bodies are attached to a revolving shaft in different transverse planes. The weights and positions of the bodies are indicated in the accompanying table, the reference plane being the transverse plane in which the mass center of the 6-lb body (W_3) lies.

W	θ	r	a
5 lb	30°	2 ft	−1 ft
4 lb	45°	1½ ft	2 ft
6 lb	150°	1 ft	0 ft
4 lb	240°	2 ft	½ ft

The given masses are to be balanced by two masses, one mass to be placed in plane 4 at a radial distance of 1½ ft, and the other to be placed in the reference plane at a radial distance of 2 ft. Find the weights and values of θ for the two masses.

Ans. $W_o = 2.93$ lb; $W'_o = 4.85$ lb.

773. The crankshaft of a gas engine carries two flywheels A and B, the planes of revolution of which are 3.5 ft. apart. The plane of revolution of the crank is between the flywheels and 1 ft 7 in. from the plane of A. The crank arms and pin are equivalent to a weight of 108 lb at a radial distance of 10 in. from the crankshaft and in the plane of revolution of the crank. What weights placed at a radial distance of 2 ft, one in each flywheel, will balance the crank? Solve algebraically.

Ans. $W_A = 24.6$ lb; $W_B = 20.4$ lb.

Appendix

FIRST MOMENTS AND CENTROIDS
MOMENTS OF INERTIA

§ 1 First Moments and Centroids

156 First moment. In the preceding chapters, moments of forces about points or axes have frequently been considered. In the analysis of many problems in engineering, however, expressions are frequently met that represent moments of volumes, masses,* areas, or lines. Since the mathematical procedure in determining the moment of a volume, mass, or line is precisely the same as that followed in determining the moment of an area, the further discussion of first moments and centroids will, for the most part, be confined to areas. An area, unlike a concentrated force, is a distributed quantity, and its moment about a line or axis cannot be defined as the product of the area and the distance of the area from the axis (similar to the manner in which the moment of a force was defined), since the different parts of the area are at different distances from the axis, and hence *the distance of the area from the axis* is indefinite and meaningless. The area may, however, be thought of as being made up of very small (differential) elements in a manner similar to the treatment of distributed forces (Art. 28), and the moment of an element of the area about an axis can then be defined as the product of the area of the element and the distance of the element from the axis. The moment of an area about a line or axis in the plane of the area may then be defined as the algebraic sum of the moments of the elements of area about the axis. Thus, the moments about the X and the Y axes of an area in the xy plane (denoted by Q_x and Q_y, respectively) may be defined by the equations

$$Q_x = \int y\, dA \quad \text{and} \quad Q_y = \int x\, dA$$

In a similar way the moment of an area, volume, mass, etc., with respect to a *plane* may be defined.

---

* For a definition of mass see Art. 91. As it is here used, it is sufficient to think of mass as the inert material or matter of which bodies are composed, the quantitative expression of which is the volume of the body times a density factor.

The moment thus defined is frequently called the *first moment* when it is desired to distinguish it from the moment of inertia (or second moment), since the distances of the various elements of area from the axis or plane with respect to which moments are taken enter into the expression for the first moment to the first power and into the expression for the moment of inertia or second moment to the second power. The first moment of an area is frequently called the *statical moment* of the area. Second moments will be considered in the next section.

SIGN, DIMENSIONS, AND UNITS. The sign of the moment of an element of an area about an axis may be positive or negative, according to whether the co-ordinate of the element is positive or negative. Likewise, the moment of an area about an axis may be positive, negative, or zero, according to whether the sum of the positive moments of the elements of the area is larger than, smaller than, or equal to the sum of the negative moments of the elements.

Furthermore, the dimensional expression for the moment of a line is length squared (L^2) expressed in such units as inch^2, foot^2. Similarly, the dimensions of the moments of an area and of a volume are, respectively, length cubed (L^3) and length to the fourth power (L^4).

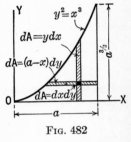

FIG. 482

Illustrative Problems

Problem 774. Find the moments about the X and Y axes of the area (Fig. 482) bounded by the curve $y^2 = x^3$, the X axis, and the line $x = a$. What are the numerical values of the moments if $a = 2$ in.?

SOLUTION. *First Method.* By taking as the element of area $dA = dx\, dy$, the moments of the area about the X and Y axes may be found as follows:

$$Q_x = \int y\, dA = \int_0^a \int_0^{x^{3/2}} y\, dy\, dx = \int_0^a [\tfrac{1}{2}y^2]_0^{x^{3/2}}\, dx = \int_0^a \tfrac{1}{2}x^3\, dx = \tfrac{1}{8}a^4$$

$$Q_y = \int x\, dA = \int_0^{a^{3/2}} \int_{y^{2/3}}^a x\, dx\, dy = \int_0^{a^{3/2}} [\tfrac{1}{2}x^2]_{y^{2/3}}^a\, dy = \tfrac{1}{2}\int_0^{a^{3/2}} (a^2 - y^{4/3})\, dy$$

$$= \tfrac{1}{2}[a^2 y - \tfrac{3}{7}y^{7/3}]_0^{a^{3/2}} = \tfrac{1}{2}[a^{7/2} - \tfrac{3}{7}a^{7/2}] = \tfrac{2}{7}a^{7/2}$$

Second Method. The moments of the area about the X and Y axes may also be found by selecting as the elements of area $dA = (a - x)\, dy$ and $dA = y\, dx$, respectively. Thus,

$$Q_x = \int_0^{a^{3/2}} y(a - x)\, dy = \int_0^{a^{3/2}} y(a - y^{2/3})\, dy = [\tfrac{1}{2}ay^2 - \tfrac{3}{8}y^{8/3}]_0^{a^{3/2}} = \tfrac{1}{2}a^4 - \tfrac{3}{8}a^4 = \tfrac{1}{8}a^4$$

and

$$Q_y = \int_0^a xy \, dx = \int_0^a x \cdot x^{3/2} \, dx = \tfrac{2}{7}[x^{7/2}]_0^a = \tfrac{2}{7}a^{7/2}$$

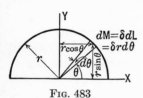

When $a = 2$ in., $Q_x = 2$ in.^{3} and $Q_y = 3.23$ in.^{3}

Problem 775. Find the moment, about the X axis, of the mass of one half of the homogeneous rim of a wheel (Fig. 483) in which the thickness of the rim is negligible compared to the radius r. The moment of the mass of the rim may be assumed to be the same as the moment of the semi-circular arc (line) times a density factor.

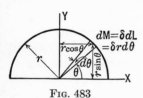

$dM = \delta dL$
$= \delta r d\theta$

FIG. 483

SOLUTION. The element of mass dM, expressed in polar co-ordinates, is the product of a density factor δ (mass per unit length of arc) and the length $dL = r \, d\theta$ of the element of the arc. Hence, the moment of the mass of the rim about the X axis is

$$Q_x = \int y \, dM = \int_0^\pi r \sin \theta \cdot \delta r \, d\theta = \delta r^2 \int_0^\pi \sin \theta \, d\theta$$

$$= -\delta r^2 [\cos \theta]_0^\pi = 2\delta r^2 = \frac{2}{\pi} Mr$$

where $M = \pi r \delta$ is the mass of the rim.

Problems

776. Find the moment of the area of a triangle of base b and altitude h, about the base of the triangle. *Ans.* $Q = \tfrac{1}{6}bh^2$.

777. Find the moment about the X axis of the area of the upper half of the circle $x^2 + y^2 = r^2$. *Ans.* $Q_x = \tfrac{2}{3}r^3$.

778. Find the moment of the volume of a right circular cone about the base. Express it in terms of r, the radius of the base, and h, the altitude of the cone.

779. The bending moment at any point in a beam that supports a uniformly distributed load is represented by the corresponding ordinate to a parabola whose equation is $y = C_1x - C_2x^2$, which is represented by the curve in Fig. 484. The moment of the area under this curve with respect to a vertical axis is used in obtaining the deflection of the beam. If $C_1 = 500$ and $C_2 = 50$, find the moment with respect to the Y axis of the area under the curve

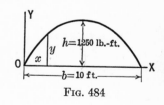

FIG. 484

between the ordinates $x = 0$ and $x = 5$ ft: (a) by the first method used in Prob. 774, (b) by the second method used in Prob. 774.

780. Determine the first moment about the Y axis of the area bounded by the curve $y^2 = 4x$ and the lines $y = 2$, $y = 4$, and $x = 0$. *Ans.* $Q_y = 6.2$.

781. Find the moment about the X axis of the area bounded by the curve $y^2 = 4x$ and the lines $x = 4$ and $y = 2$.

782. Find the moment of the volume of a hemisphere, of radius r, with respect to the base of the hemisphere. *Ans.* $Q = \tfrac{1}{4}\pi r^4$.

157 Centroids. The centroid of an area is the point in the plane of the area whose distance from any axis multiplied by the area is equal to the moment of the area about the axis. This definition expressed in mathematical form is

$$A\bar{x} = \int x \, dA \quad \text{and} \quad A\bar{y} = \int y \, dA \tag{1}$$

where A is the area and $\bar{x}$ and $\bar{y}$ (called centroidal distances) are the co-ordinates of the centroid with respect to the Y and X axes, respectively.

If the centroidal distances $\bar{x}$ and $\bar{y}$ for an area are known, the moment of the area can usually be found more conveniently from the expression $A\bar{x}$ than from $\int x \, dA$. The centroidal distances for many geometric forms of lines, areas, volumes, and masses are given in engineering handbooks, and it is important that the method of applying Eqs. 1 for determining the centroidal distances of such geometric forms, as are illustrated in the next article, be well understood.

Since $A\bar{x}$ would, by definition, be the moment of the area A if all the area were located (concentrated) at a point whose distance from the axis is $\bar{x}$, Eq. 1 may be interpreted as follows: The centroid of an area is a point at which the whole area may be conceived to be concentrated so that the moment of the concentrated area about any axis is equal to the moment of the actual distributed area about the same axis.

MASS CENTER. Although the term centroid as previously defined has been used in connection with masses as well as with volumes, areas, and lines, it is sometimes used in a restricted sense as applying only to geometrical figures (volumes, areas, and lines), in which no idea of mass is involved, and the term *mass center* or *center of mass* is used to denote that point of a physical body where the mass could be conceived to be concentrated so that the moment of the concentrated mass about any plane would be equal to the moment of the distributed mass of the body about the same plane. Hereafter, then, with reference to physical bodies the terms centroid and mass center will be regarded as synonymous. It should be noted that the centroid of a geometrical solid (volume) coincides with the centroid (or mass center) of a homogeneous physical solid (body) provided the two solids are congruent.

CENTER OF GRAVITY. Another term closely associated with centroid and mass center is center of gravity. The *center of gravity* of a body is generally defined as that point in a body through which the weight of the body acts, regardless of the position (or orientation) of the body. Now the weight of a body is the resultant of the parallel forces exerted on the particles of the body by the earth, and, since the weights of the particles are proportional to their masses, the center of gravity as previously defined coincides with the mass center. Hence, the terms mass center and center of gravity as applied to a physical body are usually regarded as synonymous and will be so used hereafter. The fundamental significance of the two terms should, however, be kept in mind, for, in finding the mass center of a body, the moment of a mass system is involved; and, in finding the center of gravity, the moment of a force system is involved.

By way of summary, then, the x co-ordinate $\bar{x}$ of the centroid of a line of length L, an area A, a volume V, or a mass M may be found from the following equations, respectively:

$$L\bar{x} = \int x \, dL; \qquad A\bar{x} = \int x \, dA; \qquad V\bar{x} = \int x \, dV; \qquad M\bar{x} = \int x \, dM$$

and the y and z co-ordinates may be found from similar equations.

158 Planes and lines of symmetry. If a geometrical figure (volume, area, or line) is symmetrical with respect to a given plane or axis, the centroid of the figure lies in the given plane or axis. This statement is evident from the fact that the moments of the parts of the figure on the opposite sides of the plane or axis are numerically equal but of opposite sign. If a figure is symmetrical with respect to each of two planes or lines, the centroid of the figure lies in the line of intersection of the two planes or at the point of intersection of the two axes. If the figure has three planes of symmetry, the centroid coincides with the point of intersection of the three planes. The foregoing statements apply also to the centroids of the masses of homogeneous physical solids which are symmetrical with respect to one or more planes. The centroids of many simple figures may be partially or completely determined from symmetry. It is well to note that axes of symmetry are always centroidal axes, but centroidal axes are not always axes of symmetry.

159 Centroids by integration. In determining the centroid of a volume, mass, area, or line by the method of integration, from the equations of Art. 157, it is possible to select the element of volume, area, etc., in various ways and to express the element in terms of either cartesian or polar co-ordinates. The resulting integral may be a single, a double, or a triple integral, depending on the way the element is selected. The integral, of course, is a definite integral, the limits of integration depending on the boundary curve or surface of the figure or body. In any case the element of volume, mass, area, or line must be taken so that:

1. All points of the element are the same distance from the line or plane about which moments are taken; otherwise, the distance from the line or plane to the element will be indefinite. Or so that:

2. The centroid of the element is known, in which case the moment of the element about the moment axis or plane is the product of the element and the distance of its centroid from the axis or plane.

The centroids of some of the common geometric figures (lines, areas, and volumes) will be found in the following illustrative problems.

Illustrative Problems

Find, by the method of integration, the centroids of the following figures with respect to the axes indicated.

Problem 783. Arc of a circle. The radius which bisects the arc will be taken as the X axis (Fig. 485). By symmetry the centroid lies on this axis. Hence, $\bar{y} = 0$. If r denotes the radius of the arc and 2α the subtended angle, then, in terms of polar co-ordinates, the element of arc dL and its distance x from the Y axis are $dL = r\, d\theta$ and $x = r \cos \theta$. Thus, the element of arc is selected in accordance with the first of the foregoing rules, and $\bar{x}$ may be found as follows:

$$L\bar{x} = \int x\, dL = \int_{-\alpha}^{+\alpha} r \cos \theta \cdot r\, d\theta = r^2 \int_{-\alpha}^{+\alpha} \cos \theta\, d\theta = 2r^2 \sin \alpha$$

Therefore,

$$\bar{x} = \frac{2r^2 \sin \alpha}{L} = \frac{2r^2 \sin \alpha}{2r\alpha} = \frac{r \sin \alpha}{\alpha}$$

If the arc is a semicircle, that is, if $\alpha = 90° = \pi/2$ radians, $\bar{x} = 2r/\pi$ (Fig. 486). That is, the distance of the centroid of a semi-circular arc from the center of the circle is slightly less than two thirds of the radius of the circle.

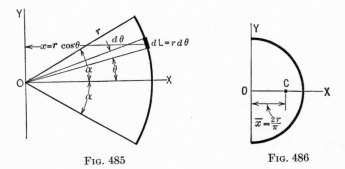

FIG. 485 FIG. 486

Problem 784. Area of a triangle. FIRST METHOD. In accordance with the first of the foregoing rules, the elements of area will be taken as strips parallel to the base of the triangle (Fig. 487). Since each element is bisected by the median drawn from the vertex opposite the base, the centroid of each element, and hence of the entire area, lies on this median. If x denotes the width of the strip, the area of the strip is $dA = x\,dy$. Thus,

$$A\bar{y} = \int xy\,dy$$

From similar triangles, the relation between x and y is $x = \dfrac{b}{h}(h - y)$. Hence,

$$A\bar{y} = \frac{b}{h}\int_0^h (h - y)y\,dy = \frac{1}{6}bh^2$$

Therefore,

$$\bar{y} = \frac{\frac{1}{6}bh^2}{\frac{1}{2}bh} = \frac{1}{3}h$$

The centroid of a triangle area, then, is on a median and at a distance of one third of the altitude from the base.

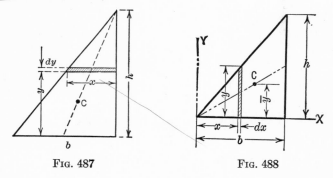

FIG. 487   FIG. 488

SECOND METHOD. In accordance with the second of the foregoing rules, the element of area will be taken as a vertical strip, as shown in Fig. 488. The moment of the element is $dA \cdot \dfrac{y}{2}$ or $y\,dx \cdot \dfrac{y}{2}$. Since $y = \dfrac{h}{b}x$, we have

$$A\bar{y} = \int \frac{y}{2}y\,dx = \frac{h^2}{2b^2}\int_0^b x^2\,dx = \frac{1}{6}h^2b$$

$$\bar{y} = \frac{\frac{1}{6}bh^2}{\frac{1}{2}bh} = \frac{1}{3}h$$

Problem 785. Sector of a circle. FIRST METHOD. The element of area will be selected in accordance with the first of the foregoing rules as indicated in Fig. 489. Since the area is symmetrical with respect to the X axis, the centroid lies on this axis, and hence $\bar{y} = 0$. The value of $\bar{x}$ may then be found from the equation

$$A\bar{x} = \int x\,dA = \int_0^r \int_{-\alpha}^{+\alpha} \rho \cos\theta \cdot \rho\,d\rho\,d\theta = \tfrac{2}{3}r^3 \sin\alpha$$

Therefore,

$$\bar{x} = \frac{\frac{2}{3}r^3 \sin\alpha}{A} = \frac{\frac{2}{3}r^3 \sin\alpha}{r^2\alpha} = \frac{2}{3}\frac{r\sin\alpha}{\alpha}$$

SECOND METHOD. In accordance with the second of the foregoing rules, the element of area will be selected as a triangle, as indicated in Fig. 490. The area of the triangle is $\frac{1}{2}r^2\, d\theta$, and the distance of its centroid from the Y axis is $\frac{2}{3}r\cos\theta$. Hence,

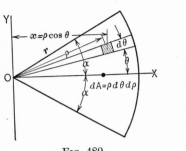

FIG. 489   FIG. 490

the moment of the triangle with respect to the Y axis is $\frac{1}{3}r^3\cos\theta\, d\theta$, and $\bar{x}$ is obtained from the equation

$$A\bar{x} = \int_{-\alpha}^{+\alpha} \frac{1}{3}r^3 \cos\theta\, d\theta = \frac{2}{3}r^3 \sin\alpha$$

Therefore,

$$\bar{x} = \frac{\frac{2}{3}r^3 \sin\alpha}{r^2\alpha} = \frac{2}{3}\frac{r\sin\alpha}{\alpha}$$

If $\alpha = 90° = \pi/2$ radians (Fig. 491), that is, if the sector is a semi-circular area, $\bar{x} = 4r/3\pi$.

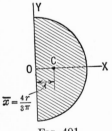

$$\overline{x} = \frac{4r}{3\pi}$$

FIG. 491   FIG. 492

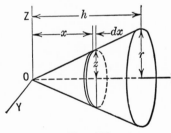

Problem 786. Find the mass center of a homogeneous right circular cone.

SOLUTION. Symmetry requires that the mass center lie on the X axis (Fig. 492). In accordance with the first of the foregoing rules, the element of mass may be taken as a thin cylindrical lamina or thin disk parallel to the base as indicated in Fig. 492. The volume of this element is $\pi z^2\, dx$ and, if the density be denoted by δ, the mass of the element is $\delta\pi z^2\, dx$. Hence, the moment of the mass of the cone with respect to the yz plane is

$$M\bar{x} = \int x\, \delta\pi z^2\, dx$$

From similar triangles, $z = \dfrac{r}{h}x$. Hence,

$$M\bar{x} = \frac{\delta\pi r^2}{h^2}\int_0^h x^3\, dx = \frac{1}{4}\delta\pi r^2 h^2$$

Therefore,

$$\bar{x} = \frac{\frac{1}{4}\delta\pi r^2 h^2}{\frac{1}{3}\delta\pi r^2 h} = \frac{3}{4}h$$

The mass center of a homogeneous right circular cone, then, lies on the geometric axis of the cone at a distance of $\frac{3}{4}h$ from the apex.

It should be noted that the mass center of a body (and also the centroid of the volume) is, in general, found from the expression for the first moment with respect to a plane and not with respect to a line.

Problems

787. A thin homogeneous disk of uniform thickness is 2 ft in diameter. How far from the center of the disk is the mass center of one half of the disk?

788. A pulley having a thin rim is 4 ft in diameter. How far from the center of the pulley is the mass center of one half of the rim?

789. Find the y co-ordinate of the centroid of the area included between the X axis, the curve $y^2 = x^3$, and the line $x = a$.   *Ans.* $\bar{y} = \frac{5}{16}a^{3/2}$.

790. Find the x and y co-ordinates of the centroid of the parabolic segment shown in Fig. 493. Select the element of area dA as indicated in the figure.

Ans. $\bar{x} = \frac{3}{5}a$; $\bar{y} = \frac{3}{8}b$.

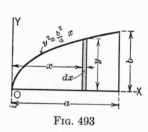

Fig. 493

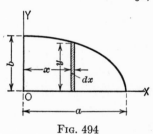

Fig. 494

791. Find the x and y co-ordinates of the centroid of the area of the quadrant of the ellipse $x^2/a^2 + y^2/b^2 = 1$ shown in Fig. 494. Select the element of area dA as indicated in the figure.

Ans. $\bar{x} = \dfrac{4a}{3\pi}$; $\bar{y} = \dfrac{4b}{3\pi}$.

792. Show that the centroid of the lateral surface of a right circular cone is on the axis of the cone at a distance of $\frac{2}{3}h$ from the apex, where h is the altitude of the cone.

793. Find the y co-ordinate of the centroid of the area under the sine curve $y = \sin x$ between ordinates corresponding to $x = 0$ and $x = \pi$.

Ans. $\bar{y} = \dfrac{\pi}{8}$.

794. Find the y co-ordinate of the centroid of the area bounded by the curve $x^2 y = 4$ and the lines $y = 0$, $x = 1$, and $x = 2$.

795. Find the centroid of the volume of the half cone shown in Fig. 495.

796. Find the z co-ordinate of the centroid of the volume of the hemisphere shown in Fig. 496. Select the element of volume dV as indicated in the figure.

Ans. $\bar{z} = \frac{3}{8}r$.

797. Locate the centroid of the curved surface of the hemisphere shown in Fig. 496.

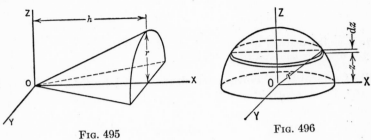

FIG. 495   FIG. 496

798. Find the centroid of the area bounded by the parabola $x^2 = \dfrac{a^2}{b} y$, the line $x = a$, and the X axis.

799. A paraboloid is generated by rotating the parabola $y^2 = px$ about the X axis. Locate the centroid of the volume included between the paraboloid and the plane $x = a$. *Ans.* $\bar{x} = \frac{2}{3}a$.

800. Find the y co-ordinate of the centroid of the area bounded by the curve $y^2 = 4x$ and the lines $x = 4$ and $y = 2$.

801. Locate the centroid of the area included between the Y axis, the line $y = b$, and the parabola $y^2 = \dfrac{b^2x}{a}$ as shown in Fig. 497. Select the element of area as shown in the figure. *Ans.* $\bar{x} = \frac{3}{10}a$; $\bar{y} = \frac{3}{4}b$.

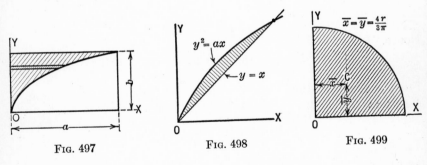

FIG. 497   FIG. 498   FIG. 499

802. Find the centroid of the area (Fig. 498) included between the curve $y^2 = ax$ and the line $y = x$.

803. Show that the centroidal distances for the area of a quadrant of a circle of radius r (Fig. 499) are $\bar{x} = \bar{y} = 4r/3\pi$.

804. The area included between the X axis, the curve $y^2 = x^3$, and the line $x = a$ is rotated about the X axis. Find the centroid of the volume generated.

805. Find the position of the mass center of a hemisphere in which the density at any point varies directly as the distance of the point from the base. *Ans.* $\bar{y} = \frac{8}{15}r$.

806. Find the mass center of a right circular cone in which the density at any point varies directly as the distance of the point from the base.

807. The density at any point of a slender rod of length l varies directly as the distance of the point from one end of the rod. Show that the mass center of the rod is $\frac{2}{3}l$ from that end.

808. Find the x co-ordinate of the centroid of the area bounded by the curves $y^2 = 3x$ and $y^2 = 6 - 6x$.

809. Find the centroid of the area bounded by the parabola $y^2 = 4x$ and the lines $y = 6$, $x = 0$, and $x = 4$.

160   Centroids of composite figures and bodies. As noted in Art. 157, if the centroid of a line, area, volume, or mass is known, the moment with respect to an axis or plane is most easily found by multiplying the line, area, volume, or mass by the distance of the centroid from the axis or plane. Thus, if a given line, area, volume, or mass can be divided into parts, the centroids of which are known, the moment of the whole line, area, etc., may be found without the use of the calculus method of integration, by obtaining the algebraic sum of the moments of the parts into which the line, area, volume, or mass is divided, the moment of each part being the product of that part and the distance of its centroid from the line or plane. Thus, for example, in the case of a composite area, if a_1, a_2, a_3, etc., denote the parts into which the area A is divided, and x'_o, x''_o, x'''_o, etc., denote the x co-ordinates of the centroids of the respective parts, then,

$$(a_1 + a_2 + a_3 + \cdots)\bar{x} = a_1 x'_o + a_2 x''_o + a_3 x'''_o + \cdots$$

or

$$\Sigma a \cdot \bar{x} = \Sigma(ax_o)$$

Hence,

$$A\bar{x} = \Sigma(ax_o) \quad \text{and, similarly,} \quad A\bar{y} = \Sigma(ay_o)$$

From similar equations the centroid of a composite line, volume, or mass may be found.

Illustrative Problems

Problem 810. Locate the centroid of the T section shown in Fig. 500.

SOLUTION. If axes be selected as indicated, it is evident from symmetry that $\bar{x} = 0$. By dividing the given area into areas a_1 and a_2 and by taking moments about the bottom edge of the area, $\bar{y}$ may be found as follows:

$$A\bar{y} = \Sigma(ay_o)$$

$$\bar{y} = \frac{12 \times 1 + 12 \times 5}{6 \times 2 + 6 \times 2} = 3 \text{ in.}$$

Problem 811. Locate the centroid of the volume of the cone and hemisphere shown in Fig. 501, the values of r and h being 6 in. and 18 in., respectively.

SOLUTION. The axis of symmetry will be taken as the Y axis. From symmetry

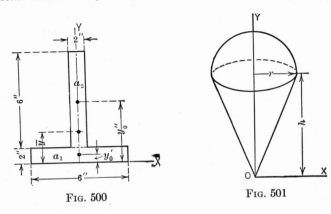

FIG. 500   FIG. 501

then $\bar{x} = 0$. If the X axis is taken through the apex of the cone as shown, the equation $V\bar{y} = \Sigma(vy_o)$ becomes

$$(\tfrac{1}{3}\pi r^2 h + \tfrac{2}{3}\pi r^3)\bar{y} = \tfrac{1}{3}\pi r^2 h \times \tfrac{3}{4}h + \tfrac{2}{3}\pi r^3(h + \tfrac{3}{8}r)$$

That is,

$$\tfrac{1}{3}\pi r^2(h + 2r)\bar{y} = \tfrac{1}{3}\pi r^2(\tfrac{3}{4}h^2 + 2rh + \tfrac{3}{4}r^2)$$

Therefore,

$$\bar{y} = \frac{\tfrac{3}{4}h^2 + 2rh + \tfrac{3}{4}r^2}{h + 2r}$$

$$= \frac{\tfrac{3}{4} \times (18)^2 + 2 \times 6 \times 18 + \tfrac{3}{4} \times (6)^2}{18 + 2 \times 6} = 16.2 \text{ in.}$$

Problems

812. A rectangular area 4 in. wide and 8 in. high has cut from it a semi-circular area the diameter of which coincides with one long side of the rectangle. Find the centroid of the remaining area.

813. From an area 8 in. square is cut out an isosceles triangle whose base coincides with one side of the square. If the centroid of the remaining area is at the vertex of the triangle, what is the altitude of the triangle?   *Ans. h = 5.07 in.*

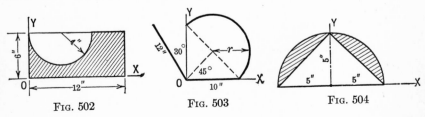

FIG. 502   FIG. 503   FIG. 504

814. Locate, with respect to the axes shown, the centroid of the shaded area in Fig. 502.

815. A wire is bent in the form shown by the heavy line in Fig. 503. Locate the centroid (or mass center) of the wire.   *Ans.* $\bar{x} = 4.42$ in.; $\bar{y} = 5.52$ in.

816. Find the centroid of the shaded area shown in Fig. 504.

817. The base of an isosceles triangle is 4 in. long. If the centroid of the area of the triangle coincides with the centroid of the three lines bounding the area, find the height of the triangle.

818. Locate, with respect to the axes shown, the centroid of the shaded area in Fig. 505.   *Ans.* $\bar{x} = 3.61$ in.; $\bar{y} = 5.24$ in.

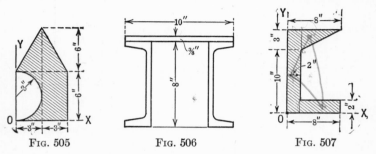

FIG. 505   FIG. 506   FIG. 507

819. Figure 506 represents the cross section of the end post of a bridge. The area of each channel section is 4.78 sq in. Find the distance from the top of the cover plate to the centroid of the section.

820. Locate, with respect to the axes shown, the centroid of the shaded area in Fig. 507.

821. A triangular corner whose area is 48 sq in. is cut from a square 12 in. on a side. What are the dimensions of the triangle if the centroid of the remaining area is 5 in. from one side of the square?

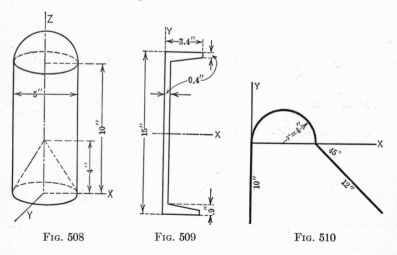

FIG. 508   FIG. 509   FIG. 510

822. In Fig. 508 is represented a homogeneous solid which consists of a hemisphere and a right circular cylinder from which a cone is removed. Locate the centroid of the solid with respect to the axes indicated.   *Ans.* $\bar{z} = 6.45$ in.

823. Find the centroid of the area of the channel section shown in Fig. 509.
$Ans.\ \bar{x} = 0.79$ in.

824. A slender steel rod is bent in the form shown in Fig. 510. Locate the centroid of the rod with respect to the axes shown. $Ans.\ \bar{x} = 5.70$ in.; $\bar{y} = -1.99$ in.

825. A homogeneous cube each edge of which is b in. long rests on a horizontal plane. On top of the cube is placed a homogeneous right circular cone having a base of diameter b in. and an altitude of b in., the base of the cone resting on the upper face of the cube. Find the distance of the center of gravity of the two bodies above the horizontal plane.
$Ans.\ 0.65b.$

826. The body of a car weighs 1000 lb and is mounted on 4 wheels, each of which weighs 100 lb, the total weight of the car being 1400 lb. The center of gravity of the car is 12 in. above the plane of the wheel axles. If each wheel is replaced by a wheel weighing 200 lb, locate the center of gravity of the car with respect to the plane of the wheel axles.

827. The shovel shown in Fig. 511 is made of steel plate of uniform thickness. Locate the center of gravity of the shovel with respect to the axes shown in the figure.

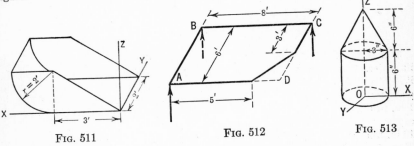

FIG. 511   FIG. 512   FIG. 513

828. If the top of the table (Fig. 512) weighs 40 lb per sq ft, find the reaction of the floor on each of the three legs at the corners A, B, and C. Neglect the weights of the legs. $Ans.\ A = 810$ lb; $B = 127.5$ lb; $C = 802.5$ lb.

829. In Fig. 513 find the z co-ordinate of the centroid of the lateral area of the cylinder and cone. $Ans.\ \bar{z} = 4.79$ in.

830. Three particles of equal mass are placed at the vertices of a triangle. Show that the mass center of the particles coincides with the centroid of the area of the triangle.

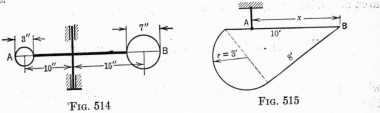

FIG. 514   FIG. 515

831. Two homogeneous spheres A and B, connected by a rod, are mounted on a vertical axis as shown in Fig. 514. The weights of the spheres are 20 lb and 50 lb, respectively, and the weight of the rod is 10 lb. How far from the axis is the center of gravity of the three bodies? $Ans.\ \bar{x} = 7.06$ in.

832. The plate in Fig. 515 has uniform thickness and is suspended by a cable attached at point A. What must be the distance x in order that the edge AB be horizontal?

833. If the cone in Fig. 513 has a density two times that of the cylinder, find the mass center of the body consisting of the cone and cylinder.   *Ans.* $\bar{z} = 4.8$ in.

834. Four bodies, A, B, C, and D, are carried by a rotating shaft as shown in Fig. 516. The weights of the bodies are 20, 15, 12, and 8 lb, respectively, and the distances of their centers of gravity from the axis of the shaft are 12, 6, 5, and 10 in., respectively. Find the center of gravity of the four bodies when in the positions shown.

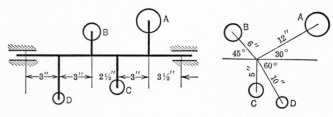

FIG. 516

835. A flywheel is 2 ft in diameter and is mounted on a horizontal axle through its center. The flywheel is balanced; that is, when turned on its shaft to any position, it is in equilibrium. A hole 1 in. in diameter and ½ in. deep is drilled on a vertical diameter of the flywheel and 6 in. from the center of the flywheel. Another hole 1 in. in diameter and 1 in. deep is drilled on a horizontal diameter 8 in. from the center. If the flywheel is to be balanced by drilling a hole 1 in. in diameter and 10 in. from the center, what should be the depth of the hole, and on what diameter of the flywheel should the hole be drilled?

161 Theorems of Pappus and Guldinus.
I. The area of a surface of revolution generated by revolving a plane curve about any non-intersecting axis in its plane is equal to the product of the length of the curve and the length of the path described by the centroid of the curve.

Proof. Let the curve AB (Fig. 517) be revolved about OX. The area of the surface generated is given by the equation

$$A = \int 2\pi y \cdot dL = 2\pi \int y \, dL = 2\pi \bar{y} \cdot L$$

where $\bar{y}$ is the distance of the centroid of the curve from OX and L is the length of the curve.

II. The volume of the solid generated by revolving any plane area about any non-intersecting line in its plane is the product of the area and the length of the path described by the centroid of the area.

Proof. Let the plane area A (Fig. 518) be rotated about the axis OX.

Each elementary area dA will generate a circular ring the volume of

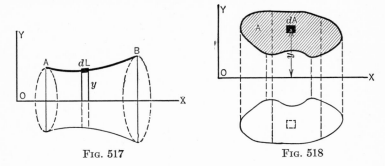

FIG. 517   FIG. 518

which is $2\pi y \, dA$, and hence the entire volume generated is given by the equation

$$V = \int 2\pi y \, dA = 2\pi \int y \, dA = 2\pi \bar{y} \cdot A$$

where $\bar{y}$ is the distance of the centroid of the area from OX.

Illustrative Problems

Problem 836. Show that the area of the surface of a hemisphere generated by rotating the quadrant of a circle (shown in Fig. 519) about the X axis is $2\pi r^2$.

SOLUTION.

$$A = L \cdot 2\pi \bar{y} = \frac{2\pi r}{4} \times 2\pi \times \frac{2r}{\pi} = 2\pi r^2 \quad \text{(see Prob. 783)}$$

Problem 837. A V-shaped groove is turned out of a cylinder as indicated by Fig. 520. Find the volume of the material removed.

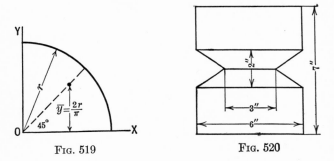

FIG. 519   FIG. 520

SOLUTION. The distance of the centroid of the triangle, which generates the volume, from the axis of the cylinder is 2.5 in., and the area of the triangle is 1.5 sq in. Hence,

$$V = A \cdot 2\pi \bar{x} = 1.5 \times 2\pi \times 2.5 = 23.55 \text{ cu in.}$$

Problems

Solve the following problems by the theorems of Pappus and Guldinus:

838. Find, in terms of the radius, the surface area and the volume of a sphere.

839. An area in the xy plane is bounded by the lines $x = 0$, $x = 6$, $y = 6$, and $2y = x$. Find the x co-ordinate of the centroid of the area. Find also the volume of the solid generated by rotating the area about the Y axis.

Ans. $\bar{x} = 2\frac{2}{3}$ in.; $V = 452$ cu in.

840. Find the lateral surface and the volume of a cone. Express the results in terms of the radius of the base and the altitude of the cone.

841. The center of a circle which lies in the xy plane and has a radius r is at a distance a from the Y axis. The solid generated by rotating the circle about the Y axis is a torus (or anchor ring) provided that a is greater than r. Find the surface area and the volume of the solid. *Ans.* $A = 4\pi^2 ar$; $V = 2\pi^2 ar^2$.

842. Find the lateral area of the solid generated by revolving the square shown in Fig. 521 about the Y axis through an angle of $90°$. *Ans.* $A = 603$ sq in.

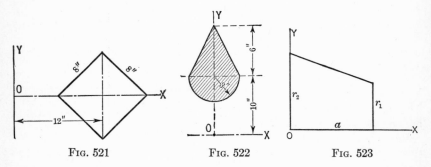

FIG. 521   FIG. 522   FIG. 523

843. Find the volume generated by revolving the shaded area shown in Fig. 522 about the X axis.

844. Find the y co-ordinate of the centroid of the trapezoid shown in Fig. 523. Determine the volume of the frustum of a cone generated by revolving the trapezoid about the X axis.

845. An isosceles triangle whose two equal sides are each c and whose base is b is rotated $360°$ about the base. Find the surface area generated by the sides of the triangle and the volume generated by the area of the triangle.

$$\text{Ans. } A = \pi c\sqrt{4c^2 - b^2};\ V = \frac{\pi b}{12}(4c^2 - b^2).$$

846. Determine the area of the surface generated by revolving the line shown in Fig. 510 about the Y axis.

847. Determine the volume generated by revolving the shaded area shown in Fig. 504 about the X axis.

848. Find the volume of the ellipsoid generated by revolving the right half of the ellipse $x^2/a^2 + y^2/b^2 = 1$ about the Y axis. *Ans.* $V = \frac{4}{3}\pi a^2 b$.

849. A $90°$ pipe elbow has an internal diameter of 24 in. The radius of curvature of the center of the pipe is 36 in. Determine the internal volume of the pipe elbow.

162 Graphical method of determining centroids of areas. If the boundary of an area is an irregular curve which cannot be represented by an equation, the centroid cannot be determined by the calculus method of integration. In such cases, however, the centroid may be determined by a graphical method which makes use of the force and string polygons. The irregular area is drawn to scale and is then divided into a large number of narrow strips parallel to one co-ordinate axis, the areas of which can be determined or estimated closely. These strips of area are then thought of as having weight and are replaced by a parallel force system in which the magnitude of each force is numerically equal to the area of the corresponding strip and acts vertically downward through the center of the strip. Now, by use of a force and a string polygon, a point on the action line of the resultant of the parallel force system is found as in Prob. 77, and the centroid of the area lies on a vertical line through this point. The distance of this line from the co-ordinate axis that is parallel to the strips gives one co-ordinate of the centroid. By dividing the area into strips parallel to the other co-ordinate axis and repeating the process, the other co-ordinate of the centroid is found.

163 Determination of center of gravity by experiment. When a body is irregular in shape, the center of gravity cannot be found by the method of integration, since the limits of the integral cannot be determined. The center of gravity of such a body, however, may be determined by the following experimental methods.

METHOD OF SUSPENSION. If a body be suspended by a cord, the center of gravity is on the (vertical) line coinciding with the axis of the cord. This statement follows from the fact that the two forces which hold the body in equilibrium (the upward tension in the cord and the downward earth pull) must be equal, opposite, and collinear, and the earth pull or weight of the body, of course, acts through the center of gravity of the body. Hence, if a body be suspended from each of two points, the center of gravity will be located in each of two lines in the body and hence is at the point of intersection of the two lines.

METHOD OF BALANCING. If a body be balanced on a knife edge the center of gravity of the body will be in a vertical plane through the knife edge. Hence, if the body be balanced on a knife edge in three different positions, three such planes in the body will be located, and the center of gravity of the body is the point in which the three planes intersect.

§ 2 Moments of Inertia of Areas

164 Moment of inertia of an area defined. In the analysis of many engineering problems, as, for example, in determining the stresses in a beam, expressions of the form $\int x^2 \, dA$ are frequently met, in which

dA represents an element of an area A, and x is the distance of the element from some axis in, or perpendicular to, the plane of the area, the limits of integration being such that each element of the area is included in the integration.   An expression of this form is called the *second moment* of the area or the *moment of inertia* of the area with respect to the given axis.   The moment of inertia of an area with respect to an

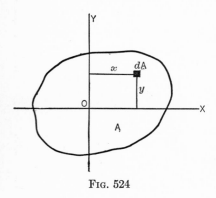

Fig. 524

axis may then be defined as the sum of the products obtained by multiplying each element of the area by the square of its distance from the given axis.

The moment of inertia of an area with respect to an axis will be denoted by I for an axis in the plane of the area and by J for an axis perpendicular to the plane of the area.   The particular axis about which the moment of inertia is taken will be denoted by subscripts.

Thus, the moments of inertia of the area A (Fig. 524) with respect to the X and Y axes are expressed as follows:

$$I_x = \int y^2 \, dA \quad \text{and} \quad I_y = \int x^2 \, dA$$

UNITS AND SIGN.   Since the moment of inertia of an area is the sum of terms, each of which is the product of an area and the square of a distance, the moment of inertia of an area is expressed as a length to the fourth power.   If, then, the inch (or foot) be taken as the unit of length, the moment of inertia will be expressed as inches (or feet) to the fourth power (written in.^{4} or ft^4).   Furthermore, the sign of each of the products $x^2 \, dA$ is always positive since x^2 is always positive, whether x is positive or negative, and dA is essentially positive.   Therefore, the moment of inertia, or second moment, of an area is always positive.   In this respect it differs from the first moment of an area, which may be positive, negative, or zero, depending on the position of the moment axis.

165   Polar moment of inertia.   The moment of inertia of an area with respect to a line perpendicular to the plane of the area is called the *polar moment of inertia* of the area and, as noted in Art. 164, will be denoted by J.   Thus, the polar moment of inertia, with respect to the Z axis, of an area in the xy plane (Fig. 525) may be expressed as follows:

$$J_z = \int r^2 \, dA = \int (x^2 + y^2) \, dA = \int x^2 \, dA + \int y^2 \, dA$$

Therefore,

$$J_z = I_y + I_x$$

Hence, the following proposition may be stated:

> The polar moment of inertia of an area with respect to any axis is equal to the sum of the moments of inertia of the area with respect to any two rectangular axes in the plane of the area that intersect on the given polar axis.

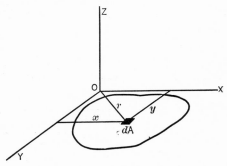

FIG. 525

166   Radius of gyration. Since the moment of inertia of an area is dimensionally a length to the fourth power, it may be expressed as the product of the total area A and the square of a distance k. Thus:

$$I_x = \int y^2 \, dA = A k_x^2 \quad \text{and} \quad J_z = \int r^2 \, dA = A k_z^2$$

The distance k is called the radius of gyration of the area with respect to the axis, the subscript denoting the axis with respect to which the moment of inertia is taken. The radius of gyration of an area with respect to an axis, then, may be regarded as the distance from the axis at which the area may be conceived to be concentrated and have the same moment of inertia with respect to the axis as does the actual (or distributed) area.

From the equation $I_y = \int x^2 \, dA = A k_y^2$, it will be noted that k_y^2,

the square of the radius of gyration with respect to the Y axis, is the mean of the squares of the distances, from the Y axis, of the equal elements of area into which the given area may be divided, and that it is *not* the square of the mean of these distances. The mean distance ($\bar{x}$) of the elements of area from the Y axis is the centroidal distance as discussed in Section 1.   Hence, $A\bar{x}^2$ does *not* represent the moment of inertia of an area with respect to the Y axis.   In other words, the mean of the squares of various lengths is *not* equal to the square of the mean of these lengths.

167   Parallel-axis theorem for areas.   If the moment of inertia of an area with respect to a centroidal axis in the plane of the area is known, the moment of inertia with respect to any parallel axis in the plane may be determined, without integrating, by means of a proposition which may be established as follows: In Fig. 526 let YY be any axis through the centroid C of an area, and let $Y'Y'$ be any axis parallel to

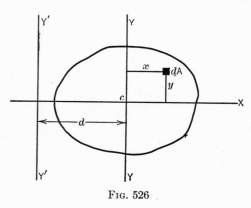

FIG. 526

YY and at a distance d therefrom.   Furthermore, let the moment of inertia of the area with respect to the axis YY be denoted by $\bar{I}$ and the moment of inertia with respect to $Y'Y'$ by I.   By definition, then,

$$I = \int (x + d)^2 \, dA$$

$$= \int x^2 \, dA + 2d \int x \, dA + d^2 \int dA$$

Therefore,

$$I = \bar{I} + Ad^2 \quad \text{since} \quad \int x \, dA = A\bar{x} = 0$$

Hence the following proposition may be stated:

> The moment of inertia of an area with respect to any axis in the plane of the area is equal to the moment of inertia of the area with respect to a parallel centroidal axis plus the product of the area and the square of the distance between the two axes.

This proposition is called the *parallel-axis theorem.*

A corresponding relation exists between the radii of gyration of the area with respect to two parallel axes, one of which passes through the centroid of the area. For, by replacing I by Ak^2 and $\bar{I}$ by $A\bar{k}^2$, the above equation becomes

$$Ak^2 = A\bar{k}^2 + Ad^2$$

whence

$$k^2 = \bar{k}^2 + d^2$$

where k denotes the radius of gyration of the area with respect to any axis in the plane of the area and $\bar{k}$ denotes the radius of gyration of the area with respect to a parallel centroidal axis.

Similarly, for polar moments of inertia and radii of gyration, it can be shown that

$$J = \bar{J} + Ad^2$$

and

$$k^2 = \bar{k}^2 + d^2$$

where $\bar{J}$ and $\bar{k}$ denote the polar moment of inertia and radius of gyration, respectively, of the area with respect to a centroidal axis, and J and k denote the polar moment of inertia and radius of gyration, respectively, of the area with respect to an axis parallel to the centroidal axis and at a distance d therefrom.

168 Moments of inertia by integration. In determining the moment of inertia of a plane area with respect to a line, from the equations of Art. 164, it is possible to select the element of area in various ways and to express the area of the element in terms of either Cartesian or polar co-ordinates. Furthermore, the integral may be either a single or a double integral, depending on the way in which the element of area is selected; the limits of integration are determined, of course, from the boundary curve of the area. In any case, however, the elementary area must be taken so that:

1. All points in the element are equally distant from the axis with respect to which the moment of inertia is to be found; otherwise, the distance x in the expression $x^2\, dA$ would be indefinite. Or so that

2. The moment of inertia of the element, with respect to the axis about which the moment of inertia of the whole area is to be found, is known; the moment of inertia of the area is then found by summing up the moments of inertia of the elements. Or so that

3. The centroid of the element is known and also the moment of inertia of the element with respect to an axis which passes through the centroid of the element and is parallel to the given axis; the moment of

inertia of the element may then be expressed by means of the parallel-axis theorem.

The moments of inertia of some of the simple areas will now be found in the following illustrative problems.

Illustrative Problems

Problem 850. Determine the moment of inertia of a rectangle, in terms of its base b and altitude h, with respect to: (a) a centroidal axis parallel to the base, and (b) an axis coinciding with the base.

SOLUTION. (a) *Centroidal Axis.* The element of area will be selected in accordance with rule 1 of Art. 168, as indicated in Fig. 527. The moment of inertia of the rectangular area with respect to the centroidal axis, then, is

$$\bar{I}_x = \int y^2 \, dA = \int_{-h/2}^{+h/2} y^2 b \, dy = \tfrac{1}{12} b h^3$$

(b) *Axis Coinciding with the Base.* The student should show by integration that the moment of the rectangular area about an axis coincident with the base is $I_b = \tfrac{1}{3} b h^3$ and should check the result by use of the parallel-axis theorem.

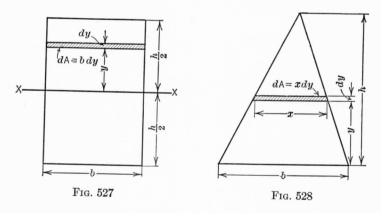

FIG. 527   FIG. 528

Problem 851. Determine the moment of inertia of a triangle, in terms of its base b and altitude h, with respect to: (a) an axis coinciding with its base and (b) a centroidal axis parallel to the base.

SOLUTION. (a) *Axis Coinciding with the Base.* The elementary area will be selected as shown in Fig. 528. The moment of inertia of the area of the triangle with respect to the base, then, is

$$I_b = \int y^2 \, dA = \int y^2 x \, dy$$

But, from similar triangles,

$$\frac{x}{b} = \frac{h - y}{h} \quad \text{or} \quad x = \frac{b}{h}(h - y)$$

Therefore,

$$I_b = \frac{b}{h} \int_0^h y^2(h - y) \, dy = \frac{1}{12} bh^3$$

(b) *Centroidal Axis Parallel to the Base.* The centroidal axis parallel to the base is at a distance $\frac{1}{3}h$ from the base (see Prob. 784). By use of the parallel-axis theorem, the moment of inertia of the triangular area with respect to the centroidal axis is found to be

$$\bar{I}_x = I_b - A(\tfrac{1}{3}h)^2$$

$$= \tfrac{1}{12}bh^3 - \tfrac{1}{2}bh \times \tfrac{1}{9}h^2 = \tfrac{1}{36}bh^3$$

Problem 852. Determine the moment of inertia of the area of a circle, in terms of its radius r, with respect to an axis coinciding with the diameter: (a) using Cartesian co-ordinates, (b) using polar co-ordinates.

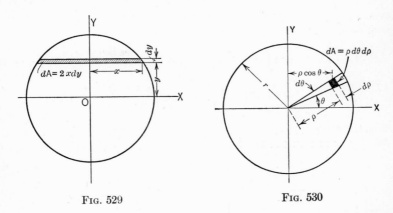

Fig. 529   Fig. 530

SOLUTION. (a) *Cartesian Co-ordinates.* The element of area will be selected as shown in Fig. 529. The moment of inertia of the circular area with respect to the diameter, then, is

$$\bar{I}_x = \int y^2 \, dA = \int y^2 2x \, dy$$

$$= 2 \int_{-r}^{+r} y^2 \sqrt{r^2 - y^2} \, dy = \tfrac{1}{4}\pi r^4$$

(b) *Polar Co-ordinates.* The element of area will be selected as shown in Fig. 530. Hence,

$$\bar{I}_x = \int y^2 \, dA = \int_0^r \int_0^{2\pi} (\rho \sin \theta)^2 \rho \, d\rho \, d\theta$$

$$= \int_0^r \int_0^{2\pi} \rho^3 \sin^2 \theta \, d\rho \, d\theta = \frac{r^4}{4} \int_0^{2\pi} \sin^2 \theta \, d\theta = \frac{r^4}{4} \times \pi = \frac{1}{4}\pi r^4$$

Problem 853. Determine the polar moment of inertia of the area of a circle of radius r with respect to a centroidal axis: (a) by integration, (b) by use of the theorem of Art. 165.

SOLUTION.   (a) *By Integration.*   If the element of area is selected as indicated in Fig. 531, the polar moment of inertia of the circular area is

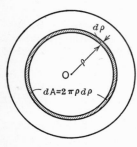

$$J_z = \int \rho^2 \, dA = \int_0^r \rho^2 2\pi\rho \, d\rho = \tfrac{1}{2}\pi r^4$$

(b) *By Use of Theorem of Art. 165.* Since I_x and I_y are each equal to $\tfrac{1}{4}\pi r^4$ (Prob. 852), the polar moment of inertia of the area of the circle is

$$J_z = I_x + I_y = \tfrac{1}{4}\pi r^4 + \tfrac{1}{4}\pi r^4 = \tfrac{1}{2}\pi r^4$$

Problem 854. Find the moment of inertia, with respect to the X axis, of the area bounded by the parabola $y^2 = 2x$, and the line $x = 8$ in.

FIG. 531   SOLUTION. *First Method.* The element of area will be selected in accordance with rule 1 of Art. 168 as indicated in Fig. 532.   The moment of inertia of the given area with respect to the X axis, then, is

$$I_x = \int y^2 \, dA = 2 \int y^2 (8 - x) \, dy$$

$$= 2 \int_0^4 y^2 \left(8 - \frac{y^2}{2} \right) dy = 2 \left[\frac{8y^3}{3} - \frac{y^5}{10} \right]_0^4 = 136.5 \text{ in.}^4$$

Second Method. The elementary area will be selected in accordance with rule 2 of Art. 168 as indicated in Fig. 533.   Since each elementary area is a rectangle of

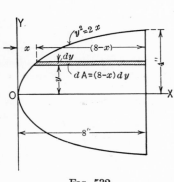

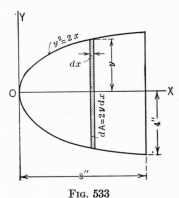

FIG. 532   FIG. 533

width dx and height $2y$, the moment of inertia of the element with respect to the X axis is $\tfrac{1}{12} \, dx (2y)^3 = \tfrac{2}{3} y^3 \, dx$ (see Prob. 850).   Hence, the moment of inertia of the given area is

$$I_x = \tfrac{2}{3} \int_0^8 y^3 \, dx = \tfrac{2}{3} \int_0^8 (2x)^{3/2} \, dx$$

$$= \frac{4\sqrt{2}}{3} \int_0^8 x^{3/2} \, dx = \frac{4\sqrt{2}}{3} \left[\frac{2}{5} x^{5/2} \right]_0^8 = 136.5 \text{ in.}^4$$

Problems

855. Determine the moment of inertia of the area of a circle, with respect to an axis tangent to the circle, in terms of r the radius of the circle: (a) by use of the parallel-axis theorem, and (b) by integration.

856. Determine, by use of the theorem of Art. 165, the polar moment of inertia of the area of a rectangle of base b and altitude d with respect to the centroidal axis.

$$Ans. \ \bar{J} = \tfrac{1}{12}bd(b^2 + d^2).$$

857. Find, by use of the theorem of Art. 165, the polar moment of inertia, with respect to a centroidal axis, of the area of an isosceles triangle having a base b and altitude h. $Ans. \ J = \tfrac{1}{12}bh(\tfrac{1}{4}b^2 + \tfrac{1}{3}h^2).$

858. In Fig. 534 is shown the cross section of an angle section the area of which is A. The X axis passes through C, the centroid of the area of the cross section. Determine the moment of inertia of the area with respect to the X axis. Assume that the thickness t of each leg is so small that the area of each leg may be considered to be concentrated along the longitudinal axis of the leg.

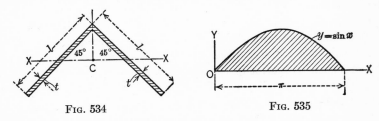

FIG. 534   FIG. 535

859. Find the moments of inertia with respect to the X and Y axes of the shaded area shown in Fig. 535. $Ans. \ I_x = 0.444; \ I_y = 5.86.$

860. Show by integration that the polar moment of inertia of an annular ring with respect to a centroidal axis is $J = \tfrac{1}{2}A(r_1^2 + r_2^2)$ in which $A = \pi(r_2^2 - r_1^2)$ is the annular area and r_1 and r_2 represent the inner and outer radii, respectively.

861. Find by integration the moment of inertia of the area of a right triangle of base b and altitude h about the base of the triangle. Select the element of area as stated under rule 2 of Art. 168, and use the result of Prob. 850b.

862. Calculate the moment of inertia and radius of gyration of a circular area 10 in. in diameter, with respect to a diameter. $Ans. \ I = 492 \ in.^4; \ k = 2.5 \ in.$

863. Find by integration the moment of inertia of a triangular area of base b and altitude h about an axis coinciding with the base. Select the element of area as shown in Fig. 536 in accordance with rule 3 of Art. 168.

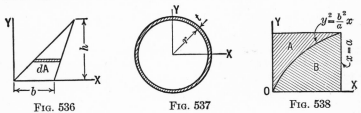

FIG. 536   FIG. 537   FIG. 538

864. Show by integration that the approximate value of the moment of inertia about the X axis of the area of the thin annular ring shown in Fig. 537 is $\tfrac{1}{2}Ar^2$

if the ratio of t to r is very small and A is the approximate area of the ring ($A = 2\pi rt$).

865. In Fig. 538 show that the first moments with respect to the X axis of the areas A and B are each equal to $\frac{1}{4}ab^2$, and find the second moment of each of the two areas with respect to the X axis.   *Ans.* $I_x = \frac{1}{5}ab^3$; $I_x = \frac{2}{15}ab^3$.

866. Determine by integration the polar moment of inertia of a sector of a circular area about an axis passing through the center of the circle. Assume the radius of the circle to be r and the central angle of the sector to be 2α.

867. Determine the moments of inertia of the area of an ellipse, the principal axes of which are $2a$ and $2b$, with respect to the principal axes.
    Ans. $I_a = \frac{1}{4}\pi ab^3$; $I_b = \frac{1}{4}\pi ba^3$.

868. The base of a triangle is 6 in., and its altitude is 10 in. Calculate the moment of inertia and radius of gyration of the area of the triangle with respect to the base.

869. Find, by use of the proposition in Art. 165, the polar moment of inertia and radius of gyration of the area of a square, each side of which is 12 in., with respect to an axis through one corner of the square.

169   Moments of inertia of composite areas.

When a composite area can be divided into a number of simple areas, such as triangles, rectangles, and circles, for which the moments of inertia are known, the moment of inertia of the entire area may be obtained by finding the sum of the moments of inertia of the several areas. Likewise, the moment of inertia of the part of an area that remains after one or more simple areas are removed may be found by subtracting, from the moment of inertia of the total area, the sum of the moments of inertia of the several parts removed.

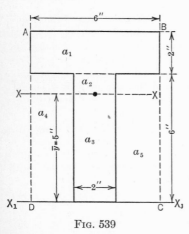

FIG. 539

Illustrative Problems

Problem 870. Locate the horizontal centroidal axis XX of the T section shown in Fig. 539, and find the moment of inertia of the area with respect to this centroidal axis.

SOLUTION. *First Method.* The distance $\bar{y}$ of the centroid of the area from the axis X_1X_1 may be found from the equation

$$A\bar{y} = \Sigma(ay_o)$$

Thus,

$$\bar{y} = \frac{12 \times 7 + 12 \times 3}{12 + 12} = 5 \text{ in.}$$

The moment of inertia with respect to the XX axis is the sum of the moments of inertia of the three parts, a_1, a_2, and a_3, with respect to that axis. Thus,

$$\bar{I}_x = \tfrac{1}{12} \times 6 \times (2)^3 + 12 \times (2)^2 + \tfrac{1}{3} \times 2 \times (1)^3 + \tfrac{1}{3} \times 2 \times (5)^3$$

$$= 4 + 48 + 0.67 + 83.33 = 136 \text{ in.}^4$$

Second Method. The moment of inertia of the T section may also be determined as follows: First find the moment of inertia of the T section with respect to the axis X_1X_1 by subtracting the moments of inertia of the parts a_4 and a_5 from the moment of inertia of the rectangular area $ABCD$, and then find $\bar{I}_x$ for the T section by use of the parallel-axis theorem. Thus, the moment of inertia I_{x1} of the T section with respect to the X_1X_1 axis is

$$\bar{I}_{x1} = \tfrac{1}{3} \times 6 \times (8)^3 - 2 \times \tfrac{1}{3} \times 2 \times (6)^3 = 736 \text{ in.}^4$$

and

$$\bar{I}_x = I_{x1} - Ad^2 = 736 - 24 \times (5)^2 = 136 \text{ in.}^4$$

Problem 871. Find the moment of inertia of the channel section shown in Fig. 540, with respect to the line XX. Find also the moment of inertia with respect to the parallel centroidal axis.

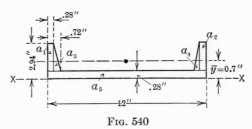

FIG. 540

SOLUTION. The area may be divided into triangles and rectangles as shown in the figure. The values used in the solution may be put in tabular form as shown in the accompanying table, where a denotes the area of any part, y_o the distance of the centroid of the part from the line XX, I_o the moment of inertia of the part with respect to its own centroidal axis parallel to XX, and I'_x the moment of inertia of the part with respect to the axis XX.

Part	a	y_o	ay_o	I_o	ay_o^2	$I'_x = I_o + ay_o^2$
a_1	0.745	1.61	1.20	0.44	1.93	2.37
a_2	0.745	1.61	1.20	0.44	1.93	2.37
a_3	0.585	1.17	0.68	0.23	0.80	1.03
a_4	0.585	1.17	0.68	0.23	0.80	1.03
a_5	3.360	0.14	0.47	0.02	0.07	0.09
	6.02 in.^{2}		4.23 in.^{3}			6.89 in.^{4}

Thus, the moment of inertia I_x of the area with respect to the XX axis is

$$I_x = \Sigma I'_x = 6.89 \text{ in.}^4$$

Further, the total area is $A = \Sigma a = 6.02$ in.^{2}, and the moment of the area with respect to the XX axis is $\Sigma(ay_o) = 4.23$ in.^{3} Hence, the distance $\bar{y}$, of the centroid of the area from the XX axis is

$$\bar{y} = \frac{\Sigma(ay_o)}{A} = \frac{4.23}{6.02} = 0.70 \text{ in.}$$

Therefore, the moment of inertia with respect to a line through the centroid and parallel to XX is given by the equation

$$\bar{I}_x = I_x - Ad^2 = 6.89 - 6.02 \times (0.70)^2 = 3.94 \text{ in.}^4$$

Problems

872. From the area of an equilateral triangle, each side of which is 10 in. long, is cut the largest possible circular area. Find the moment of inertia of the remaining area with respect to an axis passing through the centroid of the triangle and parallel to one side.

873. In Fig. 541 is shown the cross section of a standard $3\frac{1}{4}$-in. by 5-in. Z bar (fillets are neglected). Find the moments of inertia of the section with respect to the centroidal axes XX and YY.   *Ans.* $I_x = 19.2$ in.^{4}; $I_y = 9.04$ in.^{4}

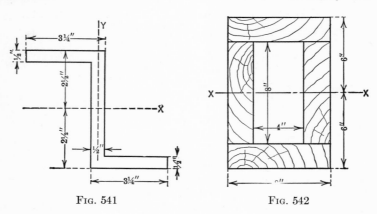

Fig. 541   Fig. 542

874. A wooden column is built up of four 2-in. by 8-in. planks as shown in Fig. 542. Find the moment of inertia of the cross section with respect to the centroidal axis XX.   *Ans.* $I_x = 981$ in.^{4}

875. Solve Prob. 860 by finding the difference of the polar moments of inertia of the two circular areas whose radii are r_1 and r_2.

876. Determine the position of the centroid O of the shaded area shown in Fig. 543, and then find the moment of inertia of the area about the X axis.

Ans. $I_x = 272$ in.^{4}

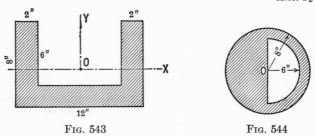

Fig. 543   Fig. 544

877. In Fig. 544 a semi-circular area is removed from a circular area. Calculate the polar moment of inertia of the remaining (shaded) area with respect to an axis passing through O.   *Ans.* $J = 5420$ in.^{4}

878. Calculate, without integrating, the moment of inertia of the shaded area in Fig. 549 with respect to the Y axis.   *Ans.* $I_y = 71.6$ in.^{4}

879. In Fig. 545 is represented a 16-in. circular plate in which there are drilled five 2-in. holes and one 4-in. hole as shown. Find the moment of inertia of the area of the holes with respect to the XX axis and also with respect to the YY axis.

Ans. $I_x = 252$ in.^{4}; $I_y = 224$ in.^{4}

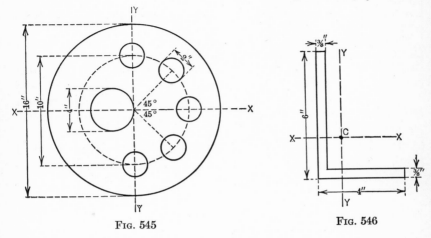

FIG. 545   FIG. 546

880. Find the moment of inertia of the angle section (Fig. 546) with respect to each of the centroidal axes parallel to the two legs of the angle.

881. Calculate the moment of inertia, about the X axis, of the shaded area in Fig. 502 (see Prob. 814).

882. Determine the moment of inertia of the area shown in Fig. 507 about the Y axis.

883. From a square area 12 in. on a side is cut a triangular corner whose area is 48 sq in., the base of the triangle being parallel to one of the diagonals of the square. Calculate, with respect to this diagonal, the moment of inertia of the remaining area.

170 Moments of inertia of areas by graphical and approximate methods.
If the bounding curve of an area is not defined by a mathematical equation, the moment of inertia of the area cannot be found by integration. It is then necessary to use graphical or approximate methods. Several graphical methods are available which are usually discussed in texts on graphical statics. An approximate method that can be applied to any area is here described. For convenience, however, a simple area will be selected so that the approximate value of the moment of inertia as determined by this method may be compared with the exact value. Thus, let the moment of inertia of the area of a rectangle, with respect to an axis coinciding with its base, be found. The area may be divided into any convenient number of equal narrow strips parallel to the base, as shown in Fig. 547. (The narrower the strips, the more closely will the result agree with the exact result.) Let the area be divided into ten such strips each 0.2 in. in width. The moment of

inertia of the rectangle is equal to the sum of the moments of inertia of the strips. The moment of inertia of any particular strip with respect

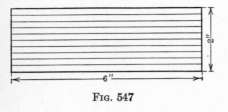

to the base of the rectangle is

$$\tfrac{1}{12} \times 6 \times (\tfrac{1}{5})^3 + 6 \times \tfrac{1}{5} \times y^2$$

where y is the distance of the centroid of the particular strip from the base. The first term is small and may be omitted without serious error. The moment

FIG. 547

of inertia of each strip then is approximately equal to the product of the area of the strip and the square of the distance of its centroid from the base. Hence, the moment of inertia of the rectangle is

$$I = \tfrac{6}{5}(0.1^2 + 0.3^2 + 0.5^2 + 0.7^2 + 0.9^2 + \overline{1.1}^2 + \overline{1.3}^2$$
$$+ \overline{1.5}^2 + \overline{1.7}^2 + \overline{1.9}^2)$$
$$= \tfrac{6}{5} \times 13.3 = 15.96 \text{ in.}^4$$

According to Prob. 850, the exact value is

$$I = \tfrac{1}{3}bh^3 = \tfrac{1}{3} \times 6 \times 2^3 = 16 \text{ in.}^4$$

The determination of the moment of inertia of an irregularly shaped area would require the use of a drafting board in order that the area be drawn to scale and the necessary distances be accurately measured. In the following problems the student is expected to draw the area to scale and divide it into elements. Measurements of the dimensions of the elements and the distances from the centroids of the elements to the axis are to be made, and the moment of inertia of each element is to be calculated from these measurements.

Problems

884. Determine the moment of inertia about the X axis of the area shown in

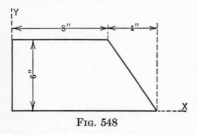

FIG. 548

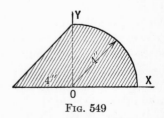

FIG. 549

Fig. 548 by use of the approximate method discussed in Art. 170.

885. Determine the moment of inertia about the X axis of the shaded area shown in Fig. 549 by use of the approximate method discussed in Art. 170.

886. Determine the moment of inertia about the X axis of the shaded area shown in Fig. 522 by use of the approximate method discussed in Art. 170.

§ 3 Moments of Inertia of Bodies

171 Moment of inertia of mass defined. In the analysis of the motion of a body, the body is frequently regarded as a system of particles, and expressions are met in the analysis that involve the mass of a particle and the square of its distance from a line or plane. This product is called the *second moment* of the mass of the particle or, more frequently, the *moment of inertia of the mass* of the particle (or, briefly, the moment of inertia of the particle) with respect to the line or plane. The moment of inertia of a system of particles (mass system or body) with respect to a line or plane is the sum of the moments of inertia of the particles with respect to the given line or plane. Thus, if the masses of the particles of a system are denoted by m_1, m_2, $m_3 \cdots$, and the distances of the particles from a given line are denoted by r_1, r_2, $r_3 \cdots$, the moment of inertia of the system may be expressed as follows:

$$I = m_1 r_1{}^2 + m_2 r_2{}^2 + m_3 r_3{}^2 + \cdots = \Sigma m r^2$$

If the mass system constitutes a continuous body, the summation in the above equation may be replaced by a definite integral, and the expression for the moment of inertia of the body then becomes

$$I = \int r^2 \, dM$$

where dM represents an element of mass of the body and r is the distance of the element from the given line or plane. The limits of the integral must, of course, be so chosen that each element of mass of the body is included in the integration. Therefore, the moment of inertia of a body with respect to a line or plane may be defined as the sum of the products obtained by multiplying each elementary mass of the body by the square of its distance from the given line or plane. The moment of inertia of the mass of a body (or, more briefly, the moment of inertia of a body) has a physical significance, since common experience teaches that, if a body is free to rotate about an axis, the farther from the axis the material is placed, that is, the greater the moment of inertia of the body becomes, the greater is the moment of the forces required to produce a given angular acceleration of the body. Thus, let a rod be free to rotate about a vertical axis through its mid-point and carry two spheres one on either side of the axis, each sphere being free to move along the rod. Experience shows that, the farther from the axis the spheres are placed, the greater is the torque required to produce a definite angular acceleration. This fact is expressed in quantitative form by one of the equations of motion, namely, $\Sigma T_o = I_o \alpha$ (see Art. 101).

UNITS. No special one-term name has been given to the unit of moment of inertia of a body; hence, the units of mass and length used are specified. Thus, if the *mass* of a body is expressed in pounds and the dimensions of the body are expressed in feet, the moment of inertia of the body is expressed in pound foot^2 units (written lb ft^2). In engineering problems, however, the pound is generally used as the *unit of force*, in which case the unit of mass is g (32.2) times the mass of 1 lb and is called a *slug* (see Art. 93). Therefore, the moment of inertia of a body, in engineering problems, is expressed in slug ft^2 units.

172 Radius of gyration. It is frequently convenient to express the moment of inertia of a body in terms of factors, one of which is the mass of the whole body. Since each term in the expression for moment of inertia as previously defined is one dimension in mass and two dimensions in length, the moment of inertia of a body may be expressed as the product of the mass M of the whole body and the square of a length. This length is defined as the *radius of gyration* of the body and will be denoted by k. Thus, the moment of inertia I of a body with respect to a given line or plane may be expressed by the product Mk^2, and, hence,

$$I = Mk^2 \quad \text{or} \quad k = \sqrt{\frac{I}{M}}$$

The radius of gyration of a body with respect to any axis, then, may be regarded as the distance from the axis at which the mass may be conceived to be concentrated and have the same moment of inertia with respect to the axis as does the actual (or distributed) mass.

Viewed differently, the radius of gyration of a body with respect to an axis is a distance such that the square of this distance is the mean of the squares of the distances from the axis of the (equal) elements of mass into which the given body may be divided (*not* the square of the mean of the distances).

173 Parallel-axis theorem for masses. If the moment of inertia of a body with respect to an axis passing through its mass center is known, the moment of inertia of the body with respect to any parallel axis may be found, without integrating, by use of the following proposition:

> The moment of inertia of a body with respect to any axis is equal to the moment of inertia of the body with respect to a parallel

axis through the mass center of the body plus the product of the mass of the body and the square of the distance between the two axes.

This proposition may be stated in equational form as follows:

$$I = \bar{I} + Md^2$$

where $\bar{I}$ denotes the moment of inertia of the body with respect to an axis through the mass center and I denotes the moment of inertia with respect to a parallel axis which is at a distance d from the axis through the mass center.

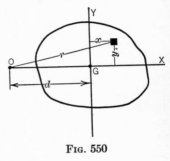

Proof. Let Fig. 550 represent the cross section of a body containing the mass center G. Furthermore, let the moment of inertia of the body with respect to an axis through G and perpendicular to this section be denoted by $\bar{I}$ and let the mo-

FIG. 550

ment of inertia with respect to a parallel axis through the point O be denoted by I. The expression for I, then, is

$$I = \int r^2 \, dM = \int [(x + d)^2 + y^2] \, dM$$

$$= \int (x^2 + y^2) \, dM + d^2 \int dM + 2d \int x \, dM$$

But

$$\int (x^2 + y^2) \, dM = \bar{I} \quad \text{and} \quad \int x \, dM = M\bar{x} = 0$$

Therefore,

$$I = \bar{I} + Md^2$$

This theorem is frequently called the *parallel-axis theorem* for moments of inertia of masses. A similar relation may be found between the radii of gyration with respect to the two axes. Thus, if the radii of gyration with respect to the two parallel axes be denoted by k and $\bar{k}$, the above equation may be written

$$Mk^2 = M\bar{k}^2 + Md^2$$

Hence,

$$k^2 = \bar{k}^2 + d^2$$

174 Moments of inertia with respect to two perpendicular planes. The determination of the moment of inertia of a body with respect to a line is frequently simplified by making use of the following theorem:

> The sum of the moments of inertia of a body with respect to two perpendicular planes is equal to the moment of inertia of the body with respect to the line of intersection of the two planes.

Proof. If the moment of inertia of the body (Fig. 551) with respect to xy and xz planes be denoted by I_{xy} and I_{xz}, respectively, the expressions for the moments of inertia are

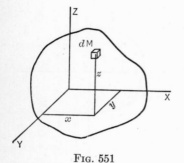

FIG. 551

$$I_{xy} = \int z^2 \, dM \quad \text{and} \quad I_{xz} = \int y^2 \, dM$$

By adding these two equations, the resulting equation is

$$I_{xy} + I_{xz} = \int (z^2 + y^2) \, dM = I_x$$

175 Moments of inertia of solids by integration. In determining the moment of inertia of a body with respect to an axis by the calculus method of integration, the mass of the body may be divided into elements in various ways, and either Cartesian or polar co-ordinates may be used, leading to a single, double, or triple integration, depending on the way the element is chosen. The elements of mass should always be selected, however, so that:

1. All points in the element are equally distant from the axis (or plane) with respect to which the moment of inertia is to be found; otherwise, the distance from the axis to the element would be indefinite. Or, if condition 1 is not satisfied, the element should be selected so that

2. The moment of inertia of the element with respect to the axis about which the moment of inertia of the body is to be found is known; the moment of inertia of the body is then found by summing up the moments of inertia of the elements. Or so that

3. The mass center of the element is known, and the moment of inertia of the element with respect to an axis through its mass center and parallel to the given axis is known, in which case the moment of inertia of the element may be expressed by use of the parallel-axis theorem (Art. 173).

The moments of inertia of some of the simpler solids are found in the problems following Art. 176.

176 Moments of inertia of bodies by experimental methods.

If a body is irregular in shape, the moment of inertia cannot be found by methods of integration, since it is impossible to determine the limits of the integral. The moments of inertia of such bodies may be determined experimentally, however, by methods which make use of the laws of motion of a pendulum as explained in Art. 146.

NOTE. The symbol δ will be used in the following pages to denote the density (mass per unit volume) of a body.

Illustrative Problems

Problem 887. Determine the moment of inertia of a homogeneous right circular cylinder with respect to its geometrical axis.

SOLUTION. In accordance with the first of the foregoing rules, the element of mass may be selected as indicated in Fig. 552. The volume of this element is $h\rho\,d\rho\,d\theta$, and, if the density be denoted by δ, the mass of the element is $\delta h\rho\,d\rho\,d\theta$. Hence, the expression for the moment of inertia becomes

$$\bar{I} = \int \rho^2\,dM = \int_0^r \int_0^{2\pi} \rho^2\,\delta h\rho\,d\rho\,d\theta$$

$$\tfrac{1}{2}\pi\,\delta h r^4 = \tfrac{1}{2}(\pi r^2 h\delta)r^2 = \tfrac{1}{2}Mr^2$$

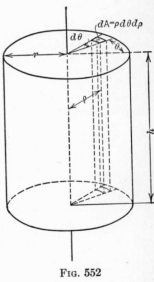

Problem 888. Determine the moment of inertia of a homogeneous sphere with respect to a diameter.

SOLUTION. The cross section of the sphere in the xy plane is shown in Fig. 553. In accordance with the second rule of Art. 175, the element of volume may be taken as a thin circular disk or lamina included between two planes parallel to the xz plane, as shown in cross section. This element, then, may be regarded as a circular cylinder of radius x and altitude dy. The mass of the elemental cylinder is $\delta\pi x^2\,dy$, and its moment of inertia with respect to the Y axis is $\tfrac{1}{2}\delta\pi x^4\,dy$ (Prob. 887). Hence, the moment of inertia of the entire sphere with respect to the Y axis is

FIG. 552

$$\bar{I} = \tfrac{1}{2}\delta\pi \int_{-r}^{+r} x^4\,dy$$

$$= \tfrac{1}{2}\delta\pi \int_{-r}^{+r} (r^2 - y^2)^2\,dy$$

$$= \tfrac{8}{15}\delta\pi r^5$$

$$= \tfrac{2}{5}(\tfrac{4}{3}\delta\pi r^3)r^2$$

$$= \tfrac{2}{5}Mr^2$$

Problem 889. Show that the moment of inertia of a homogeneous thin circular disk or lamina, with respect to an axis through the mass center, parallel to the bases of the lamina, is approximately $\frac{1}{4}Mr^2$, in which M is the mass of the lamina and r is the radius.

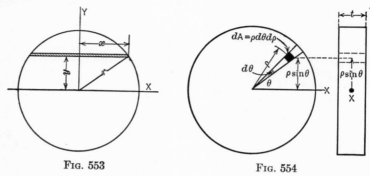

FIG. 553   FIG. 554

SOLUTION. A top view and an end view of the lamina are shown in Fig. 554. The element of volume will be taken as a prism of altitude t and cross section $\rho\,d\rho\,d\theta$, as indicated in the figure. The mass of the element is $\delta t\rho\,d\rho\,d\theta$. Now, if the thickness t is relatively small, all points in any elementary prism are approximately at the same distance ($y = \rho\sin\theta$) from the X axis except for those prisms that are near the axis, and these prisms contribute little to the moment of inertia of the lamina with respect to the X axis. Thus, the moment of inertia of the lamina with respect to an axis through its mass center parallel to the bases of the lamina is approximately

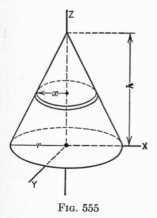

$$I_x = \int_0^r \int_0^{2\pi} \delta t\rho^3 \sin^2\theta\,d\rho\,d\theta$$

$$= \tfrac{1}{4}\delta t\pi r^4 = \tfrac{1}{4}(\delta t\pi r^2)r^2 = \tfrac{1}{4}Mr^2$$

It should be noted that, the smaller the value of t becomes, the closer is the approximation. The above expression is also a close approximation to the moment of inertia of the lamina with respect to a diameter of either base of the lamina.

Problem 890. Determine the moment of inertia of a homogeneous right circular cone with respect to a diameter of the base.

SOLUTION. In accordance with the third of the foregoing rules, the element of volume may be taken as a thin cylindrical lamina parallel to the base, as indicated in Fig. 555. The mass of this element is

FIG. 555

$\delta\pi x^2\,dz$, and its moment of inertia with respect to its centroidal axis parallel to the X axis is $\frac{1}{4}\delta\pi x^4\,dz$ (see Prob. 889). The moment of inertia with respect to the X axis, according to the parallel-axis theorem (Art. 173), is $\frac{1}{4}\delta\pi x^4\,dz + \delta\pi x^2z^2\,dz$. Hence, the moment of inertia of the entire cone with respect to the X axis is

$$I_x = \int_0^h \tfrac{1}{4}\delta\pi x^4\,dz + \int_0^h \delta\pi x^2z^2\,dz$$

From similar triangles, $x = \dfrac{r}{h}(h - z)$. Hence,

$$I_x = \tfrac{1}{4}\delta\pi\frac{r^4}{h^4}\int_0^h (h - z)^4\, dz + \delta\pi\frac{r^2}{h^2}\int_0^h z^2(h - z)^2\, dz$$

$$= \tfrac{1}{20}\delta\pi h r^4 + \tfrac{1}{30}\delta\pi r^2 h^3 = \tfrac{1}{3}\delta r^2 h(\tfrac{3}{20}r^2 + \tfrac{1}{10}h^2)$$

$$= M(\tfrac{3}{20}r^2 + \tfrac{1}{10}h^2) = \tfrac{1}{20}M(3r^2 + 2h^2)$$

Problem 891. Determine the moment of inertia of a homogeneous right circular cylinder with respect to a diameter of one of the bases.

SOLUTION. *First Method.* In accordance with the third of the foregoing rules, the element of volume may be taken as a thin circular lamina parallel to the base as indicated in Fig. 556. The mass of the element is $\delta\pi r^2\, dz$, and the moment of inertia of the element with respect to a centroidal axis parallel to the X axis, as found in the preceding problem, is $\tfrac{1}{4}\delta\pi r^4\, dz$. The moment of inertia of the element with respect to the X axis, then, as found by the parallel-axis theorem (Art. 173), is

$$\tfrac{1}{4}\delta\pi r^4\, dz + \delta\pi r^2 z^2\, dz$$

Hence, the moment of inertia of the entire cylinder with respect to the X axis is

$$I = \int_0^h \tfrac{1}{4}\delta\pi r^4\, dz + \int_0^h \delta\pi r^2 z^2\, dz$$

$$= \tfrac{1}{4}\delta\pi r^4 h + \tfrac{1}{3}\delta\pi r^2 h^3 = \tfrac{1}{12}\delta\pi r^2 h(3r^2 + 4h^2)$$

$$= \tfrac{1}{12}M(3r^2 + 4h^2)$$

Second Method. The moment of inertia with respect to the X axis may also be

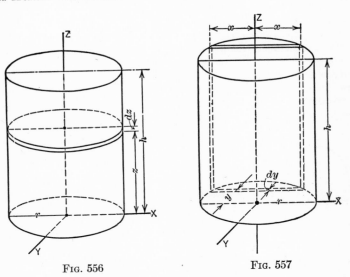

FIG. 556   FIG. 557

found by adding the moments of inertia with respect to the xy and xz planes (Art. 174). Thus, in Fig. 557,

$$I_x = I_{xy} + I_{xz}$$

The moment of inertia with respect to the end (xy) plane is

$$I_{xy} = \tfrac{1}{3}Mh^2 \quad \text{(see Prob. 896)}$$

To find the moment of inertia with respect to the xz plane, an element of mass may be selected as indicated in Fig. 557. Thus,

$$I_{xz} = \int y^2\, dM = \int_{-r}^{+r} y^2(\delta h 2x\, dy)$$

$$= 2\delta h \int_{-r}^{+r} y_2 \sqrt{r^2 - y^2}\, dy = \tfrac{1}{4}\delta h \pi r^4 = \tfrac{1}{4}Mr^2$$

Therefore,

$$I_x = \tfrac{1}{3}Mh^2 + \tfrac{1}{4}Mr^2 = \tfrac{1}{12}M(3r^2 + 4h^2)$$

Problems

892. A thin-walled cylinder has the cross section shown in Fig. 537. Determine the moment of inertia of the cylinder with respect to an axis perpendicular to the xy plane and passing through the center of the cylinder. Since t is small compared to r, it may be assumed that all particles are a distance r from the center.

893. A homogeneous slender rod of length l rotates about an axis through one end. If the ratio of the square of the radius of gyration to the centroidal distance (both with respect to the axis of rotation) is 4 ft, find the length of the rod. The moment of inertia with respect to the axis of rotation is $I = \tfrac{1}{3}Ml^2$.

894. A solid of revolution is generated by rotating about the X axis the area bounded by the parabola $y^2 = ax$, the line $x = b$, and the X axis. A homogeneous body has the same form as the solid so generated. Find the moment of inertia of the body about its axis of symmetry.　　　　　　　　　　　*Ans.* $I = \tfrac{1}{3}Mab$.

895. In Fig. 558 is shown the cross section of the web of a crankshaft (see Fig. 164a). If the equation of the line bounding the cross section is assumed to be the ellipse $x^2/a^2 + y^2/b^2 = 1$ and the web is of uniform thickness t, find the moment of inertia with respect to an axis through the origin O and perpendicular to the xy plane. By use of the parallel-axis theorem, find the moment of inertia with respect to the axis through the point O'. This axis passes through the center of the journal (such as B in Fig. 164a) and is the axis of rotation of the crankshaft.

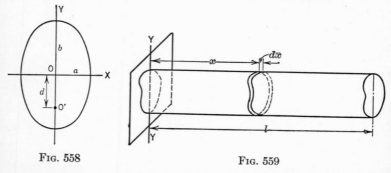

FIG. 558　　　　　　　　　　　FIG. 559

896. Show that the moment of inertia of a homogeneous right prism (Fig. 559) having a cross section of any shape, with respect to a *plane* coinciding with one of the bases of the prism, is $I = \frac{1}{3}Ml^2$, in which M is the mass of the rod and l is the length of the rod. Furthermore, show that for a *slender* rod the above expression closely approximates the moment of inertia of the rod with respect to an *axis* passing through one end of the rod and perpendicular to the rod.

897. A homogeneous cylindrical rod is 2 ft long, and the radius is 2 in. If the moment of inertia is found with respect to a line through one end of the rod perpendicular to its axis by using the approximate formula of Prob. 896, what is the error in the result, in per cent?   *Ans.* 0.52 per cent.

898. Determine the moment of inertia of a homogeneous right circular cone about an axis through the center of gravity perpendicular to the geometrical axis.
$$Ans. \ \tfrac{3}{20}M(r^2 + \tfrac{1}{4}h^2).$$

899. Calculate the moment of inertia of a steel cylinder 8 in. in diameter and 12 in. high, about its geometric axis. Assume the weight of steel to be 490 lb/cu ft.

900. Show that the moment of inertia of a homogeneous slender rod with respect to an axis through the mid-point of the rod and perpendicular to the rod is approximately $\frac{1}{12}Ml^2$.

901. A right circular cone has an altitude of 16 in. and a base of radius 6 in. Its weight is 0.20 lb/cu in. Calculate the moment of inertia of the cone with respect to a line that is parallel to its geometric axis and passes through a point on the circumference of the base.

902. The density at any point of a right circular cylinder varies directly as the distance of the point from the geometric axis. Derive the expression for the moment of inertia of the cylinder with respect to the geometric axis.   *Ans.* $\bar{I} = \frac{3}{5}Mr^2$.

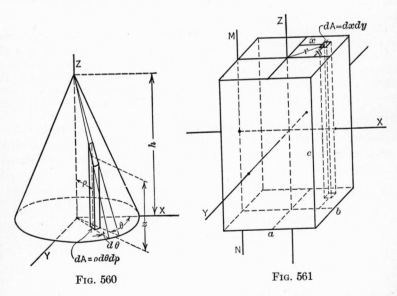

FIG. 560   FIG. 561

903. Determine the moment of inertia of a homogeneous right circular cone about its geometrical axis. Select the element of mass as indicated in Fig. 560.
$$Ans. \ I_z = \tfrac{3}{10}Mr^2.$$

904. Determine the moment of inertia of a homogeneous rectangular parallelepiped with respect to a central axis parallel to an edge. Select the element of mass as indicated in Fig. 561.   *Ans.* $I_z = \frac{1}{12}M(a^2 + b^2)$.

905. Determine by use of the theorem of Art. 174 the moment of inertia about the Z axis of the homogeneous rectangular parallelepiped in Fig. 561.

906. A thin disk whose radius is 10 in. rolls on a horizontal plane. If the radius of gyration of the disk is 12 in. with respect to an axis perpendicular to the disk and passing through the point of contact between the thin disk and plane, determine the radius of gyration with respect to a parallel axis passing through the mass center.

907. Find, by the parallel-axis theorem, the moment of inertia of the parallelepiped in Fig. 561 about the axis MN.

908. Determine the moment of inertia of a sphere with respect to a central axis if the density at any point varies directly as the distance of the point from a central plane perpendicular to the axis.   *Ans.* $I = \frac{1}{3}Mr^2$.

909. Calculate the moment of inertia, with respect to a central axis, of a cast-iron sphere 8 in. in diameter. Assume the weight of cast iron to be 450 lb/cu ft.
         Ans. $I = 0.0964$ slug ft^2.

910. Find, by integration, the moment of inertia of a right circular cylinder with respect to a plane containing the central longitudinal axis of the cylinder. Express, in terms of M, the mass of the cylinder, and r, the radius of the cylinder.
         Ans. $I = \frac{1}{4}Mr^2$.

911. Calculate the moment of inertia of a sphere having a radius of 10 in. and a weight of 64.4 lb about a line tangent to the sphere.

912. The dimensions of a rectangular parallelepiped are 4 in. by 4 in. by 12 in., and the weight of the parallelepiped is 16.1 lb. Calculate the moment of inertia of the parallelepiped with respect to a central axis perpendicular to one 4-in. × 12-in. face: (*a*) by the approximate formula (see Prob. 900), and (*b*) by the exact formula (see Prob. 904).

913. Determine the moment of inertia of a homogeneous ellipsoid, the principal axes of which are $2a$, $2b$, and $2c$, about the axis $2a$.   *Ans.* $I = \frac{1}{5}M(b^2 + c^2)$.

914. Determine the moment of inertia of a homogeneous elliptic cylinder, in which the principal axes of the cross section are $2a$ and $2b$, with respect to: (*a*) the geometrical axis, and (*b*) an axis through the center of gravity coincident with the axis $2a$ of the cross section.   *Ans.* (*a*) $I = \frac{1}{4}M(a^2 + b^2)$; (*b*) $I = \frac{1}{12}M(h^2 + 3b^2)$.

177   Moments of inertia of composite bodies.

If a body can be divided into several finite parts, the moment of inertia of each of which is known, the moment of inertia of the given body may be obtained by adding the moments of inertia of the several parts. In like manner, if parts of a body are removed, the moment of inertia of the remaining part may be obtained by subtracting from the moment of inertia of the original body the sum of the moments of inertia of the parts removed.

FIG. 562

Illustrative Problems

Problem 915. In Fig. 562 is shown the cross section of a homogeneous, hollow circular cylinder. Determine the moment of inertia of the cylinder with respect to its geometric axis, in terms of its mass M and its inner and outer radii r_1 and r_2.

SOLUTION. Let I_2 and M_2 denote the moment of inertia and the mass of a solid cylinder of radius r_2, and let I_1 and M_1 have similar meanings for the cylinder of radius r_1 which is removed. Then,

$$I = I_2 - I_1 = \tfrac{1}{2}M_2r_2{}^2 - \tfrac{1}{2}M_1r_1{}^2$$
$$= \tfrac{1}{2}\delta\pi r_2{}^4h - \tfrac{1}{2}\delta\pi r_1{}^4h = \tfrac{1}{2}\delta\pi h(r_2{}^4 - r_1{}^4)$$
$$= \tfrac{1}{2}\delta\pi h(r_2{}^2 - r_1{}^2)(r_2{}^2 + r_1{}^2) = \tfrac{1}{2}M(r_1{}^2 + r_2{}^2)$$

Problem 916. Determine the moment of inertia of the cast-iron flywheel shown in Fig. 563 with respect to the axis of rotation. Assume the weight of cast iron to be 450 lb/cu ft.

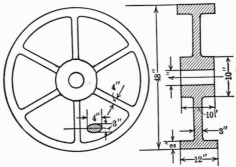

FIG. 563

SOLUTION. The rim and hub are hollow cylinders and the spokes may be regarded as slender rods.

The weight of the rim $= \pi[(\tfrac{24}{12})^2 - (\tfrac{22}{12})^2] \times \tfrac{12}{12} \times 450 = 903$ lb

The weight of the hub $= \pi[(\tfrac{5}{12})^2 - (\tfrac{2}{12})^2] \times \tfrac{10}{12} \times 450 = 172$ lb

The weight of each spoke $= \pi \times \dfrac{1.5}{12} \times \dfrac{2}{12} \times \dfrac{17}{12} \times 450 = 41.7$ lb

For the rim, $\qquad I = \dfrac{1}{2}\dfrac{903}{32.2}\left[\left(\dfrac{24}{12}\right)^2 + \left(\dfrac{22}{12}\right)^2\right] = 102.3$ slug ft^2

For the hub, $\qquad I = \dfrac{1}{2} \times \dfrac{172}{32.2}\left[\left(\dfrac{5}{12}\right)^2 + \left(\dfrac{2}{12}\right)^2\right] = 0.54$ slug ft^2

For the spokes, $\qquad I = 6\left[\dfrac{1}{12}\times\dfrac{41.7}{32.2}\times\left(\dfrac{17}{12}\right)^2 + \dfrac{41.7}{32.2}\times\left(\dfrac{13.5}{12}\right)^2\right] = 11.1$ slug ft^2

Hence, the moment of inertia of the flywheel is

$$I = 102.3 + 0.54 + 11.1 = 113.9 \text{ slug ft}^2$$

Problems

917. Determine the moment of inertia of the frustum of a homogeneous right circular cone with respect to the geometrical axis, the radii of the bases being r_2 and r_1. $\qquad Ans.\ I = \dfrac{3}{10}\ M\ \dfrac{r_2{}^5 - r_1{}^5}{r_2{}^3 - r_1{}^3}.$

918. A wooden block has a rectangular cross section 8 in. by 10 in. and a height of 30 in. A cylindrical hole 2 in. in diameter is cut from the block, the axis of the hole being parallel to the longitudinal centroidal axis of the block. The distance between the two axes is 3 in. The wood weighs 40 lb/cu ft. Find the moment of inertia of the remaining portion of the block with respect to the longitudinal axis of the original block.

919. In Fig. 564 a sphere A is attached to a cylinder B by a slender rod C. The weights of A, B, and C are 96.6 lb, 32.2 lb, and 64.4 lb, respectively. Calculate the moment of inertia of the whole body about the axis YY.   *Ans. $I = 18.1$ slug ft².*

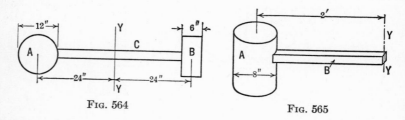

Fig. 564   Fig. 565

920. The body shown in Fig. 565 consists of a cylinder A that weighs 96.6 lb and a slender rod B that weighs 32.2 lb. Calculate the moment of inertia of the body about the axis YY.

921. Three slender rods are joined so that they form an equilateral triangle. Each rod is 2 ft long and weighs 8.05 lb. Calculate the moment of inertia of the three rods about an axis passing through one of the vertices of the triangle and perpendicular to the plane of the triangle.   *Ans. $I = 1.5$ slug ft².*

922. Assume that the thin-walled cylinder whose cross section is shown in Fig. 537 weighs 12 lb and has attached to its circumference a small body B whose weight is 4 lb. The radius r of the cylinder is 1 ft. Locate the axis parallel to the longitudinal axis of the cylinder about which the moment of inertia of the cylinder and body B is the least. Determine the moment of inertia about this axis.

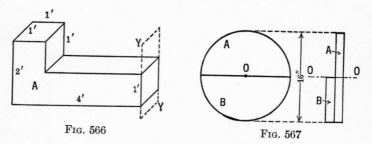

Fig. 566   Fig. 567

923. In Fig. 566, A is a wooden block. Calculate the moment of inertia of the block with respect to the plane YY. Assume the weight of wood to be 40 lb/cu ft.
      Ans. $I = 41.8$ slug ft².

924. In Fig. 567 a circular disk A has its mass increased by the addition of a semi-circular disk B. The weight of A is 100 lb. What is the weight of B if the moment of inertia about an axis through O perpendicular to the disk is increased 40 per cent by the addition of B?

925. From a round steel disk which is 24 in. in diameter and 4 in. thick are bored four holes, each 4 in. in diameter. The axes of the holes are parallel to the geometric axis of the disk and 8 in. therefrom. Calculate the moment of inertia of the remainder of the disk with respect to its geometric axis. Assume the weight of steel to be 490 lb/cu ft.   *Ans. I* = 7.16 slug ft².

926. Two spheres are connected by a horizontal rod and are free to rotate about a vertical axis midway between the spheres. The diameter of each sphere is 10 in., the distance between their centers is 2 ft, and the diameter of the rod is 2 in. Find the moment of inertia of the rod and spheres with respect to the axis of rotation. Assume that the rod and spheres are made of cast iron which weighs 450 lb/cu ft.

927. The head of the mallet shown in Fig. 568 is a rectangular parallelepiped, and the handle is a right circular cylinder. If the weight of the material is ¼ lb/cu in., find the moment of inertia of the mallet with respect to the line *YY*.

        Ans. I = 3.81 slug ft².

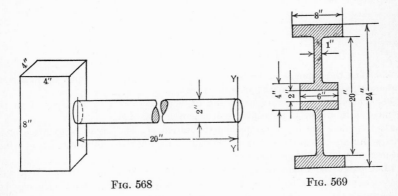

Fig. 568   Fig. 569

928. The wheel shown in Fig. 569 is made of cast iron and has a solid web. Determine the moment of inertia of the wheel with respect to the axis of rotation. Assume the weight of cast iron to be 450 lb/cu ft.

929. A slender rod 9 ft long rotates about an axis perpendicular to the rod 3 ft from one end. The rod weighs 20 lb. Find the moment of inertia of the rod about the axis of rotation.   *Ans. Ī* = 5.59 slug ft².

930. Two wooden spheres, each weighing 16.1 lb and having a diameter of 10 in., are connected by a cylindrical rod 16 in. long and 4 in. in diameter, the distance between the centers of the spheres being 26 in. The rod weighs 0.25 lb/cu in. Find the moment of inertia of the spheres and rod with respect to an axis perpendicular to the rod and midway between the spheres.

Review Questions
First Moments and Centroids

1. Define the moment of a line about a co-ordinate axis: (*a*) in words, and (*b*) by a mathematical expression.

2. What is the value of the moment of the lateral surface area of a right circular cone that has a base of radius *r* and an altitude *h* about a plane in which the axis of the cone lies?

3. What are the dimensions of the moment of an area about an axis? Of a volume about a plane?

4. What is the expression for the moment of the area of the base of a right circular cone about a plane parallel to the base and passing through the vertex of the cone? The known quantities are the radius r of the base and the altitude h of the cone.

5. Correct the following statement: The centroid of a plane area is a point in the area whose distance from a given axis divided by the area is equal to the moment of the area with respect to the axis.

6. In finding centroids of lines, areas, and volumes by the method of integration, what are the two general ways in which the element of the line, area, or volume may be selected?

7. Complete the following inadequate statement: The mass center of a physical body is that point at which the mass of the body may be thought of as being located or concentrated.

8. One of the theorems of Pappus and Guldinus states that the area of a surface of revolution is equal to the product of two lines. Describe the two lines.

Moment of Inertia of Areas

9. Define the moment of inertia of an area with respect to a iine: (a) in a word statement, and (b) as a mathematical expression.

10. What are the dimensions of the moment of inertia of an area? Can the moment of inertia of an area be zero or negative? Explain.

11. Complete the following inadequate statement: The radius of gyration of an area with respect to an axis may be thought of as a distance from the axis at which the area may be considered to be concentrated.

12. Correct the following statement: The radius of gyration of an area with respect to an axis is equal to the square of the quotient found by dividing the moment of inertia of the area about the given axis by the area.

13. Prove and give a word statement of the formula $J_z = I_x + I_y$.

14. Prove the parallel-axis theorem for moments of inertia of areas.

15. In deriving, by the calculus method, an expression for the moment of inertia of an area about a line, what are the three general ways of selecting the element of area?

Moment of Inertia of Bodies

16. Define the moment of inertia of a body or mass with respect to a line or plane: (a) in a word statement, and (b) as a mathematical expression.

17. What are the dimensions of the moment of inertia of a mass?

18. Point out and correct the error in the following statement: The moment of inertia of a mass with respect to a line or plane is the product of the mass and the square of the distance of the mass center from the line or plane.

19. Complete the following inadequate statement: The radius of gyration of a body with respect to a line or plane is the distance from the line or plane at which the mass of the body may be considered to be concentrated.

20. State in words and prove the parallel-axis theorem for the moment of inertia of a mass.

21. In determining by integration an expression for the moment of inertia of a mass, what are the three general methods of selecting the element of mass?

INDEX

The numbers refer to pages.

Absolute motion, 193
Acceleration, absolute, 194
  angular, 186
  axial components of, 190
  components of, 183
  Coriolis, 200
  linear, 169
  normal, 183
  of gravity, 6
  relative, 196
  tangential, 183
Acceleration-time curve, 171
Amplitude of oscillation, 179, 353, 373
Angle, of friction, 132
  of repose, 133
Angular acceleration, 186
Angular displacement, 157
Angular impulse, 319
Angular momentum, 344, 345
Angular velocity, 160, 163
Anti-resultant, 9
Axis, instantaneous, 216
  of precession, 346
  of rotation, 216
  of spin, 344
  of zero acceleration, 217
  of zero velocity, 216
  torque, 346

Balancing, 379
  dynamic, 384
  of elongated rotor, 389
  of rotating masses, 385
  static, 384
Base point, 209
Belt friction, 146
Benedetti, Father, 17
Body, rigid, 4
Bow's notation, 7, 38
British thermal unit, 302

Cable, catenary, 115

Cable, parabolic, 112
  stress in, 101, 111
Center, of gravity, 397
  of mass, 397
  of percussion, 270
  of pressure, 53
Centrifugal couple, 386
Centrifugal force, 265, 385
Centroids, 394
  graphical method for finding, 410
  of composite bodies, 404
  of lines, areas, volumes, and masses, 398–408
Circular frequency, 190, 355
Coefficient, of damping, 370
  of friction, 131
  of restitution, 342
  of rolling resistance, 151
Composition, of couples, 63
  of forces, 8
Compound pendulum, 361
Concurrent forces, 16
Conservation, of energy, 312
  of momentum, 336
Conservative systems, 312
Coriolis, G., 200
  component of acceleration, 200
Couples, 8, 23
  characteristics of, 24
  composition of, 27, 63
  gyroscopic, 346
  resolution of, 27
  system of, 388
  transformation of, 25
  vector representation of, 27
Critical damping, 370
Critical speed, 377
Curvilinear motion, 156
Cycle, 353

D'Alembert's principle, 245, 249
Damped vibration, 368, 379

Damping factor, 371
da Vinci, Leonardo, 17
Decrement, logarithmic, 372
Degree of freedom, 353
Dimensional equation, 32
Displacement, angular, 157
  components, of, 156
  linear, 156
  radial, 158
  relative, 194
  transverse, 158
Displacement-time curve, 165
Dissipation of energy, 314
Distance-time curve, 160
Distributed forces, 53
Dynamics, 4
Dynamometers, 314
Dyne, 228

Effective force, 236, 244
Efficiency, 314
Energy, 293
  conservation of, 312
  dissipation of, 314
  kinetic, 294, 296, 297
  mechanical, 294
  non-mechanical, 301
  of rigid body, 298
  potential, 294
  thermal, 301
Equations of equilibrium, *see* Equilibrium
Equations of motion, for particle, 228
  for plane motion, 273
  for rotation, 256
  for translation, 249
Equilibrant, 9
Equilibrium, 8
  algebraic conditions of, 67
  equations of, 66, 72, 81, 86, 120, 123, 125
  graphical conditions of, 67
  of system of couples, 388
  of three forces, 75
Equilibrium polygon, 66
Erg, 290
Exciting force, harmonic, 371
  non-harmonic, 378

First moments, 394
  see also Centroid

Force, 3
  centrifugal, 265
  characteristics of, 4
  components of, 8, 13, 14
  concept of, 4
  effective, 236, 244
  exciting, 357
  external effect of, 4
  impulsive, 318
  inertia, 235
  internal, 70, 73
  moment of, 17
  units of, 6
  vector representation of, 7
Force polygon, 38, 41, 50, 83
Force systems, characteristics of, 224
  classification of, 37
  resultant of, 36
  statically determinate, 66
  statically indeterminate, 66
  unbalanced, 223
Forced vibration, 373
  torsional, 378
  with damping, 378
  without damping, 373
Forces, classification of, 8
  distributed, 53
  parallelogram of, 9
  triangle of, 10
Fourier series, 378
Free-body diagrams, 69
  internal force in, 70
Free vibrations, 2, 38, 373
Frequency, 179, 353
  circular, 180, 355
  first harmonic, 378
  higher harmonic, 378
Friction, 130
  angle of, 132
  belt, 146
  coefficient of, 131
  kinetic, 130
  laws of, 133
  limiting, 130
  pivot, 142
  rolling, 151
  of screw, 143
  static, 130
Funicular (or string) polygon, 38, 42, 50, 83

G-pound or geepound, 228
Graphical methods, *see* Methods of solving problems
Gravity, acceleration of, 6
  center of, 397
Guldinus, theorem of, 408
Gyroscope, 344
  precession of, 346
  torque axis of, 346
Gyroscopic couple, 346

Harmonic motion, 178, 354
Hoop tension in flywheel, 267
Horsepower, 291
Horsepower-hour, 291

Impact, 319, 341
Impulse, 319
  angular, 319
  components of, 320
  linear, 319
  moment of, 320
Impulse and momentum, principle of, 328
Impulsive force, 318
Inertia, 225
  moment of, 411
Inertia force, 235
  for a body, 250
  for a particle, 235, 263
  method of, 235, 263
Instantaneous center, of rotation, 216
  of zero acceleration, 217
  of zero velocity, 216

Jerk, 171

Kilowatt, 291
Kilowatt-hour, 291
Kinematics, 4, 155
Kinetic energy, *see also* Energy
  of a particle, 296
  of a system of particles, 297
  of rigid bodies, 298
Kinetic system of units, 227
Kinetics, 4, 155, 223, 243

Lami, Bernard, 19
Linear acceleration, 169
Linear displacement, 156

Linear impulse, 319
Linear momentum, 322, 324
Linear velocity, 158

Magnification factors for steady-state vibration, 376
Mass, 225
  units of, 227
Mass center, 397
  motion of, 247
  rotation about, 263
Mechanical vibrations, *see* Vibration
Mechanics, laws of, 3
  science of, 3
Methods of solving problems, 30, 94, 229
  algebraic, 30, 44, 48, 57, 78
  graphical, 30, 37, 42 48, 57, 78, 92, 135
  in kinetics, 229
  in statics, 94
  trial and error, 30
Moment, first and second, 394, 412
  of a couple, 23
  of a force, 17
  of line, area, volume, mass, 395, 411
  principles of, 14, 42
Moment arm, 18
Moment center, 18
Moment of inertia, about perpendicular planes, 427
  graphical, experimental, and approximate methods for, 423, 429
  of areas, 411
  of bodies or masses, 425
  of composite areas and bodies, 420, 434
  parallel axis theorem for, 414, 426
  polar, 412
Momentum, 318, 322
  angular, 322, 324
  components of, 322
  linear, 322, 324
  moment of, 322, 324
Motion, absolute, 193
  curvilinear, 156
  laws of, 226
  linear, 156
  non-uniform, 156
  of a projectile, 176
  of rotation, 207
  of translation, 206
  plane, 208

Motion, plane of, 207, 208
  relative, 193
  uniform, 156, 159
  uniformly accelerated, 175

Natural period of vibration, 240
Newton, Sir Isaac, 19
  laws of motion, 226
Nodal point in torsional vibration, 363
Non-conservative systems, 338
Normal pressure, 130

Oscillation, *see also* Vibrations
  period of, 179, 240

Pappus, theorem of, 408
Parabolic cable, 112
Parallelogram law, 9
Particle, 155, 223, 243
  equations of motion for, 228
  kinetic energy of, 294–297
Pendulum, compound, 361
  simple, 361
  torsional, 362
Period, in harmonic motion, 179, 240
  of oscillation, 240, 353, 371
Phase angle, 355
Pivot friction, 142
Plane of motion, 207, 208
Poinsot, Louis, 23
Polar moment of inertia, 412
Pole of force polygon, 40
Potential energy, 294
Power, 290
Precession, axis of, 346
  velocity of, 346
Pressure, center of, 53
  normal, 130
Principle, of conservation of energy, 312
  of conservation of momentum, 329
  of impulse and momentum, 328
  of moments, 19, 42
  of motion of the mass center, 245
  of transmissibility, 6
  of work and energy, 303
Procedure in problem solution, in kinetics, 229
  in statics, 94
Prony brake, 314

Radius of gyration, 413
Reactions, types of, 69
Rectilinear motion, 175
Reduction of vibration, 379
Relative motion, 194–196, 200
Resolution, of a couple, 27
  of a force, 13
  of a force and couple, 28
  of two parallel forces, 16
Resonance, 240, 377, 379
Restitution, coefficient of, 342
Resultant, 8
  of system of couples, 61
  of various force systems, 36
Reversed effective force, 250
Rigid body, 4
Rolling friction, 151
  coefficient of, 151
Rolling resistance, 151
Rotation, 206
  center of, 207
  pure, 207

Scalar quantity, 7, 283
Screw, for lifting weights, 142
  pitch angle of, 144
Second moment, *see* Moment of inertia
Simple harmonic motions, 178
Slug, 228
Space diagram, 7, 39
Speed, 158
Speed-time curve, 160
Spring constant, 238, 353, 357, 364
Statical moment, 395
  see also First moment
Statically indeterminate forces, 66
Statics, 4
Steady-state forced vibration, 376
Stresses in trusses, 101
String (or funicular) polygon, 38, 42, 50
Superelevation of rail, 267
Symmetry, lines of, 398
  planes of, 398

Time, 3
Translation, curvilinear, 206
  rectilinear, 206
Transmissibility, in forced vibrations, 380
  principle of, 6

Triangle law, 10
Trusses, graphical analysis of stresses in, 108
  method of joints, 102
  method of sections, 102
Tuning in vibrations, 379
Two-force member, 73

Uniform motion, 156, 159
Uniformly accelerated motion, 175, 186
Units, absolute system of, 228
  engineers' system of, 227
  gravitational system of, 227
  kinetic system of, 227
  of energy and work, 283, 294
  of impulse, 319
  of mass, 227
  of moment of force, 18
  of momentum, 322
  of power, 290

Varignon, Pierre, 19
  theorem of, 19
Vector addition and subtraction, 155
Vector diagram, 17, 39
Vector quantity, 7
Velocity, angular, 160
  components of, 164

Velocity, linear, 158
  relative, 195
Vibration, critical damping, 370
  damped, 240, 357
  damping factor, 370
  forced, 240, 373
  free, 240, 353, 356
  frequency of, 179
  isolation of, 379
  logarithmic decrement, 372
  overdamped, 370
  period of, 179
  reduction of, 379
  steady state forced, 376
  transient, 376
  viscous damping of, 368

Watt, 291
Weight, 6
Work, 281, 303
  done by couple, 283
  done by force system, 285
  done by variable force, 282
  graphical representation of, 284
  sign of, 283
  units of, 283
Work and kinetic energy, principle of, 303
Working component of force, 281